FINITE ELEMENT COMPUTATIONAL FLUID MECHANICS

Series in Computational Methods in Mechanics and Thermal Sciences

W. J. Minkowycz and E. M. Sparrow, *Editors*

Baker, Finite Element Computational Fluid Mechanics
Patankar, Numerical Heat Transfer and Fluid Flow
Shih, Numerical Heat Transfer

PROCEEDINGS
Shih, Editor, Numerical Properties and Methodologies in Heat Transfer: Proceedings of the Second National Symposium

FINITE ELEMENT COMPUTATIONAL FLUID MECHANICS

A. J. Baker

Department of Engineering Science and Mechanics
The University of Tennessee, Knoxville

HEMISPHERE PUBLISHING CORPORATION
Washington New York London

McGRAW-HILL BOOK COMPANY
New York St. Louis San Francisco Auckland Bogotá
Hamburg Johannesburg London Madrid Mexico
Montreal New Delhi Panama Paris São Paulo
Singapore Sydney Tokyo Toronto

FINITE ELEMENT COMPUTATIONAL FLUID MECHANICS

2 3 4 5 6 7 8 9 0 B R B R 8 9 8 7 6 5 4

This book was set in Press Roman by Hemisphere Publishing Corporation. The editors were Rodger Klas and Brenda Munz Brienza; the production supervisor was Miriam Gonzalez; and the typesetters were Sandra F. Watts and Wayne Hutchins. Braun-Brumfield, Inc., was printer and binder.

Library of Congress Cataloging in Publication Data

Baker, A. J., date
Finite element computational fluid mechanics.

(Series in computational methods in mechanics and thermal sciences)
Includes bibliographies and index.
1. Fluid mechanics. 2. Finite element method.
I. Title. II. Series.
TA357.B27 1983 620.1′06′01515353 83-36
ISBN 0-07-003465-6

To
Mary Ellen and the Gang

CONTENTS

PREFACE

A dozen or so texts have appeared on the market during the past decade dealing with the theory and application of finite-element numerical methodology in mechanics. By far, the majority address problems in design-oriented structural mechanics. Conversely, others tend to be mathematically quite formal in content, without addressing the design issue. In both instances, however, the fundamental theoretical concept involves formulation of a variational boundary value problem statement of system "energy" and generating a discretized approximation of its extremum using finite-element concepts and procedures. For engineers and scientists whose expertise lies generally outside mathematics or structural analysis, and in fluid mechanics in particular, these approaches are probably confusing if not rather incomprehensible and frustrating. The astute engineer or scientist, with a basic interest in fluid mechanics, has probably sensed that finite-element solution methodology may possess considerable power and versatility for the problem class. However, with no comprehensive and readable literature reference, this individual will most likely resort directly to finite differences rather than spending the time to gain the apparent required theoretical proficiencies.

This text addresses this dilemma. It derives, develops, and applies finite-element solution methodology directly to the differential equation systems governing distinct and practical problem classes in fluid mechanics. It is principally a text on fluid mechanics and the theory of its computational simulation. The text's goal is to firmly quantize accuracy—as well as the always-present sources of discrete approximation error—for flow predictions at practical (large) Reynolds numbers that may also be turbulent. To bridge the gap between variational boundary value problems, and the highly nonlinear Navier-Stokes equations, the initial chapters focus on the steady heat conduction equation. This permits the dual problem formulation and introduces concepts of admissible approximation functions, accuracy, error measurement, and convergence. Highly instructive illustrative examples amplify key theoretical and computational features of this elementary problem specification that is widely understood. The linearity of this problem definition permits effective communication between the elegant theory and the less well (theoretically) understood nonlinear equation system algorithm. The net result is a rapid exposition of the essential aspects of finite-element concepts, for progressively more nonlinear differential equation descriptions for fluid mechanics, expressed in terminology that is comprehensible to both the up-to-date practicing engineer as well as the analytically oriented scientist and/or student.

While the finite-element concept originally burst on the fluid mechanics scene in the guise of a triangle, the more exact analysis determines it to effectively return the power of classical applied mechanics, calculus, and vector field theory to numerical algorithm construction. In particular, and as amply illustrated here, familiar finite-difference recursion formulas can always be established from the finite-element algorithm statement in elementary contexts. In this sense, the finite-element algorithm is perhaps most easily interpreted as an approximate transformation of a partial differential equation (system) into a larger system of lower order differential equations. The computational mesh is formed by the union (summation) of nonoverlapping subdomains, called finite elements, and the mesh can be "arbitrarily" nonregular. Approximation polynomials (of degree k) are prescribed on a local basis within each finite element, to represent all dependent variables and parameters, such as viscosity, Reynolds stress, and thermal conductivity. These approximation basis function sets are "cardinal," i.e., they reduce to zeroes and ones at predetermined locations, within or on the boundary of each computational subdomain, called nodes. The boundary of the solution domain need not coincide with surfaces of a global coordinate system. Nevertheless, the "natural" elliptic boundary condition specification, relating the dependent variable and its normal derivative, is routinely implemented along any (all) disconnected portions of the solution domain boundary. The ultimate algebraic equation solution matrix structure produced by the finite-element algorithm is sparse and banded, with band width being a function of problem dimension, the degree of interpolation, and the discretization node numbering. The resultant system is directly solvable, or an iterative procedure may be developed using tensor matrix products. For parent equation systems exhibiting initial-value character, the algorithm yields a system of ordinary differential equations that can be integrated using any explicit or implicit procedure.

This text has evolved over several year's experience with presentation of similarly entitled courses to senior and graduate engineering students. On several occasions, select topics have been extracted to form both continuing-education overviews and intensive short course presentations. With selective emphasis in the later chapters, the material can constitute a full-semester or two-quarter sequence at an introductory level. Considerable amplification and extension, according to the instructor's particular interests, can produce an effective one-year sequence that will provide a firm foundation for consideration of practical problem analysis and/or more theoretical aspects at an advanced level.

I am deeply indebted to many colleagues and friends, and a complete acknowledgement is impossible. I am particularly indebted to Mr. Paul Murray of Bell Aerospace Company, who started me into this topic in 1967 with an offer for summer employment to investigate the reported new finite-element applications in heat transfer, and to Dr. John Morgenthaler, who thereafter provided a permanent research scientist position for full-time pursuit of the exciting first phases of the research in fluid mechanics. I appreciate the guidance and counsel and the opportunity to work directly with Dr. Irving Shames, Faculty Distinguished Professor at State University of New York at Buffalo, who encouraged me as a graduate student into continuum mechanics and the broader view. I am indebted to Old Dominion University, and in particular Dr. Sid Roberts, for the Visiting Professorship during 1974–1975, that provided the opportunity to initiate organization of these notes. To my many colleagues at NASA/Langley, USAF/Wright-Patterson, and USN/NADC, I appreciate the encouragement and contract support required to transform theory into practice. My special thanks go to Mss. Eunice Hinkle, Jenny Wren, and Gwen Lunden, at University of Tennessee, Ms. Lillian Miller at Old Dominion, and Mrs. Jan Gomesky at Bell Aerospace, who have typed and retyped this manuscript numerous times, always with persistent smiles. And finally, to my good colleagues Messrs. Paul Manhardt and Joe Orzechowski, and Drs. Darrell Pepper and Osama Soliman, without whose collective close collaboration this work could not have been accomplished, I extend my most sincere appreciation and thanks.

A. J. Baker

FINITE ELEMENT COMPUTATIONAL FLUID MECHANICS

CHAPTER

ONE

INTRODUCTION

1.1 OVERVIEW

The finite-element method is an approximation procedure for solving differential equations of boundary and/or initial-value type in engineering and mathematical physics. The procedure employs subdivision of the solution domain into many smaller regions of convenient shapes, such as triangles and quadrangles, and uses approximation theory to quantize behavior on each finite element. Suitably disposed coordinates are specified for each element, and the action of the differential equation is approximately replaced using values of the dependent variables at these nodes. Using a variational principle, or a weighted-residual method, the governing differential equations are then transformed into finite-element equations governing the (each) isolated element. These local equations are collected together to form a global system of ordinary differential or algebraic equations including a proper accounting of boundary conditions. The nodal values of the dependent variables are determined from solution of this matrix equation system.

The purpose of this text is to provide a substantive exposition of finite-element solution theory and practice applied to the linear and nonlinear equations governing a wide range of problems in fluid mechanics. Fluid mechanics is an extremely broad subject, and it is difficult to narrow the scope without excluding important aspects. The approach taken herein is to assume that the reader is versed in engineering and in fluid mechanics, but is not necessarily as adept at the mathematics. Therefore, the physical subject is presented first. The numerical ideas are then introduced and immediately employed to generate solutions to elementary but informative problems. After the basic ideas are presented, the available mathematical theory is developed and additional numerical results are generated to firmly quantize the concepts of accuracy and convergence. The progression within each chapter addresses a sequentially more difficult problem description.

As succinctly stated by Bruce Irons in his reflections on teaching the finite-element method, "Most people, mathematicians apart, abhor abstraction." Booker T. Washington expressed the same thought in stating "An ounce of application is worth a ton of abstraction." These precepts are the watchwords for the developments in this text. This chapter reviews some of the basic ideas concerning differential equations, construction of solutions, and functional forms, following a brief discussion of the history. Thereafter, this development of finite-element computational fluid mechanics presents practice before theory, to convince the reader by example that developing an understanding of the theory is indeed a worthwhile activity. *Bon voyage*!

1.2 A BRIEF HISTORY

The finite-element method was originally developed by engineers in the 1950s to analyze large structural systems for aircraft. Turner et al. (1956) presented the first paper on the subject; these authors were followed by Clough (1960) and Argyris (1963), among others. Application of the finite-element method to nonstructural problems, such as elementary flow and electromagnetism, was first reported by Zienkiewicz and Cheung (1965). Applications to a wide class of problems in nonlinear mechanics were contributed by Oden (1972). As the finite-element method matured in applications, the concept of "force balance" was replaced by a robust theoretical analysis founded in the classical variational calculus and Rayleigh-Ritz methods (Rayleigh, 1877; Ritz, 1909). There have been many contributions to the development of the mathematical theory of finite elements, including those of Babuska and Aziz (1972), Ciarlet and Raviart (1972), Aubin (1972), Strang and Fix (1973), Oden and Reddy (1976), and the pioneering works of Lions and Magenes (1972).

The direct extension of these classical theoretical concepts to algorithm construction for most problem classes in fluid mechanics is not possible. The principal difficulty is that the typical eulerian reference frame renders the expression for conservation of momentum explicitly nonlinear. Therefore, a variational principle is not assured even to exist, let alone be found. For this reason, at least, the most widely practiced construction for approximation procedures for fluid mechanics has been direct replacement of derivatives by divided difference quotients, that is, finite differences (Richtmyer and Morton, 1967; Roache, 1972). A variation of this concept has been the integration of conservation equations over a discretization, using the divergence theorem and replacing cell fluxes with difference quotients, yielding finite volumes (Patankar, 1980). The *particle in cell method* (Evans and Harlow, 1957), employs the cell flux concept, but uses pseudolagrangian particle distributions to approximately enforce the basic conservation laws.

Most of the difference quotient-based algorithm constructions in fluid mechanics can be viewed in a unified manner as specific criteria within a weighted-residuals framework. Here, the error in the approximate satisfaction of the conservation equations is not set to zero itself, but instead its integral with respect to selected "weights" is required to vanish (Finlayson, 1972). Within weighted residuals, the *collocation method* reproduces the classical finite difference quotients. Conversely, the family of finite volume algorithms is retrieved by using constant weights. Generalizing the weights to be functions and defining them as identical to the approximation functions for the conservation variables yields the *Galerkin criteria*, named after the original (nondiscretized) procedure of B. G. Galerkin (1915). For a linear elliptic differential equation, this definition reproduces exactly the classical variational principle extremization, the successor formulation of the original finite-element concept. Finally, defining the weights to be the differential approximation error itself yields the *least-squares method.*

Pioneering research on finite element applications to fluid mechanics problems has employed several of these weighted-residuals criteria. Oden (1972) was among the first to derive the basic theoretical analog for the Navier-Stokes equations. Baker (1971, 1973, 1974) published results for an elementary incompressible flow with recirculation, obtained using the Galerkin criteria. Olson (1972) published a pseudo-variational finite-element algorithm for the biharmonic equation streamfunction analog for two-dimensional incompressible flow. Lynn (1974) utilized the least-squares criteria to develop a finite-element algorithm for laminar boundary-layer flow that preserved a symmetric matrix structure. Popinski and Baker (1976) developed a Galerkin criteria algorithm for laminar boundary-layer flow and published direct comparisons with results of a Crank-Nicolson finite-difference algorithm. Chung and Chiou (1976) published a similar algorithm construction for laminar boundary-layer flow behind a shock.

From the current perspective, it appears that the Galerkin criteria weighted-residuals formulation is most representative of a direct extension from the classical concepts. Therefore, in this text, the finite-element algorithm is synonymous with Galerkin weighted residual when addressed to a nonlinear problem definition. Thereby, for the introductory linear problem classes, we always retrieve the classical variational principle extremization. Let us now review some basic analytical solution procedures for linear differential equations, as a means of reviewing terminology and concepts appropriate to the important developments.

1.3 BASIC SOLUTION CONCEPTS

Consider the axial flow of heat in a thin, homogeneous rod with constant properties. The governing one-dimensional partial differential equation is

$$L(T) = \frac{1}{\alpha}\frac{\partial T}{\partial t} - \frac{\partial^2 T}{\partial x^2} = 0 \tag{1.1}$$

where α is the thermal diffusivity. Equation (1.1) is in canonical, that is, standard, form and is parabolic. Hence, one can specify the initial distribution of temperature along the x axis, and the temperature and/or its x derivative at locations $x = 0$ and $x = L$. For our purposes, let

$$T(0, t) = 0 = T(L, t) \qquad T(x, 0) = f(x) \tag{1.2}$$

A separation of variables solution for (1.1)-(1.2) assumes that time and space dependence is separable, i.e.,

$$T(x, t) \equiv F(x)G(t) \tag{1.3}$$

Substituting (1.3) into (1.1), and dividing by T yields

$$\frac{1}{F}\frac{d^2F}{dx^2} = \frac{1}{\alpha G}\frac{dG}{dt} \equiv -\beta^2$$

since arbitrary functions of x and t can be equal only if they are identically a constant $(-\beta^2)$. Hence, the governing ordinary differential equation for $F(x)$ is

$$\frac{d^2F}{dx^2} + \beta^2 F = 0$$

the solution of which is

$$F(x) = A\cos\beta x + B\sin\beta x \tag{1.4}$$

where A and B are arbitrary constants. Applying the homogeneous boundary conditions (1.2), A must equal zero and the separation constant β is the set of eigenvalues, i.e., characteristic values β_n.

$$\beta_n = \frac{n\pi}{L} \qquad n = 0, 1, 2, \ldots, \tag{1.5}$$

Solving the time-dependent equation yields

$$G(t) = C\exp(-\alpha\beta_n^2 t) \tag{1.6}$$

where C is an arbitrary constant. Combining these two solutions, using (1.3), produces the characteristic solution T_n:

$$T_n(x, t) = \sin\frac{n\pi x}{L}\exp(-\alpha\beta_n^2 t) \tag{1.7}$$

Since (1.1) is linear and homogeneous, the fundamental theorem states that the general solution is the linear combination of the characteristic solutions

$$T(x, t) = \sum_{n=0}^{\infty} B_n \sin\frac{n\pi x}{L}\exp(-\alpha\beta_n^2 t) \tag{1.8}$$

The solution (1.8) is made unique by enforcing the initial condition (1.2). Therefore,

$$T(x, 0) \equiv f(x) \equiv \sum_{n=0}^{\infty} B_n \sin\frac{n\pi x}{L}$$

Since $\sin(n\pi x/L)$ are solutions to a Sturm-Liouville differential equation, they possess the special properties of orthogonality and completeness. Using the orthogonality property, the unknown expansion coefficients B_n are determined by integration over the solution domain R^1 (the x axis) yielding

$$\int_0^L f(x) \sin \frac{m\pi x}{L} \, dx = \sum_{n=0}^{\infty} \int_0^L B_n \sin \frac{n\pi x}{L} \sin \frac{m\pi x}{L} \, dx = \frac{L}{2} B_n \delta_{nm} \quad (1.9)$$

where δ_{nm} is the Kronecker delta, which is unity for $n = m$ and otherwise vanishes. Hence, the expansion coefficient set B_n, for the general solution (1.8), is determined by an integration over R^1, that is,

$$B_n = \frac{2}{L} \int_0^L f(x) \sin \frac{n\pi x}{L} \, dx \quad (1.10)$$

We will see that the finite-element algorithm, for numerical solution of similar equation systems, employs concepts identical to (1.10) for establishing the expansion coefficients.

Proceeding to a multidimensional problem in steady heat conduction, the governing partial differential equation

$$L(T) = \frac{\partial^2 T}{\partial x^2} + \frac{\partial^2 T}{\partial y^2} + \frac{\partial^2 T}{\partial z^2} \equiv \nabla^2 T = 0 \quad (1.11)$$

is elliptic and in canonical form. There is no initial condition, and boundary conditions are required on each coordinate plane $0 = x = a$, $0 = y = b$, $0 = z = c$. For illustration, assume

$$T(0, y, z) = T(z, y, z) = T(x, 0, z) = T(x, b, z) = 0$$

$$T(x, y, 0) = 0 \qquad T(x, y, c) = f(x, y)$$

The separated-variables solution is

$$T(x, y, z) = X(x)Y(y)Z(z) \quad (1.12)$$

Applying the specified homogeneous boundary conditions, the characteristic solution is

$$T_{nm} = \sin \frac{n\pi x}{a} \sin \frac{m\pi y}{b} \sinh \left[\pi \sqrt{\left(\frac{n}{a}\right)^2 + \left(\frac{m}{b}\right)^2} \right] z \quad (1.13)$$

From the fundamental theorem, the general solution is

$$T(x, y, z) = \sum_{n=0}^{\infty} \sum_{m=0}^{\infty} C_{nm} T_{nm} \quad (1.14)$$

Applying the remaining boundary condition yields,

$$T(x, y, c) = f(x, y) = \sum_{n=1}^{\infty} \sum_{m=1}^{\infty} C_{nm} \sin \frac{n\pi x}{a} \sin \frac{m\pi y}{b} \sinh \gamma_{nm} c \qquad (1.15)$$

where γ_{nm}, the eigenvalues of the solution, are

$$\gamma_{nm} \equiv \sqrt{\left(\frac{n}{a}\right)^2 + \left(\frac{m}{b}\right)^2} \qquad (1.16)$$

Thus, using the orthogonality property of the characteristic solution, the expansion coefficients for the series solution are again determined by an integration over the solution domain.

$$C_{nm} = \frac{4}{ab} \int_0^b \int_0^a f(x, y) \sin \frac{n\pi x}{a} \sin \frac{m\pi y}{b} \, dx \, dy \qquad \begin{array}{l} m = 1, 2, \ldots \\ n = 1, 2, \ldots \end{array} \qquad (1.17)$$

Problems

1 Consider a rod of length L, initially at uniform temperature T_1. At $t = 0$, $T(L, t)$ is raised to T_2 and held constant. Find the transient and steady-state temperature distributions for $T(0, t) = T_1$. (Hint: solve for the difference between the steady state and initial distributions.)

2 (*a*) Separating variables, find solutions $\phi(x, y)$ to Laplace's equation on $0 \leqslant x \leqslant a$, $0 \leqslant y \leqslant b$, $\partial^2\phi/\partial x^2 + \partial^2\phi/\partial y^2 = 0$.

(*b*) Find the particular solution satisfying the boundary conditions $\phi(0, y) = 0$, $\partial\phi(x, 0)/\partial y = \partial\phi(x, b)/\partial y = 0$, and $\phi(a, y) = \cos(3\pi y/b)$.

3 Find the solution to Laplace's equation $\nabla^2\phi = 0$ in the interior of a right circular cylinder, centered on and including the z axis, and of length L and outer radius a, subject to the boundary conditions

(*a*) $\phi(r, \theta, 0) = \phi(a, \theta, z) = 0$, $\phi(r, \theta, L) = V(r)$ (easy)

(*b*) $\phi(r, \theta, 0) = \phi(a, \theta, z) = 0$, $\phi(r, \theta, L) = V(r, \theta)$ (harder)

(*c*) $\phi(r, \theta, 0) = \phi(r, \theta, L) = 0$, $\phi(a, \theta, z) = V(\theta, z)$ (hardest)

where V is some specified potential distribution.

1.4 PROBLEM STATEMENTS

For many scientists and engineers first pursuing the subject of finite elements, a major cause for uneasiness is that the problem statement is cast in terms of extremization of a functional. This is a key element of the formulation language, however, and the concept becomes extremely useful in the progression to the interesting nonlinear problems in fluid mechanics. The great mathematicians of the last century devised the concept of the limit and transformed difference algebra to the calculus. Digital computations were initiated about 50 years ago utilizing difference quotients to replace derivatives. The finite-element functional procedure may be correctly viewed as returning calculus, vector field theory, and classical mechanics to formulation of numerical approximations, a feature we will confirm to be of distinct usefulness.

Nonfamiliarity with a functional representation can be rapidly dispelled. As an introduction, consider an elementary function T of the n independent variables x_i, $1 \leqslant i \leqslant n$; that is,

$$T(x_i) = T(x_1, x_2, \ldots, x_n) \tag{1.18}$$

Suppose that at the coordinates $x_i = \bar{x}_i$, T is known to take on a minimum value. Defining an arbitrary displacement Δx_i about $\bar{x}_i$, the fact that $T(\bar{x}_i)$ is a minimum can be stated as

$$\begin{aligned}\Delta T &\equiv T(\bar{x}_1 + \Delta x_1, \bar{x}_2 + \Delta x_2, \ldots, \bar{x}_n + \Delta x_n) - T(\bar{x}_i)\\ &= T(\bar{x}_i + \Delta x_i) - T(\bar{x}_i) > 0\end{aligned} \tag{1.19}$$

If $\Delta T > 0$ only for small Δx_i, then (1.19) states the existence of a local minimum. Conversely, if $\Delta T > 0$ for arbitrary Δx_i, then (1.19) ensures the existence of an absolute minimum.

The basic requirement for the finite-element formulation is to confirm the existence of a local extremum, usually without regard to whether it is a maximum or a minimum. Recall that a necessary condition for a function to take on an extremum (stationary) value is that first derivatives with respect to all independent variables must vanish. As an example, limiting $n = 1$ in (1.18), the Taylor series about $\bar{x}_1$ is

$$T(\bar{x}_1 + \Delta x_1) = T(\bar{x}_1) + \left.\frac{dT}{dx_1}\right|_{\bar{x}_1} \Delta x_1 + \frac{1}{2}\left.\frac{d^2 T}{dx_1^2}\right|_{\bar{x}_1} \Delta x^2 + \cdots \tag{1.20}$$

Then,

$$\begin{aligned}\Delta T(\bar{x}_1 + \Delta x_1) &\equiv T(\bar{x}_1 + \Delta x_1) - T(\bar{x}_1)\\ &= \left.\frac{dT}{dx_1}\right|_{\bar{x}_1} \Delta x_1 + \frac{1}{2}\left.\frac{d^2 T}{dx_1^2}\right|_{\bar{x}_1} \Delta x_1^2 + \cdots\end{aligned} \tag{1.21}$$

Taking Δx_1 arbitrarily small, if $T(\bar{x}_1)$ is a local minimum, then ΔT must be positive and dT/dx_1 must equal zero (since Δx_1 could be negative). Correspondingly, if $T(\bar{x}_1)$ corresponds to an extremum, then dT/dx_1 must vanish and $\Delta T \gtrless 0$ dependent upon the sign of d^2T/dx_1^2 at $\bar{x}_1$. The procedure rapidly generalizes to n independent variables, whence (1.21) becomes

$$\begin{aligned}\Delta T(\bar{x}_i + \Delta x_i) &= \left.\frac{\partial T}{\partial x_1}\right|_{\bar{x}_1} \Delta x_1 + \left.\frac{\partial T}{\partial x_2}\right|_{\bar{x}_i} \Delta x_2 + \cdots + \left.\frac{\partial T}{\partial x_n}\right|_{\bar{x}_i} \Delta x_n\\ &\quad + \frac{1}{2}\left(\left.\frac{\partial^2 T}{\partial x_1^2}\right|_{\bar{x}_i} \Delta x_1^2 + 2\left.\frac{\partial^2 T}{\partial x_1\,\partial x_2}\right|_{\bar{x}_i} \Delta x_1\,\Delta x_2 + \cdots\right) + \cdots\end{aligned} \tag{1.22}$$

A necessary condition for $T(\bar{x}_i)$ to be stationary is that

$$\left.\frac{\partial T}{\partial x_i}\right|_{\bar{x}_i} = \nabla T(\bar{x}_i) = 0 \qquad \text{for all } 1 \leq i \leq n$$

In contrast to the calculus of a function, the theory and practice of finite-element formulations is based upon the *variational calculus*, which is concerned with extremum values of functions of functions, i.e., functionals. A typical form for a one-dimensional problem is

$$I(T) \equiv \int_{x_1}^{x_2} f(x, T, T_x)\, dx \tag{1.23}$$

where $f(\cdot)$ is a functional of the functions $T(x)$ and $T_x \equiv dT/dx$. The formulational procedure, equivalent to (1.21) is to determine the function $T(x)$, hence the functional $f(\cdot)$ that extremizes $I(T)$. The methodology is formal (Weinstock, 1952; Huebner, 1975) and requires the definition of a one-parameter family of functions $\phi(x)$ that lie arbitrarily close to the solution $T(x)$. A convenient form is

$$\phi(x) \equiv T(x) + \epsilon\eta(x) \tag{1.24}$$

where $\eta(x)$ is arbitrary on $x_1 < x < x_2$, but $\eta(x_1) \equiv 0 \equiv \eta(x_2)$, and ϵ is a parameter that controls the "closeness" of $\phi(x)$ and $T(x)$ for each $\eta(x)$. Specifically, for all $\eta(x)$, there is a value of $-\epsilon_0 \leq \epsilon \leq \epsilon_0$ such that the difference (distance) between $\phi(x)$ and $T(x)$ may be made arbitrarily small, i.e.,

$$|\phi(x) - T(x)| < \delta \tag{1.25}$$

where δ is (arbitrarily) small.

Determining the extremum of $I(T)$, (1.23) is now replaced by seeking the stationary value of $I(\phi, \epsilon)$

$$I(\phi, \epsilon) \equiv \int_{x_1}^{x_2} f(x, \phi(\epsilon), \phi_x(\epsilon))\, dx \tag{1.26}$$

with respect to the arbitrary parameter ϵ. It is important to note that once the functional form is derived, the distance between $\phi(x)$ and $T(x)$ vanishes on setting $\epsilon \equiv 0$ [see (1.24)]. Therefore, the formulation statement is

$$\left.\frac{dI}{d\epsilon}\right|_{\epsilon=0} \equiv 0 \tag{1.27}$$

Using (1.26) and (1.24), and noting that the limits of integration are constants, (1.27) becomes

$$\left.\frac{dI}{d\epsilon}\right|_{\epsilon=0} = \int_{x_1}^{x_2} \left[\frac{\partial f}{\partial \phi}\frac{\partial \phi}{\partial \epsilon} + \frac{\partial f}{\partial \phi_x}\frac{\partial \phi_x}{\partial \epsilon}\right] dx = \int_{x_1}^{x_2} \left[\frac{\partial f}{\partial \phi}\eta(x) + \frac{\partial f}{\partial \phi_x}\frac{d\eta}{dx}\right] dx$$

$$= \int_{x_1}^{x_2} \left[\frac{\partial f}{\partial \phi} - \frac{d}{dx}\left(\frac{\partial f}{\partial \phi_x}\right)\right] \eta(x)\, dx + \left.\frac{\partial f}{\partial \phi_x}\eta\right|_{x_1}^{x_2} \equiv 0 \tag{1.28}$$

The final form in (1.28) is achieved using integration by parts. The last term vanishes identically, since $\eta(x_1) \equiv 0 \equiv \eta(x_2)$. Since $\eta(x)$, $x_1 < x < x_2$, is completely arbitrary, (1.28) can be rendered zero in a general way only if the integrand in brackets vanishes identically. Then, setting $\epsilon = 0$ in (1.24) yields that the extremum of $I(T)$, (1.23), occurs for $f(\cdot)$ satisfying the partial differential equation

$$L(f) = \frac{\partial f}{\partial T} - \frac{d}{dx}\left(\frac{\partial f}{\partial T_x}\right) = 0 \tag{1.29}$$

Equation (1.29) is the well-known Euler-Lagrange equation, a necessary condition for (1.23) to be rendered an extremum.

Some special cases for $f(\cdot)$ warrant comment. First, should $f(\cdot) = f(x)$ only, (1.23) reduces to an elementary integration and (1.29) cannot be enforced. If $f(\cdot) = f(x, T_x)$, then (1.29) can be integrated once,

$$\frac{\partial f}{\partial T_x} = C_1 \tag{1.30}$$

where C_1 is an arbitrary constant. For $f(\cdot) = f(T_x)$, the integral of (1.29) simplifies to

$$T_x = \frac{dT}{dx} = C_2 \tag{1.31}$$

Hence, $T(x) = C_2 x + C_3$ is the function that renders $I(T)$ stationary.

Finally, letting

$$f(\cdot) = \tfrac{1}{2}T_x^2 - gT \tag{1.32}$$

where $g(x)$ is an arbitrary function of x, (1.29) yields

$$\frac{\partial f}{\partial T} - \frac{d}{dx}\left(\frac{\partial f}{\partial T_x}\right) = -g - \frac{d}{dx}\left(\frac{1}{2}T_x \cdot 2\right) = 0$$

or,

$$L(T) = \frac{d^2 T}{dx^2} + g = 0 \tag{1.33}$$

which is recognized as the steady-state, one-dimensional heat conduction equation with heat source distribution $g(x)$.

Quite obviously, then, extremization of (1.23) for $f(\cdot)$ specified by (1.32) must correspond exactly to solution of the linear, second-order partial differential equation for conservation of energy. Setting $g = 0$ for convenience, one with a finite-difference background would have no difficulty using (1.19) to form the difference algebra equivalent of d^2T/dx^2, on a uniform discretization of $x_1 \leqslant x \leqslant x_2$, as

$$\frac{d^2 T}{dx^2} = \frac{d}{dx}\left(\frac{dT}{dx}\right) \approx \frac{1}{\Delta x}\left(\frac{T_{i+1} - T_i}{\Delta x_i} - \frac{T_i - T_{i-1}}{\Delta x_{i-1}}\right) = \frac{T_{i+1} - 2T_i + T_{i-1}}{(\Delta x)^2} \tag{1.34}$$

As will be amply illustrated throughout this text, the finite-element approximate extremization of (1.23), as obtained using polynomials in x to approximate the functional $T(x)$, always yields the familiar and appropriate order-accurate difference recursion relation on a uniform discretization. Importantly, this is not usually true for nonlinear terms, source terms, boundary conditions, nonuniform discretizations, multidimensional problems, or the progression to higher order accuracy using nonlinear polynomials, wherein the finite-element algorithm statement invariably produces distinct representations.

Equation (1.31) is the elementary solution for the case $g = 0$, which states a linear function in x is adequate for extremization of (1.23). Leaving the details to the next chapter, we note that the nodal temperatures become the parameters with which the discrete finite element approximation to (1.23) is eligible for extremization. Using finite-difference notation, and for a uniform discretization, the linear element equivalent becomes the matrix operation

$$S_e \left[\frac{1}{\Delta_e} \begin{bmatrix} 1 & -1 \\ -1 & 1 \end{bmatrix} \begin{Bmatrix} T_{j-1} \\ T_j \end{Bmatrix}, \frac{1}{\Delta_e} \begin{bmatrix} 1 & -1 \\ -1 & 1 \end{bmatrix} \begin{Bmatrix} T_j \\ T_{j+1} \end{Bmatrix} \right] = \{0\}$$

where S_e is the to-be-defined matrix assembly operator. The brackets denote a square matrix, while the braces denote a column matrix. The representative difference recursion relation is established by rowwise addition of the last equation in the first product to the first equation in the second product, yielding

$$\begin{aligned} S_e[\cdot] &\Rightarrow \frac{1}{\Delta} [-T_{j-1} + T_j + (T_j - T_{j+1})] \\ &= \frac{-T_{j+1} + 2T_j - T_{j-1}}{\Delta x} = 0 \end{aligned} \tag{1.35}$$

Note that (1.35) differs from (1.34) only by a sign and an order of Δx, with the latter accountable to the integration specified for (1.23).

One should be highly encouraged by this comparison, since consistency demands that second (and higher) order accurate difference formulations belong to the hierarchy of finite-element representations. Our hope, to be confirmed, is that finite elements may yield an efficient formula for generating optimally order accurate difference relations, for comparison to accepted low-dimensional recursion formulas. This should produce the confidence required to confirm that the effort is worthwhile.

For completeness, the multidimensional Euler-Lagrange equation is

$$L(f) = \frac{\partial f}{\partial T} - \nabla \cdot \left[\frac{\partial f}{\partial (\nabla T)} \right] = 0 \tag{1.36}$$

which determines the functional $f(x, T, \nabla T)$ that corresponds to the extremum of

$$I(T) \equiv \int_{R^n} f(\mathbf{x}, T, \nabla T)\, dx \tag{1.37}$$

where R^n is the n-dimensional region spanned by the $\mathbf{x}(x_i, 1 \leqslant i \leqslant n)$ coordinate system.

Problem

1 Determine the functional form for f(•) in (1.23), corresponding to the separated variables spatial solution form for (1.1), that is, $d^2T/dx^2 + \beta^2 T = 0$.

1.5 ORTHOGONAL FUNCTIONS

There are connecting aspects between the separation of variables solution procedure and the variational calculus that warrant additional exposure, as an introduction to finite-element approximation procedures. The form of the functional $f(x)$, (1.23) or (1.37), can usually be determined, provided the equivalent partial differential equation (1.29) or (1.36) corresponds to the laplacian. Similarly, given the n-dimensional laplacian, the separation of variables procedure reduces the solution requirements to solving n, one-dimensional second-order ordinary differential equations; recall (1.4), (1.7) and (1.13).

The generalization of second-order differential equations of the form

$$L(F) = \frac{d^2F}{dx^2} + \beta^2 F = 0$$

is the Sturm-Liouville equation

$$L(u(x)) \equiv \frac{d}{dx}\left[p(x)\frac{du}{dx}\right] + [q(x) + \lambda r(x)]\,u = 0 \tag{1.38}$$

defined on the interval $a < x < b$, where parameters $p(x) > 0$ and $r(x) > 0$ are everywhere continuous. Equations of the form (1.38) result for the separated variables solution of the laplacian in cartesian coordinate systems. Their fundamental solutions are well known, for example, the trigonometric functions, Bessel functions, Legendre polynomials, and spherical harmonics. These fundamental solutions exhibit some unique and highly useful properties, specifically, orthogonality and completeness. In analogy, these concepts are basic to error minimization and the theoretical concepts of accuracy and convergence in the numerical sequel using finite elements. A brief exposition is worthwhile.

The differential equation (1.38) is completed by boundary conditions specified at the end points of the x interval. Assume the general form

$$l(u) \equiv a_{1i}u(x_i) + a_{2i}\left.\frac{du}{dx}\right|_{x_i} = 0 \qquad i = 1, 2 \tag{1.39}$$

The differential operator $L(\cdot)$ is called a self-adjoint operator provided

$$\int_{x_1}^{x_2} [vL(u) - uL(v)]\; dx = 0 \tag{1.40}$$

where u and v are solutions to $L(\cdot)$ and satisfy boundary conditions $l(\cdot)$, for example (1.38)–(1.39). The Sturm-Liouville equation defines a self-adjoint operator; by direct substitution of (1.38) into (1.40)

$$\int_{x_1}^{x_2} [vL(u) - uL(v)]\, dx = \int_{x_1}^{x_2} \left[v \frac{d}{dx}\left(p \frac{du}{dx}\right) - u \frac{d}{dx}\left(p \frac{dv}{dx}\right) + v(q + \lambda r)u - u(q + \lambda r)v \right] dx = 0 \quad (1.41)$$

The last two terms cancel identically. Integrating by parts the remaining two terms, and substituting (1.39) yields another identical cancellation.

Therefore, (1.38) defines a self-adjoint operator. As a consequence, for solutions to the Sturm-Liouville equation there exists an ordered set of numbers λ_n, $n = 0, 1, \ldots, N, \ldots,$ such that $\lambda_0 < \lambda_1 < \lambda_2 < \ldots < \lambda_N < \ldots$, with the limit $\lambda_N \to \infty$ as $n \to \infty$ for which (1.38) possesses a nontrivial solution. Members of the set λ_n are called eigenvalues (principle values), and the corresponding solutions $u_n(x)$, $n = 0, 1, 2, \ldots, N, \ldots,$ are called eigenfunctions (principle functions). For the heat conduction equation example in Sec. 1.3, $\beta_n = n\pi/L$ are the eigenvalues and $u_n = \sin \beta_n x$ are the eigenfunctions.

The eigenfunction solutions of the Sturm-Liouville equation exhibit a property termed orthogonality. In (1.40), letting $u \equiv u_n$ and $v \equiv u_m$, and substituting (1.38) yields the identity

$$(\lambda_n - \lambda_m) \int_{x_1}^{x_2} r(x) u_n(x) u_m(x)\, dx = 0 \quad (1.42)$$

Only for $n = m$ does the left side of (1.42) vanish identically; otherwise, since λ_n and λ_m cannot be equal, the integral itself must vanish. Recalling the Kronecker delta, (1.42) can be rewritten as

$$\int_{x_1}^{x_2} r(x) u_n(x) u_m(x)\, dx = a_n \delta_{nm} \quad (1.43)$$

where a_n is the value of the integral (1.42) for $n = m$. Hence, the eigenfunctions $u_n(x)$ and $u_m(x)$ are defined as orthogonal on the interval $x_1 \leqslant x \leqslant x_2$, since the integral of their product with respect to the weight $r(x)$, contained in (1.38), vanishes for all $n \neq m$. This property was utilized for the heat conduction example problem [see (1.9)] to determine the expansion coefficients B_n of the general solution (1.8). The finite-element procedure will lead us to establishment of locally orthogonal approximation functions exhibiting such preferred properties. The analogy to (1.43) is almost exact, with the exception that the integral fails to vanish on select subintervals (finite elements) of $x_1 \leqslant x \leqslant x_2$ following discretization. Furthermore, since the perpendicular distance is a minimum measure, the error in the finite-element approximate solution will become orthogonal to the space of approximation functions, as a consequence of the formulational procedure.

A second useful property of the eigenfunctions of the Sturm-Liouville equation is completeness. A function set $u_n(x)$ is defined as complete on $x_1 \leqslant x \leqslant x_2$, if for every $\delta > 0$ there exists a number $N > 0$ such that the distance between an arbitrary, square-integrable function $f(x)$, and an expansion in $u_n(x)$ can be made arbitrarily small:

$$\int_{x_1}^{x_2} \left[f(x) - \sum_{n=0}^{N} C_n u_n(x) \right]^2 dx < \delta \tag{1.44}$$

Using (1.43), (1.44) is assured by defining the expansion coefficients C_n to be

$$C_n \equiv \int_{x_1}^{x_2} f(x) u_n(x)\, dx \tag{1.45}$$

Note that (1.45) is the identity used for determining the coefficients B_n in the heat conduction example. The separated variables procedure yields infinite series to be evaluated for the solution [see (1.8)]. This is never accomplished in practice, however. Instead, the solution is projected onto its first N eigenfunctions, that is, the infinite series is truncated at $n = N$. Viewing (1.44), one is guaranteed a level of accuracy for the solution $f(x)$, by selection of N sufficiently large, provided the functions $u_n(x)$ form a complete set.

In the finite-element numerical sequel, the theoretical statements on accuracy and convergence rate with discretization refinement require that the locally orthogonal, polynomial approximation functions be complete to a consistent degree. Increasing this degree invariably yields solution improvements on sufficiently refined grids, which corresponds in analogy to increasing N in (1.44). Hopefully, these commonalities will be of use to the reader in establishing a firm appreciation of the elegance and practical utility of finite-element procedures in fluid mechanics.

1.6 MATRIX ALGEBRA AND EQUATION SOLVING

The remaining introductory topic is matrix algebra and equation solving. The finite-element approximation, applied to the differential equations of fluid mechanics, eventually produces a large, usually nonlinear algebraic equation system. The usual presentation is in the form of a matrix statement, and the structure of some of these matrices can be nonelementary. For example, some may contain matrix elements that are themselves matrices. Nevertheless, developed matrix formalisms and notation are highly descriptive and readily translatable into FORTRAN notation. Many excellent introductory treatises exist for this subject (Kreyszig, 1967, Chap. 7). This section introduces the essence of matrix algebra and equation solving, primarily to review concepts and specific nomenclature.

A matrix, denoted by a bracket, $[\cdot]$, is an $m \times n$ rectangular array of numbers that obeys certain rules of manipulation. The elements of a matrix $[A]$ are the entries a_{ij}, where $1 \leqslant i \leqslant m$ and $1 \leqslant j \leqslant n$. The rows of a matrix are the horizontal arrays, denoted by subscript i, and the columns are the vertical arrays denoted by subscript j.

There are names given to matrices possessing certain properties. For example, $[A]$ is

real: if all a_{ij} have zero imaginary parts
square: if $m = n$
symmetric: if $a_{ij} = a_{ji}$
skew-symmetric: if $a_{ij} = -a_{ji}$, hence $a_{ii} = 0$
triangular: if $a_{ij} = 0$ for $i < j$ or $j < i$ (upper, lower)
diagonal: if $a_{ij} = 0$ for $i \neq j$
row matrix: if $a_{ij} = 0$ for $i > 1$
column matrix: if $a_{ij} = 0$ for $j > 1$

The algebra of matrices follows familiar rules. The addition of two matrices $[A]$ and $[B]$ defines a new matrix $[C]$,

$$[C] \equiv [A] + [B] \tag{1.46}$$

the elements of which are determined by ordinary addition as

$$c_{ij} \equiv a_{ij} + b_{ij} \tag{1.47}$$

The product of a matrix $[A]$ with a scalar g defines a new matrix $[C]$,

$$[C] \equiv g[A] \tag{1.48}$$

each element of which is the multiple

$$c_{ij} = g a_{ij} \qquad \begin{cases} 1 \leqslant i \leqslant m \\ 1 \leqslant j \leqslant n \end{cases} \tag{1.49}$$

The difference between two matrices $[A]$ and $[B]$ is defined by (1.46)–(1.47), by setting $g = -1$ in (1.48), yielding

$$[C] = [A] + (-1)[B] \tag{1.50}$$

hence,

$$c_{ij} \equiv a_{ij} + (-1) b_{ij} \tag{1.51}$$

The operations of addition and subtraction are associative, commutative, and distributive; for example,

$$[D] = ([A] + [B]) + [C] = [A] + ([B] + [C]) = ([A] + [C]) + [B]$$

The transpose of a matrix $[A]$ is denoted $[A]^T$, and the elements a_{ij}^T are defined as

$$a_{ij}^T = a_{ji} \qquad \begin{cases} 1 \leqslant i \leqslant m \\ 1 \leqslant j \leqslant n \end{cases} \tag{1.52}$$

The product of two matrices is denoted without a special symbol. For example,

$$[C] \equiv [A][B] \tag{1.53}$$

defines the matrix $[C]$ as the product of $[A]$ and $[B]$. The elements of $[C]$ are formed by summing products of rows of $[A]$ and columns of $[B]$ as

$$c_{ij} \equiv \sum_{k=1}^{p} a_{ik} b_{kj} \qquad \begin{cases} 1 \leqslant i \leqslant m \\ 1 \leqslant j \leqslant n \end{cases} \tag{1.54}$$

where p is the number of columns in $[A]$, which must equal the number of rows of $[B]$. Adding a subscript notation to (1.53) for clarity,

$$[C]_{m \times n} = [A]_{m \times p} [B]_{p \times n} \tag{1.55}$$

signifies the number of rows × columns for each matrix. Multiplication is associative and distributive,

$$([A][B])[C] = [A]([B][C])$$

$$[A]([B] + [C]) = [A][B] + [A][C]$$

but not commutative:

$$[A][B] \neq [B][A]$$

Denoting a column matrix by braces $\{\cdot\}$, and a row matrix as the transpose $\{\cdot\}^T$, special products of specific use include:

Row × square: $\{A\}^T_{1 \times m} [B]_{m \times n} = \{C\}_{1 \times n}$

Row × column: $\{A\}^T_{1 \times n} \{B\}_{n \times 1} = c_{1 \times 1}$

Column × row: $\{A\}_{m \times 1} \{B\}^T_{1 \times n} = [C]_{m \times n}$

Identity × square: $[I]^T_{m \times m} [A]_{m \times m} = [A]_{m \times m}$

Quadratic forms play a special role in finite element methodology and in the resultant matrix statements. Given the n variables x_i, $1 \leqslant i \leqslant n$, and the $n \times n$ square symmetric matrix $[A]$, a quadratic form is the scalar function $f(x_i)$

$$f(x_i) \equiv \tfrac{1}{2} \{x\}^T_{1 \times n} [A]_{n \times n} \{x\}_{n \times 1} \tag{1.56}$$

or, in terms of the elements of $\{x\}$ and $[A]$.

$$f(x_i) \equiv \frac{1}{2} \sum_{i=1}^{n} \sum_{j=1}^{n} a_{ij} x_i x_j \tag{1.57}$$

The form of (1.56) is the typical construction for the finite-element energy functional $I(T)$ introduced earlier [see (1.23)]. The theoretical construction is to seek its extremum or stationary value, which is accomplished by differentiation with respect to each of the independent variables. The derivative of (1.56) with respect to x_i is easy to construct, using (1.57), as

$$\frac{\partial f}{\partial x_k} = \frac{1}{2}\frac{\partial}{\partial x_k}\sum_{i=1}^{n}\sum_{j=1}^{n} a_{ij}x_i x_j = \frac{1}{2}\sum_{j=1}^{n} a_{ij}x_j\delta_{ik} + \frac{1}{2}\sum_{i=1}^{n} a_{ij}x_i\delta_{jk} = \sum_{j=1}^{n} a_{jk}x_j \tag{1.58}$$

accounting for the interchangeability of dummy indices and the symmetry of $[A]$. By the same token, in matrix notation, the derivative of (1.56) with respect to $\{x\}$ is

$$\frac{\partial f}{\partial \{x\}} = \frac{1}{2}\frac{\partial}{\partial \{x\}}(\{x\}^T[A]\{x\}) = \frac{1}{2}([A]\{x\} + (\{x\}^T[A])^T) = [A]\{x\} \tag{1.59}$$

since $[A]$ is symmetric and the transpose of a matrix product is the product of the transposed matrices.

Equation (1.59) is the basic formulational step for a finite-element algorithm, in that it locates the extremum with respect to all elements of $\{x\}$. Simply stated, (1.59) must vanish identically at the extremum.

$$[A]\{x\} \equiv \{0\} \tag{1.60}$$

Equation (1.60) is a homogeneous system of (linear) algebraic equations, the solution of which will determine the elements of the column matrix $\{x\}$. Cramer's rule defines the formal solution of a matrix equation in terms of the matrix inverse $[A]^{-1}$. For (1.60), the solution statement is

$$\{x\} = [A]^{-1}\{0\} \tag{1.61}$$

which makes little sense, since it yields the trivial solution $\{x\} = \{0\}$ if the matrix inverse $[A]^{-1}$ exists. Therefore, $[A]^{-1}$ must not exist, which means $[A]$ is a singular matrix.

Before getting into this terminology, the flaw in (1.60) is that all elements x_i of $\{x\}$ are not independent. At least one must be constrained by a boundary condition. Multiplying these known data by the appropriate a_{ij} and transporting the numbers to the right side yields the reduced matrix statement

$$[A^r]\{x^r\} = \{b\} \tag{1.62}$$

The matrix $[A^r]$ is nonsingular; therefore its inverse exists and is finite, and, via Cramer's rule,

$$\{x^r\} = [A^r]^{-1}\{b\} \tag{1.63}$$

is the solution for the $1 \leqslant i \leqslant r < n$ elements of $\{x\}$. Of course, there are much superior matrix methods for equation solving (1.62) for the $[A^r]$ produced by the finite-element algorithm. This topic is expanded in context with the equation developments in succeeding chapters.

Returning to terminology, the inverse $[A]^{-1}$ of the square matrix $[A]$ is defined as the matrix of cofactors of $[A]$, transposed, and divided by the determinant of $[A]$:

$$[A]^{-1} = \frac{1}{\det [A]} [C]^T \tag{1.64}$$

The scalar d ($\equiv \det[A]$) is defined as the determinant of order n, of the $n \times n$ square matrix $[A]$, and is evaluated using expansion by cofactors on any row or column of the matrix $[A]$:

$$d \equiv a_{i1}c_{i1} + a_{i2}c_{i2} + \cdots + a_{in}c_{in}$$

or

$$a_{1i}c_{1i} + a_{2i}c_{2i} + \cdots + a_{ni}c_{ni} \qquad 1 \leqslant i \leqslant n \tag{1.65}$$

The cofactor c_{ij} is the signed minor of the element a_{ij} of $[A]$,

$$c_{ij} \equiv (-1)^{i+j} \det [M] \tag{1.66}$$

and the minor is the determinant of the matrix M formed by deleting the ith row and jth column from the matrix $[A]$. Hence, d is determined by n determinants of order $n-1$, which are each evaluated by $n-1$ determinants of order $n-2$, etc., until one arrives at evaluation of a second-order determinant where c_{ij} is a single number. The operations count required for evaluating $\det[A]$ is one reason why (1.64) is rarely used.

Some additional pertinent terminology includes:

order (n) $\equiv$ the number of rows or columns of a matrix $[A]$
submatrix $\equiv$ any matrix formed by deleting rows and/or columns from a matrix $[A]$
rank (r) $\equiv$ the order of the largest submatrix of $[A]$ for which the determinant is nonvanishing
nonsingular $\equiv$ matrix $[A]$ for which $r = n$
singular $\equiv$ a matrix $[A]$ for which $r < n$

This completes the key introductory elements.

Problems

1 Let $A = \begin{bmatrix} 2 & 1 \\ 1 & 3 \end{bmatrix}$, $B = \begin{bmatrix} -2 & 0 \\ 3 & 4 \end{bmatrix}$, $C = \begin{bmatrix} 3 & 2 & 0 \\ 1 & 0 & 4 \end{bmatrix}$

If they exist, evaluate

(*a*) $A + B$, $B + A$ (*b*) $(A + B)^T$, $A^T + B^T$ (*c*) AB (*d*) BC
(*e*) AC^T (*f*) AB^TC (*g*) $\det A$ (*h*) $\det AB$

2 Determine the rank of $D = \begin{bmatrix} 6 & 1 & 8 & 3 \\ 2 & 3 & 0 & 2 \\ 4 & -1 & -8 & -3 \end{bmatrix}$

3 Solve the system of equations for x, y and z.

$$\begin{bmatrix} 2 & -1 & 3 \\ -1 & 2 & 1 \\ 3 & 1 & -4 \end{bmatrix} \begin{Bmatrix} x \\ y \\ z \end{Bmatrix} = \begin{Bmatrix} 8 \\ 4 \\ 0 \end{Bmatrix}$$

4 Find all the solutions of the equation system

$$\begin{bmatrix} -4 & 3 & -1 \\ 8 & 1 & 2 \end{bmatrix} \begin{Bmatrix} x \\ y \\ z \end{Bmatrix} = \{0\}$$

5 Solve the equation system by Gauss elimination

$$\begin{bmatrix} 1 & -1 & 3 & -3 \\ -5 & 2 & -5 & 4 \\ -3 & -4 & 7 & -2 \\ 2 & 3 & 1 & -11 \end{bmatrix} \begin{Bmatrix} w \\ x \\ y \\ z \end{Bmatrix} = \begin{Bmatrix} 3 \\ -5 \\ 7 \\ 1 \end{Bmatrix}$$

6 Find the inverse of A and check $A^{-1}A = I$.

$$A = \begin{bmatrix} 0 & 0 & 1 \\ 0 & 1 & 0 \\ 1 & 0 & 0 \end{bmatrix}$$

REFERENCES

Argyris, J. H. (1963). *Recent Advances in Matrix Methods of Structural Analysis,* Pergamon, Elmsford, N.Y.

Aubin, J. P. (1972). *Approximation of Elliptic Boundary Value Problems,* Wiley-Interscience, New York.

Babuska, I. and Aziz, A. K. (1972). Lectures on the Mathematical Foundations of the Finite Element Method, in A. K. Aziz (ed.), *Mathematical Foundations of the Finite Element Method with Applications to Partial Differential Equations,* Academic, New York, pp. 1–345.

Baker, A. J. (1971). A Finite Element Computational Theory for the Mechanics and Thermodynamics of a Viscous Compressible Multi-Species Fluid. Bell Aerospace Research Rept. 9500-920200.

Baker, A. J. (1973). Finite Element Solution Algorithm for Viscous Incompressible Fluid Dynamics. *Int. J. Num. Meth. Eng.,* vol. 6, pp. 89–101.

Baker, A. J. (1974). A Finite Element Algorithm for the Navier-Stokes Equations. NASA CR-2391.

Chung, T. J. and Chiou, J. N. (1976). Analysis of Unsteady Compressible Boundary Layer Flow Via Finite Elements. *Computers Fluids,* vol. 4, pp. 1–12.

Ciarlet, P. G. and Raviart, P. A. (1972). General Lagrange and Hermite Interpolation in R^n with Applications to the Finite Element Method. *Arch. Rat. Mech. Anal.,* vol. 46, pp. 177–199.

Clough, R. W. (1960). The Finite Element Method in Plane Stress Analysis. *Proc. 2d Conf. Electronic Computation,* American Society of Civil Engineers, Pittsburgh, Pennsylvania, pp. 345–378.

Evans, M. E. and Harlow, F. H. (1957). The Particle-in-Cell Method for Hydrodynamic Calculations. Los Alamos Scientific Lab., Rept. No. LA-2139, Los Alamos, New Mexico.

Finlayson, B. A. (1972). *The Method of Weighted Residuals and Variational Principles,* Academic, New York.

Galerkin, B. G. (1915). Series Occurring in Some Problems of Elastic Stability of Rods and Plates. *Eng. Bull.,* vol. 19, pp. 897–908.

Huebner, K. H. (1975). *Finite Element Method for Engineers,* Wiley, New York.

Kreyszig, E. (1967). *Advanced Engineering Mathematics,* Wiley, New York.

Lions, J. L. and Magenes, E. (1972). Non-Homogeneous Boundary-Value Problems and Applications, Vol. I (Trans. from 1963 French Edition by P. Kenneth), Springer-Verlag.

Lynn, P. O. (1974). Least Squares Finite Element Analysis of Laminar Boundary Layers. *Int. J. Num. Meth. Eng.,* vol. 8, pp. 865–876.

Oden, J. T. (1972). *Finite Elements of Nonlinear Continua,* McGraw-Hill, New York.

Oden, J. T. and Reddy, J. N. (1976). *Introduction to Mathematical Theory of Finite Elements,* Wiley, New York.

Olson, M. E. (1972). Formulation of a Variational Principle-Finite Element Method for Viscous Flows. *Proc. Variational Meth., Eng.,* Southampton University, pp. 5.27–5.38.

Patankar, S. V. (1980). *Numerical Heat Transfer and Fluid Flow,* Hemisphere, Washington, D.C.

Popinski, Z. and Baker, A. J. (1976). An Implicit Finite Element Algorithm for the Boundary Layer Equations, *J. Comp. Phys.,* vol. 21, no. 1, pp. 55–84.

Rayleigh, J. W. S. (1877). *Theory of Sound,* 1st Ed., Revised, Dover, New York, 1945.

Richtmyer, R. D. and Morton, K. W. (1967). Difference Methods of Initial-Value Problems, 2d Ed., Interscience, New York.

Ritz, W. (1909). *Uber Eine Neue Methode zur Losung Gewisser Variations–Probleme der Mathematischen Physik, J. Reine Angew. Math.,* vol. 135, no. 1, p. 1.

Roache, P. J. (1972). *Computational Fluid Mechanics,* Hermosa, Albuquerque, New Mexico.

Strang, G. and Fix, G. J. (1973). *An Analysis of the Finite Element Method,* Prentice Hall, Englewood Cliffs, New Jersey.

Turner, M., Clough, R., Martin, H., and Topp, L. (1956). Stiffness and Deflection Analysis of Complex Structures, *J. Aero. Sci.,* vol. 23, no. 9, pp. 805–823.

Weinstock, R. (1952). *The Calculus of Variations,* McGraw-Hill, New York.

Zienkiewicz, O. C. and Cheung, Y. K. (1965). Finite Elements in the Solution of Field Problems, *The Engineer,* pp. 507–510.

CHAPTER

TWO

THE FINITE-ELEMENT METHOD, AN INTRODUCTION

2.1 OVERVIEW

Many of the finite-element techniques in use today were founded in structural analysis about 20 years ago, although the original concepts date back almost a century. The balance of forces in a stationary structure was the foundation for the initial formulation. However, mathematicians soon recognized the existence of an equivalent variational principle, and the powerful variational calculus became the theoretical foundation for numerical structural design analysis. The engineer could then rely on existence of bounds on predicted system behavior as a consequence of the theoretical basis.

As a result of this evolution, the partial differential equation description of structural mechanics rarely finds use as the means for developing or utilizing the algorithm. This accounts in large part for the unfamiliarity that a fluid dynamicist feels, for example, with the finite-element method. However, a connection must exist between finite-element variational principles and finite-difference handling of partial differential equations in fluid mechanics. The connecting concepts have emerged, and this chapter is designed to bridge the gap between linear mechanics problems, cast in terms of a variational principle, and the corresponding partial differential equation description. This will place the finite-element algorithm on a firm foundation for analysis of the more general problems in fluid mechanics as characterized by systems of partial differential equations. The restriction to linearity also provides for development of the essence of accuracy and convergence, hence development of the theoretical foundation for later use in nonlinear problem analysis.

2.2 STRAIN ENERGY MINIMIZATION FOR THE FIRST LAW*

In classical mechanics, one may directly apply momentum principles (Newton's law) or use the alternative approach of energy minimization. Finite-element principles and procedures have evolved using the latter. Consider the free-body diagram of a device under thermal and mechanical loading shown in Fig. 2.1. The energy imparted to the device is expressed by the first law of thermodynamics,

$$de \equiv đQ - đW \tag{2.1}$$

which states that an incremental change in internal energy de of the system results from an increment $đQ$ of the heat added to, and increment $đW$ of work done by, the device on the surroundings. The differential overbar signifies that both processes may be path dependent.

Neglecting heat addition for the moment, the external (constraint) forces place the device in a state of stress. The total potential (strain) energy imparted to the body equals the work (force $\times$ distance) performed by the force increments $d\mathbf{F}_i$. Expressing forces in terms of stress τ (force/area), and distance in terms of strain ϵ (length change/length), the strain energy I of the body (Shames, 1964, pp. 341–347) is the integral of the incremental work on the n-dimensional domain R^n occupied by the device:

$$I \equiv \int_{R^n} de = \int_{R^n} \int_0^{\epsilon} \tau \, d\epsilon \, dv \tag{2.2}$$

For a perfect (linear isotropic) elastic medium, the stress tensor τ and the strain tensor ϵ are related linearly by Hooke's law. Hence, the integrand in (2.2) can be expressed as an exact quadratic differential in either stress or strain:

$$I = \int_{R^n} \int_0^{\epsilon} f(\epsilon, \nu, E) \, d\epsilon \, dv = \int_{R^n} \int_0^{f} df(\tfrac{1}{2}\epsilon^2, \nu, E) \, dv \tag{2.3}$$

In (2.3), f is a known function of its argument, and ν and E (Poisson's ratio and Young's modulus, respectively) are the constitutive properties of R^n that identify the material.

The primary determination of a finite-element analysis is the resultant vector displacement field $\mathbf{u}(x_i)$, $1 \leqslant i \leqslant n$, on R^n, and on its boundary ∂R, due to the loading. This is accomplished by minimization of the strain energy (2.3) with respect to all admissible displacement fields (Zienkiewicz, 1977, Chap. 2). The exact solution is that field $\mathbf{u}_0(x_i)$ that analytically renders (2.3) a minimum. To determine the discrete approximation $\mathbf{u}^h$ to $\mathbf{u}_0$, it is necessary first to subdivide the domain

*This section is intended primarily to acquaint the engineer who has a finite-element structures background with a nomenclature. The nonstructures-oriented engineer might proceed directly to the next section after reading the first paragraph.

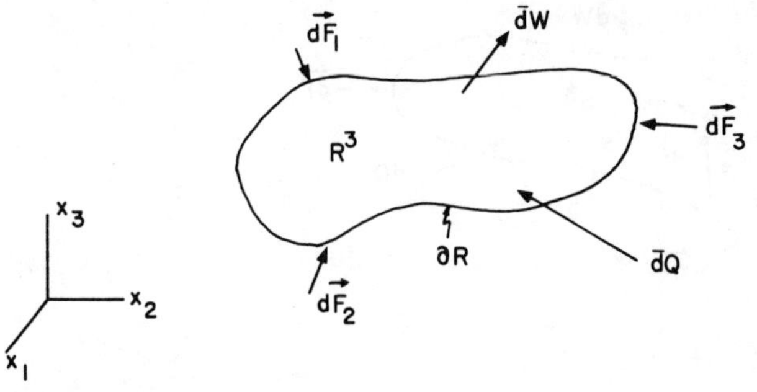

Figure 2.1 A region of R^3 subjected to external force and thermal loading.

R^n into a system of disjoint interior subdomains R_e^n, named finite elements (see Fig. 2.2). Within each finite-element domain, one assumes a functional expression for the local displacement field $\mathbf{u}_e^h(x_i)$. For example, one candidate is a truncated power series in the coordinates x_i, modified by expansion coefficients expressing $\mathbf{u}^h$ in terms of its scalar components parallel to the coordinate axes. Denoting these displacements as u, v, and w, and signifying a column matrix as $\{\cdot\}$, and a row matrix as the transpose $\{\cdot\}^T$, the finite-element approximation to the local displacement field could be (see Problem 1 at the end of this section):

$$\begin{aligned}\mathbf{u}_e^h(x_i) &\equiv u_e^h(x_i)\,\hat{\mathbf{i}} + v_e^h(x_i)\,\hat{\mathbf{j}} + w_e^h(x_i)\,\hat{\mathbf{k}} \\ &= [a_1 + a_2x + a_3y + a_4z + a_5xy + \cdots + \cdots]\,\hat{\mathbf{i}} \\ &\quad + [b_1 + b_2x + b_3y + \cdots \qquad + \cdots]\,\hat{\mathbf{j}} \\ &\quad + [c_1 + c_2x + c_3y + \cdots \qquad + \cdots]\,\hat{\mathbf{k}} \end{aligned} \tag{2.4}$$

Note that the terms in brackets are similar in form. Leaving the details for later, the matrix equivalent of (2.4) is

$$\mathbf{u}_e^h(x_i) = \{N_k(x_i)\}^T\{U\}_e\,\hat{\mathbf{i}} + \{N_k(x_i)\}^T\{V\}_e\,\hat{\mathbf{j}} + \{N_k(x_i)\}^T\{W\}_e\,\hat{\mathbf{k}} \tag{2.5}$$

The elements of the column matrix $\{N_k(x_i)\}$ are kth degree polynomials written on the coordinates x_i, $1 \leqslant i \leqslant n$, and are termed a cardinal basis, that is, a standardized form. Since each scalar displacement is interpolated by the same $\{N_k\}$, (2.5) can be equivalently written as

$$\begin{aligned}\mathbf{u}_e^h(x_i) &= \{N_k(x_i)\}^T[\{U\}_e\,\hat{\mathbf{i}} + \{V\}_e\,\hat{\mathbf{j}} + \{W\}_e\,\hat{\mathbf{k}}] = \{N_k(x_i)\}^T\{\mathbf{U}\}_e \\ &= \{N_k(x_i)\}^T\{UJ\}_e\,\hat{\mathbf{e}}_j \end{aligned} \tag{2.6}$$

where $1 \leqslant (j, J) \leqslant 3$ is associated one-to-one with scalar components x, y, z (x_1, x_2, x_3) and displacements u, v, and w.

The elements of the column matrix $\{UJ\}_e$ are the approximation to the displacements at the node points of R_e^n parallel to the x, y, and z coordinate directions. (Using higher degree polynomials, one can also introduce derivatives of the displacements as expansion coefficients, as will be illustrated.) Continuing to avoid detail, insert (2.6) into (2.3) to form the finite-element approximation I^h to

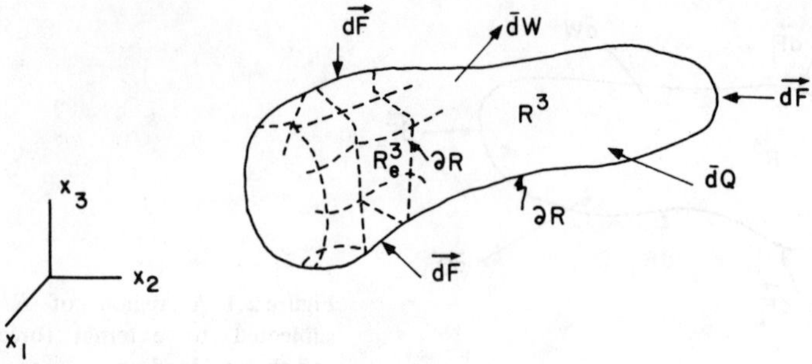

Figure 2.2 A region of R^3 subjected to external loading and discretized for a finite element analysis.

total strain energy of the loaded structure. The integral over R^n now becomes summation of the integrals over each finite-element domain R_e^n.

$$I^h \equiv \sum_{e=1}^{M} I_e = \sum_{e=1}^{M} \sum_{J=1}^{n} \int_{R_e^n} f(\tfrac{1}{2}\{UJ\}_e^T \{N_k(x_i)\}\{N_k(x_i)\}^T \{UJ\}_e, \nu, E)\, dv \quad (2.7)$$

where M is the total number of finite elements. Since the elements of $\{UJ\}$ are constants, they can be extracted from the integrand, yielding

$$I^h = \sum_{e=1}^{M} \sum_{J=1}^{n} \{UJ\}_e^T \int_{R_e^n} f(\tfrac{1}{2}\{N_k(x_i)\}\{N_k(x_i)\}^T, \nu, E)\, dv \{UJ\}_e \quad (2.8)$$

For ν and E constant, the integrand in (2.8) contains polynomials up to degree $2k$. Their integration is easy, and the integral yields a square matrix of order equal to $\{UJ\}_e$. Performing the summations over $1 \leqslant J \leqslant n$ and $1 \leqslant e \leqslant M$, the approximation I^h to I, Eq. (2.3), becomes

$$I^h \equiv \tfrac{1}{2}\{U\}^T [K(\nu, E)]\{U\} \quad (2.9)$$

The order of the column matrix of unknowns $\{U\}$ in (2.9) is equal to the total number of unknown displacements for the entire structure.

The numerical determination of the displacement field, resulting from the applied load distribution, occurs for (2.9) taking its minimum value. The sole variables remaining in (2.9) are the elements U_γ of the global discrete displacement matrix $\{U\}$. Hence, minimization of (2.9) is achieved by differentiation with respect to each element of $\{U\}$ and setting the resultant equation to zero. Therefore,

$$\frac{\partial I^h}{\partial U1} \equiv 0$$

$$\frac{\partial I^h}{\partial U2} \equiv 0$$

$$\frac{\partial I^h}{\partial UJ} \equiv 0$$

$$\vdots$$

or, in compact matrix notation,

$$\frac{\partial I^h}{\partial \{U\}} \equiv \{0\} \tag{2.10}$$

Substituting (2.9) into (2.10), and using the matrix equivalent of the chain rule for differentiation, yields the linear algebraic equation system.

$$[K(\nu, E)]\,\{U\} = 0 \tag{2.11}$$

One additional step is required, since $[K]$ in (2.11) must be singular, recall Sec. 1.6. The matrix $\{U\}$ includes one node (at least) whose displacement must be fixed (to prevent rigid body translation). Several other nodes might be fixed as well, by the geometry of the problem, and these all constitute known parameters of the solution. It is necessary to account for the known displacements; conceptually, this is accomplished by partitioning (2.11) into the form

$$\begin{bmatrix} [K_{\alpha\alpha}] & [K_{\alpha\beta}] \\ [K_{\beta\alpha}] & [K_{\beta\beta}] \end{bmatrix} \begin{Bmatrix} \{U_\alpha\} \\ \{U_\beta\} \end{Bmatrix} = \{0\} \tag{2.12}$$

In (2.12), the elements of submatrix $\{U_\beta\}$ contain node point displacements fixed by problem constraints. Performing the matrix inner product between $[K_{\alpha\beta}]$ and $\{U_\beta\}$, and placing this contribution on the right side of (2.12) yields the final equation system

$$[K_{\alpha\alpha}]\,\{U_\alpha\} = -[K_{\alpha\beta}]\,\{U_\beta\} \tag{2.13}$$

This operation has reduced the rank of (2.11) to be identical with the total number of unknown node point displacements. Formally, the solution of (2.13) is

$$\{U_\alpha\} = -[K_{\alpha\alpha}]^{-1}\,[K_{\alpha\beta}]\,\{U_\beta\} \tag{2.14}$$

where $[K_{\alpha\alpha}]^{-1}$ is the inverse matrix of $[K_{\alpha\alpha}]$. The second set of equations in (2.12) is discarded, since the $\{U_\beta\}$ are constrained. The solution (2.14) yields the finite-element approximation $\{U_\alpha\}$ to the nodal displacement field. Coupled with the fixed displacements $\{U_\beta\}$, (2.9) has been minimized to produce the approximation to the displacement vector $\mathbf{u}_0(x_i)$ at the nodes of the finite-element discretization. Using (2.4) or (2.5), displacements can then be established anywhere throughout a finite-element domain R_e^n, hence, the entire physical domain R^n and its boundary ∂R. Therefore, the solution is complete.

This brief exposition has introduced the finite-element approximate minimization of the strain energy functional for the first law. Throughout fluid mechanics, however, the analyst is more familiar with the requirement to generate approximate solutions to partial differential equation systems. The vehicle for the development remains energy conservation, assisted with a modest exposure to variational principles to achieve transition.

Problem

1. Establish the form of (2.5) for a two-dimensional displacement field, $\mathbf{u}_e^h(x, y) = u_e^h(x, y)\hat{\mathbf{i}} + v_e^h(x, y)\hat{\mathbf{j}}$, assuming that u_e^h and v_e^h vary over the two-dimensional domain R_e^2 in a linear fashion, that is,

$$u_e^h(x, y) = a_1 + a_2 x + a_3 y$$
$$v_e^h(x, y) = b_1 + b_2 x + b_3 y$$

2.3 VARIATIONAL FORMULATION FOR STEADY-STATE HEAT CONDUCTION

We now seek the finite-element algorithm construction for the first law of thermodynamics (2.1), for the case where no work is done by the external forces but heat is added ($\bar{d}Q \neq 0$) (see Fig. 2.1). For the linear steady-state case, the energy functional and finite-element algorithm approximation are easily established. The one-dimensional case serves the purpose. As introduced in the previous chapter, we require identification of the function $w(x)$ that (1) is twice differentiable on x; (2) satisfies fixed constraints at the ends of the interval R^1, i.e., $w(x_1) \equiv w_1$, $w(x_2) \equiv w_2$; and yields the solution $T(x)$ that minimizes the energy functional

$$I = \int_{R^1} f\left(x, w, \frac{dw}{dx}\right) dx \tag{2.15}$$

From Chap. 1, we know the answer is that $w(x)$ is the solution to the Euler-Lagrange equation

$$L(w) = \frac{d}{dx}\left[\frac{\partial f}{\partial(dw/dx)}\right] - \frac{\partial f}{\partial w} = 0 \tag{2.16}$$

As the elementary example, the differential equation corresponding to one-dimensional steady-state conduction is

$$L(T) = k\frac{d^2 T}{dx^2} = 0 \tag{2.17}$$

where k is the thermal conductivity, assumed to be constant. The functional f that renders the extremum of (2.15) the equivalent of (2.17) is established by inspection as

$$f = \frac{k}{2}\left(\frac{dT}{dx}\right)^2 \tag{2.18}$$

That this is the appropriate functional is readily verified by direct substitution.

$$\frac{d}{dx}\left[\frac{\partial f}{\partial(dT/dx)}\right] - \frac{\partial f}{\partial T} = \frac{1}{2}\, k \frac{d}{dx}\left(2\frac{dT}{dx}\right) - 0 = k\frac{d^2T}{dx^2} = 0$$

Hence, minimization of the integral

$$I = \int_{R^1} \frac{1}{2}\, k \left(\frac{dT}{dx}\right)^2 dx \tag{2.19}$$

is formally equivalent to solution of the one-dimensional, steady-state heat conduction equivalent of the first law (2.1), with boundary constraints $T(x_1) = T_1$ and $T(x_2) = T_2$.

While (2.15)-(2.16) could serve immediate requirements, generalization to a multidimensional solution domain and more useful boundary conditions is important. The multidimensional equivalent of d/dx is the gradient ∇ with scalar components $\partial/\partial x_i$. The corresponding n-dimensional Euler-Lagrange equation is

$$L(w) = \nabla\cdot\left[\frac{\partial f}{\partial(\nabla w)}\right] - \frac{\partial f}{\partial w} = 0 \tag{2.20}$$

Equation (2.20) is a partial differential equation on $w(x_i)$ that can be equivalently re-expressed in terms of a functional $f(x_i, w, \nabla w)$, and the extremization of the integral

$$I = \int_{R^n} f(x_i, w, \nabla w)\, d\tau \tag{2.21}$$

Recalling (2.15), implied in (2.21) is that $w(x_i)$ is known everywhere on the boundary ∂R of the solution domain R^n. This is inappropriate for the heat conduction form of the first law, (2.1), however, since it is rare that the boundary temperature $T(\bar{x}_i)$ is known everywhere. However, (2.21) is readily generalized to the case where the normal derivative of $w(x_i)$ is constrained in the form

$$\bar{f}(\bar{x}_i, w, \nabla w\cdot\hat{\mathbf{n}}) = 0 \tag{2.22}$$

Employing a Lagrange multiplier λ, the integral expression (2.21) for extremization becomes (Weinstock, 1952).

$$I = \int_{R^n} f(x_i, w, \nabla w)\, d\tau + \lambda \int_{\partial R} g(\bar{x}_i, w, \nabla w)\, d\sigma \tag{2.23}$$

Minimizing (2.23) with respect to the class of admissible functions $w(x_i)$ yields again that $f(x_i, w, \nabla w)$ satisfies the Euler-Lagrange equation (2.20) on R^n. In addition, extremization requires that the relationship

$$\int_{\partial R} \left[\frac{\partial f}{\partial(\nabla w)} \cdot \hat{\mathbf{n}} + \lambda \frac{\partial g}{\partial w} \right] d\sigma = 0 \tag{2.24}$$

hold on those portions of ∂R where (2.22) is applied, that is,

$$\bar{f}(\bar{x}_i, w, \nabla w \cdot \hat{\mathbf{n}}) \equiv \frac{\partial f}{\partial(\nabla w)} \cdot \hat{\mathbf{n}} + \lambda \frac{\partial g}{\partial w} = 0 \tag{2.25}$$

Elsewhere, on the remainder of ∂R, the dependent variable w still satisfies the constraint

$$w(\bar{x}_i) = C(\bar{x}_i)$$

where C is specified. Enforcing the equality in (2.25) determines the appropriate value of λ in (2.23). (See Problem 1 at the end of this section.)

The inverse statement is required for the finite-element algorithm for the steady conduction form of the first law (2.1). In this instance, the partial differential equation and its boundary conditions are well known. Specifically, $T(x_i)$ is a solution on R^n to

$$L(T) = \nabla \cdot k \nabla T + \rho \dot{q} = 0 \tag{2.26}$$

where $\rho \dot{q}$ is some distributed source term. On specified segments of ∂R, $T(\bar{x}_i)$ also satisfies

$$l(T) = k \nabla T \cdot \hat{\mathbf{n}} + h(T - T_r) = 0 \tag{2.27}$$

where h is the convection coefficient for heat exchange with reservoir at temperature T_r. Elsewhere, on the remainder of ∂R, the temperature is fixed, that is,

$$T(\bar{x}_i) = T_b(\bar{x}_i) \tag{2.28}$$

The formulation statement is now determination of the functionals f and g, (2.23), for the integral whose minimization yields (2.26)-(2.28). These functionals are determined by inspection to be

$$f(x_i, T, \nabla T) = \tfrac{1}{2} k \nabla T \cdot \nabla T - \rho \dot{q} T \tag{2.29}$$

$$g(\bar{x}_i, T, \nabla T) = h(\tfrac{1}{2} T^2 - T T_r) \tag{2.30}$$

and $\lambda = +1$ in (2.23). Thus, the energy functional whose minimization is completely equivalent to the heat conduction-convection differential equation statement (2.26)-(2.28) of the first law (2.1) is

$$I = \int_{R^n} (\tfrac{1}{2} k \nabla T \cdot \nabla T - \rho \dot{q} T)\, d\tau + \int_{\partial R} h(\tfrac{1}{2} T - T_r) T \, d\sigma \tag{2.31}$$

Identification of the form (2.31) is the crucial formulational step. Construction of the finite-element approximate solution to (2.26)-(2.28) is based upon an approximate evaluation of (2.31), followed by construction of the extremum. As for the structural problem definition discussed in the previous section, the solution domain R^n with boundary ∂R is discretized into a set of nonoverlapping finite-element domains R_e^n with coincident boundaries ∂R_e; see Fig. 2.2. In each finite-element domain, the temperature distribution is assumed to be adequately represented by a power series truncated at degree k

$$T_e(x) = a + bx + cy + dz + ex^2 + \cdots + pz^k$$
$$\equiv \{N_k(\mathbf{x})\}^T \{Q\}_e \tag{2.32}$$

The second form in (2.32) has explicitly extracted the expansion coefficients as the temperatures at the node points of R_e^n. When the power series is written in this form, the matrix $\{N_k(\mathbf{x})\}$ is called a cardinal, i.e., standardized, basis, and the elements are functions of $\mathbf{x}$ and the nodal coordinates of R_e^n. (Considerable attention is focused on this operation as this chapter develops.)

With identification of (2.32), the energy functional (2.31) can be evaluated approximately as the sum of integrals over R_e^n, that is,

$$I^h \equiv \sum_{e=1}^{M} \int_{R_e^n} f_e(\mathbf{x}, T_e, \nabla T_e)\, d\tau + \int_{\partial R_e \cap \partial R} g_e(\mathbf{x}, T_e)\, d\tau \tag{2.33}$$

For the heat conduction problem, the analytical forms for f_e and g_e are given in (2.29)-(2.30). Hence,

$$f_e \equiv \tfrac{1}{2} k\, \nabla T_e \cdot \nabla T_e - \rho \dot{q} T_e \tag{2.34}$$

$$g_e \equiv \tfrac{1}{2} h T_e^2 - h T_r T_e \tag{2.35}$$

can be evaluated directly using the finite-element approximation (2.32). Specifically, noting that (2.32) is a scalar, and using transposition and the chain rule,

$$f_e = \tfrac{1}{2} k \{Q\}_e^T \nabla \{N_k\} \cdot \nabla \{N_k\}^T \{Q\}_e - \rho \dot{q} \{Q\}_e^T \{N_k\} \tag{2.36}$$

$$g_e = \tfrac{1}{2} h \{Q\}_e^T \{N_k\} \{N_k\}^T \{Q\}_e - h T_r \{Q\}_e^T \{N_k\} \tag{2.37}$$

Assuming $\nabla \{N_k\}$ exists, and is finite and nonzero, one merely inserts (2.36)-(2.37) into (2.33), performs the integrals (which is easy, since they involve only polynomials), and sums over all M. This produces the finite-element approximation to the energy functional as

$$I^h \equiv \sum_{e=1}^{M} I_e = \sum_{e=1}^{M} \left(\int_{R_e^n} f_e\, d\tau + \int_{\partial R_e \cap \partial R} g_e\, d\tau \right)$$
$$\equiv \tfrac{1}{2} \{Q\}^T [K(k, h)] \{Q\} - \{Q\}^T \{F(\dot{q}, hT_r)\} \tag{2.38}$$

In (2.38), each of the element nodal temperatures in $\{Q\}_e$ has been entered in the appropriate location in the global matrix of unknowns $\{Q\}$. This bookkeeping procedure also defines the location for the element matrix contributions in the global "thermal stiffness" matrix $[K(k, h)]$ and "data" matrix $\{F(\dot{q}, hT_r)\}$. Note in particular [see (2.37)] that the thermal stiffness matrix also contains the boundary heat convection coefficient h.

The quadratic form of the first term in (2.38) is functionally identical to the corresponding term in the structural problem statement [see (2.9)]. Using the finite-element approximation (2.32), the scalar I^h has become solely dependent upon the unknown node temperature distribution $\{Q\}$. The gradient of temperature, embedded as an independent variable within the analytical functional form f, (2.29), has disappeared because of the availability of (2.32) to support the differential operations in (2.36). Therefore, the extremum of (2.38) can only be established by differentiation with respect to each available element q_γ of $\{Q\}$, that is,

$$\frac{\partial I^h}{\partial q_1} \equiv 0$$

$$\frac{\partial I^h}{\partial q_2} \equiv 0$$

$$\vdots$$

$$\frac{\partial I^h}{\partial q_n} \equiv 0$$

Recalling the appropriate developments in Sec. 1.6, see (1.57)–(1.59), the equivalent expression is

$$\frac{\partial I^h}{\partial \{Q\}} = \{0\} \tag{2.39}$$

By inserting (2.38) into (2.39), noting the timely occurrence of the one-half's, the "finite-element" steady-state temperature distribution on R^n, and on appropriate segments of ∂R, is determined by solution of the algebraic equation system

$$[K(k, h)]\,\{Q\} = \{F\} \tag{2.40}$$

Note that (2.40) is formally identical to (2.11) for the structures problem. As occurred in that case, the general form (2.39), of the extremization of I^h, can include elements q_β of $\{Q\}$ that in fact are constrained by the Dirichlet boundary condition (2.28). Since these values are known and fixed, they are not available for modification to extremize I^h. Hence, the matrices in (2.40) are partitioned to localize those elements $\{Q_\beta\}$ that are fixed by (2.28). The resultant form for (2.40) is

$$\begin{bmatrix} [K_{\alpha\alpha}] & [K_{\alpha\beta}] \\ [K_{\beta\alpha}] & [K_{\beta\beta}] \end{bmatrix} \begin{Bmatrix} \{Q_\alpha\} \\ \{Q_\beta\} \end{Bmatrix} = \begin{Bmatrix} \{F_\alpha\} \\ \{F_\beta\} \end{Bmatrix} \tag{2.41}$$

Completing the matrix multiplications involving $\{Q_\beta\}$, and discarding the lower partition equation system as inconsistent with $\{Q_\beta\}$ fixed (if retained, they correspond to enforcing an adiabatic wall boundary condition), the equation system of precisely correct rank for determination of $\{Q_\alpha\}$ is

$$[K_{\alpha\alpha}]\,\{Q_\alpha\} = \{F_\alpha\} - [K_{\alpha\beta}]\,\{Q_\beta\} \tag{2.42}$$

The formal solution for the node point temperature distribution is

$$\{Q_\alpha\} = [K_{\alpha\alpha}]^{-1}(\{F_\alpha\} - [K_{\alpha\beta}]\,\{Q_\beta\}) \tag{2.43}$$

As noted, and in comparison to (2.11), the "thermal stiffness" matrix $[K]$ contains both thermal conductivity and boundary convection contributions, while the matrix $\{F\}$ contains data from thermal input loads throughout R^n and on ∂R, as well as the loads due to fixed boundary temperatures. Hence, the extremization of the approximation I^h to the energy functional (2.31) has yielded an approximate solution to the more familiar statement (2.26)-(2.28). Hopefully, this overview presentation has served to dispel some of the typical initial uneasiness. The next step is to fill in the details for an elementary but highly informative problem.

Problems

1 Prove that the functionals f and g, (2.29) and (2.30), indeed yield the partial differential equation description (2.26) and (2.27), upon minimization of the functional (2.31) with the definition $\lambda = 1$.

2 Obtain the forms for f_e and g_e, (2.36)-(2.37), using (2.32) in (2.34)-(2.35).

2.4 A SOLUTION USING LINEAR FINITE ELEMENTS

In Chap. 1, we determined the analytical solution for one-dimensional heat conduction in a thin rod. For the considerable insight it provides, the one-dimensional heat conduction problem is pursued throughout this chapter for illustration. Furthermore, since error is an intrinsic part of numerical solutions, the example problem is chosen such that a truncated power series cannot yield the exact solution. Therefore (see Fig. 2.3), consider the radial conduction of heat through an axisymmetric cylinder on R^1, that is, $r_1 \leqslant r \leqslant r_2$, with thermal loading provided by convection on the interior surface ∂R, that is, $r = r_1$. The governing differential equation statement (2.26)-(2.28) is

$$L(T) = \frac{1}{r}\frac{d}{dr}\left(rk\frac{dT}{dr}\right) = 0 \qquad r_1 < r < r_2 \tag{2.44}$$

$$l(T) = a_1 hT + k\,\nabla T\cdot\hat{\text{n}} - a_3 hT_r = 0 \qquad r = r_1 \tag{2.45}$$

$$T(r_2) = T_b \qquad r = r_2 \tag{2.46}$$

Note that for $a_1 = 1 = a_3$, (2.45) defines convection at $r = r_1$. Setting $a_1 = 0$ and $a_3 = 1$ produces the companion case of a fixed flux $F \equiv hT_r$.

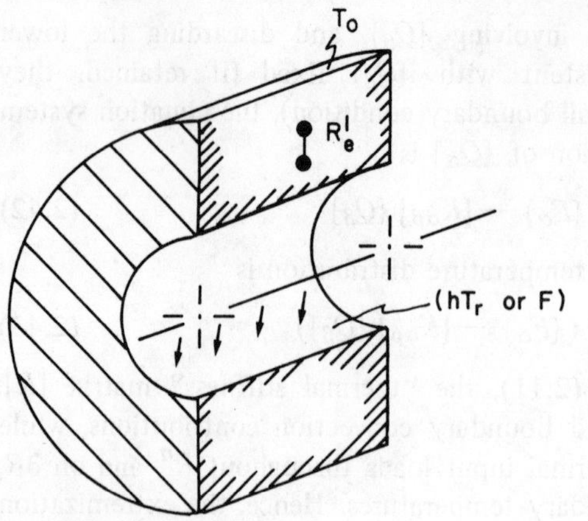

Figure 2.3 Radial conduction in a convectively loaded circular cylinder.

The analytical solution for (2.44)–(2.46) is available (Carslaw and Jaeger, 1959, Chap. 7). The general solution is

$$T(r) = A + B \ln r \tag{2.47}$$

The coefficients A and B are determined by enforcing (2.45)–(2.46). It is left as an exercise to verify that the solution satisfying (2.44)–(2.46) is

$$T(r) = T_b - \left[\frac{a_3 T_r - a_1 T_b}{k/r_1 h - a_1 \ln (r_1/r_2)} \right] \ln \left(\frac{r}{r_2} \right) \tag{2.48}$$

The finite element domain R_e^1 for a one-dimensional problem is a line segment. Referring to (2.34), the lowest degree approximation permitted is the linear polynomial $T_e(r) = a + br$, since only the first derivative of the approximation is required to form the conductivity approximation term (2.36). The first step is to express the finite-element approximation function $T_e = a + br$ in terms of the linear cardinal basis $\{N_1(x)\}$. This is an elementary task on one-dimensional space. Referring to Fig. 2.4, a typical finite-element domain R_e^1, denote the temperature at the left node (1) as $Q1$ and at the right node (2) as $Q2$. Further, define the coordinate translation $\bar{x} = r - R1$, where $R1$ is the radial coordinate of the left node. Then,

$$T_e(r) = a + br = a + b(\bar{x} + R1) \tag{2.49}$$

Evaluate (2.49) at the left and right nodes of R_e^1, yielding

$$T_e(R1) \equiv Q1 = a + b(R1) \tag{2.50}$$
$$T_e(R2) \equiv Q2 = a + b(R2)$$

Equation (2.50) is the matrix system

$$\begin{bmatrix} 1, R1 \\ 1, R2 \end{bmatrix} \begin{Bmatrix} a \\ b \end{Bmatrix} = \begin{Bmatrix} Q1 \\ Q2 \end{Bmatrix}_e \tag{2.51}$$

with solution

$$\begin{Bmatrix} a \\ b \end{Bmatrix} = \begin{bmatrix} 1, R1 \\ 1, R2 \end{bmatrix}^{-1} \begin{Bmatrix} Q1 \\ Q2 \end{Bmatrix}_e \tag{2.52}$$

Substituting (2.52) into (2.49) yields

$$\begin{aligned} T_e(r) &= \{1, r\}\begin{Bmatrix} a \\ b \end{Bmatrix} = \{1, \bar{x} + R1\}\frac{1}{R2 - R1}\begin{bmatrix} R2, & -R1 \\ -1, & 1 \end{bmatrix}\begin{Bmatrix} Q1 \\ Q2 \end{Bmatrix}_e \\ &= \left\{1 - \frac{\bar{x}}{\Delta_e}, \frac{\bar{x}}{\Delta_e}\right\}\begin{Bmatrix} Q1 \\ Q2 \end{Bmatrix}_e \end{aligned} \tag{2.53}$$

where $\Delta_e \equiv R2 - R1$ is the characteristic measure, i.e., length, of the finite element domain R_e^1.

Equation (2.53) defines the elements of the linear cardinal basis $\{N_1(\bar{x})\}$; recall (2.32). For simplicity, define $\zeta_1 \equiv 1 - \bar{x}/\Delta_e$, and $\zeta_2 \equiv \bar{x}/\Delta_e$. Hence,

$$\{N_1(\bar{x})\} = \begin{Bmatrix} \zeta_1 \\ \zeta_2 \end{Bmatrix} \equiv \begin{Bmatrix} 1 - \dfrac{\bar{x}}{\Delta_e} \\ \dfrac{\bar{x}}{\Delta_e} \end{Bmatrix} \tag{2.54}$$

Referring again to Fig. 2.4, note that ζ_1 is the normalized coordinate that is unity at node 1 and zero at node 2. Conversely, ζ_2 is unity at node 2 and zero at node 1. Hence, ζ_i is the (linearly dependent) natural coordinate system spanning R_e^1, the components of which form the elements of the linear cardinal basis $\{N_1(\bar{x})\}$. (We will see that the concept of natural coordinates extends to multidimensional domains, Chap. 3, and to construction of more complete, i.e., higher degree, approximation polynomials.)

Therefore, the cardinal basis form of the linear finite element approximation (2.49) is

$$T_e(r) = \{N_1(\bar{x})\}^T \{Q\}_e \tag{2.55}$$

The algorithm formulation step is to evaluate the element functionals f_e and g_e; see (2.36)-(2.37). Substituting the derivative of (2.53) into (2.36),

Figure 2.4 One-dimensional finite element and natural coordinate system.

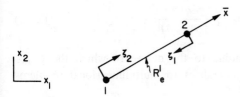

$$f_e = \frac{k}{2\Delta_e^2}\{Q\}_e^T\begin{Bmatrix}-1\\1\end{Bmatrix}\{-1, 1\}\{Q\}_e = \frac{k}{2\Delta_e^2}\{Q\}_e^T\begin{bmatrix}1 & -1\\-1 & 1\end{bmatrix}\{Q\}_e \qquad (2.56)$$

is the approximation to the thermal conductivity term in I_e. Assuming the left node of the first element of the discretization coincides with the convection surface (Fig. 2.3), then $\zeta_1 \doteq 1$ and $\zeta_2 = 0$, in (2.53), yielding for (2.37)

$$g_e = g_1 = \frac{h}{2}\{Q\}_1^T\begin{bmatrix}1 & 0\\0 & 0\end{bmatrix}\{Q\}_1 - hT_r\{Q\}_1\begin{Bmatrix}1\\0\end{Bmatrix} \qquad (2.57)$$

In (2.57), the subscript notation $e \Rightarrow 1$ emphasizes that this contribution occurs only in formation of I_1.

Equations (2.56)-(2.57) permit evaluation of the thermal conductivity and convection contribution to the elemental energy functional I_e, hence determination of the energy approximation I^h (2.38). For the radial problem, $d\tau = r\,dr\,d\theta = 2\pi r\,dr$ and $d\sigma = r_1\,d\theta = 2\pi r_1$. Hence,

$$I_e \equiv \int_{R_e^1} f_e\,d\tau + \int_{\partial R_e} g_e\,d\sigma = \frac{2\pi k}{2\Delta_e^2}\{Q\}_e^T\begin{bmatrix}1 & -1\\-1 & 1\end{bmatrix}\{Q\}_e\int_{R_e^1} r\,dr$$
$$+\ \delta_{e1}2\pi r_1\left(\frac{h}{2}\{Q\}_e^T\begin{bmatrix}1 & 0\\0 & 0\end{bmatrix}\{Q\}_e - hT_r\{Q\}_e^T\begin{Bmatrix}1\\0\end{Bmatrix}\right) \qquad (2.58)$$

In (2.58), δ_{e1} is the element Kronecker delta, which is zero except when $e = 1$, that is, the first element. The only integral remaining to evaluate is $\int r\,dr = \frac{1}{2}r^2 + C$, where C depends upon the specific element. To unify the process, and expose a concept, note that since r varies linearly on R^1, it can be interpolated on R_e^1 in terms of its nodal values using the linear cardinal basis $\{N_1(\bar{x})\}$. Therefore,

$$r(r) = \{N_1(\bar{x})\}^T\{R\}_e \qquad (2.59)$$

and the elements of $\{R\}_e$ are $R1$ and $R2$; see (2.50). Hence, noting that $dr = d\bar{x}$

$$\int_{R_e^1} r\,dr = \{R\}_e^T\int_{R_e^1}\{N_1(\bar{x})\}\,d\bar{x} = \Delta_e\{R\}_e^T\begin{Bmatrix}\frac{1}{2}\\\frac{1}{2}\end{Bmatrix} \qquad (2.60)$$

The integrals in (2.60) are easy to evaluate by direct substitution of ζ_1 and ζ_2, (2.54). However, they are even easier to evaluate using the closed form solution

$$\int_{R_e^1}\zeta_1^p\zeta_2^q\,d\bar{x} = \Delta_e\frac{p!q!}{(1+p+q)!} \qquad (2.61)$$

In (2.61), p and q are integers corresponding to the degree to which the ζ_i are raised. Importantly, this expression also generalizes to multidimensional problems and to more complete cardinal bases.

With (2.60) the final form for I_e (2.58), using the linear element approximation (2.55) is at hand. Deleting the 2π multiplier for convenience, substituting (2.60) into (2.58) and rearranging, the finite-element approximation I^h to the thermal energy functional (2.31) is

$$I^h \equiv \sum_{e=1}^{M} \left[\frac{1}{2} \{Q\}_e^T \left(\frac{k}{\Delta_e} \{R\}_e^T \begin{Bmatrix} \frac{1}{2} \\ \frac{1}{2} \end{Bmatrix} \begin{bmatrix} 1 & -1 \\ -1 & 1 \end{bmatrix} \{Q\}_e \right) + \frac{1}{2} \{Q\}_e^T \left(hr_1 \delta_{e1} \begin{bmatrix} 1 & 0 \\ 0 & 0 \end{bmatrix} \{Q\}_e - 2hT_r \delta_{e1} \begin{Bmatrix} 1 \\ 0 \end{Bmatrix} \right) \right] \tag{2.62}$$

Recalling (2.38)-(2.39), the extremization of (2.62) with respect to each eligible member of the set of unknowns in $\{Q\}$ yields the final solution equation statement (2.40). The practical difficulty is that $I^h = I^h(\{Q\}_e)$ in (2.62), rather than $I^h(\{Q\})$. Only for a one-element discretization of R^1 is $\{Q\}_e = \{Q\}$. Otherwise, a bookkeeping procedure is required to track where specific elements of $\{Q\}_e$ are located in $\{Q\}$, which is called the matrix assembly algorithm. This concept is one of the least-publicized "black box" arts of finite-element practice. A detailed derivation is presented in Sec. 2.9. The following two examples specifically illustrate the mechanics of the extremization of (2.62), without the burden of the general formulation.

Example 2.1 Single element solution Determine the extremum of (2.62), hence, solve for the nodal temperature distribution for the thick axisymmetric cylinder problem on R^1 (Fig. 2.3), using a one-element discretization. Assume $r_1 = 1m$, $r = 2m$, $k = 10$ W/m K, $h = 20$ W/m K, $T_r = 1500$ K, and $T_b(r_2) = 306.85282$ K. (Note: For these data, and setting $T_b \equiv 306.85282$ K, the analytical solution for the hot surface temperature is exactly 1000.0 K, for easy accuracy comparisons. Nondimensionalization could also yield numbers for easy reference, but it is important to illustrate insertion of nonhomogeneous data.) Noting that $M = 1$ is the summation limit in (2.62), the energy functional approximation I^h becomes

$$I^h = \sum_{e=1}^{1} \frac{1}{2} \{Q\}_1^T \left(\frac{10}{1} \{1, 2\}_1^T \begin{Bmatrix} \frac{1}{2} \\ \frac{1}{2} \end{Bmatrix} \begin{bmatrix} 1 & -1 \\ -1 & 1 \end{bmatrix} \{Q\}_1 \right) + \frac{1}{2} \{Q\}_1^T \left(20 \begin{bmatrix} 1 & 0 \\ 0 & 0 \end{bmatrix} \{Q\}_1 - 40(1500) \begin{Bmatrix} 1 \\ 0 \end{Bmatrix} \right)$$
$$= \frac{1}{2} \{Q\}^T \left(\begin{bmatrix} 15 + 20, & -15 \\ -15, & 15 \end{bmatrix} \{Q\} - \begin{Bmatrix} 40(1500) \\ 0 \end{Bmatrix} \right) \tag{2.63}$$

The second line in (2.63) explicitly recognizes $\{Q\}_1 = \{Q\}$, and has combined the conduction and convection contributions into the thermal stiffness matrix $[K(k, h)]$, [see (2.38)].

The extremum of (2.63) is evaluated [recall (1.59)] as

$$\frac{\partial I^h}{\partial \{Q\}} = \begin{bmatrix} 35 & -15 \\ -15 & 15 \end{bmatrix} \{Q\} - \begin{Bmatrix} 20(1500) \\ 0 \end{Bmatrix} \equiv \{0\} \tag{2.64}$$

In forming (2.64), we failed to enforce the fact that $T(r_2) = T_b = 306.85282$ K is fixed. Since the second entry in $\{Q\}$ is the nodal temperature at $r = r_2$, partitioning (2.64) and substituting T_b yields

$$\left[\begin{array}{c:c} 35 & -15 \\ \hdashline -15 & 15 \end{array}\right] \left\{\begin{array}{c} Q1 \\ \hdashline 306.8\cdots \end{array}\right\} = \left\{\begin{array}{c} 20(1500) \\ \hdashline 0 \end{array}\right\} \tag{2.65}$$

Deleting the second equation in (2.65), recall (2.41)–(2.42), the matrix solution for $Q1$ is trivial, yielding

$$\{Q\} = \begin{Bmatrix} Q1 \\ Q2 \end{Bmatrix} = \begin{Bmatrix} 988.65120 \\ 306.85282 \end{Bmatrix} \text{K} \tag{2.66}$$

As noted, the analytical surface temperature is 1000.0 K. Hence, this most rudimentary finite-element solution (linear interpolation on one element with convection boundary condition) underpredicts this temperature by only 11.35°, a 1.135 percent error! This surely can be improved by increasing the number and decreasing the span Δ_e of a uniform finite element discretization of R^1. See the following example.

Example 2.2 Two-element discretization solution Discretize the solution domain R^1 into two finite elements of uniform measure $\Delta_e = 0.5$ m (see Fig. 2.5). Proceeding as in Example 2.1, for the first element R_1^1 spanning $1.0 \leqslant r \leqslant 1.5$, the corresponding conductivity contribution to I^h is

$$I_1 = \tfrac{1}{2} \{Q\}_1^T \left(25 \begin{bmatrix} 1 & -1 \\ -1 & 1 \end{bmatrix} \{Q\}_1 \right) \tag{2.67}$$

The convection boundary condition contribution to (2.67) is identical to that in (2.63), since the evaluation is unaffected by the measure Δ_1. For R_2^1, the second element, the conductivity contribution is

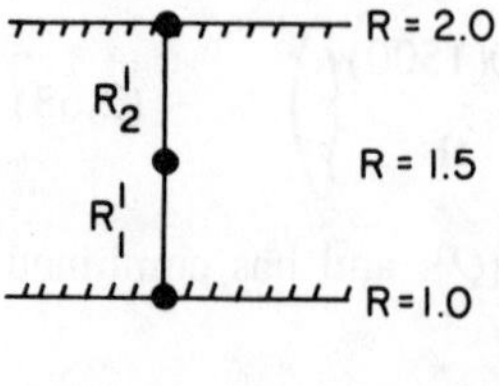

Figure 2.5 Two-element discretization of thick circular cylinder.

$$I_2 = \tfrac{1}{2}\{Q\}_2^T\left(35\begin{bmatrix} 1 & -1 \\ -1 & 1 \end{bmatrix}\{Q\}_2\right) \tag{2.68}$$

and there is no convection contribution. Hence, the approximate energy functional (2.62) for the two-element discretization solution is

$$I^h \equiv \sum_{e=1}^{2} I_e = \tfrac{1}{2}\{Q\}_1^T\left(\begin{bmatrix} 25+20, & -25 \\ -25, & 25 \end{bmatrix}\{Q\}_1 - \begin{Bmatrix} 40(1500) \\ 0 \end{Bmatrix}\right)$$

$$+\tfrac{1}{2}\{Q\}_2^T\begin{bmatrix} 35, & -35 \\ -35, & 35 \end{bmatrix}\{Q\}_2 \tag{2.69}$$

Noting in (2.69) that the second element in $\{Q\}_1$ is identical to the first element in $\{Q\}_2$, that is, the finite-element nodal temperature approximation to $T(r = 1.5)$, the element matrices can be stored, i.e., assembled, into the global equivalent form.

$$I^h = \tfrac{1}{2}\{Q\}^T\left(\begin{bmatrix} 25+20 & -25 & 0 \\ -25 & 25+35 & -35 \\ 0 & -35 & 35 \end{bmatrix}\{Q\} - \begin{Bmatrix} 40(1500) \\ 0 \\ 0 \end{Bmatrix}\right) \tag{2.70}$$

Note that zero elements have been added appropriately to the global $[K(k, h)]$ matrix, yielding the familiar banded (tridiagonal) matrix structure. Further note the matrix $\{Q\}$ is devoid of a subscript, i.e., it is the global dependent variable.

Differentiating (2.70) with respect to $\{Q\}$, [see (2.39)], the solution matrix statement is

$$\left[\begin{array}{cc:c} 45 & -25 & 0 \\ -25 & 60 & -35 \\ \hdashline 0 & -35 & 35 \end{array}\right]\{Q\} = \left\{\begin{array}{c} 20(1500) \\ 0 \\ \hdashline 0 \end{array}\right\} \tag{2.71}$$

Partitioning as indicated, to account for the fixed exterior temperature, reduces the order to a rank exactly equal to the number of unknowns. Discarding the last equation, which is written on the fixed boundary temperature, and transferring the thermal load contribution in the second equation to the right-hand side, yields the final matrix statement.

$$\begin{bmatrix} 45, & -25 \\ -25, & 60 \end{bmatrix}\begin{Bmatrix} Q_1 \\ Q_{1.5} \end{Bmatrix} = \begin{Bmatrix} 30{,}000.0 \\ 10{,}739.84868 \end{Bmatrix} \tag{2.72}$$

The solution of (2.72) for the inner wall and midpoint temperatures, Q_1 and $Q_{1.5}$ respectively, yields

$$\{Q\} = \begin{Bmatrix} Q_1 \\ Q_{1.5} \\ Q_2 \end{Bmatrix} = \begin{Bmatrix} 996.86565 \\ 594.35816 \\ 306.85282 \end{Bmatrix} \text{K} \tag{2.73}$$

The improvement in accuracy of the interior wall temperature compared to the one-element solution is substantial. The two-element solution has also produced an approximation to the midcylinder temperature. A four-element solution further improves the prediction accuracy. Table 2.1 lists nodal solutions as a function of M, for a range of conductivities and convection coefficients.

In addition to cardinal basis and discretization, the specified form of the boundary conditions affects solution accuracy. For example, repeat Example 2.2 replacing the convection boundary condition with the specified heat flux as a gradient boundary condition that yields the surface temperature of 1000.0 K. The exact solution to (2.44)-(2.46), for $a_1 = 0$ in (2.45), yields $F = 10{,}000$ W/m^2.

Example 2.3 Two-element discretion with fixed flux boundary The conductivity contributions of Example 2.2 are unchanged. The boundary condition contribution for R_1^1 is altered, and now becomes only the second term in I_1 [see (2.69)], i.e.,

$$-\tfrac{1}{2}\{Q\}_1^T \begin{Bmatrix} 40(1500) \\ 0 \end{Bmatrix}$$

The extremization of I^h, recall (2.69)-(2.71), yields the matrix solution statement

$$\left[\begin{array}{cc:c} 25 & -25 & 0 \\ -25 & 60 & -35 \\ \hdashline 0 & -35 & 35 \end{array}\right] \{Q\} = \left\{\begin{array}{c} 10{,}000 \\ 0 \\ \hdashline 0 \end{array}\right\} \tag{2.74}$$

Comparing (2.74) with (2.71), note the change in the (1,1) element of $[K(k, h)]$ as well as the load vector. The solution of (2.74), after partitioning to account for the fixed exterior surface temperature, is

$$\{Q\} = \begin{Bmatrix} Q_1 \\ Q_{1.5} \\ Q_2 \end{Bmatrix} = \begin{Bmatrix} 992.56710 \\ 592.56710 \\ 306.85282 \end{Bmatrix} \text{K} \tag{2.75}$$

Comparing (2.75) to (2.73), the accuracy of the predicted surface temperature for fixed flux is appreciably poorer, even though the specified heat flux was exact. Hence, the form of the boundary condition indeed influences accuracy, as would be expected.

Table 2.1 Finite-element predicted node temperature distributions radial conduction in thick axisymmetric cylinder

Boundary condition	No. of finite elements	Thermal conductivity, W/m K	Node radial coordinates 1.0	1.25	1.50	1.75	2.0
Convection, $h = 20$,	1		1416.75717				306.85282
W/m² K	2	1.0	1418.91230		770.21095		306.85282
	4		1419.51460	1061.80180	769.12778	521.48048	306.85282
Analytical		1.0	1419.72336	1061.45907	768.73583	521.24185	306.85282
Convection, $h = 20$	1		988.65120				306.85282
	2	10.0	996.86565		594.35816		306.85282
	4		999.19105	776.60929	594.49694	440.40188	306.85282
Analytical ‡		10.0	1000.00000	776.85645	594.53489	440.38421	306.85282
Fixed flux	1		973.51949				306.85282
	2	10.0	992.56710		592.56710		306.85282
	4		998.07272	775.85049	594.03231	440.18615	306.85282
Convection, $h = 20$	1		605.13962				306.85282
	2	40.0	611.48614		433.78337		306.85282
	4		613.30383	514.78204	434.17329	365.96589	306.85282
Analytical		40.0	613.93833	515.07888	434.30482	366.01133	306.85282

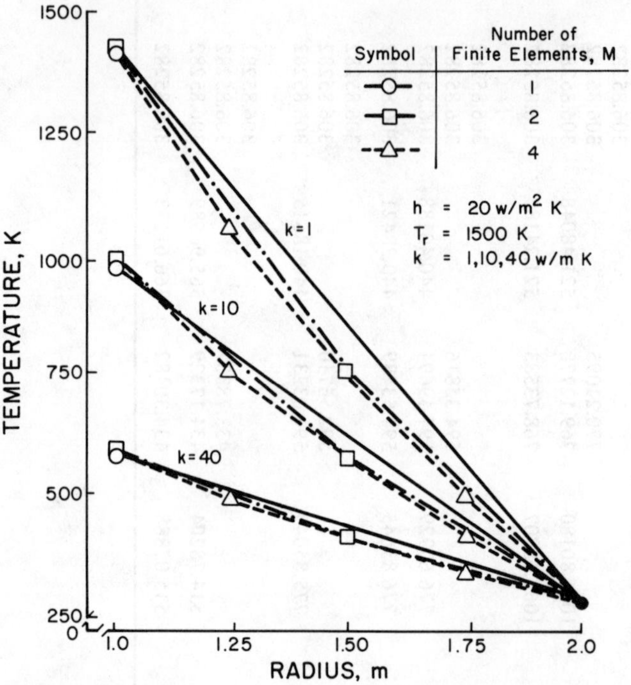

Figure 2.6 Computed steady-state temperature distributions in axisymmetric cylinder, linear finite-element solution.

These elementary examples have illustrated several key aspects of finite-element solution methodology, in particular formation of the approximate energy functional (2.62), assembly of finite element contributions into the global functional, cf. (2.70), extremization of the approximation (2.71), and reduction of matrix rank of the resultant algebraic equation system to account for fixed temperature boundary conditions, cf. (2.72). These numerical solution data are graphed in Fig. 2.6. The accuracy of the approximate solutions improves uniformly as the number of finite elements spanning R^1 increases (Table 2.1). Furthermore, the absolute accuracy depends on the boundary condition statement, for any discretization, as well as the levels of thermal properties. It is now appropriate to correlate these observations and data within a theoretical framework, and then to expand upon factors affecting solution accuracy.

Problems

1 Verify the analytical solution (2.48) for the radial heat conduction equation system (2.44)–(2.46).

2 Verify (2.53).

3 Verify (2.60) by direct integration and using (2.61).

4 Verify (2.63).

5 Verify the scalar multipliers 25 and 35 in (2.67) and (2.68), respectively.

6 Sum the element contributions I_e to form I^h, (2.69)-(2.70).

7 Verify the solution (2.73).

8 Derive (2.74).

2.5 NUMERICAL ERROR AND CONVERGENCE WITH DISCRETIZATION REFINEMENT

The results for the radial conduction problem have introduced the essence of a finite element solution. The linear basis (2.53) is the lowest degree polynomial allowing evaluation of the thermal conductivity contribution (2.36) to the approximate energy functional. The examples confirmed that accuracy was improved by refining the computational grid, such that each elementary approximation spans a smaller domain. These two concepts, i.e., a simple local approximation and grid refinement, account for the considerable success enjoyed by the algorithm in computational mechanics. We now establish a formal statement of solution character, approximation error, and rate of convergence with discretization refinement.

Consider first the alternatives that exist for definition of the finite element approximation. Present purposes are served by a one-dimensional problem domain spanned by the cartesian coordinate x. In place of the sequence of linear finite element polynomials, which generates the approximate temperature solution,

$$T^h(x) \equiv \sum_{e=1}^{M} T_e(x) \equiv \sum_{e=1}^{M} \{N_1(x)\}^T \{Q\}_e \tag{2.76}$$

we could have selected (say) the first N eigenfunctions $\phi_j(x)$ of the separation of variables solution to (2.44) (or an allied problem). Letting C_j represent the unknown expansion coefficients, the approximation (2.76) would then be replaced by

$$T^h(x) = \sum_{j=1}^{N} C_j \phi_j(x) \tag{2.77}$$

In (2.77), each of the $\phi_j(x)$ spans the entire solution domain R^1, that is, $x_1 \leqslant x \leqslant x_2$. Recalling the one-dimensional example of Chap. 1, candidate eigenfunctions ϕ_j could be

$$\phi_j(x) = \sin \frac{j\pi x}{\Delta} = \sin \lambda_j x \tag{2.78}$$

and $\lambda_j = j\pi/\Delta$ is the jth eigenvalue.

The energy functional (2.31), corresponding to the differential equation statement (2.26)-(2.28), can be evaluated directly using (2.77), for no boundary convection, $h = 0$ in (2.30), and $T(0) = T(\Delta) = 0$ for (2.28). The approximate energy functional I^h becomes

$$I^h = \sum_{j=1}^{N} \left[\frac{k\Delta}{4} C_j^2 \lambda_j^2 - \int_0^{\Delta} \rho \dot{q} C_j \phi_j(x)\, dx \right] \tag{2.79}$$

The simple form for the first term in (2.79) occurs since each member of the approximation set is orthogonal to all other members. Minimizing I^h (2.79), with respect to the admissible variables, which are now C_j,

$$\frac{\partial I^h}{\partial C_j} = 0 \qquad 1 \leqslant j \leqslant N$$

produces the (diagonal) matrix equation system

$$C_j = \frac{2}{k\,\Delta\lambda_j^2} \int_0^{\Delta} \rho \dot{q} \phi_j(x)\, dx \tag{2.80}$$

Hence, as occurs in the separation of variables solution, orthogonality of the $\phi_j(x)$ is responsible for each C_j being determined independently, and

$$T^h(x) = \sum_{j=1}^{N} \left(\frac{2}{k\,\Delta\lambda_j^2} \int_{\Delta} \rho \dot{q} \phi_j\, dx \right) \phi_j(x) \qquad j = 1, 2, \ldots, N \tag{2.81}$$

Hence, the approximation (2.77) has projected the exact solution

$$T(x) = \sum_{j=1}^{\infty} \left(\frac{2}{k\,\Delta\lambda_j^2} \int_{\Delta} \rho \dot{q} \phi_j\, dx \right) \phi_j(x) \qquad j = 1, 2, \ldots, N, \ldots, \tag{2.82}$$

onto its first N eigenfunctions. This corresponds identically to the separation of variables solution, and higher accuracy can be achieved by increasing N. However, this theoretical appeal is rather mitigated by the constraints placed on the formulation, specifically, no convection at the boundary and vanishing temperature at $x = 0$ and Δ. These are difficult to overcome in a general way, and extension of the concept to a general purpose, multidimensional computational procedure appears unfeasible.

A second alternative (to using piecewise local interpolation) could be to extend the approximate solution in a power series spanning the entire solution domain, i.e.,

$$T^h(x) = T(0) + \sum_{j=1}^{N} C_j x^j \tag{2.83}$$

The approximate functional I^h (2.31) is readily evaluable, and (2.83) can be adjusted easily to include the convection boundary condition. Minimizing the approximation I^h with respect to the variables C_j and equating to zero yields the matrix system

$$\sum_{j=1}^{N} K_{ij} C_j = f_i \qquad 1 \leq i \leq N \tag{2.84}$$

Equation (2.84) is identical to the original Galerkin procedure (Finlayson and Scriven, 1966). For a one-dimensional problem, the concept is viable for $N < 6$, after which round-off error in determining the matrix coefficients of $[K]$ becomes intolerable. The contributing factor to this loss of precision is that the polynomials in (2.83) do not form an orthogonal set. Hence, this formulation is completely devoid of the desirable properties of the previous construction (2.77), that is, $K_{ij} \rightarrow [K]$ is not a diagonal matrix nor even banded. Hence, solutions with consistently improved accuracy for increasing N cannot be assured and further examination of the concept appears unfruitful.

The summary observations from this exercise are twofold. Approximation by expansion into a series of functions, completely orthogonal on the interval R^1, severely constrains boundary condition flexibility and can yield difficult integral forms to implement the algorithm. However, it does admit improved solution accuracy with use of a more complete basis. The power series expansion (2.83) improves boundary condition flexibility, on one-dimensional space at least. However, since these polynomials are not orthogonal, numerical error eventually swamps the solution as attempts to improve accuracy are made by using a more complete, i.e., higher degree, basis.

The desirable middle ground requires approximations possessing some modicum of orthogonality coupled with assurance of certified reducible error. This is precisely the finite element procedure! Consider Fig. 2.7, the abscissa of which is the x axis discretized into M finite elements, $i = 1, \ldots, j-1, j, j+1, \ldots, M$, with corresponding nodal coordinates $0, \ldots, x_{k-1}, x_k, x_{k+1}, \ldots, \Delta$. Graphed is the spatial dependence in the elements of the local linear polynomial interpolation of

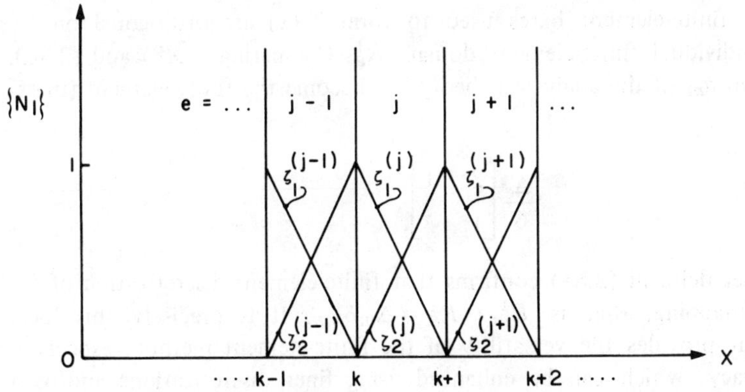

Figure 2.7 Discretization of one-dimensional solution domain illustrating linear basis finite-element solution.

temperature, $T^h = \Sigma_e T_e$ (2.76). The functional dependence in each element R_e^1 is identical with that of the natural coordinates, i.e., expressed in the manner of (2.83), (2.76) becomes

$$T^h(x) = \sum_{e=1}^{M} T_e(x) = \sum_{e=1}^{M} \{N_1(\bar{x})\}^T \{Q\}_e = \sum_{e=1}^{M} \sum_{j=1}^{2} \zeta_j Q_j^e \tag{2.85}$$

Recall (Sec. 1.5), that a function set is orthogonal with respect to a weight function $r(x)$ on the interval $x_1 \leqslant x \leqslant x_2$ provided

$$\int_{x_1}^{x_2} r(x) u_m(x) u_n(x)\, dx = a_m \delta_{nm} \tag{2.86}$$

where δ_{nm} is the Kronecker delta. For the finite element approximation (2.85), the functions similar to $u_n(x)$ are $\zeta_i(x)$, $i = 1, 2$. For $r(x)$ constant, and on a representative finite element domain R_e^1, (2.86) evaluated using (2.85) yields,

$$\int_{R_e^1} \{\zeta\}_e \{\zeta\}_e^T\, dx = \frac{\Delta_e}{6} \begin{bmatrix} 2 & 1 \\ 1 & 2 \end{bmatrix} \tag{2.87}$$

using the integration formula (2.61). Thus, the elements $\zeta_i(x)$ of the finite-element linear basis are not orthogonal on R_e^1. However, extending the interval of integration to the entire domain R^1, the union of R_e^1, (2.87) evaluated for the mth and nth finite elements R_m^1 and R_n^1 yields

$$\int_{R^1 = \cup R_e^1} \{\zeta\}_m \{\zeta\}_n^T\, dx = \frac{\Delta_m}{6} \begin{bmatrix} 2 & 1 \\ 1 & 2 \end{bmatrix} \delta_{nm} \tag{2.88}$$

In (2.88), δ_{nm} is the Kronecker delta, and the equation vanishes unless $m = n$. Thus, the linear finite-element bases used to form $T_e(x)$ are orthogonal on R^1 except on the individual finite-element domain R_e^1. Comparing (2.88) and (2.86), the scalar constant a_m of the analytical theory has become the finite-element (mass) matrix

$$\frac{\Delta_e}{6} \begin{bmatrix} 2 & 1 \\ 1 & 2 \end{bmatrix}$$

and the Kronecker delta in (2.88) confirms that finite-element discretization of R^1 must be nonoverlapping, that is, $R_m^1 \cap R_n^1 = \Delta_m \delta_{mn}$. It is precisely this local orthogonality that provides the versatility of the finite-element method, especially concerning accuracy, which can be enhanced using finer discretizations and/or a more complete basis, as shall be developed.

Therefore, the fundamental question is, "How well can a sequence of linear finite element interpolations approximate the (assumed) smoothly continuous behavior of the exact solution that minimizes the energy functional I, (2.31)?"

Alternatively, as the measure (span) Δ_e of each finite-element domain is reduced, and their total number is correspondingly increased, at what rate does the generated numerical solution converge to the exact solution? Can adequate accuracy be obtained for a practical problem within the bounds of present-day computer hardware resources? The allied question is, therefore, "What is the order of magnitude of the error in a finite-element solution obtained using linear (or other) elements of reasonable size?" And in particular, "How does one measure the accuracy of a finite element solution?" Specifically, is there a scalar measure that is intrinsic to efficient quantization of approximation error? The answers to these questions will each reflect favorably on the finite element method as a viable numerical solution procedure. Unfortunately, their rigorous establishment requires mathematical dexterity beyond that assumed for the reader at the introductory level of this development. Strang and Fix (1973, Chap. 1) develop these answers in mathematical completeness. Herein, we only highlight the results.

The basic requirement is to establish the error measure for the finite-element solution. The development is presently restricted to the linear basis spanning one-dimensional finite-element domains. The fundamental question is, "How close is the finite-element solution

$$T^h(x) \equiv \sum_{e=1}^{M} T_e \equiv \sum_{e=1}^{M} \{N_1(\bar{x})\}^T \{Q\}_e \tag{2.76}$$

to the solution $T(x)$ of Eqs. (2.26)–(2.28)?" The answer, quite simply, is that the finite-element solution lies *as close as possible* to the exact solution in the sense that the "energy" in the approximation error ϵ^h

$$\epsilon^h \equiv T - T^h \tag{2.89}$$

is minimized. The energy functional for the heat conduction problem is (2.31).

$$I \equiv I(T, T) = \int_{R^n} (\tfrac{1}{2} k \nabla T \cdot \nabla T - \rho \dot{q} T)\, d\tau + \int_{\partial R} h(\tfrac{1}{2} T - T_r) T\, d\sigma \tag{2.31}$$

The mathematical definition of the energy inner product is the totality of terms appearing quadratically in the energy functional. Hence, for (2.31), the corresponding energy inner product is

$$E \equiv E(T, T) = \int_{R^n} \tfrac{1}{2} k\, \Delta T \cdot \nabla T\, d\tau + \int_{\partial R} \tfrac{1}{2} h T^2\, d\sigma \tag{2.90}$$

Should the temperature-dependent boundary convection not be applied, the second term in (2.90) is deleted. [Note: the general expression of the energy inner product of u and v is

$$E(u, v) \equiv \sum_{i,j=0}^{m} \int_{R^n} \left(\frac{\partial^i u}{\partial x^i} \frac{\partial^j v}{\partial x^j} \right) dx \tag{2.91}$$

where $2m$ is the order of the differential equation associated with (2.31).]

The proof of the following theorem (Strang and Fix, 1973, pp. 39–41) assures that the energy in ϵ^h is minimum for the extremization of the finite-element approximation to (2.31). $T(x)$ minimizes (2.31), i.e., it is the true solution. Assume $\bar{T}$ is a set containing all (linear) functions admissible for evaluation of (2.31), i.e., all those functions possessing a first derivative that exists and is finite on R_e^1. The finite element solution T^h therefore belongs to the set $\bar{T}$. Another member of $\bar{T}$ would be the linear interpolate of the exact solution $T(x)$, for example. Then:

Theorem I

1. The minimum of the energy functional $I(\bar{T}, \bar{T})$, (2.31), and the minimum of the energy inner product $E(\bar{T}, \bar{T})$, (2.90), is achieved by the same function T^h (2.76) as $\bar{T}$ ranges over all linear function sets, i.e.,

$$E(T - T^h, T - T^h) = \min E(T - \bar{T}, T - \bar{T}) \tag{2.92}$$

2. With respect to the energy inner product (2.90), T^h is the projection of the true solution T onto the space of finite-element basis $\{N_1(\bar{x})\}^T\{Q\}_e$. Equivalently, the error ϵ^h in the finite-element solution is orthogonal to the finite element approximation, i.e.,

$$E(\epsilon^h, T^h) = E(T - T^h, T^h) = 0 \tag{2.93}$$

3. The approximation that minimizes the energy inner product (2.90) is the solution

$$T^h \equiv \sum_{e=1}^{M} T_e(x) \tag{2.76}$$

where T_e is the finite-element interpolation on R_e^1

$$T_e(x) = \{N_1(\bar{x})\}^T\{Q\}_e \tag{2.94}$$

for which the totality of expansion coefficients $\{Q\}_e$, $e = 1, 2, \ldots, M$ are determined by solution of the finite-element algorithm statement (2.38)-(2.39), i.e.,

$$\frac{\partial I^h}{\partial \{Q\}} = \frac{\partial}{\partial \{Q\}} \sum_{e=1}^{M} I_e(\{Q\}_e) \equiv \{0\}$$

4. The energy in the finite-element solution T^h underestimates the energy in the true solution T.

$$E(T - T^h, T - T^h) = E(T, T) - E(T^h, T^h) \tag{2.95}$$

This results directly from (2.92)-(2.93), and states that the energy in the error is equal to the error in the energy. Furthermore, since the left side of (2.95) is a symmetric quadratic form, which must be non-negative,

$$E(T^h, T^h) \leqslant E(T, T) \tag{2.96}$$

Therefore, the energy in the finite element solution always underestimates the energy in the true solution.

Before proceeding further, we can illustrate these concepts by using the example problem data. These evaluations also introduce convergence and error estimation. The energy inner product (2.90), evaluated for the analytical solution (2.48), involves

$$\nabla T \cdot \hat{r} = -\frac{a_3 T_r - a_3 T_b}{k/r_1 h - a_1 \ln(r_1/r_2)} \frac{1}{r} \equiv -\frac{A}{r} \tag{2.97}$$

Hence, for (2.90)

$$E(T, T) = \int_{r_1}^{r_2} \frac{1}{2} k \, \nabla T \cdot \nabla T \, d\tau + 2\pi \left(\frac{1}{2} h T^2 \right) \Bigg|_{r=r_1}$$

$$= 2\pi \left[\frac{A^2 k}{2} \int_{r_1}^{r_2} \frac{1}{r^2} r \, dr + \frac{1}{2} h T(r_1)^2 \right] = 2\pi \left[\frac{A^2 k}{2} \ln\left(\frac{r_2}{r_1}\right) + \frac{1}{2} h T(r_1)^2 \right] \tag{2.98}$$

The evaluation of (2.98) for the example problem with variation on k is summarized in Table 2.2. Note the significance of E_h for all k.

The energy inner product (2.90) for the finite element solution T^h is easy to evaluate. By definition,

$$E(T^h, T^h) = \int_{R^1} \tfrac{1}{2} k \, \nabla T^h \cdot \nabla T^h \, d\tau + \int_{\partial R} \tfrac{1}{2} h T^h T^h \, d\sigma$$

$$= \sum_{e=1}^{M} \left(\int_{R_e^1} \tfrac{1}{2} k \, \nabla T_e \cdot \nabla T_e \, d\tau + \int_{\delta R_e \cap \delta R} \tfrac{1}{2} h T_e T_e \, d\sigma \right) \tag{2.99}$$

Table 2.2 Energy inner product for thermal conduction in convectively loaded axisymmetric cylinder

	Energy inner product, $E/2\pi$		
Thermal conductivity, k	E_k, conduction	E_h, convection	$E_k + E_h$ conduction + convection
1.0	8.93375 (5)	2.01562 (7)	2.10496 (7)
10.0	3.46574 (6)	1.00000 (7)	1.34657 (7)
40.0	2.72097 (6)	3.76920 (6)	6.49017 (6)

The integrals in (2.99) have already been evaluated as the finite element thermal conductivity and boundary convection matrices [see (2.58)–(2.62)]. Denoting these as $[K]_e$ and $[H]_e$, respectively, (2.99) becomes

$$E(T^h, T^h) = \tfrac{1}{2} \sum_{e=1}^{M} \{Q\}_e^T([K]_e + [H]_e)\{Q\}_e \tag{2.100}$$

where

$$[K]_e \equiv \frac{2\pi k}{\Delta_e} \begin{bmatrix} 1 & -1 \\ -1 & 1 \end{bmatrix} \{\tfrac{1}{2}, \tfrac{1}{2}\} \{R\}_e$$

$$[H]_e \equiv 2\pi r_1 h \begin{bmatrix} 1 & 0 \\ 0 & 0 \end{bmatrix} \delta_{e1} \tag{2.101}$$

Therefore, the energy inner product (2.99) is formed by pre- and post-multiplication of $[K]_e$ and $[H]_e$ by the finite-element nodal matrix $\{Q\}_e$, and summing over $1 \leqslant e \leqslant M$.

As an example, for the one-element solution with boundary convection, see Table 2.1; $\{Q\}_1 = \{988.65120, 306.85282\}^T = \{Q\}$, and (2.100) becomes

$$E(T^h, T^h) = \tfrac{1}{2} \sum_{e=1}^{2} \{Q\}_1^T([K]_1 + [H]_1)\{Q\}_1$$

$$= 2\pi \left[\tfrac{1}{2} \{988.65120, \quad 306.85282\} \left(15 \begin{bmatrix} 1 & -1 \\ -1 & 1 \end{bmatrix} + 20 \begin{bmatrix} 1 & 0 \\ 0 & 0 \end{bmatrix} \right) \begin{Bmatrix} 988.65120 \\ 306.85282 \end{Bmatrix} \right] = 2\pi(1.32607 \times 10^7) \tag{2.102}$$

Comparing to the appropriate entry in Table 2.2, the single-element solution has underpredicted the analytical energy inner product by about 1.52 percent. Recall that the surface temperature error was about 1.135 percent. For the two-element solution, (2.100) is

$$E(T^h, T^h) = \tfrac{1}{2} \sum_{e=1}^{2} \{Q\}_e^T([K]_e + [H]_e)\{Q\}_e$$

$$= 2\pi \left[\tfrac{1}{2} \{996.86565, \quad 594.35816\} \left(25 \begin{bmatrix} 1 & -1 \\ -1 & 1 \end{bmatrix} + 20 \begin{bmatrix} 1 & 0 \\ 0 & 0 \end{bmatrix} \right) \begin{Bmatrix} 996.86565 \\ 594.35816 \end{Bmatrix} + \tfrac{1}{2} \{594.35816, \quad 306.85282\} \right. \tag{2.103}$$

$$\times \begin{bmatrix} 1 & -1 \\ -1 & 1 \end{bmatrix} \begin{Bmatrix} 594.35816 \\ 306.85282 \end{Bmatrix} \Bigg] = 2\pi[1.34091(7)] \qquad (2.103) \text{ (Cont.)}$$

and the error has been reduced to 0.42 percent. The error for the four-element solution (see Table 2.1) is 0.108 percent. For the cases where the convection boundary condition is replaced by (the analytically exact) fixed-flux (see Example 2.3), the energy inner product evaluations are

$$M = 1: \qquad E(T^h, T^h) = 3.33333(6)$$
$$M = 2: \qquad E(T^h, T^h) = 3.42857(6)$$
$$M = 4: \qquad E(T^h, T^h) = 3.45610(6)$$

Comparing these data to the analytical solution Table 2.2, the percent errors are correspondingly 3.82, 1.07, and 0.278. Therefore, for either problem specification, refining the discretization by a factor of two reduces the error in energy by a factor of about four.

With this insight, we now formulate the statement of error in the finite element solution in terms of the energy inner product. Recall from (2.89) that the error ϵ^h is the difference between the true solution T and the finite element prediction T^h. From the first statement (2.92) in Theorem I,

$$E(\epsilon^h, \epsilon^h) = \min E(T - \bar{T}, T - \bar{T}) \leqslant E(T - \bar{T}, T - \bar{T}) \qquad (2.104)$$

which states that the energy in the finite element solution error is bounded by the error in energy associated with any other approximate solution. Of course, the true solution T is typically unknown, and one is required to estimate the size of (2.104). The key lies in the inequality; an approximate solution arbitrarily close to T is its linear interpolate T_I, and (2.104) states that the energy in the error in T^h is at least as small as that for the linear interpolate, $\bar{T} \equiv T_I$. Hence,

Theorem II The error in the energy inner product (2.90) for the linear finite element solution (2.76) satisfies the inequality

$$E(T - T^h, T - T^h) \leqslant C\, \Delta_e^2 \max |T''(x)|^2 \qquad (2.105)$$

where C is a constant independent of Δ_e, the measure of the uniform finite element discretization of R^1, and $T'' \equiv d^2T/dx^2$ is assumed continuous everywhere on R^1. The proof of (2.105) (Strang and Fix, 1973, p. 44), centers on evaluation of the difference between the true solution T and the linear interpolate T_I on a typical finite-element domain R_e^1. Referring to Fig. 2.8, since T_I interpolates $T(x)$ at the nodes x_k of the discretization, then the difference

$$e(x) \equiv T(x) - T_I(x) \qquad (2.106)$$

vanishes at $x = x_k$, $k = 1, 2, \ldots, n$. Therefore, $e'(x) \equiv de/dx$ must vanish somewhere on the interval $x_k \leqslant x \leqslant x_{k+1}$, that is, on R_e^1. Denoting $x = \alpha$ as that point, and using y as a dummy variable,

$$\int_\alpha^x e''(y)\, dy = \int_\alpha^x [T''(y) - T_I''(y)]\, dy = \int_\alpha^x T''(y)\, dy \tag{2.107}$$

since T_I is a linear function on R_e^1. Also,

$$\int_\alpha^x e''(y)\, dy = e'(x) - e'(\alpha) = e'(x) \tag{2.108}$$

since $e'(\alpha)$ vanishes identically. Assuming $T''(x)$ continuous on R_e^1, and using the mean value theorem of calculus (Thomas, 1962, Chap. 3), (2.107)-(2.108) are combined to yield

$$|e'(x)| \leqslant \Delta_e \max |T''(x)| \tag{2.109}$$

where $\Delta_e = (x_{k+1} - x_k)$, the measure of R_e^1. The maximum value of $e(x)$ will occur where e' vanishes, i.e., at $x = \alpha$ (see Fig. 2.8). Assuming this occurs closer to the right end of R_e^1 than to the left, expand $e(x_{k+1})$ in a Taylor series about $x = \alpha$

$$e(x_{k+1}) = e(\alpha) + (x_{k+1} - \alpha)e'(\alpha) + \frac{(x_{k+1} - \alpha)^2}{e} e''(\alpha) + \cdots \tag{2.110}$$

Since $e(x_{k+1})$ vanishes identically, as does $e'(\alpha)$ by definition, and since $(x_{k+1} - \alpha) < \frac{1}{2}\Delta_e$, $e''(x) = T''(x)$ and $|e(x)| < |e(\alpha)|$, (2.110) can be expressed as

$$|e(x)| \leqslant \tfrac{1}{8}\, \Delta_e^2 \max |T''(x)| \tag{2.111}$$

From (2.109) and (2.111) and the definition of error in the linear interpolate (2.106), therefore

$$\max |T(x) - T_I(x)| \leqslant \tfrac{1}{8}\, \Delta_e^2 \max |T''(x)| \tag{2.112}$$

$$\max |T'(x) - T_I'(x)| \leqslant \Delta_e \max |T''(x)| \tag{2.113}$$

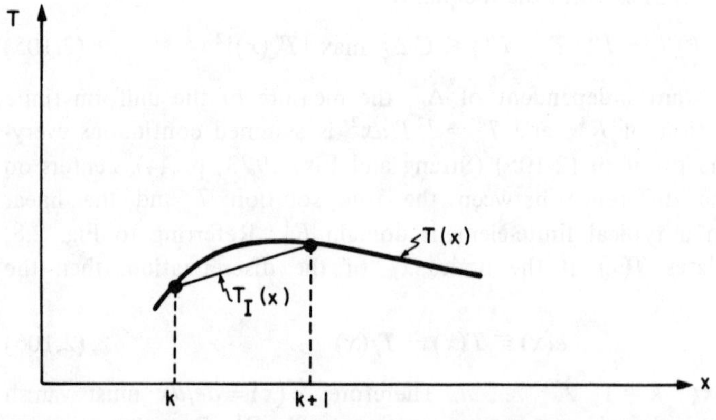

Figure 2.8 Illustration of the linear interpolate $T_I(x)$ of the temperature distribution $T(x)$.

The error in the energy inner product $E(e_I, e_I)$ formed by the linear interpolate T_I is therefore

$$E(e_I, e_I) \equiv E(T - T_I, T - T_I) = \int_{R^1} \tfrac{1}{2} k(T' - T_I')^2 \, d\tau + \int_{\partial R} \tfrac{1}{2} h(T - T_I)^2 \, d\sigma$$

$$\leqslant C \, \Delta_e^2 \max |T''(x)| \tag{2.114}$$

using (2.112)–(2.113). Then, by Theorem I, see (2.104), since the energy error must be less for $\bar{T}$ identified with T^h, the finite-element approximation, the desired result is proved. Hence, the error in the energy inner product for the linear basis finite-element solution decreases as the square of the mesh measure Δ_e under discretization refinement, which proves (2.105).

The imperfection in (2.105) is the requirement that $T''(x)$ be continuous on R^1. This can be relaxed to where the second derivative need only possess finite energy, i.e., is square-integrable

$$\|T''\|^2 \equiv \int_{R^1} (T'')^2 \, d\tau < \infty \tag{2.115}$$

Referring to Strang and Fix (1973, p. 45) for the sharper proof, the statement is:

Theorem III The error in the finite element solution

$$\epsilon^h \equiv T - T^h \tag{2.89}$$

satisfies the inequality in the energy inner product

$$E(\epsilon^h, \epsilon^h) \leqslant C_1 \, \Delta_e^2 \|T''\|^2 \leqslant C_2 \, \Delta_e^2 \|F\|^2 \tag{2.116}$$

where C_1 and C_2 are constants, Δ_e is the measure of the discretization of R^1, and $\|F\|$ is the L_2 norm of the "data" of the problem specification.

$$\|F\| \equiv \left[\int_{R^1} (\rho \dot{q})^2 \, d\tau + \int_{\partial R} (hT_r)^2 \, d\sigma \right]^{1/2} \tag{2.117}$$

Hence, (2.116) and (2.117) state that the finite-element solution error in energy decreases in proportion to the square of the measure of the uniform discretization, and depends continuously on the data of the problem specification.

Theorem IV follows as a direct consequence of Theorem III.

Theorem IV The error in the finite-element solution T^h converges to zero in energy, as the number of finite-element domains spanning R^1 increases without limit, i.e.,

$$E(\epsilon^h, \epsilon^h) \to 0 \quad \text{as} \quad \Delta_e \to 0 \tag{2.118}$$

Finally, finite-element practice generally employs the cardinal basis interpolation (2.94) for distribution of parameters, for example, $\rho\dot{q}$, on R^1_e. In particular,

$$\int_{R^1} \{N_1\}\rho\dot{q}_e \, d\tau \rightarrow \int_{R^1} \rho\{N_1\}\{N_1\}^T\{QDOT\}_e \, d\tau$$

where the matrix elements of $\{QDOT\}_e$ are the nodal values of the linear interpolate $\dot{q}_I$ of the heat generation term $\dot{q}$ on R^1_e. Denoting $\tilde{T}^h$ as the finite-element solution of (2.31) with these data replaced by the interpolate, Strang and Fix (1973, p. 50) prove that the error in the energy satisfies the inequality

$$E(T - \tilde{T}^h, T - \tilde{T}^h) \leqslant C_q \, \Delta_e^4 \, \|F\|^2 \tag{2.119}$$

Hence, the additional error introduced by interpolation of the data goes to zero faster, i.e., to order Δ_e^4, than the error in the corresponding finite-element solution itself. Hence, interpolation of "data" using (2.94) is appropriate, which reduces input to the nodal specification $\{QDOT\}$ only.

Returning to the sample problems, Table 2.3 summarizes the percent error in the energy inner product (2.90) for the various finite-element solutions. Observe indeed that the error decreases monotonically by essentially a factor of four. As the number of finite elements spanning R^1 is further increased, the factor of four becomes exact, confirming the theoretical value of 2.0 for the exponent on Δ_e in (2.116). Hence, as the number of finite elements increases without bound, the error in the energy decreases to zero in the limit.

It is instructive to evaluate the actual bound on the error (2.116) to determine its quantitative usefulness. The square of the L_2 norm of the data (2.117), for the convectively loaded cylinder is

$$\|F\|^2 = \int_{\partial R} (hT_r)^2 \, d\sigma = 2\pi r_1 (hT_r)^2 = 2\pi[9.000(8)] \tag{2.120}$$

Table 2.3 Percent error in energy inner product, finite-element solution for conduction in axisymmetric cylinder

No. of elements, M	Energy in the error, $E(\epsilon^h, \epsilon^h)$: Convection, $k = 1$	Convection, $k = 10$	Convection, $k = 40$	Fixed flux, $k = 10$
1	0.255	1.52	2.45	3.82
2	0.0694	0.42	0.683	1.07
4	0.0171	0.108	0.177	0.278

Therefore, Eq. (2.116) yields

$$E(\epsilon^h, \epsilon^h) \leqslant C_2 \, \Delta_e^2 \|F\| = C_2 \, \Delta_e^2 2\pi[9.000(8)] \tag{2.121}$$

Since the energy in the error equals the error in the energy, (2.95), from Table 2.2 and (2.102)–(2.103), the energy in the error for the one- and two-element discretization solutions is

$$\begin{aligned} M = 1: \quad & E(\epsilon^h, \epsilon^h) = 2\pi[1.34657(7) - 1.32607(7)] = 2\pi[2.05(5)] \\ M = 2: \quad & E(\epsilon^h, \epsilon^h) = 2\pi[0.566(5)] \end{aligned} \tag{2.122}$$

Comparing (2.122) and (2.120), the computed energy in the error is four orders of magnitude smaller than the bound. Therefore, the practical approach to determination of absolute accuracy is to compute solutions on progressively refined discretizations, and compare results to the theoretical convergence rate, i.e., the exponent on Δ_e in (2.116).

This completes the introduction on accuracy and error estimation for the linear basis finite-element algorithm. The energy norm is indeed the natural way to measure a computed solution and shall repeatedly be employed. However, other measures of error will also prove useful, and consideration will not be limited to the energy inner product. For example, surface temperature and/or surface heat flux are parameters of considerable importance in assessing solution acceptability (accuracy). Ample use will be made of such engineering norms, in the assessment of finite-element solutions.

Problems

1 Verify (2.79)–(2.80).

2 Prove (2.88).

3 Verify (2.96) using (2.93) and (2.95).

4 Verify (2.103).

5 Prove (2.111).

2.6 IMPROVED ACCURACY USING A HIGHER ORDER ELEMENT BASIS

Improving the accuracy of the linear finite-element solution using successively finer grids is formalized. Consider now the alternative of improvement through definition and use of a more complete finite element basis,

$$T_e(x) \equiv \{N_k(\bar{x})\}^T \{Q\}_e \tag{2.123}$$

with $k > 1$. Recall for the linear basis,

$$\{N_1(\dot{x})\} = \{\zeta(\bar{x})\} \tag{2.124}$$

and
$$\{\zeta(\bar{x})\} \equiv \begin{Bmatrix} 1 - \dfrac{x}{\Delta_e} \\ \dfrac{x}{\Delta_e} \end{Bmatrix} \tag{2.125}$$

The quadratic cardinal basis, $k = 2$ in (2.123), can be constructed from the power series

$$T_e(x) = \sum_{i=0}^{2} a_i \bar{x}^i = a_0 + a_1 \frac{\bar{x}}{\Delta_e} + a_2 \left(\frac{\bar{x}}{\Delta_e}\right)^2 \tag{2.126}$$

where $\bar{x}$ is the local coordinate and the expansion coefficients a_i are to be determined. Referring to Fig. 2.9, since three expansion coefficients must now be determined, specify an additional node for R_e^1 at the midspan. Denoting the corresponding nodal temperature as $Q\frac{1}{2}$, (2.123) becomes

$$T_e(x) = \{N_2(\bar{x})\}^T \begin{Bmatrix} Q1 \\ Q\frac{1}{2} \\ Q2 \end{Bmatrix}_e \tag{2.127}$$

The elements comprising $\{N_2(\bar{x})\}$ are determined simply by equating (2.126) and (2.127).

$$T_e(x) = a_1 + a_2 \left(\frac{\bar{x}}{\Delta_e}\right) + a_3 \left(\frac{\bar{x}}{\Delta_e}\right)^2 \equiv \{N_2(\zeta(\bar{x}))\}^T \{Q\}_e \tag{2.128}$$

Evaluating (2.128) at the three nodal coordinates of R_e^1 yields

$$\begin{bmatrix} 1 & 0 & 0 \\ 1 & 1 & 1 \\ 1 & \frac{1}{2} & \frac{1}{4} \end{bmatrix} \begin{Bmatrix} a_1 \\ a_2 \\ a_3 \end{Bmatrix} = \begin{Bmatrix} Q1 \\ Q2 \\ Q\frac{1}{2} \end{Bmatrix} \tag{2.129}$$

Solving for $\{a\}$, (2.126) becomes

$$T_e(x) = Q1 + (-3Q1 - Q2 + 4Q\tfrac{1}{2}) \frac{\bar{x}}{\Delta_e} + (2Q1 + 2Q2 - 4Q\tfrac{1}{2}) \left(\frac{\bar{x}}{\Delta_e}\right)^2 \tag{2.130}$$

Rewriting (2.130) in the (transposed) matrix form of (2.127), recalling (2.125) and appropriately adding and subtracting unity, we can write (2.130) in the symmetric form

$$T_e(x) = \{Q1, Q\tfrac{1}{2}, Q2\}_e \begin{Bmatrix} \zeta_1(2\zeta_1 - 1) \\ 4\zeta_1\zeta_2 \\ \zeta_2(2\zeta_2 - 1) \end{Bmatrix} \tag{2.131}$$

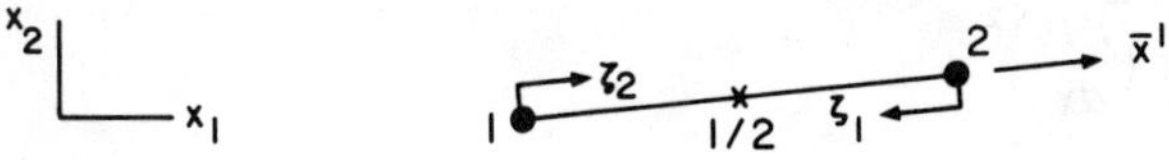

Figure 2.9 One-dimensional finite element with midpoint node for $\{N_2\}$.

Comparing (2.127) and (2.131), the elements of the quadratic cardinal basis on R_e^1 are

$$\{N_2(\bar{x})\} \equiv \begin{Bmatrix} \zeta_1(2\zeta_1 - 1) \\ 4\zeta_1\zeta_2 \\ \zeta_2(2\zeta_2 - 1) \end{Bmatrix} \tag{2.132}$$

The ζ_i in (2.132) are the natural coordinates (2.125) of the linear basis (2.124).

In implementing the finite-element algorithm (2.34)–(2.35), f_e requires establishment of ∇T_e. From (2.131), and using the chain rule,

$$\nabla T_e(x) \cdot \hat{\mathrm{i}} = \frac{dT_e}{dx} = \frac{1}{\Delta_e} \{Q1, Q\tfrac{1}{2}, Q2\}_e \begin{Bmatrix} \zeta_2 - 3\zeta_1 \\ 4(\zeta_1 - \zeta_2) \\ 3\zeta_2 - \zeta_1 \end{Bmatrix} \tag{2.133}$$

It is interesting to compare (2.133) to a finite-difference formula for a function differentiated at select points x_α over two panels of data. The general form is

$$\left.\frac{dT}{dx}\right|_{x_\alpha} = \sum_{i=1}^{n} \frac{1}{i} \delta^i T_\alpha \tag{2.134}$$

where δ^n is the nth order forward, backward, and/or central difference operator. For example, evaluating (2.133) at node 2, Fig. 2.9, yields

$$\frac{dT_e}{dx} = \frac{1}{\Delta_e} (Q1 + 3Q2 - 4Q\tfrac{1}{2}) \tag{2.135}$$

Evaluating (2.134) at node 2, using a second-order accurate ($n = 2$) backward difference formula, for a uniform panel length l, yields

$$\left.\frac{dT}{dx}\right|_{x_2} = \frac{1}{l}\left[(Q2 - Q\tfrac{1}{2}) + \frac{1}{2}(Q2 - Q\tfrac{1}{2} + Q1) + \cdots\right] = \frac{1}{2l} (Q1 + 3Q2 - 4Q\tfrac{1}{2}) \tag{2.136}$$

Since $\Delta_e = 2l$, (2.135) and (2.136) are identical. With this interpretation, (2.133) evaluated at the three nodes of R_e^1 yields respectively, a second-order accurate forward difference at x_1, a second-order backward difference at x_2, and a second-order central difference at the midpoint $\frac{1}{2}(x_1 + x_2)$.

Equations (2.132)–(2.133) permit evaluation of the approximations f_e and g_e, (2.34)–(2.35), hence I^h. For the conductivity term

$$f_e \equiv \frac{1}{2} k \nabla T_e \cdot \nabla T_e = \frac{1}{2} k \left(\frac{dT_e}{dx} \right)^2$$

$$= \frac{k}{2\,\Delta_e} \{Q\}_e^T \begin{Bmatrix} \zeta_2 - 3\zeta_1 \\ 4(\zeta_1 - \zeta_2) \\ 3\zeta_2 - \zeta_1 \end{Bmatrix} \{\zeta_2 - 3\zeta_1, 4(\zeta_1 - \zeta_2), 3\zeta_2 - \zeta_1\} \{Q\}_e \quad (2.137)$$

Therefore, for the axisymmetric cylinder example problem,

$$\int_{R_e^1} f_e \, d\tau = \int_{R_e^1} f_e r \, dr \, d\theta = 2\pi \int f_e \{R\}^T \{N_1\} \, d\bar{x} = \frac{2\pi k \{Q\}_e^T \{R\}_e^T}{2\,\Delta_e^2}$$

$$\cdot \int_{R_e^1} \begin{Bmatrix} \zeta_1 \\ \zeta_2 \end{Bmatrix} \begin{bmatrix} (\zeta_2 - 3\zeta_1)^2, & 4(\zeta_2 - 3\zeta_1)(\zeta_1 - \zeta_2), & (3\zeta_2 - \zeta_1)(\zeta_2 - 3\zeta_1) \\ & 16(\zeta_1 - \zeta_2)^2, & 4(3\zeta_2 - \zeta_1)(\zeta_1 - \zeta_2) \\ (\text{sym}) & & , (3\zeta_2 - \zeta_1)^2 \end{bmatrix} d\bar{x} \{Q\}$$

(2.138)

In (2.138), the scalar $\{R\}_e^T\{N_1\}$ has been moved to follow directly $\{Q\}_e^T$, which permits placement of $\{R\}_e^T$ outside the integral. Further, the square matrix defined in (2.137) has been expanded.

Equation (2.138) involves definition of a matrix premultiplication with a column matrix, which is an undefined operation in ordinary matrix algebra. Recall, however, that a scalar multiple of a matrix can be replaced by multiplying each element of the matrix by the scalar. Then, each element of the 3×3 matrix in (2.138) can be considered multiplied by two scalars, ζ_1 and ζ_2. Since arrays are denoted as $\{\cdot\}$, then, for example, the upper left matrix element in (2.138) can be written as

$$\int_{R_e^1} \begin{Bmatrix} \zeta_1 \\ \zeta_2 \end{Bmatrix} \begin{bmatrix} (\zeta_2 - 3\zeta_1)^2, & \cdot, & \cdot \\ & \cdot, & \cdot \\ (\text{sym}) & & , \cdot \end{bmatrix} d\bar{x} = \int_{R_e^1} \begin{bmatrix} \begin{Bmatrix} \zeta_1(\zeta_2 - 3\zeta_1)^2 \\ \zeta_2(\zeta_2 - 3\zeta_1)^2 \end{Bmatrix} & \cdots \\ & \ddots \end{bmatrix} d\bar{x}$$

$$= \int_{R_e^1} \begin{bmatrix} \begin{Bmatrix} \zeta_1\zeta_2^2 - 6\zeta_1^2\zeta_2 + 9\zeta_1^3 \\ \zeta_2^3 - 6\zeta_1\zeta_2^2 + 9\zeta_1^2\zeta_2 \end{Bmatrix}, & \cdots \\ & \ddots \end{bmatrix} d\bar{x}$$

$$= \Delta_e \begin{bmatrix} \begin{Bmatrix} \frac{1}{12} - \frac{6}{12} + \frac{9}{4} \\ \frac{1}{4} - \frac{6}{12} + \frac{9}{12} \end{Bmatrix}, & \cdots \\ & \ddots \\ & , \cdot \end{bmatrix} = \frac{\Delta_e}{6} \begin{bmatrix} \begin{Bmatrix} 11 \\ 3 \end{Bmatrix}, & \cdot, & \cdot \\ & \cdot, & \cdot \\ & & , \cdot \end{bmatrix} \quad (2.139)$$

The integrals defined in the second line of (2.139) are each evaluated using (2.61), yielding the third line. The fourth line has extracted the common denominator. The remaining five terms in (2.138) are evaluated in exactly the same manner, verifying the great usefulness of (2.61). Therefore, the conductivity contribution to I^h, as formed using the quadratic cardinal basis $\{N_2(\zeta)\}$, is

$$\int_{R_e^1} f_e \, d\tau = \frac{2\pi k \{Q\}_e^T}{12\, \Delta_e} \left(\{R\}_e^T \begin{bmatrix} \begin{Bmatrix} 11 \\ 3 \end{Bmatrix} & \begin{Bmatrix} -12 \\ -4 \end{Bmatrix} & \begin{Bmatrix} 1 \\ 1 \end{Bmatrix} \\ & \begin{Bmatrix} 16 \\ 16 \end{Bmatrix} & \begin{Bmatrix} -4 \\ -12 \end{Bmatrix} \\ \text{(sym)} & & \begin{Bmatrix} 3 \\ 11 \end{Bmatrix} \end{bmatrix} \right) \{Q\}_e \qquad (2.140)$$

Equation (2.140) introduces a notational structure that is highly useful in algorithm construction for nonlinear problems. The 3×3 square matrix is termed a *hypermatrix* of degree one, since its elements are themselves column matrices (2×1 in this specific instance). A degree-two hypermatrix would possess elements that were square matrices, not necessarily of rank equal to the square matrix, e.g., as occurs in (2.140). What the hypermatrix construction permits is "once-and-for-all" formation of the element-independent characterization of, in this instance, the conductivity contribution to I^h. A computer program would possess as a DATA statement the integers in $[\cdot]$ and the common denominator. As a preprocessor to a solution, this element "master matrix" is called into use and the denominator is divided out to available machine accuracy. Thereafter, within an element *DO* loop on $1 \leqslant e \leqslant M$, the left contraction with $\{R\}_e^T$ is applied first, yielding the specific element thermal stiffness matrix. This is then multiplied by Δ_e, k, and the remaining constants and is stored into the global stiffness matrix as the consequence of forming the extremization of I^h. This procedure is quite efficient, and the degree k of the finite-element basis becomes an input parameter that accesses the appropriate master matrix from the DATA statement. Furthermore, (2.140) is appropriate in form for a variable thermal conductivity problem, for example in a rectangular coordinate description, by replacing $\{R\}_e$ with $\{K\}_e$, the element nodal thermal conductivity (see Problem 2 in this section).

This step completed, the remaining term in I^h for the cylinder problem is the boundary convection term (2.35). Hence, using (2.131)-(2.132),

$$g_e \equiv \frac{1}{2} h T_e^2 - h T_r T_e = \frac{h}{2} \{Q\}_e^T \{N_2\} \{N_2\}^T \{Q\}_e - h T_r \{Q\}_e^T \{N_2\} \qquad (2.141)$$

Noting again that appropriate matrix elements of the cardinal basis $\{N_2\}$ vanish at nodes of R_e^1 [recall (2.57)] and assuming that convection is applied at the left-hand node of R_1^1 (Fig. 2.9) the integral of (2.141) becomes

$$\int_{\partial R_1 \cap \partial R} g_e \, d\sigma = \int g_e r_1 \, d\theta$$

$$= \delta_{e1} 2\pi r_1 \left(\frac{h}{2} \{Q\}_e^T \begin{bmatrix} 1 & 0 & 0 \\ 0 & 0 & 0 \\ 0 & 0 & 0 \end{bmatrix} \{Q\}_e - hT_r \{Q\}_e^T \begin{Bmatrix} 1 \\ 0 \\ 0 \end{Bmatrix} \right) \tag{2.142}$$

Note that (2.142) is *identical* to the $\{N_1\}$ algorithm basis statement [see (2.58)] to within addition of a row and column of zeros to match the order of $\{Q\}_e$. Therefore, the algorithm equivalent of a nonhomogeneous gradient boundary condition constraint is independent of the degree k of the approximation on R_e^1.

Example 2.4 Determine the finite-element algorithm approximate solution for the temperature distribution in the convection-loaded axisymmetric cylinder of Example 2.1 using a one-element ($M = 1$) discretization of R^1. Evaluating (2.140),

$$\int_{R_e^1} f_e \, d\tau = \frac{2\pi(10)}{12(1)} \{Q\}_1^T \{1, 2\}_1 \begin{bmatrix} \begin{Bmatrix} 11 \\ 3 \end{Bmatrix} & \begin{Bmatrix} -12 \\ -4 \end{Bmatrix} & \begin{Bmatrix} 1 \\ 1 \end{Bmatrix} \\ & \begin{Bmatrix} 16 \\ 16 \end{Bmatrix} & \begin{Bmatrix} -4 \\ -12 \end{Bmatrix} \\ & & \begin{Bmatrix} 3 \\ 11 \end{Bmatrix} \end{bmatrix} \{Q\}_1$$

$$= \frac{10\pi}{6} \{Q\}_1^T \begin{bmatrix} 17 & -20 & 3 \\ & 48 & -28 \\ & & 25 \end{bmatrix} \begin{Bmatrix} Q1 \\ Q\tfrac{1}{2} \\ 306.85282 \end{Bmatrix}_1 \tag{2.143}$$

Equation (2.142) becomes

$$\int_{\partial R_1} g_e \, d\sigma = 20\pi \{Q\}_1^T \begin{Bmatrix} Q1 - 2(1500) \\ 0 \\ 0 \end{Bmatrix}_1 \tag{2.144}$$

Hence, inserting (2.143)-(2.144) in the energy functional approximation I^h and extremizing [(2.39)-(2.40)], and accounting for $Q2$ fixed yields the matrix solution statement

$$\begin{bmatrix} 17 + 12 & -20 \\ -20 & 48 \end{bmatrix} \begin{Bmatrix} Q1 \\ Q\tfrac{1}{2} \end{Bmatrix} = \begin{Bmatrix} 17079.44154 \\ 8591.87894 \end{Bmatrix} \tag{2.145}$$

The solution is elementary, and the nodal distribution of the discrete approximate solution is

$$\{T\} \equiv \sum_{e=1}^{M} \{Q\}_e = \begin{Bmatrix} Q_1 \\ Q_{1.5} \\ Q_2 \end{Bmatrix} = \begin{Bmatrix} 999.64796 \\ 595.51746 \\ 306.85282 \end{Bmatrix} \text{K} \tag{2.146}$$

When these data are compared to the linear basis predictions summarized in Table 2.1, it is found that the surface temperature for the one-element discretization solution using $\{N_2\}$ is more accurate than the four-element $\{N_1\}$ solution. Further, the size (rank) of the $\{N_2\}$ matrix solution statement is identical to the two-element $\{N_1\}$ solution. Therefore, for half the computational work, i.e., CPU, a significant improvement in accuracy is gained by the modest expenditure of effort required to form (2.140) and (2.142). The two-element discretization $\{N_2\}$ solution data are compared to (2.146) and to the linear basis results in Table 2.4. The sequential rate of improvement in accuracy is noteworthy.

Evaluating the energy norm (2.99) using (2.146) yields

$$E(T^h, T^h) = 2\pi\left(\tfrac{1}{2}\{999.64796,\ 595.51746,\ 306.85282\}\left(\frac{10}{6}\begin{bmatrix} 17 & -20 & 3 \\ & 48 & -28 \\ (\text{sym}) & & 25 \end{bmatrix} + 20\begin{bmatrix} 1 & 0 & 0 \\ & 0 & 0 \\ & & 0 \end{bmatrix}\right)\begin{Bmatrix} 999.64796 \\ 595.51746 \\ 306.85282 \end{Bmatrix}\right) = 2\pi[1.34597(7)] \tag{2.147}$$

Using the data in Table 2.2, the error in energy for the $M = 1$ quadratic algorithm is found to be only 0.045 percent. For the two-element $\{N_2\}$ solution, the error in

Table 2.4 Finite element predicted node temperature distributions on axisymmetric cylinder using linear and quadratic finite elements ($k = 10$, $h = 20$, $T_r = 1500$ K)

Degree of F.E. interpolation	No. of finite elements	Node radial coordinate 1.0	1.25	1.5	1.75	2.0
Linear $\{N_1(x)\}$	1	988.65120				306.85282
	2	996.96565		594.35816		306.85282
	4	999.19105	776.60929	594.49694	440.40188	306.85282
Quadratic $\{N_2(x)\}$	1	999.64796		595.51746		306.85282
	2	999.97043	776.98428	594.54106	440.42236	306.85282
Analytical	–	1000.00000	776.60929	594.49694	440.40188	306.85282

the energy is only 0.00712 percent. Generalization of the theoretical statement of accuracy and convergence as a function of $\{N_k\}$ is deferred pending development of the cubic basis formulation in the next section.

Problems

1 Verify (2.140).

2 Rearrange the form (2.140) for a one-dimensional problem domain spanned by a rectangular cartesian coordinate, for the case of linearly variable element thermal conductivity k_e on R_e^1. How would this form change if the conductivity varied (*a*) quadratically; (*b*) not at all?

3 Derive the master matrix form (2.140) appropriate for point symmetric conduction on a one-dimensional space R^1 spanned by spherical coordinates. The differential element is $d\tau = r^2 \sin\phi \, dr \, d\phi \, d\theta$, where ϕ is the polar angle (measured from the z axis), $0 \leqslant \phi \leqslant \pi$, and θ is the circumferential angle with range $0 \leqslant \theta \leqslant 2\pi$.

4 Verify (2.142).

5 Obtain (2.145) using (2.143)–(2.144).

6 Using (2.140) and (2.142), generate the two-element discretization $\{N_2\}$ solution of Table 2.4 and compare results to (2.146).

2.7 A CUBIC FINITE-ELEMENT BASIS FOR ONE DIMENSION

The significant accuracy improvement associated with the quadratic basis $\{N_2(\bar{x})\}$, (2.132), leads one to consideration of a cubic form. The corresponding Taylor series is

$$T_e(x) = a + b\,\frac{\bar{x}}{\Delta_e} + c\left(\frac{\bar{x}}{\Delta_e}\right)^2 + d\left(\frac{\bar{x}}{\Delta_e}\right)^3 \tag{2.148}$$

The finite-element cardinal basis equivalent is

$$T_e(x) = \{N_3(\bar{x})\}^T \{Q\}_e \tag{2.149}$$

Two options now exist concerning definition of the expansion coefficient set $\{Q\}_e$ in (2.149). One could proceed as in Sec. 2.6 and designate two interior nodes within R_e^1 at $\Delta_e/3$ and $2\Delta_e/3$ (see Fig. 2.9). The alternative is to specify derivative degrees of freedom, i.e., the first x derivative of T, at node coordinates 1 and 2. For this case, $\{Q\}_e$ in (2.149) is defined as

$$\{Q\}_e^T = \left\{Q1,\ Q2,\ \frac{dQ}{d\bar{x}}\bigg|_1,\ \frac{dQ}{d\bar{x}}\bigg|_2\right\}_e \equiv \{Q1,\ Q2,\ Q1',\ Q2'\}_e \tag{2.150}$$

Recalling the natural coordinate definition,

$$\{\zeta\} = \begin{Bmatrix} 1 - \dfrac{\bar{x}}{\Delta_e} \\ \dfrac{\bar{x}}{\Delta_e} \end{Bmatrix} \tag{2.151}$$

the cardinal basis form (2.149)-(2.150) is determined simply by evaluating (2.148), and the x derivatives of (2.148), at nodes 1 and 2 of R_e^1. The resultant algebraic equation system is readily solved for the expansion coefficients a, b, c, and d, yielding

$$\{N_3'(\bar{x})\} = \begin{Bmatrix} 1-(\zeta_2)^2(1+2\zeta_1) \\ (\zeta_2)^2(1+2\zeta_1) \\ \zeta_2(\zeta_1)^2\Delta_e \\ -\zeta_1(\zeta_2)^2\Delta_e \end{Bmatrix} \tag{2.152}$$

The superscript prime in (2.152) is a reminder that (2.150) is the nodal variable set.

For the radial conduction problem, one is again required to establish $\nabla\{N_3'(\bar{x})\}$ for the conductivity contribution f_e, (2.36). Proceeding through the details, as in Sec. 2.6, it is left as an exercise to confirm the form.

$$\nabla\{N_3'(\bar{x})\}\cdot\hat{\imath} = \frac{1}{\Delta_e}\begin{Bmatrix} -6\zeta_2(1-\zeta_2) \\ 6\zeta_2(1-\zeta_2) \\ [1-4\zeta_2+3\zeta_2^2]\,\Delta_e \\ [-2\zeta_2+3\zeta_2^2]\,\Delta_e \end{Bmatrix} \tag{2.153}$$

The correctness of (2.152)-(2.153) is readily verified by noting that the matrix elements are either unity or zero at node points 1 and 2 of R_e^1, as required for a cardinal basis.

The thermal conductivity contribution to I^h (2.38) is constructed as illustrated, using $\{N_2\}$ in the previous section. Hence, using (2.153),

$$f_e \equiv \tfrac{1}{2}k\,\nabla T_e\cdot\nabla T_e = \tfrac{1}{2}k\left(\frac{dT_e}{dx}\right)^2 = \frac{k}{2\,\Delta_e^2}\{Q\}_e^T\begin{Bmatrix} -6\zeta_2(1-\zeta_2) \\ 6\zeta_2(1-\zeta_2) \\ (1-4\zeta_2+3\zeta_2^2)\,\Delta_e \\ (-2\zeta_2+3\zeta_2^2)\,\Delta_e \end{Bmatrix}\{\cdot\}^T\{Q\}_e \tag{2.154}$$

where $\{\cdot\}$ contains the column matrix elements as a row matrix. Then, for example, the (1,1) term in the matrix defined in (2.154) takes the form

$$\int_{R_e^1} f_e\,d\tau = \int_{R_e^1} f_e\,r\,dr\,d\theta$$

$$= \frac{2\pi k}{2\,\Delta_e^2}\{Q\}_e^T\{R\}_e^T\int_{R_e^1}\begin{Bmatrix}\zeta_1\\ \zeta_2\end{Bmatrix}[(-6\zeta_2(1-\zeta_2))^2,\ldots,]\,d\bar{x}\,\{Q\}_e \tag{2.155}$$

$$\int_{R_e^1} f_e \, d\tau = \frac{2\pi k}{5(2\,\Delta_e)} \{Q\}_e^T \{R\}_e^T \begin{bmatrix} \begin{Bmatrix} 3 \\ \cdots \\ 3 \end{Bmatrix} \cdots \end{bmatrix} \{Q\}_e \qquad (2.155) \text{ (Cont.)}$$

using (2.61) to evaluate the defined integrals of polynomials in ζ_i. Proceeding throughout the lengthy computations, the final form of (2.155) for $\{N_3'\}$ is

$$\int_{R_e^1} f_e \, d\tau = \frac{2\pi k}{120} \{Q\}_e^T \{R\}_e^T \begin{bmatrix} \dfrac{36}{\Delta_e} \left(\begin{Bmatrix} 1 \\ 1 \\ -1 \\ -1 \end{Bmatrix} \begin{Bmatrix} -1 \\ -1 \\ 1 \\ 1 \end{Bmatrix} \right) & 6 \left(\begin{Bmatrix} 0 \\ 1 \\ 0 \\ -1 \end{Bmatrix} \begin{Bmatrix} 1 \\ 0 \\ -1 \\ 0 \end{Bmatrix} \right) \\ \text{(sym)} & \Delta_e \left(\begin{Bmatrix} 6 \\ 2 \\ -1 \\ -1 \end{Bmatrix} \begin{Bmatrix} -1 \\ -1 \\ 2 \\ 6 \end{Bmatrix} \right) \end{bmatrix} \qquad (2.156)$$

The structure of (2.156) deserves some comment. Definition and use of the (Hermite) cubic basis $\{N_3'\}$ has yielded the master matrix dependent upon Δ_e. The upper left partition displays the essential character of the linear element conductivity matrix [see (2.56)]. The top right partition is somewhat similar but without the $1/\Delta_e$ multiplier. The lower right partition displays an entirely new structure, including the multiplication by Δ_e.

It is important to confirm that the convection boundary condition contribution to I^h, (2.37), remains unchanged from the linear and quadratic basis construction. Proceeding through the operations, and noting that only the first matrix element of $\{N_3'(\bar{x})\}$ is nonvanishing at node 1, yields

$$\int_{\partial R_1} g_e \, d\sigma = \int_{\partial R_1} g_e r_1 \, d\theta$$

$$= \delta_{e1} 2\pi r_1 \left(\frac{h}{2} \{Q\}_e^T \begin{bmatrix} 1 & 0 & 0 & 0 \\ & 0 & 0 & 0 \\ & & 0 & 0 \\ & & & 0 \end{bmatrix} \{Q\}_e - hT_r \{Q\}_e^T \begin{Bmatrix} 1 \\ 0 \\ 0 \\ 0 \end{Bmatrix} \right) \qquad (2.157)$$

Comparison of (2.157) to the quadratic and linear basis statements [see (2.57) and (2.142)], shows that they indeed differ only in the matrix order.

Identification of (2.156) and (2.157) allows solution of a one-dimensional heat conduction problem using $\{N_3'\}$. Therefore,

Example 2.5 Establish the steady-state temperature distribution in an axisymmetric cylinder, employing a one-element discretization of the solution domain

R^1, using the cubic finite element basis (2.150) and (2.152). For (2.156), noting that $\Delta_1 = 1$,

$$\int_{R_e^1} f_e\, d\tau = \frac{2\pi(10)\{Q\}_1^T\{1,2\}}{120}\begin{bmatrix} \begin{Bmatrix}36\\36\end{Bmatrix} & \begin{Bmatrix}-36\\-36\end{Bmatrix} & \begin{Bmatrix}0\\6\end{Bmatrix} & \begin{Bmatrix}6\\0\end{Bmatrix} \\ & \begin{Bmatrix}36\\36\end{Bmatrix} & \begin{Bmatrix}0\\-6\end{Bmatrix} & \begin{Bmatrix}-6\\0\end{Bmatrix} \\ & & \begin{Bmatrix}6\\2\end{Bmatrix} & \begin{Bmatrix}-1\\-1\end{Bmatrix} \\ (\text{sym}) & & & \begin{Bmatrix}2\\6\end{Bmatrix}\end{bmatrix}\{Q\}_1$$

$$= \pi\{Q\}_1^T\begin{bmatrix}18 & -18 & 2 & 1\\ & 18 & -2 & -1\\ & & \frac{5}{3} & -\frac{1}{2}\\ (\text{sym}) & & & \frac{7}{3}\end{bmatrix}\{Q\}_1$$

For the convection boundary condition, (2.157) becomes

$$\int_{\partial R_1} g_e\, d\sigma = 40\pi\{Q\}_1^T\begin{Bmatrix}\frac{1}{2}Q1 - 1500\\ 0\end{Bmatrix}_1$$

Performing the extremization (2.39), the resultant matrix statement is

$$\begin{bmatrix}18 & -18 & 2 & 1\\ & 18 & -2 & -1\\ & & \frac{5}{3} & -\frac{1}{2}\\ (\text{sym}) & & & \frac{7}{3}\end{bmatrix}\begin{Bmatrix}Q1\\Q2\\Q1'\\Q2'\end{Bmatrix}_1 = \begin{Bmatrix}-20Q1 + 20(1500)\\0\\0\\0\end{Bmatrix}_1 \tag{2.158}$$

Before solving, the order of (2.158) must be modified to account for the boundary condition statements. As before, the outer wall temperature is fixed, hence $Q2 \equiv 306.85282$ K. As a departure from previous experience, the interior nodal derivative degree of freedom $Q1'$ is constrained by the derivative boundary constraint (2.45), that is,

$$Q1' \equiv \left.\frac{dT}{dx}\right|_{r_1} = \frac{h}{k}[Q1 - T_r] = 2[Q1 - 1500] \tag{2.159}$$

Fixing $Q2$, enforcing (2.159), and carrying all $Q1$ dependence to the left side of (2.158), the reduced order matrix statement is

$$\begin{bmatrix} 42 & 1 \\ 0 & \frac{7}{3} \end{bmatrix} \begin{Bmatrix} Q1 \\ Q2' \end{Bmatrix} = \begin{Bmatrix} 41{,}523.35075 \\ -1{,}193.14718 \end{Bmatrix} \tag{2.160}$$

Note that (2.160) is not a symmetric matrix, this property having been destroyed by enforcing (2.159). The last equation in (2.160) is easily solved, yielding

$$Q2' = -511.34879 \text{ K/m}$$

The solution for $Q1$ is then

$$Q1 = 1000.82618 \text{ K}$$

The other nodal derivative variable is determined from (2.159) and $Q1$ as

$$Q1' = -998.34764 \text{ K/m}$$

Referring to Table 2.4, the accuracy of the $\{N_3'\}$ inside wall temperature $Q1$ is comparable to the quadratic one-element solution. Differentiating the analytical solution (2.48), the exact values of the two derivative degrees of freedom are

$$\left.\frac{dT}{dr}\right|_{r_1} = -1000.0 \text{ K/m} \qquad \left.\frac{dT}{dr}\right|_{r_1} = -500.0 \text{ K/m}$$

The errors in the derivative degrees of freedom of the one-element $\{N_3'\}$ solution are somewhat greater compared to those of the nodal temperatures. Note that physical significance of the derivative degree of freedom accrues by multiplication by the thermal conductivity, since $-kT'(r_2)$ is the energy efflux across the outer surface of the cylinder.

Example 2.6 Determine the approximate temperature distribution in an axisymmetric cylinder by discretizing the domain into two equal-measure finite elements and employing the $\{N_3'\}$ finite-element cardinal basis. Referring to Fig. 2.5, and noting that $\Delta_1 = 0.5$, the contribution to I^h from the first finite element R_1^1 is:

$$\int_{R_1^1} f_e \, d\sigma = \pi \{Q\}_1^T \begin{bmatrix} 30 & -30 & 1.5 & 1.0 \\ & 30 & -1.5 & -1.0 \\ & & 0.75 & -0.208333 \\ & & & 0.916667 \end{bmatrix} \begin{Bmatrix} Q1 \\ Q2 \\ Q1' \\ Q2' \end{Bmatrix}_1$$

The convection contribution remains

$$\int_{R_1^1} g_e \, d\sigma = 40\pi \{Q\}_1^T \begin{Bmatrix} \frac{1}{2}Q1 - 1500 \\ 0 \\ 0 \\ 0 \end{Bmatrix}_1$$

For the second element, the sole contribution to I^h is

$$\int_{R_2^1} f_e \, d\tau = \pi \{Q\}_2^T \begin{bmatrix} 42 & -42 & 2 & 1.5 \\ & 42 & -2 & -1.5 \\ & & 1.08333 & -0.291667 \\ & & & 1.25 \end{bmatrix} \begin{Bmatrix} Q1 \\ Q2 \\ Q1' \\ Q2' \end{Bmatrix}_2,$$

Assembling the individual matrices into the global energy statement (2.38), differentiating by $\{Q\}^T$ to extremize I^h, and rearranging slightly, yields the matrix statement

$$\begin{bmatrix} 3.0 & 0.15 & -3.0 & 0.10 & 0 & 0 \\ 0.15 & 0.075 & -0.15 & -0.0208333 & 0 & 0 \\ -3.0 & -0.15 & (3.0 + 4.2) & (-0.10 + 0.20) & -4.2 & 0.15 \\ 0.10 & -0.0208333 & (-0.10 + 0.20) & \begin{pmatrix} 0.1083333 \\ +0.0916666 \end{pmatrix} & -0.20 & -0.0291666 \\ 0 & 0 & -4.2 & -0.20 & 4.2 & -0.15 \\ 0 & 0 & 0.15 & -0.0291666 & -0.15 & 0.125 \end{bmatrix}$$

$$\begin{Bmatrix} Q_1 \\ Q_1' \\ Q_{1.5} \\ Q_{1.5}' \\ Q_2 \\ Q_2' \end{Bmatrix} = \begin{Bmatrix} 2(-Q_1 + 1500) \\ 0 \\ 0 \\ 0 \\ 0 \\ 0 \end{Bmatrix}$$

Enforcing the boundary conditions $Q_2 = 306.85282$ and $Q_1' = 2(Q_1 - 1500)$ reduces the order, yielding

$$\begin{bmatrix} 3.0 + 2.0 + 2(0.15) & -3.0 & 0.10 & 0 \\ -3.0 - 2(0.15) & 7.2 & 0.10 & 0.15 \\ 0.10 - 2(0.0208333) & 0.10 & 0.20 & -0.0291666 \\ 0 & 0.15 & -0.0291666 & 0.125 \end{bmatrix} \begin{Bmatrix} Q_1 \\ Q_{1.5} \\ Q_{1.5}' \\ Q_2' \end{Bmatrix}$$

$$= \begin{Bmatrix} 2(1500) + 2(0.15)(1500) \\ -2(0.15)(1500) + 4.2(306.85282) \\ -2(0.0208333)(1500) + 0.2(306 \cdots) \\ 0.15(306.85282) \end{Bmatrix} \tag{2.161}$$

Solving (2.161) and using (2.159), the nodal dependent variable solution $\{Q\}$ is

$$\{Q\} = \begin{Bmatrix} Q_1 \\ Q_1' \\ Q_{1.5} \\ Q_{1.5}' \\ Q_2 \\ Q_2' \end{Bmatrix} = \begin{Bmatrix} 1000.10270 \\ -999.79460 \\ 594.59097 \\ -667.71389 \\ 306.85282 \\ -501.08532 \end{Bmatrix} \tag{2.162}$$

The accuracy of all nodal variables is commendable; however, the effort in obtaining these results is substantial. The next section generalizes the theory and presents data quantizing accuracy and confirming convergence rates with discretization refinement.

Problems 4-6 at the end of this section suggest repeating these analyses using the (Lagrange) cubic interpolation for T_e, (2.149) that specifies nodal temperature (only) degrees of freedom uniformly spaced on R_e^1. Hence, (2.150) is replaced by

$$\{Q\}_e^T \equiv \{Q1,\ Q\tfrac{1}{3},\ Q\tfrac{2}{3}, Q2\}_e \tag{2.163}$$

The corresponding cardinal basis $\{N_3(\bar{x})\}$ is

$$\{N_3(\bar{x})\} = \frac{9}{2}\begin{Bmatrix} \zeta_1(\zeta_2^2 - \zeta_2 + \frac{2}{9}) \\ \zeta_1\zeta_2(2 - 3\zeta_2) \\ \zeta_1\zeta_2(3\zeta_2 - 1) \\ \zeta_2(\zeta_2^2 - \zeta_2 + \frac{2}{9}) \end{Bmatrix} \tag{2.164}$$

where the natural coordinates are specified in (2.151). The gradient of $\{N_3(\bar{x})\}$, required for the thermal conductivity contribution, is

$$\nabla\{N_3(\bar{x})\}\cdot\hat{\mathbf{i}} = \frac{9}{2\,\Delta_e}\begin{Bmatrix} -3\zeta_2^2 + 4\zeta_2 - \frac{11}{9} \\ 9\zeta_2^2 - 10\zeta_2 + 2 \\ -9\zeta_2^2 + 8\zeta_2 - 1 \\ 3\zeta_2^2 - 2\zeta_2 + \frac{2}{9} \end{Bmatrix} \tag{2.165}$$

A considerable amount of labor yields the corresponding thermal conductivity term [cf. (2.156)]

$$\int_{R_e^1} f_e \, d\tau = \frac{2\pi k \{Q\}_e^T \{R\}_e^T}{80\,\Delta_e} \begin{bmatrix} \begin{Bmatrix} 262 \\ 34 \end{Bmatrix} & \begin{Bmatrix} -327 \\ -51 \end{Bmatrix} & \begin{Bmatrix} 78 \\ 30 \end{Bmatrix} & \begin{Bmatrix} -13 \\ -13 \end{Bmatrix} \\ & \begin{Bmatrix} 594 \\ 270 \end{Bmatrix} & \begin{Bmatrix} -297 \\ -297 \end{Bmatrix} & \begin{Bmatrix} 30 \\ 78 \end{Bmatrix} \\ & & \begin{Bmatrix} 270 \\ 594 \end{Bmatrix} & \begin{Bmatrix} -51 \\ -327 \end{Bmatrix} \\ & & & \begin{Bmatrix} 34 \\ 262 \end{Bmatrix} \end{bmatrix} \{Q\}_e \tag{2.166}$$

Note that although cubic polynomials were employed in both instances, (2.166) differs considerably from (2.156). However, the convection boundary condition contribution is unchanged from (2.157). For a one-element discretization of R^1, the nodal solution obtained using the cubic cardinal basis (2.163)–(2.164) is

$$\{Q\} = \begin{Bmatrix} 999.98931 \\ 712.11327 \\ 488.90648 \\ 306.85282 \end{Bmatrix} \text{K} \tag{2.167}$$

The two-element solution is

$$\{Q\} = \sum_e \{Q\}_e = \{999.99971, 845.82033, 712.28454, 594.53503, 489.16671, \\ 393.85567, 306.85282\}^T \tag{2.168}$$

There is essentially six-place accuracy for every computed node point temperature in this solution (cf. Table 2.1).

Problems

1 Derive $\{N_3'(\bar{x})\}$, (2.152), using (2.148)–(2.151).

2 Verify (2.153) for $\nabla \{N_3'(\bar{x})\}$.

3 Verify some terms in (2.156).

4 Derive the one-dimensional cubic finite element cardinal basis $\{N_3(\bar{x})\}$ employing temperature degrees of freedom at the end points and at the one-third coordinates of R_e^1.

5 Establish the thermal conductivity term (2.166). (This is a lengthy problem.)

6 Establish the $M = 1$ and 2 finite-element solutions, analogous to Examples 2.6 and 2.7, using the results obtained in Problems 4 and 5.

2.8 ACCURACY AND CONVERGENCE GENERALIZED

Having established the concepts and mechanics of higher degree cardinal basis, we are ready to generalize the theoretical statement of accuracy and convergence developed in Sec. 2.5. Theorem I established that, for all admissible approximations $\bar{T}$ to the true solution T, the finite-element approximation T^h extremized the energy functional $I(\bar{T}, \bar{T})$ and the energy inner product $E(\bar{T}, \bar{T})$. Now consider that $\bar{T}$ and T^h are polynomials of equal degree k, and that the finite-element solution is defined as

$$T_k^h(x) \equiv \sum_{e=1}^{M} T_e(x) \tag{2.169}$$

where, on R_e^1

$$T_e(x) \equiv \{N_k(\zeta)\}^T \{Q\}_e \tag{2.170}$$

Restatement of (2.92), generalized to arbitrary degree, is

$$E(\epsilon_k^h, \epsilon_k^h) \equiv E(T - T_k^h, T - T_k^h) = \min E(T - \bar{T}_k, T - \bar{T}_k) \tag{2.171}$$

for all admissible approximation functions of degree k, that is, $\bar{T}_k$. The generation and use of kth degree finite element cardinal basis does not affect the assertion that the discrete approximation in the finite-element solution is orthogonal to the selected cardinal basis forming the approximation subspace. Hence,

$$E(T - T_k^h, T_k^h) = 0 \tag{2.172}$$

Therefore, using (2.171) and (2.172), and for degree k, the energy in the error equals the error in the energy (inner product), i.e.,

$$E(T - T_k^h, T - T_k^h) = E(T, T) - E(T_k^h, T_k^h) \tag{2.173}$$

Then, if T is the solution to an mth-order variational statement [hence, the parent partial differential equation is of order $2m$; see (2.26)], the discrete approximation error is bounded in energy of the form (Strang and Fix, 1973, Chap. 2).

$$E(T - T_k^h, T - T_k^h) \leqslant C\, \Delta_e^{2(k+1-m)} \|T\|_{k+1}^2 \tag{2.174}$$

In (2.174), C is a constant independent of Δ_e, the measure of a uniform finite element discretization of R^1, and $\|T\|_{k+1}$ is the root mean square (norm) of the $(k+1)$st derivative of the correct solution T,

$$\|T\|_{k+1} \equiv \left[\int_{R^1} \left(\frac{d^{k+1}T}{dx^{k+1}}\right)^2 dx\right]^{1/2} \tag{2.175}$$

This norm can be replaced by the L_2 norm of derivatives of order $(k + 1 - 2m)$ of the data F; see (2.116).

For the example heat conduction problem from (2.26), $2m = 2$, hence $m = 1$. For the linear finite-element cardinal basis, $k = 1$; hence, $k + 1 = 2$ and

$k+1-m=1$. Then, (2.174) with (2.175) is identical with (2.105), and the theoretical and numerically confirmed convergence rate is quadratic. For the quadratic finite-element basis, $k=2$, hence $k+1-m=2$. Therefore, the exponent of Δ_e in (2.174) is $2(k+1-m)=4$, and a fourth-degree convergence rate in energy is predicted. Similarly, for both cubic elements, $k=3$ and convergence should be sixth degree in the energy norm.

Figure 2.10 graphs computed discrete approximation error $E(\epsilon^h, \epsilon^h)$ in the energy norm as a function of degree of the finite-element cardinal basis for both the fixed flux and convection boundary conditions. The lines are drawn at indicated integer slopes. The confirmed convergence rates for the $1 \leqslant k \leqslant 3$ solutions are identical with the theoretical prediction for $M \geqslant 4$. For $M < 4$, $k > 1$, the error in energy is just smaller than theory, indicative of a trend toward coarse grid accuracy. (Additional numerical results for progressively more complex problem descriptions will confirm this as a general trend in finite-element solution methodology.) For $k = 3'$, the cubic element with derivative degrees of freedom, the highest degree complete polynomial is only 2, since the nodal derivatives are interpolated one degree lower than temperature, see (2.153). Thus, the numerically confirmed convergence rate of 4 for these cubics also agrees with theory.

To lend "engineering credence" to use of energy, convergence in alternative "norms" has also been quantized (Baker and Soliman, 1979). Figure 2.11 graphs the error in computed temperature at the interior surface, which is loaded by convection. This norm is primarily responsive to the order of accuracy with which the finite-element algorithm applies the nonhomogeneous gradient boundary condi-

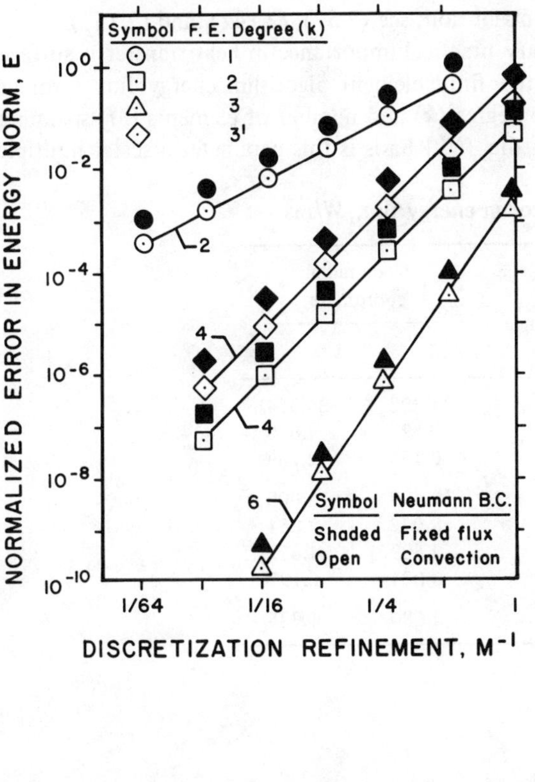

Figure 2.10 Normalized error in energy norm for one-dimensional equation with nonhomogeneous Neumann boundary condition.

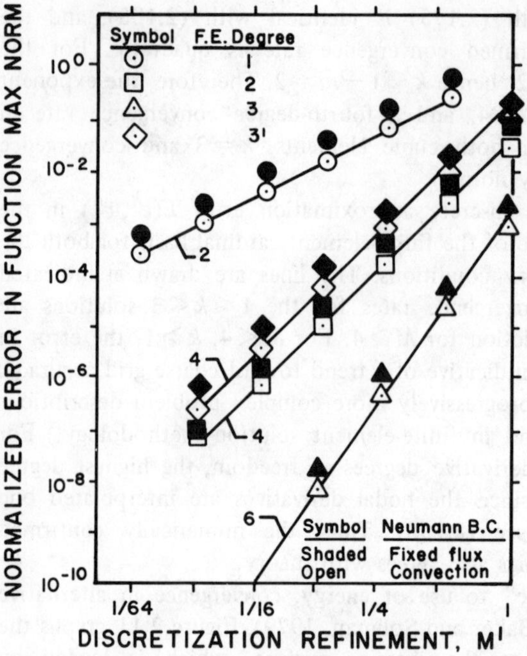

Figure 2.11 Normalized error in function max norm for one-dimensional equation with nonhomogeneous Neumann boundary condition.

tion. As can be seen, the order of accuracy is at least equal to that of the parent differential equation. This is of particularly fundamental importance, since it was observed that using a more complete cardinal basis R_e^1 did not alter in any way the equivalent boundary convection contribution; see (2.57), (2.142), and (2.157).

A solution parameter of primary practical importance in heat transfer is surface heat flux. Table 2.5 summarizes the finite-element algorithm energy flux error at both surfaces as a function of the degree (k) and number of elements (M) spanning the domain R^1. Note that only for the $\{N_3'\}$ basis is this parameter a scalar multiple

Table 2.5 Computed percentage error in energy flux, W/m²

No. of finite elements on R^1	Finite element degree	Finite difference order	Node radial coordinate 1.0	2.0
1	1	1	31.823	−36.354
	2	2	7.627	7.628
	3′	—	0.165	−2.269
2	1	1	19.499	−15.000
	1	2	8.072	7.854
	2	2	2.609	1.372
	3′	—	0.021	−0.197
4	1	2	2.680	1.376

of a degree of freedom. For the linear and quadratic basis solution, a second- or third-order accurate finite difference formula was used to estimate surface heat flux, consistent with the number of data points available for interpolation. Comparing results, the $\{N_3'\}$ algorithm data accuracy is truly remarkable, even for the single-element discretization. Figure 2.12 graphs normalized error in the interior surface heat flux prediction for each of the four basis formulations. The curves are drawn at noninteger slopes interpolating the data. The indicated third and fourth degree convergence rates for the cubics is in agreement with theory. The linear and quadratic basis data exhibit higher convergence rates than the 1 and 2 that is predicted theoretically. Hence, on all comparison bases, the finite-element algorithm produces quite acceptable accuracy and convergence rates for linear variational problems constrained by gradient boundary conditions.

2.9 THE FINITE-ELEMENT ASSEMBLY ALGORITHM

For the elementary one- and two-element discretizations considered thus far, formation of the energy functional I^h (2.38), and differentiation by $\{Q\}$ to achieve extremization (2.39), has been easily accomplished. The latter operation becomes very tedious as M increases, however. It can be replaced by defining a matrix element summation, termed the "finite element assembly algorithm," that permits construction of (2.39) on an element basis. Recall that (2.36)-(2.37) define each finite-element contribution to total system energy I^h (2.38). By the summation process $1 \leqslant e \leqslant M$, the global form (2.38) is established for extremization with respect to the totality of node point temperatures $\{Q\}$ located at those coordinates

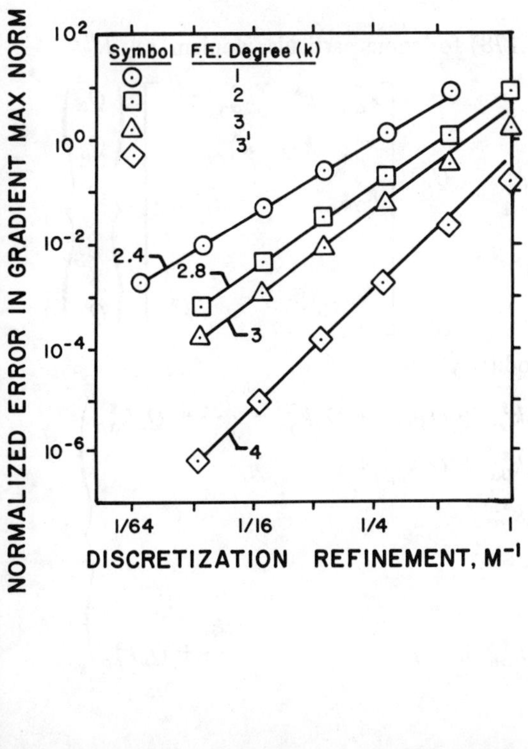

Figure 2.12 Normalized error in gradient max norm for one-dimensional equation with convection Neumann boundary condition.

of the finite-element discretization which are not explicitly constrained by the boundary condition statement (2.28).

This extremization with respect to $\{Q\}$ can be replaced by an operation on the elemental variable $\{Q\}_e$, by identification of a matrix summation. The sole requirement is that the elemental operation produce the identical matrix statement (2.40) of the global operation. This assembly algorithm is of fundamental importance for deriving finite-element algorithms for computational fluid mechanics. Of greatest practical significance, it permits direct assembly of the matrix solution statement (2.40), without proceeding through the formal construction of I^h.

The assembly algorithm is developed by induction. From (2.36)-(2.38), the form of I^h is

$$I^h \equiv \sum_e I_e = \{Q\}^T \left[\frac{1}{2} \left(\sum_e \int_{R_e^n} k \, \nabla\{N_k\} \cdot \nabla\{N_k\}^T \, d\tau \right) \{Q\} + \cdots \right] \tag{2.176}$$

Reexpressing (2.176) as the equivalent element operation yields

$$I^h \equiv \sum_e I_e = \sum_e \left[\frac{1}{2} \{Q\}_e^T \int_{R_e^n} k \, \nabla\{N_k\} \cdot \nabla\{N_k\}^T \, d\tau \{Q\}_e + \cdots \right] \tag{2.177}$$

The integrals in (2.177) are directly evaluated, as has been illustrated for $n = 1$ in the example problems. All functional dependence is known, and each integral produces a square or column master matrix. Thus, at the element level, the equivalent of (2.38) is the form

$$I^h = \sum_e [\tfrac{1}{2} \{Q\}_e^T [K]_e \{Q\}_e + \cdots] \tag{2.178}$$

Expanding the inner expression in (2.178) for some particular domain, say R_s^n

$$\frac{1}{2} \{Q\}_s^T [K]_s \{Q\}_s = \frac{1}{2} \{Q_\alpha, Q_\beta, Q_\gamma, \ldots, Q_\rho\}_s \begin{bmatrix} k_{\alpha\alpha}^s & k_{\alpha\beta}^s & k_{\alpha\gamma}^s & & \\ k_{\beta\alpha}^s & k_{\beta\beta}^s & k_{\beta\gamma}^s & & \\ k_{\gamma\alpha}^s & & \cdot & & \\ & & & \ddots & \\ & & & & k_{\rho\rho}^s \end{bmatrix}_s \begin{Bmatrix} Q_\alpha \\ Q_\beta \\ Q_\gamma \\ \vdots \\ Q_\rho \end{Bmatrix}_s$$

Proceeding through the first inner product yields

$$\frac{1}{2} \{Q_\alpha, Q_\beta, Q_\gamma, \ldots, Q_\rho\}_s \begin{Bmatrix} Q_\alpha k_{\alpha\alpha}^s + Q_\beta k_{\alpha\beta}^s + Q_\gamma k_{\alpha\gamma}^s + \cdots + Q_\rho k_{\alpha\rho}^s \\ Q_\alpha k_{\beta\alpha}^s + Q_\beta k_{\beta\beta}^s + \cdots \\ Q_\alpha k_{\gamma\alpha}^s \\ \vdots \\ Q_\alpha k_{\rho\alpha}^s + \cdots \qquad \cdots + Q_\rho k_{\rho\rho}^s \end{Bmatrix}_s$$

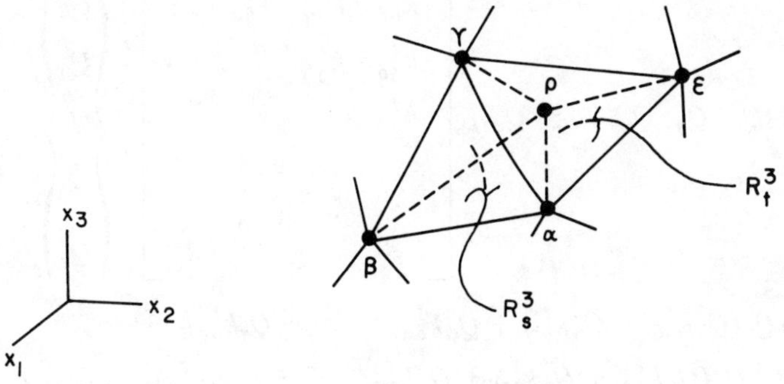

Figure 2.13 Close up of adjacent finite elements discretizing a three-dimensional solution domain R^3.

Completing the remaining matrix multiplication, the contribution I_s to I^h for the finite-element domain R_s^n is

$$\begin{aligned}\tfrac{1}{2}\{Q\}_s^T[K]_s\{Q\}_s = &\tfrac{1}{2}Q_\alpha(Q_\alpha k_{\alpha\alpha}^s + Q_\beta k_{\alpha\beta}^s + Q_\gamma k_{\alpha\gamma}^s + \cdots + Q_\rho k_{\alpha\rho}^s)_s \\ &+ \tfrac{1}{2}Q_\beta(Q_\alpha k_{\beta\alpha}^s + Q_\beta k_{\beta\beta}^s + Q_\gamma k_{\beta\gamma}^s + \cdots \qquad)_s \\ &+ \tfrac{1}{2}Q_\gamma(Q_\alpha k_{\gamma\alpha}^s + \cdots \qquad)_s \\ &\vdots \\ &+ \tfrac{1}{2}Q_\rho(Q_\alpha k_{\rho\alpha}^s + Q_\beta k_{\rho\beta}^s + \cdots + Q_\rho k_{\rho\rho}^s)_s\end{aligned} \tag{2.179}$$

As Figs. 2.13-2.15 illustrate, there will be some other finite-element domain, say R_t^n, that will share at least n nodes (hence, node point variables or "degrees of freedom" of the finite element discretization of R^n) with R_s^n, where n is the dimension of the parent problem definition (2.26). (Note: Finite-element discretizations can share $N > n$ nodal degrees of freedom, using higher degree cardinal basis, as examined using $\{N_3'\}$ on R_e^1.) For R_t^n then, proceeding through operations identical to those yielding (2.179), the appropriate contribution is

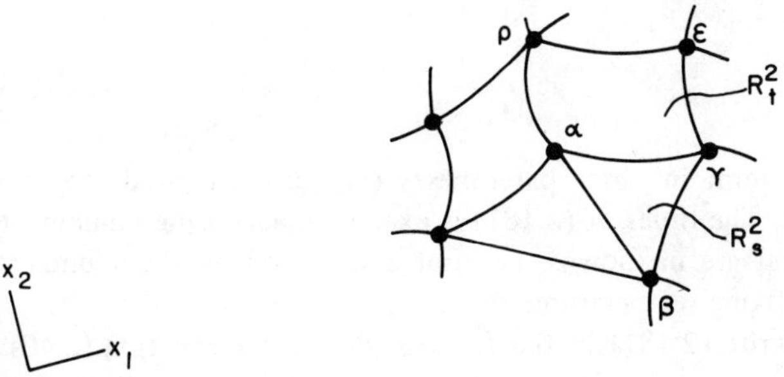

Figure 2.14 Adjacent finite elements discretizing a two-dimensional solution domain R^2.

$$\tfrac{1}{2}\{Q\}_t^T[K]_t\{Q\}_t = \tfrac{1}{2}\{Q_\delta, Q_\gamma, Q_\alpha, \ldots, Q_\epsilon\}_t \begin{bmatrix} k^t_{\delta\delta} & k^t_{\delta\gamma} & k^t_{\delta\alpha} & \cdots \\ k^t_{\gamma\delta} & k^t_{\gamma\gamma} & & \\ k^t_{\alpha\delta} & \cdot & \cdot & \\ \vdots & & \ddots & \\ & & \cdot & k^t_{\epsilon\epsilon} \end{bmatrix}_t \begin{Bmatrix} Q_\delta \\ Q_\gamma \\ Q_\alpha \\ \vdots \\ Q_\epsilon \end{Bmatrix}_t$$

$$\begin{aligned} &= \tfrac{1}{2}Q_\delta(Q_\delta k^t_{\delta\delta} + Q_\gamma k^t_{\delta\gamma} + Q_\alpha k^t_{\delta\alpha} + \cdots + Q_\epsilon k^t_{\delta\epsilon})_t \\ &\quad + \tfrac{1}{2}Q_\gamma(Q_\delta k^t_{\gamma\delta} + Q_\gamma k^t_{\gamma\gamma} + Q_\alpha k^t_{\gamma\alpha} + \cdots + Q_\epsilon k^t_{\gamma\epsilon})_t \\ &\quad + \tfrac{1}{2}Q_\alpha(Q_\delta k^t_{\alpha\delta} + Q_\gamma k^t_{\alpha\gamma} + Q_\alpha k^t_{\alpha\alpha} + \cdots \qquad)_t \\ &\quad + \cdots + \tfrac{1}{2}Q_\epsilon(Q_\delta k^t_{\epsilon\delta} + Q_\gamma k^t_{\epsilon\gamma} + Q_\alpha k^t_{\epsilon\alpha} + \cdots + Q_\epsilon k^t_{\epsilon\epsilon})_t \end{aligned} \tag{2.180}$$

Now, forming the extremization of the global energy functional I^h (2.38), using (2.179) and (2.180) as representative contributions to I_e, yields for (2.39),

$$\frac{\partial I^h}{\partial\{Q\}} = \begin{Bmatrix} \begin{aligned} &([(Q_\alpha k^s_{\alpha\alpha} + \tfrac{1}{2}Q_\beta k^s_{\alpha\beta} + \tfrac{1}{2}Q_\gamma k^s_{\alpha\gamma} + \cdots + \tfrac{1}{2}Q_\rho k^s_{\alpha\rho}) \\ &\qquad + (\tfrac{1}{2}Q_\beta k^s_{\beta\alpha} + 0 + \cdots + 0) + (\tfrac{1}{2}Q_\gamma k^s_{\gamma\alpha} + \cdots + 0) \\ &\qquad + \cdots \qquad + (\tfrac{1}{2}Q_\rho k^s_{\rho\alpha})] \\ &\quad + [(0 + 0 + \tfrac{1}{2}Q_\delta k^t_{\delta\alpha} + 0 + \cdots + 0) + (0 + 0 + \tfrac{1}{2}Q_\gamma k^t_{\gamma\alpha} + 0 + \cdots + 0) \\ &\qquad + (\tfrac{1}{2}Q_\delta k^t_{\alpha\delta} + \tfrac{1}{2}Q_\gamma k^t_{\alpha\gamma} + Q_\alpha k^t_{\alpha\alpha} + \cdots + Q_\epsilon k^t_{\alpha\epsilon}) \\ &\qquad + \cdots \qquad + (0 + 0 + \tfrac{1}{2}Q_\epsilon k^t_{\epsilon\alpha} + 0 + \cdots + 0)])_{k=\alpha}, \\ &([\cdots \qquad)_{k=\beta}, \\ &([(0 + 0 + \tfrac{1}{2}Q_\alpha k^s_{\alpha\gamma} + \cdots + 0) + (0 + 0 + \tfrac{1}{2}Q_\beta k^s_{\beta\gamma} + \cdots) \\ &\quad + (\tfrac{1}{2}Q_\alpha k^s_{\gamma\alpha} + \tfrac{1}{2}Q_\beta k^s_{\gamma\beta} + Q_\gamma k^s_{\gamma\gamma} + \cdots) + (\qquad)] \\ &\quad + [(0 + \tfrac{1}{2}Q_\delta k^t_{\delta\gamma} + 0 + \cdots + 0) + (\tfrac{1}{2}Q_\delta k^t_{\delta\gamma} + Q_\gamma k^t_{\gamma\gamma} + \tfrac{1}{2}Q_\alpha k^t_{\gamma\alpha} + \cdots) \\ &\quad + (0 + \tfrac{1}{2}Q_\alpha k^t_{\alpha\gamma} + \cdots + 0) + (0 + \tfrac{1}{2}Q_\epsilon k^t_{\epsilon\gamma} + 0 + \cdots + 0)])_{k=\gamma} \\ &(\cdots) \end{aligned} \end{Bmatrix} \tag{2.181}$$

Note in (2.181) that each term in outer parentheses $(\cdot)_{k=\alpha}$ corresponds to one element of a column matrix. The order of (2.181) is exactly equal to the number of node point temperatures that are unknowns, i.e., not constrained by the boundary condition statement (2.28) fixing temperature.

The final step is to rewrite (2.181) in the form of the matrix equation (2.40).

Recalling that each of the element matrices $[K]_e$ is symmetric, for linear steady-state heat conduction, see (2.178), the form for (2.181) is

$$\frac{\partial I^h}{\partial \{Q\}} = \begin{bmatrix} (k^s_{\alpha\alpha} + k^t_{\alpha\alpha}), & k^s_{\alpha\beta}, & (k^s_{\alpha\gamma} + k^t_{\alpha\gamma}), & k^t_{\alpha\delta}, & k^t_{\alpha\epsilon}, \ldots, & k^s_{\alpha\rho}, \\ \cdots & , \cdots, & \cdots & , & & \\ (k^s_{\gamma\alpha} + k^t_{\gamma\alpha}), & k^s_{\gamma\beta}, & (k^s_{\gamma\gamma} + k^t_{\gamma\gamma}), & k^t_{\gamma\delta}, & k^t_{\gamma\epsilon}, \ldots, & k^s_{\gamma\rho}, \\ & & \ddots & & & \\ & & & & & , k^s_{\rho\rho} \end{bmatrix} \begin{Bmatrix} Q_\alpha \\ Q_\beta \\ Q_\gamma \\ Q_\delta \\ Q_\epsilon \\ \vdots \\ Q_\rho \end{Bmatrix} \tag{2.182}$$

Equation (2.182) is the explicit form for the global assembly of the extremization of the quadratic portions of (2.38) for two finite elements sharing two nodal degrees of freedom, i.e., the temperature unknowns Q_α and Q_γ. The symmetry of the parent element matrices $[K]_e$ leads to symmetry in global form (2.182).

The finite-element assembly algorithm is derived by showing that (2.182) can formally result from extremization of the local functional I_e with respect to the element degrees of freedom $\{Q\}_e$ without regard to their eligibility for constraint by a Dirichlet boundary condition (2.28) should $\partial R_e \cap \partial R \neq 0$. A postoperation is then required to account for Dirichlet boundary conditions; recall the example problems. The minimization of I_e with respect to $\{Q\}_e^T$ is particularly easy to evaluate [cf. (2.36)-(2.38)].

$$\frac{\partial I_e}{\partial \{Q\}_e} = \int_{R_e^n} k\, \nabla \{N_k\} \cdot \nabla \{N_k\}^T \, d\tau \{Q\}_e - \int_{R_e^n} \rho \dot{q} \{N_k\} \, d\tau + \int_{\partial R_e \cap \partial R} h \{N_k\}(\{N_k\}^T \{Q\}_e - T_r) \, d\sigma \tag{2.183}$$

Writing (2.183) for each finite-element domain R_e^n, and summing over the range $1 \leqslant e \leqslant M$, produces a matrix expression that is defined as

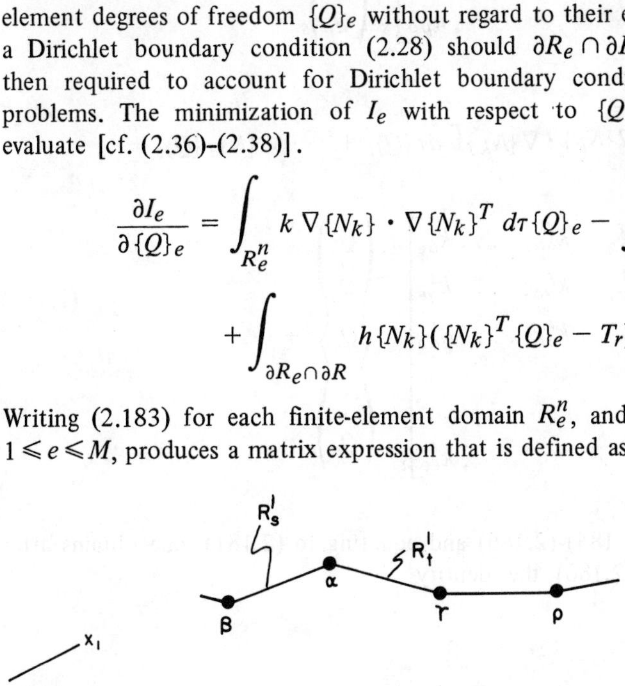

Figure 2.15 Adjacent finite elements discretizing a one-dimensional solution domain R^1.

$$S_e\left[\frac{\partial I_e}{\partial \{Q\}_e}\right] \equiv \{0\} \tag{2.184}$$

Equation (2.184) defines the matrix summation operator S_e, the form of which is required derived. [Note: In the context of this introductory development, S_e is defined as a special summation operator. More properly, it is interpreted as a linear mapping between the space of the finite-element discrete approximation $T^h(\bar{x}) = \Sigma_{e=1}^{M} \{N_k\}^T \{Q\}_e$ and the function space of the global approximation (2.38).] In the spirit of (2.178)-(2.180), a general term of (2.180) for two elements R_e^n, $e = s$ and t, sharing the node pair $\mathbf{x}_\alpha$ and $\mathbf{x}_\beta$, with corresponding unknown temperatures Q_α and Q_β, becomes

$$\frac{\partial I_s}{\partial \{Q\}_s^T} = \int_{R_s^n} k\, \nabla \{N_k\} \cdot \nabla \{N_k\}^T \, d\tau \{Q\}_s + \cdots \equiv [K]_s \{Q\}_s + \cdots$$

$$= \begin{bmatrix} k_{\alpha\alpha}^s, & k_{\alpha\beta}^s, & k_{\alpha\gamma}^s, & \ldots, & k_{\alpha\rho}^s \\ & k_{\beta\beta}^s, & k_{\beta\gamma}^s, & \ldots, & k_{\beta\rho}^s \\ & & k_{\gamma\gamma}^s, & \ldots, & k_{\gamma\rho}^s \\ & & & \ddots & \\ \text{(sym)} & & & & k_{\rho\rho}^s \end{bmatrix}_s \begin{Bmatrix} Q_\alpha \\ Q_\beta \\ Q_\gamma \\ \vdots \\ Q_\rho \end{Bmatrix}_s + \cdots \tag{2.185}$$

$$\frac{\partial I_t}{\partial \{Q\}_t^T} = \int_{R_t^n} k\, \nabla \{N_k\} \cdot \nabla \{N_k\}^T \, d\tau \{Q\}_t + \cdots \equiv [K]_t \{Q\}_t + \cdots$$

$$= \begin{bmatrix} k_{\delta\delta}^t, & k_{\delta\gamma}^t, & k_{\delta\alpha}^t, & \ldots, & k_{\delta\epsilon}^t \\ & k_{\gamma\gamma}^t, & k_{\gamma\alpha}^t, & \ldots, & k_{\gamma\epsilon}^t \\ & & k_{\alpha\alpha}^t, & \ldots, & k_{\alpha\epsilon}^t \\ & & & \ddots & \\ \text{(sym)} & & & & k_{\epsilon\epsilon}^t \end{bmatrix}_t \begin{Bmatrix} Q_\delta \\ Q_\gamma \\ Q_\alpha \\ \vdots \\ Q_\epsilon \end{Bmatrix}_t + \cdots \tag{2.186}$$

Forming (2.184), using (2.185)-(2.186) and equating to (2.181), one obtains after modest rearrangement of (2.186), the identity

$$
\begin{bmatrix}
(k^s_{\alpha\alpha}+k^t_{\alpha\alpha}), & k^s_{\alpha\beta}, & (k^s_{\alpha\gamma}+k^t_{\alpha\gamma}), & k^t_{\alpha\delta}, & k^t_{\alpha\epsilon}, \ldots, k^s_{\alpha\rho} \\
 & k^s_{\beta\beta}, & \cdots & , & \\
 & , & (k^s_{\gamma\gamma}+k^t_{\gamma\gamma}), & k^t_{\gamma\delta}, & k^t_{\gamma\epsilon}, \ldots, k^s_{\gamma\rho} \\
 & & & \ddots & \\
\text{(sym)} & & & & \ddots, k^s_{\rho\rho}
\end{bmatrix}
\begin{Bmatrix} Q_\alpha \\ Q_\beta \\ Q_\gamma \\ Q_\delta \\ \vdots \\ Q_\rho \end{Bmatrix}
$$

$$
\equiv S_e \left(\begin{bmatrix}
k^s_{\alpha\alpha}, & k^s_{\alpha\beta}, & k^s_{\alpha\gamma}, \ldots, k^s_{\alpha\rho} \\
, & k^s_{\beta\beta}, & \ldots \\
 & , & k^s_{\gamma\gamma}, \ldots \\
 & & \ddots \\
\text{(sym)} & & \cdot \quad k^s_{\rho\rho}
\end{bmatrix}_s
\begin{Bmatrix} Q_\alpha \\ Q_\beta \\ Q_\gamma \\ \vdots \\ Q_\rho \end{Bmatrix}_s ,
\begin{bmatrix}
k^t_{\alpha\alpha}, & k^t_{\alpha\gamma}, & k^t_{\alpha\delta}, \ldots, k^t_{\alpha\epsilon} \\
, & k^t_{\gamma\gamma}, & \ldots \\
 & , & k^t_{\delta\delta}, \ldots \\
 & & \ddots \\
\text{(sym)} & & \cdot \quad k^t_{\epsilon\epsilon}
\end{bmatrix}
\begin{Bmatrix} Q_\alpha \\ Q_\gamma \\ Q_\delta \\ \vdots \\ Q_\epsilon \end{Bmatrix}_t \right) \tag{2.187}
$$

From the definition (2.187), the matrix operator S_e corresponds to rowwise addition of matrix elements of the element matrices $[K]_s$ and $[K]_t$, at locations of node point degree-of-freedom commonality, after accounting for the order of node point unknowns in each specific finite-element column matrix $\{Q\}_e$. Specifically, (2.187) defines the operation

$$
\frac{\partial I^h}{\partial \{Q\}} \equiv S_e \left[\frac{\partial I_e}{\partial \{Q\}_e} \right] \equiv \{0\} \tag{2.188}
$$

The first observation from (2.188) is that each finite-element matrix $\{Q\}_e$ must be a linearly independent subset of the global vector $\{Q\}$, that is,

$$
\begin{aligned}
&\{Q\}_e \in \{Q\} \\
&\{Q\}_s \neq \{Q\}_t, \qquad s \neq t
\end{aligned} \tag{2.189}
$$

Thus, each finite-element domain R^n_e of the discretization of the solution domain must be unique. Therefore, (2.188) must vanish identically for each $\{Q\}_e$, employing the concept of linear independence (Kreyczig, 1962, p. 100).

The matrix equation system definition (2.188) basically involves assembly of each element of the global coefficient matrix $[K]$ from the corresponding finite-element domain matrices (2.185), i.e.,

$$
[K] \equiv S_e [K]_e \tag{2.190}
$$

Let k_{ij} be the (i, j) matrix element of the global matrix $[K]$. Each element is formed by rowwise addition of the matrix elements $k^e_{\alpha\beta}$, of the eth elemental matrices $[K]_e$, over common nodal degrees of freedom. Specifically,

$$k_{ij} \equiv \sum_e k^e_{\alpha\beta} \tag{2.191}$$

where i = the integer location in $\{Q\}$ where Q_α is stored
j = the integer location in $\{Q\}$ where Q_β is stored
α = the integer location in $[K]_e$ corresponding to Q_α in $\{Q\}_e$
β = the integer location in $[K]_e$ corresponding to Q_β in $\{Q\}_e$
e = ranges over all finite-element domains containing both Q_α and Q_β.

Since the rule for ordering entries into the global matrix is basically (yes, no), or a (0,1) operation, as determined by whether the node point degree of freedom is common to an element pair or not, the matrix element summation (2.191) is fundamentally a "Boolean" operation. Since (2.191) is defined on degree-of-freedom commonality, the operation is independent of the dimension n of the problem, cf. (2.26), as well as the degree of the finite-element approximation (2.32). As indicated at the beginning of this section, the assembly algorithm (2.190)-(2.191) is fundamental to finite-element operations, and is a concept with which the user should become familiar. It is suggested that the problems of Examples 2.2 and 2.5 be repeated using (2.190)-(2.191) for familiarization.

A few additional comments are required regarding Dirichlet boundary conditions fixing nodal degrees of freedom on appropriate boundary segments ∂R. Independent of whether extremization of I^h (2.176) is performed on $\{Q\}$, or on the totality of $\{Q\}_e$ (2.188), and for arbitrary dimension, the order (size) of the global matrix equation system equals the total number of defined node point variables. As discussed in Sec. 2.3, those members $\{Q_\beta\}$ of $\{Q\}$ that are fixed by Dirichlet boundary conditions are placed in the lower partition $\{Q\}$ [cf. (2.41)]. Hence, (2.188) is the form

$$S_e\left[\frac{\partial I_e}{\partial \{Q\}_e}\right] = [K]\{Q\} - \{F\} \equiv \{0\}$$

$$= \begin{bmatrix} [K_{\alpha\alpha}] & [K_{\alpha\beta}] \\ [K_{\beta\alpha}] & [K_{\beta\beta}] \end{bmatrix} \begin{Bmatrix} \{Q_\alpha\} \\ \{Q_\beta\} \end{Bmatrix} - \begin{Bmatrix} \{F_\alpha\} \\ \{F_\beta\} \end{Bmatrix} \equiv \{0\} \tag{2.192}$$

In (2.192), the order of $[K_{\alpha\alpha}]$ is identical to the number of degrees of freedom $\{Q_\alpha\}$. Hence, the solution matrix statement is

$$[K_{\alpha\alpha}]\{Q_\alpha\} = \{F_\alpha\} - [K_{\alpha\beta}]\{Q_\beta\} \tag{2.193}$$

By discarding the lower partition equations in (2.192), since they correspond to specification of a homogeneous (adiabatic wall) gradient boundary condition (2.27) rather than the specified Dirichlet constraint (2.28), the nodal solution $\{Q\}^T = \{Q_\alpha, Q_\beta\}$ is completed by solving (2.193).

$$\{Q_\alpha\} = [K_{\alpha\alpha}]^{-1}(\{F\}_\alpha - [K_{\alpha\beta}]\{Q_\beta\}) \tag{2.194}$$

With identification of the assembly algorithm (2.190)–(2.191) completed, the direct global matrix statement for extremization of I^h becomes

$$S_e\left[\int_{R_e^n} k\,\nabla\{N_k\}\cdot\nabla\{N_k\}^T\,d\tau\,\{Q\}_e + \int_{\partial R_e\cap\partial R} h\{N_k\}\{N_k\}^T\,d\sigma\,\{Q\}_e \right.$$
$$\left. - \int_{R_e^n} \rho\dot{q}\{N_k\}\,d\tau - \int_{\partial R_e\cap\partial R} hT_r\{N_k\}\,d\sigma\right] = \{0\} \tag{2.195}$$

Note that (2.195) exhibits an appearance similar to the parent differential equation statement (2.26)–(2.27). Therefore, no need exists to form the scalars f_e and g_e, or even I^h, in actual practice. The computer program embodiment of (2.195) is a *DO* loop on $1 \leqslant e \leqslant M$, with S_e the Boolean operator for storing the element matrix contributions into the global solution matrices. Reflecting on the several example problems discussed in this chapter, observe that (2.195) is the final solution form established in each instance. The direct formation of the extremization matrix statement (2.195) is the procedure followed throughout the remainder of this text.

Problems

1 Repeat the problems of Examples 2.2 and 2.5 using S_e, (2.190)–(2.191).

2 Repeat Example 2.2, for an $M = 4$ discretization of R_e^1, using the assembly algorithm (2.190)–(2.191) to establish the corresponding matrix equation statement.

2.10 THE STATIC CONDENSATION ALGORITHM

In addition to the assembly algorithm, there is one other operation intrinsic to finite-element methodology for linear boundary value problems that should be introduced. Static condensation enables a reduction of rank of the global statement of energy minimization. This is accomplished by "reducing out" the degrees of freedom Q_α corresponding to minimization of energy at the element level. There is an entire class of so-called serendipity finite elements (in analogy to the Princes of Serendip, who always transformed adversity to advantage) that are formulated for $k > 1$ without any nodes internal to the boundary of the finite element R_e^n (Zienkiewicz, 1977, p. 107). For the example problem pursued in this chapter, recall that both the quadratic and nonderivative cubic basis defined interior nodes. The additional degrees of freedom associated with these nodes can be removed at the element level of computation, hence do not appear in the global matrix equation system. The formulation and associated matrix operations for the quadratic basis algorithm of Sec. 2.6 are presented herein.

Consider the generalized matrix equivalent of the thermal conduction problem

(2.195) with convection boundary condition. On the finite-element domain R_e^1, and prior to assembly, the matrix statement is

$$[K]_e\{Q\}_e = \{F\}_e \qquad (2.196)$$

The column matrix of unknowns $\{Q\}_e$ contains degrees of freedom at nodes on the boundary ∂R_e and at the nodes interior to R_e^n. Partition $\{Q\}_e$ into $\{Q_\alpha\}_e$ into $\{Q_\beta\}_e$, such that all nodes not lying on the boundary have their degrees of freedom cast into $\{Q_\beta\}_e$. Equation (2.196) thus reorganized is

$$\begin{bmatrix} K_{\alpha\alpha} & \vdots & K_{\alpha\beta} \\ \hdashline K_{\beta\alpha} & \vdots & K_{\beta\beta} \end{bmatrix}_e \begin{Bmatrix} Q_\alpha \\ \hdashline Q_\beta \end{Bmatrix}_e = \begin{Bmatrix} F_\alpha \\ \hdashline F_\beta \end{Bmatrix} \qquad (2.197)$$

The lower partition of (2.197) is solved for $\{Q_\beta\}_e$, yielding

$$\{Q_\beta\}_e = [K_{\beta\beta}]_e^{-1}(\{F_\beta\}_e - [K_{\beta\alpha}]_e\{Q_\alpha\}_e) \qquad (2.198)$$

The resultant solution statement for the upper partition, inserting (2.198), is

$$([K_{\alpha\alpha}]_e - [K_{\alpha\beta}]_e[K_{\beta\beta}]_e^{-1}[K_{\beta\alpha}]_e)\{Q_\alpha\}_e = \{F_\alpha\}_e - [K_{\alpha\beta}]_e[K_{\beta\beta}]_e^{-1}\{F_\beta\}_e \qquad (2.199)$$

The matrix system (2.199) is formally identical to the extremization operation yielding (2.196), however with the degrees of freedom $\{Q_\beta\}_e$ removed. Dropping the subscript α notation, (2.199) is

$$[K^a]_e\{Q\}_e \equiv \{F^a\}_e \qquad (2.200)$$

Comparing (2.200) to (2.199),

$$[K^a]_e \equiv [K_{\alpha\alpha}]_e - [K_{\alpha\beta}]_e[K_{\beta\beta}]_e^{-1}[K_{\beta\alpha}]_e \qquad (2.201)$$

$$\{F^a\}_e \equiv \{F_\alpha\}_e - [K_{\alpha\beta}]_e[K_{\beta\beta}]_e^{-1}\{F_\beta\}_e \qquad (2.202)$$

Upon assembly of the element statements (2.200), using (2.190)-(2.191), solution of the resultant global equation system yields the matrix elements of $\{Q\}$ corresponding to $\{Q_\alpha\}_e$ only. The remaining elements $\{Q_\beta\}_e$ are obtained as a post operation at the element level by evaluating (2.198). For illustration:

Example 2.7 Using the static condensation and assembly algorithms, determine the steady-state temperature distribution in an axisymmetric cylinder using the quadratic finite element basis on a two-element discretization of R^1. On R_1^1,

$$\{R\}_1^T = \{1., \quad 1.5\}_1$$

$$\int_{R_1^1} \nabla\{N_2(\bar{x})\}^T \cdot k\,\nabla T_e\,d\tau = \frac{40\pi}{6}\begin{bmatrix} 15.5 & 2.5 & -18. \\ & 19.5 & -22. \\ \text{(sym)} & & 40. \end{bmatrix}\begin{Bmatrix} Q1 \\ Q2 \\ Q_2^1 \end{Bmatrix}_1 \qquad (2.203)$$

$$\int_{\partial R_1 \cap \partial R} \{N_2(\bar{x})\} h[T_e - T_r]\, d\sigma = 40\pi \begin{Bmatrix} Q1 - 1500 \\ 0 \\ 0 \end{Bmatrix}_1 \tag{2.204}$$

On the second element R_2^1,

$$\{R\}_2^T = \{1.5, \quad 2.0\}_2$$

$$\int_{R_2^1} \nabla \{N_2(\bar{x})\} \cdot k\, \nabla T_e\, d\tau = \frac{40\pi}{6} \begin{bmatrix} 22.5 & 3.5 & -20.0 \\ & 26.5 & -30.0 \\ \text{(sym)} & & 56.0 \end{bmatrix} \begin{Bmatrix} Q1 \\ Q2 \\ Q\frac{1}{2} \end{Bmatrix} \tag{2.205}$$

Static condensation of (2.203) can remove $Q\frac{1}{2}$ from $\{Q\}_1$. From (2.201), neglecting the scalar multiplier,

$$[K^a]_1 \equiv \begin{bmatrix} 15.5 & 2.5 \\ 2.5 & 19.5 \end{bmatrix} - \begin{Bmatrix} -18.0 \\ -22.0 \end{Bmatrix} \frac{1}{40} \{-18.0, \quad -22.0\} = \begin{bmatrix} 7.4 & -7.4 \\ -7.4 & 7.4 \end{bmatrix} \tag{2.206}$$

The thermal load matrix (2.204) is unaffected by condensation. On R_2^1, condensing out $Q\frac{1}{2}$ from $\{Q\}_2$ yields

$$[K^a]_2 \equiv \begin{bmatrix} 22.5 & 3.5 \\ 3.5 & 26.5 \end{bmatrix} - \begin{Bmatrix} -26.0 \\ -30.0 \end{Bmatrix} \frac{1}{56} \{-26.0, \quad -30.0\} = \begin{bmatrix} 10.43 & -10.43 \\ -10.43 & 10.43 \end{bmatrix} \tag{2.207}$$

Assembling (2.206)-(2.207) using (2.190)-(2.191), and inserting (2.204) into the condensed thermal load matrix yields the global matrix system

$$\left[\begin{array}{cc:c} 13.4 & -7.4 & 0. \\ -7.4 & 17.84 & -10.43 \\ \hdashline 0 & -10.43 & 10.43 \end{array}\right] \begin{Bmatrix} Q_1 \\ Q_{1.5} \\ 306.85282 \end{Bmatrix} = \left\{\begin{array}{c} 6(1500) \\ 0 \\ \hdashline 0 \end{array}\right\} \tag{2.208}$$

Partitioning (2.208) to account for Q_2 fixed, and solving determines the uncondensed nodal temperature solution.

$$\{Q\} = \begin{Bmatrix} Q_1 \\ Q_{1.5} \\ Q_{2.0} \end{Bmatrix} = \begin{Bmatrix} 999.97042 \\ 594.54107 \\ 306.85282 \end{Bmatrix} \text{K}$$

These data agree through the fourth significant digit with the standard quadratic solution (see Table 2.4), although the error is marginally larger compared to the exact solution. The temperatures at the quarter span nodes $Q_{1.25}$ and $Q_{1.75}$ are obtained using (2.198). For finite element R_1^1

$$Q_{1.25} = \frac{1}{40}\left(0 - \{-18.0, \quad -22.0\}\begin{Bmatrix}999.97042\\594.54107\end{Bmatrix}\right) = 776.98429 \text{ K}$$

and for R_2^1

$$Q_{1.75} = \frac{1}{56.}\left(0 - \{-26.0, \quad -30.0\}\begin{Bmatrix}594.54107\\306.85282\end{Bmatrix}\right) = 440.42237 \text{ K}$$

From Table 2.4, both these temperatures are marginally more accurate than the regular quadratic basis results.

The complete $M = 2$ nodal solution for $\{N_2\}$ using static condensation is

$$\{Q\} = \begin{Bmatrix}999.97042\\776.98429\\594.54107\\440.42237\\306.85282\end{Bmatrix} \text{K} \tag{2.209}$$

Note that this solution was obtained solving a matrix of rank two; see (2.208), while the rank of the standard solution procedure was four. This reduction of global rank is the primary feature of static condensation and can be used to significant advantage for large multidimensional problems. Under discretization refinement, the solutions obtained using static condensation will converge to the true solution to order 4 in Δ_e.

2.11 CLOSURE

The primary goal of this chapter was to establish and illustrate the finite-element solution algorithm applied to a linear partial differential equation system. The energy conservation law was selected for its considerable value in communication between structural energy extremization methods, the variational calculus, and analysis in heat transfer. Following derivation and use of various degree finite-element cardinal basis, and establishment of the rigorous statements of accuracy and convergence with discretization refinement, the finite element assembly algorithm was established by a direct procedure. This algorithm permits the casting of the fundamental algorithm onto a sequence of operations on a representative finite element domain. The reduction of global matrix system order to the required rank, i.e., the number of unknowns on $R^n \cup \partial R$ requiring solution, was illustrated as a post operation to assembly. The elementary example problems, and experimentation with discretization refinement, adds substance to the concept of accuracy and convergence measured in the energy norm. Hence, most of the "tools" of finite element methodology have been introduced and used in an expository fashion. We are now ready to pursue application to progressively more complex problems.

REFERENCES

Baker, A. J. and Soliman, M. O. (1979). Utility of a Finite Element Solution Algorithm for Initial-Value Problems, *J. Comp. Phys.*, vol. 32, no. 3, pp. 289–324.

Carslaw, H. S. and Jaeger, J. C. (1959). *Conduction of Heat in Solids,* 2d Ed., Oxford Press, London.

Finlayson, B. A. and Scriven, L. E. (1966). The Method of Weighted Residuals–A Review, *Appl. Mech. Rev.*, vol. 19, no. 9, pp. 735–748.

Kreyszig, E. (1962). *Advanced Engineering Mathematics,* 2d Ed., Wiley, New York.

Shames, I. H. (1964). *Mechanics of Deformable Solids*, Prentice Hall, Englewood Cliffs, New Jersey.

Strang, G. and Fix, G. J. (1973). *An Analysis of the Finite Element Method,* Prentice Hall, Englewood Cliffs, New Jersey.

Thomas, G. B. (1962). *Calculus and Analytical Geometry,* Addison-Wesley, Reading, Mass.

Weinstock, R. (1952). *The Calculus of Variations,* McGraw-Hill, New York.

Zienkiewicz, O. C. (1977). *The Finite Element Method,* McGraw-Hill, London.

CHAPTER

THREE

INVISCID POTENTIAL FLOW

3.1 INTRODUCTION

An important problem class in fluid mechanics, directly amenable to analysis using the developed finite-element concepts, is potential flow. For the steady irrotational flow of an incompressible inviscid fluid, the governing eulerian equations can be reduced to the laplacian written on either of two velocity potential functions. The same form results for the steady subsonic compressible flow about slender aerodynamic bodies in terms of the perturbation velocity potential function. Hence, for these simplifications, the governing partial differential equation is a linear elliptic boundary value problem, for which the potential energy functional is readily formed. The various forms for the potential flow equations are presented and their solutions are explored using the finite-element algorithm. The two- and three-dimensionality of this problem class provides the opportunity to present and evaluate higher dimensional finite-element spaces and curved-sided isoparametric elements. The dominance of the gradient boundary condition statement and importance of solution accuracy on the boundary emphasizes algorithm performance.

The earliest applications of finite elements to fluid analysis involved adaptation of elasticity computer programs to potential flow. DeVries and Norrie (1971) obtained a finite-element solution for two-dimensional aerodynamic flow in a cascade using straight-sided triangular elements. Two-dimensional aerodynamic configuration solutions are given by Meissner (1973). Sarpkaya and Hiriart (1975) present results for an axisymmetric thrust reverser involving a free surface of unknown location. Results using higher degree curved-sided finite elements for two-dimensional potential flows are given by Thompson (1973), Isaacs (1973), and Hirsch and Warzee (1974). The case for a specified freestream vorticity "frozen" into a two-dimensional aerodynamic flow is discussed by Vooren and Laburjere (1973) using linear elements. Applications to nonsteady, two-dimensional flows are reported by Bratanow and Ecer (1974). Baker and Manhardt (1975, 1977) report results for potential flow prediction about general airfoils at angle of attack employing linear finite elements. This chapter develops application of the finite-element algorithm for this important problem class.

A. INCOMPRESSIBLE FLOW

3.2 EQUATION SYSTEMS GOVERNING POTENTIAL FLOW

A fundamental precept in mechanics is conservation of mass, a property intrinsic to the lagrangian description of structural mechanics. However, in the eulerian description for fluid mechanics, the fundamental laws become expressed for a region in space through which mass is convected by the local velocity vector **u**. From Reynolds' transport theorem (Shames, 1982, Chap. 4), the equivalent differential statement for conservation of mass of an incompressible fluid is vanishing divergence of the velocity field

$$L(\mathbf{u}) = \nabla \cdot \mathbf{u} = 0 \tag{3.1}$$

For a potential flow field, the velocity field is also irrotational; hence, the curl of the velocity vanishes

$$\text{curl } \mathbf{u} = \nabla \times \mathbf{u} \equiv 0 \tag{3.2}$$

From vector field theory, (3.2) is identically satisfied by definition of the scalar potential function Φ as

$$\mathbf{u} \equiv -\nabla\Phi \tag{3.3}$$

where the negative sign is defined by convention. Substitution of (3.3) into (3.1) yields the differential equation governing potential flow in the form

$$L(\Phi) = \nabla \cdot \nabla\Phi = \nabla^2\Phi = 0 \tag{3.4}$$

where ∇^2 is called the laplacian (operator). Equation (3.4) is a linear elliptic partial differential equation.

The boundary condition statement for (3.4) is provided by (3.3). On segments of the solution domain boundary where the velocity vector **u** is known, and defining $\hat{\mathbf{n}}$ the local outward pointing unit normal vector, the inner product with (3.3) yields

$$\nabla\Phi \cdot \hat{\mathbf{n}} = -\mathbf{u} \cdot \hat{\mathbf{n}} \equiv -u^1 \tag{3.5}$$

where u^1 denotes the scalar component of the surface velocity vector perpendicular to the boundary segment. In the event this corresponds to an impervious surface, to which the velocity vector must be parallel, (3.5) yields

$$\nabla\Phi \cdot \hat{\mathbf{n}} = 0 \tag{3.6}$$

the familiar flow tangency condition. Finally, (3.3) defines Φ only to within an arbitrary constant; therefore, Φ may be set equal to an arbitrary constant at one point on the domain boundary. Hence, this specification for potential flow yields a linear elliptic partial differential equation for solution with Neumann boundary conditions.

For incompressible flows, an alternative vector potential function can be defined from (3.1). In two dimensions, this potential function is called streamfunction (ψ), and in steady flow computed stream lines correspond identically with the particle trajectories used extensively for flow visualization. The two-dimensional "streamfunction" is but one scalar component of a three-dimensional vector potential function $\boldsymbol{\Psi}$. From vector field theory, (3.1) can be enforced identically by definition of the (two-dimensional) velocity field as the curl of the orthogonal scalar component $\psi\hat{\mathbf{k}}$ of the vector potential function $\boldsymbol{\Psi}$ as

$$\mathbf{u} \equiv \text{curl}\, \psi\hat{\mathbf{k}} = \nabla \times \psi\hat{\mathbf{k}} \tag{3.7}$$

since the divergence of the curl vanishes identically. Since the flow is irrotational, the curl of the velocity vector must also vanish. From (3.7), and use of a vector identity, this yields

$$L(\psi) = \nabla^2 \psi = 0 \tag{3.8}$$

for ψ a divergence-free field. Hence, for two-dimensional flows, the scalar component ψ of the vector potential function also satisfies the laplacian differential equation.

The boundary conditions for (3.8) are established directly from (3.7). Along any streamline, the steady flow vector is parallel to each streamline; hence, any solid wall is a streamline. For domain boundary segments with mass efflux, integration of (3.7) in the direction perpendicular to the outward pointing unit normal $\hat{\mathbf{n}}$ yields,

$$\Delta\psi = \mathbf{u} \cdot \hat{\mathbf{n}} \equiv u^1 \tag{3.9}$$

where Δ indicates the increment in ψ across a segment with unit normal $\hat{\mathbf{n}}$. For an arbitrarily oriented boundary segment, which is neither parallel nor perpendicular to a streamline, (3.7) takes the general form of a gradient boundary condition as

$$\nabla\psi \cdot \hat{\mathbf{n}} = -u'' \tag{3.10}$$

In (3.10), u'' denotes the velocity component parallel to the boundary. Finally, a value of ψ can be arbitrarily set, since the specification in (3.7) is only to within an arbitrary constant. Therefore, the streamfunction specification for two-dimensional potential flow also yields a linear elliptic boundary value statement for solution with mixed Dirichlet and Neumann boundary conditions.

Problems

1 Verify that (3.2) is identically satisfied by (3.3).

2 Prove that (3.7) is identically the solution to (3.1).

3 Establish (3.8) using (3.7) and (3.2).

4 By direct integration of (3.7) obtain (3.9).

5 Using the dot product of (3.7) with a unit tangent vector, derive the boundary condition (3.10).

6 Using the definitions of potential and stream function, (3.3) and (3.7), for the steady, two-dimensional, isentropic flow of an incompressible fluid, prove the solution contours of Φ and ψ form an orthogonal network on the domain R^2.

3.3 FINITE-ELEMENT SOLUTION ALGORITHM

The potential flow descriptions in fluid mechanics have generated the requirement to solve a linear elliptic partial differential equation with appropriate gradient-constraint boundary conditions. Hence, each problem statement corresponds equivalently to extremization of an energy functional. It is an elementary exercise to confirm that the functionals $f(x_i, \Phi)$ and $g(\bar{x}_i, \Phi)$, see (2.23), for potential flow expressed in terms of scalar potential function are

$$f(x_i, \Phi) = \tfrac{1}{2}\, \nabla\Phi \cdot \nabla\Phi \tag{3.11}$$

$$g(\bar{x}_i, \Phi) = -u^1\, \Phi \tag{3.12}$$

The corresponding specifications for the stream function description are

$$f(x_i, \psi) = \tfrac{1}{2}\, \nabla\psi \cdot \nabla\psi \tag{3.13}$$

$$g(\bar{x}_i, \psi) = -u''\psi \tag{3.14}$$

With (3.11)–(3.14) available to replace (3.4)–(3.6) and (3.8)–(3.10), the finite-element algorithm statement is direct using the developments of Chap. 2. For the statement on Φ, on the union of the n-dimensional finite-element domains $R^n_{e_h}$, spanned by the x_i coordinate system, the finite-element approximate solution Φ^h is

$$\Phi^h = \sum_{e=1}^{M} \Phi_e(x_i) \equiv \sum_{e=1}^{M} \{N_k(x_i)\}^T \{PHI\}_e \tag{3.15}$$

In (3.15), the members of $\{N_k(x_i)\}$ are polynomials on x_i complete to degree k, as illustrated in Chap. 2 for x_i restricted to one-dimensional space. The elements of $\{PHI\}_e$ are the values of potential function at the nodes of the finite element R^n_e. For the gradient boundary conditions, the velocity normal component u^1 is interpolated on $\partial R_e \cap \partial R$ in terms of nodal values $\{UPERP\}$ as

$$u^1_e(\bar{x}_i) \equiv \{N_k(\bar{x}_i)\}^T \{UPERP\}_e \tag{3.16}$$

where the superscript bar denotes x_i constrained to ∂R.

The statement of the finite-element extremization of the approximation energy functional $I^h \equiv \Sigma_e I_e$, for (3.1)–(3.2), is directly stated in terms of the assembly operator S_e [see (2.184)] as

$$S_e \frac{\partial I^h}{\partial \{Q\}_e} = S_e\left[\int_{R_e^n} \nabla\{N_k(x_i)\}\cdot\nabla\{N_k(x_i)\}^T\{PHI\}_e\, d\tau\right.$$

$$\left.+\int_{\partial R_e\cap\partial R} \{N_k(\bar{x}_i)\}\{N_k(\bar{x}_i)\}^T\{UPERP\}_e\, d\sigma\right] \equiv \{0\} \quad (3.17)$$

Note that (3.17) is formally identical to the heat conduction statement (2.31) for zero heat source and hT_r interpreted as u^1. This commonality pervades development of the algorithm statement in the progression to the complexly nonlinear problem description for viscous and turbulent flows.

The algorithm form for the description in stream function is basically identical. The finite-element approximate solution ψ^h on the union of the two-dimensional domains R_e^2 is

$$\psi^h \equiv \sum_{e=1}^{M} \psi_e(x_i) \equiv \sum_{e=1}^{M} \{N_k(x_i)\}^T\{PSI\}_e \quad (3.18)$$

Similarly, the interpolation of u'' on $\partial R_e \cap \partial R$ is

$$u_e''(\bar{x}_i) \equiv \{N_k(\bar{x}_i)\}^T\{UPARA\}_e \quad (3.19)$$

Then, the extremization of the approximation I^h of the energy functional, using (3.13)-(3.14), yields

$$S_e \frac{\partial I^h}{\partial \{Q\}_e} = S_e\left[\int_{R_e^n} \nabla\{N_k\}\cdot\nabla\{N_k\}^T\{PSI\}_e\, d\tau\right.$$

$$\left.+\int_{\partial R_e\cap\partial R} \{N_k\}\{N_k\}^T\{UPARA\}_e\, d\sigma\right] \equiv \{0\} \quad (3.20)$$

Note that (3.17) and (3.20) are indeed formally identical.

The theoretical statement of accuracy and convergence for (3.15) and/or (3.18) is an extension of the development in Chap. 2. Recalling Sec. 2.8, the energy norm quadratic form, associated with the energy functional I for (3.4)-(3.5) [see (3.11)-(3.12)] is

$$E(\Phi, \Phi) = \tfrac{1}{2}\int_{R^n} \nabla\Phi\cdot\nabla\Phi\, d\tau \quad (3.21)$$

No contribution accrues from (3.12) since the boundary condition statement (3.5) is strictly nonhomogeneous. The finite-element approximation to (3.21) is, using (3.15)

$$E(\Phi^h, \Phi^h) \equiv \tfrac{1}{2}\sum_{e=1}^{M} E(\Phi_e, \Phi_e) \equiv \tfrac{1}{2}\sum_{e=1}^{M}\int_{R_e^n} \nabla\Phi_e\cdot\nabla\Phi_e\, d\tau \quad (3.22)$$

$$E(\Phi^h, \Phi^h) = \tfrac{1}{2} \sum_{e=1}^{M} \{PHI\}_e^T \int_{R_e^n} \nabla \{N_k\} \cdot \nabla \{N_k\}^T \, d\tau \, \{PHI\}_e \qquad (3.22)\ \text{(Cont.)}$$

The last form emphasizes the independence of elements of $\{PHI\}_e$ from x_i. From Theorem I (Sec. 2.5), the energy in the finite-element solution underestimates that of the true solution [see (2.96)].

$$E(\Phi^h, \Phi^h) \leqslant E(\Phi, \Phi) \qquad (3.23)$$

Recall that the energy in the error is defined as

$$E(\epsilon^h, \epsilon^h) \equiv E(\Phi - \Phi^h, \Phi - \Phi^h) \qquad (3.24)$$

and that the energy in the error equals the error in energy, see (2.95).

$$E(\epsilon^h, \epsilon^h) = E(\Phi, \Phi) - E(\Phi^h, \Phi^h) \qquad (3.25)$$

The statement of convergence is based upon the generalization to degree k of Theorem II, Sec. 2.5. On a one-dimensional space, recall that the energy in the error is bounded by a constant, the mesh measure to the exponent $2(k + 1 - m)$, and the square of the L_2 norm of the $k + 1$st derivative of the exact solution, see (2.174)–(2.175). The corresponding statement for a multidimensional problem must include an accounting for aspect ratio of the finite-element discretization of R^n. The necessary generalization is presented by Oden and Reddy (1976, Sec. 8.6) in terms of the H^m Sobolev norm, which for the laplacian ($m = 1$) contains the square root of the energy norm,

$$\| \cdot \|_{H^1} = E(\cdot, \cdot)^{1/2} + \cdots \qquad (3.26)$$

In (3.26), the "dot" denotes the argument, and $\| \cdot \|$ is synonymous with "norm." For reference, recalling the error definition $\epsilon^h = q - q^h$, the one-dimensional convergence statement (2.174) expressed in the H^1 norm is,

$$\| \epsilon^h \|_{H^1} \leqslant C_1 \, \Delta_e^{(k+1-m)} \| q \|_{H^{k+1}} \qquad (3.27)$$

Comparing (3.27) and (2.174), $C_1 > 0$ is a constant different from C and

$$\| \cdot \|_{k+1} \rightarrow \| \cdot \|_{H^{k+1}}$$

i.e., the H^r norm of u is

$$\| u \|_{H^r} \equiv \left[\sum_{i=0}^{r} \sum_{j=0}^{r} \int_{R^n} \frac{\partial^i u}{\partial x_k^i} \frac{\partial u^j}{\partial x_k^j} \, d\tau \right]^{1/2}, \qquad 1 \leqslant k \leqslant n \qquad (3.28)$$

For the homogeneous differential equation (3.4) or (3.8), with boundary conditions (3.5) or (3.9)–(3.10) [which for convenience can be uniformly expressed as $l(\cdot) = g(u)$], for well-posedness, Oden and Reddy (1976, Eq. 8.74) assume the exact solution $q(\phi$ or $\psi)$ depends continuously on the boundary data in the H^r norm,

$$\| q \|_{H^r(R)} \leqslant C \| g(u) \|_{H^{r-s-\frac{1}{2}}(\partial R)} \qquad (3.29)$$

where $C>0$, $r \geqslant m$, $s \geqslant \frac{1}{2}$ and (R) and (∂R) indicate domain of the H norm. For the potential flow descriptions, assuming $r \equiv m = 1$ and the smallest value for s, (3.29) states the boundary data need only be sufficiently smooth to be square integrable (H^0), and that the square root of the energy (H^1) in q is bounded by these data. Correspondingly, on a sufficiently refined uniform discretization of R^n, such that Δ_e is uniformly the measure, combining (3.27) and (3.29) yields the convergence statement for error in the finite-element approximation q^h

$$\|\epsilon^h\|_{H^\alpha(R)} \leqslant C\, \Delta_e^\gamma \|g(u)\|_{H^p(\partial R)} \tag{3.30}$$

where $\alpha = m$, $\gamma = k+1-m$ and $p \geqslant \frac{1}{2}$.

A nonuniform discretization of R^n requires adaptation of (3.30) for variable aspect-ratio finite elements. Referring to Fig. 3.1, which illustrates a segment of a two-dimensional discretization using triangles, a suitable measure pair for R_e^2 is ρ_e, the diameter of the maximum inscribed circle, and h_e, the extremum chord of the circumscribed circle. Then, the H^m norm of the error (3.27) is bounded by the H^{k+1} norm of the exact solution, evaluated on an element-by-element basis as

$$\|\epsilon^h\|_{H^1} \leqslant C_1 \sum_{e=1}^{M} \frac{h_e^{k+1}}{\rho_e^m} \|q\|_{H^{k+1}} \tag{3.31}$$

Let $\Delta_e \equiv \max(h_e)$ and $\rho \equiv \min(\rho_e)$; then, $\Delta_e/\rho \leqslant \sigma$ for all $h_e/\rho_e \leqslant \sigma$, and (3.31) evaluated on $\cup R_e^n$ becomes

$$\|\epsilon^h\|_{H^1} \leqslant C_2\, \Delta_e^{k+1}\left(\frac{\Delta_e}{\sigma}\right)^{-m} \|q\|_{H^{k+1}} \leqslant C_2\, \Delta_e^\gamma \|q\|_{H^r} \tag{3.32}$$

where $\gamma = \min(k+1-m,\ r-m)$. Oden and Reddy (1976, Theorem 8.6) then prove that (3.30) remains the statement of convergence for $\alpha \leqslant m$ and $\gamma = \min(k+1-m,\ p+s+\frac{1}{2}-m,\ m-\alpha)$. In the energy norm, the equivalent of (3.30) is

$$E(\epsilon^h, \epsilon^h) \leqslant C_3\, \Delta_e^{2\gamma} \|g(u)\|^2_{H^p(\partial R)} \tag{3.33}$$

and $\gamma \leqslant (k+1-m)$ is dependent upon the extremum discretization aspect ratio. In the worst instance, γ can be independent of k, which can destroy the utility of the higher degree cardinal basis.

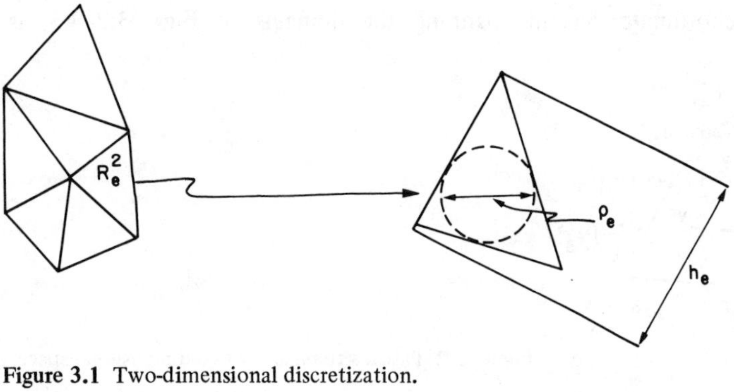

Figure 3.1 Two-dimensional discretization.

3.4 NATURAL COORDINATE FINITE-ELEMENT BASIS

With completion of the theoretical statement, the practical aspect of a finite-element solution for potential flow is selection of suitable multidimensional finite-element domains. Progressing beyond the one-dimensional domain of Chapter 2 opens up Pandora's box concerning acceptable finite-element shapes and associated kth-degree interpolation functions (Zienkiewicz, 1977, Chaps. 7 and 8). The basic demarcation, on complexity of the associated calculus operations, is whether the finite elements are straight- or curved-sided. This section develops the former class, for element shapes spanned by the natural coordinate concept introduced in Chapter 2. Section 3.6 introduces the tensor-product basis including the transition to curved-sided isoparametric elements.

On two-dimensional space, for example, the linear interpolation of a function is expressible as a simple power series involving three coefficients

$$\phi(x_i) = a_1 + a_2 x + a_3 y \tag{3.34}$$

A quadratic would involve six coefficients a_i, $1 \leqslant i \leqslant 6$. The basic geometric shape on two-dimensional space appropriate for convenient redefinition of a_i in terms of dependent variable nodal values is the triangle.

Pascal's triangle (Fig. 3.2) provides a geometric interpretation of desirable node-point distributions for this finite element for degree k of the interpolation function $\{N_k(x_i)\}$ spanning the domain. For example, $\{N_1(x_i)\}$ employs three nodes located at the vertices of the triangle. Six nodes are required for the second degree function $\{N_2(x_i)\}$, and all can lie on the boundary ∂R_e of the finite element in symmetric fashion. The nodes of the cubic $\{N_3(x_i)\}$ can also be symmetrically disposed on a triangle, with nine nodes on ∂R_e and the tenth node at the element centroid (corresponding to the location of xy in Fig. 3.2). The three-dimensional equivalent of Pascal's triangle is the tetrahedron, with node coordinates illustrated in Fig. 3.3 for linear and quadratic interpolations.

If attention is restricted to these two- and three-dimensional domain shapes, the practical requirement of the algorithm is to evaluate the integrals defined in (3.17) or (3.20). The n-dimensional natural coordinate system is appropriate as the direct extension of the one-dimensional formulations. A coordinate, of the linearly dependent natural coordinate system spanning the domains of Figs. 3.2–3.3, is

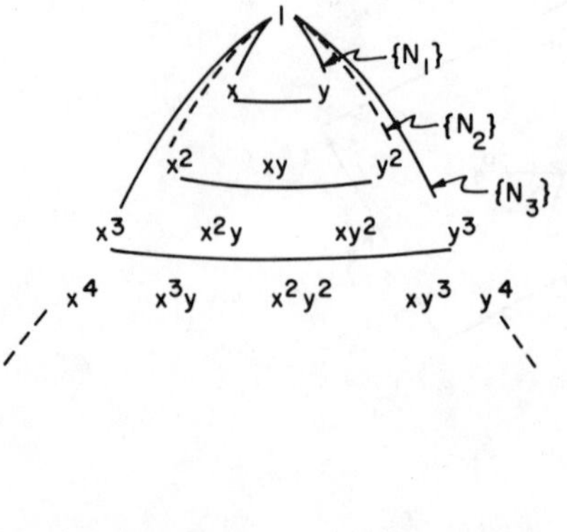

Figure 3.2 Pascal's triangle for two-dimensional space.

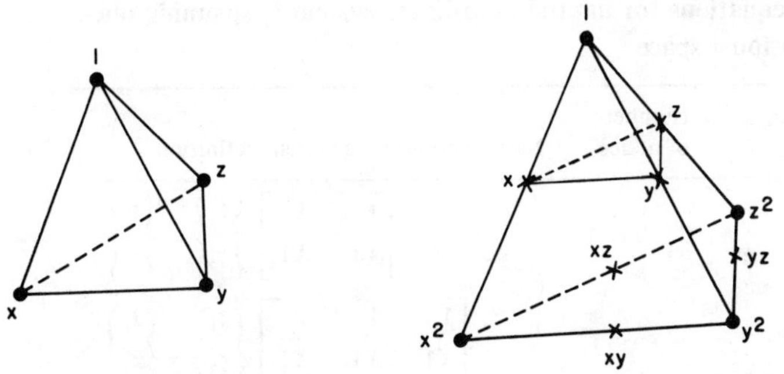

Figure 3.3 Representation of Pascal's tetrahedrons for three-dimensional space.

defined for every vertex node. The value of the coordinate at its node is unity; it is defined perpendicular to the element boundary segment opposite this node and thereupon takes the value zero. Hence, for an n-dimensional specification, there are $n + 1$ natural coordinates (see Fig. 3.4).

The derivation of the n-dimensional natural coordinate system is direct. Denoting ζ_i as the elements of $\{N_1\}$, that is, the natural coordinate system, the interpolation of a constant is

$$1 \equiv \zeta_1 + \zeta_2 + \zeta_3 \equiv \{N_1(\zeta)\}^T \{ONE\} \tag{3.35}$$

The remaining n equations require that ζ_i interpolate exactly the cartesian coordinate system x_i spanning the same domain. Hence,

$$x_i = \{N_1(\zeta)\}^T \{XI\}_e \qquad 1 \leqslant (i, I) \leqslant n \tag{3.36}$$

where $\{XI\}_e$ is the array of the nodal coordinates (constants) on R_e^n. Denoting the corresponding matrix elements as XI_l, where l is node number, the expansion of (3.35)-(3.36) on one-, two-, and three-dimensional space is presented in Table 3.1. The explicit expression for the natural coordinate system ζ_i accrues with solution of the linear algebraic equation system, (3.35)-(3.36). This is simplified by defining an alternative local rectangular cartesian coordinate system $\bar{x}_i$. The coefficient matrices for (3.35)-(3.36) (see also Table 3.1) become upper triangular by selecting the

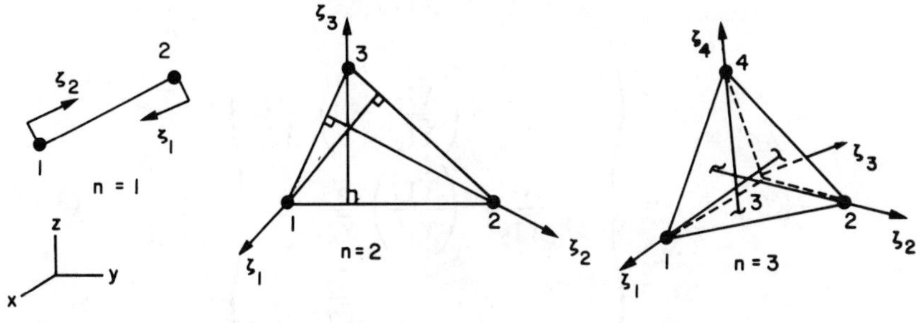

Figure 3.4 Natural coordinate systems spanning R^n, $1 \leqslant n \leqslant 3$.

Table 3.1 Definition equations for natural coordinate system ζ_i spanning one-, two-, and three-dimensional space

Dimension of space	Element shape	Number of nodes	Natural coordinate system definition
1	Line	2	$\begin{bmatrix} 1 & 1 \\ X1_1 & X1_2 \end{bmatrix} \begin{Bmatrix} \zeta_1 \\ \zeta_2 \end{Bmatrix} = \begin{Bmatrix} 1 \\ x_1 \end{Bmatrix}$
2	Triangle	3	$\begin{bmatrix} 1 & 1 & 1 \\ X1_1 & X1_2 & X1_3 \\ X2_1 & X2_2 & X2_3 \end{bmatrix} \begin{Bmatrix} \zeta_1 \\ \zeta_2 \\ \zeta_3 \end{Bmatrix} = \begin{Bmatrix} 1 \\ x_1 \\ x_2 \end{Bmatrix}$
3	Tetrahedron	4	$\begin{bmatrix} 1 & 1 & 1 & 1 \\ X1_1 & X1_2 & X1_3 & X1_4 \\ X2_1 & X2_2 & X2_3 & X2_4 \\ X3_1 & X3_2 & X3_3 & X3_4 \end{bmatrix} \begin{Bmatrix} \zeta_1 \\ \zeta_2 \\ \zeta_3 \\ \zeta_4 \end{Bmatrix} = \begin{Bmatrix} 1 \\ x_1 \\ x_2 \\ x_3 \end{Bmatrix}$

origin of $\bar{x}_i$ at node 1, aligning the $\bar{x}_1$ axis with the line connecting nodes 1 and 2, and defining the $\bar{x}_3$ plane as containing the node triad (1, 2, 3). Figure 3.5 illustrates the system for one-, two-, and three-dimensional elements.

The coordinate transformation from x_i to $\bar{x}_i$ is affine and involves a rotation with direct cosines α_{ij} and a translation (vector) **r** with scalar components equal to the global coordinates of node 1, that is, XI_1. Therefore,

$$\bar{x}_i \equiv \sum_j \alpha_{ij} x_j - XI_1 \tag{3.37}$$

In terms of the local cartesian system $\bar{x}_i$, with node coordinates $\bar{X}I_j$, the ζ_i are

$$R_e^1: \qquad \{\zeta(\bar{x}_1)\} = \begin{Bmatrix} 1 - \dfrac{\bar{x}_1}{\bar{X}1_2} \\[2ex] \dfrac{\bar{x}_1}{\bar{X}1_2} \end{Bmatrix} \tag{3.38}$$

$$R_e^2: \qquad \{\zeta(\bar{x}_1, \bar{x}_2)\} = \begin{Bmatrix} 1 - \dfrac{\bar{x}_1}{\bar{X}1_2} + \left(\dfrac{\bar{X}1_3}{\bar{X}1_2} - 1\right)\dfrac{\bar{x}_2}{\bar{X}2_3} \\[2ex] \dfrac{\bar{x}_1}{\bar{X}1_2} - \left(\dfrac{\bar{X}1_3}{\bar{X}1_2}\right)\dfrac{\bar{x}_2}{\bar{X}2_3} \\[2ex] \dfrac{\bar{x}_2}{\bar{X}2_3} \end{Bmatrix} \tag{3.39}$$

R_e^3:

$\{\zeta(\bar{x}_1, \bar{x}_2, \bar{x}_3)\}$

$$= \begin{Bmatrix} 1 - \dfrac{\bar{x}_1}{\bar{X}1_2} + \left(\dfrac{\bar{X}1_3}{\bar{X}1_2} - 1\right)\dfrac{\bar{x}_2}{\bar{X}2_3} + \left[\dfrac{\bar{X}2_4}{\bar{X}2_3}\left(1 - \dfrac{\bar{X}1_3}{\bar{X}1_2}\right) + \left(\dfrac{\bar{X}1_4}{\bar{X}1_2} - 1\right)\right]\dfrac{\bar{x}_3}{\bar{X}3_4} \\ \dfrac{\bar{x}_1}{\bar{X}1_2} - \left(\dfrac{\bar{X}1_3}{\bar{X}1_2}\right)\dfrac{\bar{x}_2}{\bar{X}2_3} + \left(\dfrac{\bar{X}1_3}{\bar{X}1_2}\dfrac{\bar{X}2_4}{\bar{X}2_3} - \dfrac{\bar{X}1_4}{\bar{X}1_2}\right)\dfrac{\bar{x}_3}{\bar{X}3_4} \\ \dfrac{\bar{x}_2}{\bar{X}2_3} - \left(\dfrac{\bar{X}2_4}{\bar{X}2_3}\right)\dfrac{\bar{x}_3}{\bar{X}3_4} \\ \dfrac{\bar{x}_3}{\bar{X}3_4} \end{Bmatrix} \tag{3.40}$$

The most useful feature of the ζ_i coordinate description, as illustrated for the one-dimensional exercises of Chapter 2, is the integration formula (2.61) generalized to R^n.

$$\int_{R_e^n} \zeta_1^{n_1}\zeta_2^{n_2}\zeta_3^{n_3}\zeta_4^{n_4} \prod_{i=1}^{n} d\bar{x}_i = D_e^n \frac{n_1!n_2!n_3!n_4!}{(n + n_1 + n_2 + n_4)!} \tag{3.41}$$

where R_e^n is the n-dimensional finite element, and D_e^n is the determinant of the coefficient matrix defining the ζ_i coordinate system, (3.35)-(3.36). It is left as an exercise to confirm that $D_e^2 = 2A_e$ and $D_e^3 = 6V_e$, where A_e and V_e are area and volume respectively of R_e^n.

Equation (3.41) is commonly recognized and utilized by the finite-element community (Zienkiewicz, 1977, Chap. 7). Eisenberg and Malvern (1973) present proof for $n = 2$ which establishes the general validity. With reference to Fig. 3.6, the differential element is

$$\prod_{i=1}^{2} d\bar{x}_i \equiv d\tau = \frac{(h_1\, d\zeta_1)(h_2\, d\zeta_2)}{\sin\alpha_3} = \frac{h_1 h_2}{\sin\alpha_3}\, d\zeta_1\, d\zeta_2 = 2A\, d\zeta_1\, d\zeta_2 \tag{3.42}$$

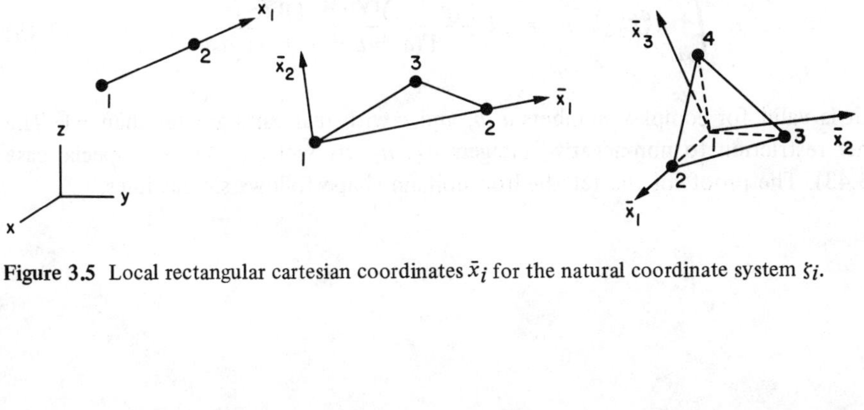

Figure 3.5 Local rectangular cartesian coordinates $\bar{x}_i$ for the natural coordinate system ζ_i.

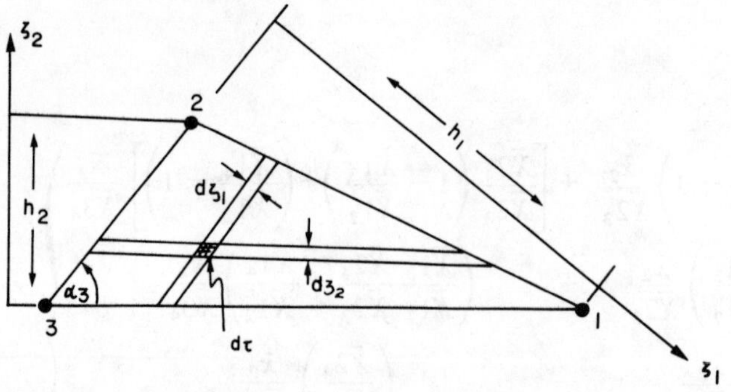

Figure 3.6 Two-dimensional integration domain.

where A is the plane area of the triangle, and $\zeta_i = s_i/h_i$ are the area coordinates of the triangle and identical to the natural coordinate description. Generalizing to noninteger exponents, the required evaluation is

$$\int_{R^2} \zeta_1^a \zeta_2^b \zeta_3^c \, d\sigma = 2A \int_0^1 \left[\int_0^{1-\zeta_1} \zeta_1^a \zeta_2^b (1 - \zeta_1 - \zeta_2)^c \, d\zeta_2 \right] d\zeta_1$$

A change of variables to $\eta = \zeta_2/(1 - \zeta_1)$ yields the symmetric form

$$\int_{R^2} \zeta_1^a \zeta_2^b \zeta_3^c \, d\sigma = 2A \int_0^1 \zeta_1^a (1 - \zeta_1)^{b+c+1} \, d\zeta_1 \int_0^1 \eta^b (1 - \eta)^c \, d\eta$$

Each of the integrals on the right side is a form of the beta function $B(z, w)$,

$$B(z, w) \equiv \int_0^1 t^{z-1}(1 - t)^{w-1} \, dt = \frac{\Gamma(z)\Gamma(w)}{\Gamma(z + w)}$$

where Γ denotes the gamma function, which satisfies the relation $\Gamma(n + 1) = n!$ for integers $n \geqslant 0$. Thus, the general expression for (3.41) is

$$\int_{R^2} \zeta_1^a \zeta_2^b \zeta_3^c \, d\sigma = 2A \frac{\Gamma(a + 1)\Gamma(b + 1)\Gamma(c + 1)}{\Gamma(a + b + c + 3)} \tag{3.43}$$

which is valid for complex numbers a, b, and c with real parts greater than -1. The further restriction to non-negative integers n_1, n_2, n_3 yields (3.41) as a special case of (3.43). The proof for the tetrahedron domain shape follows similar lines.

Problems

1 Determine the explicit representation (3.36) for the natural coordinate system spanning a three-dimensional space, in terms of the four node point coordinates of a tetrahedron, $\bar{XI}j$, $j = 1, 2, 3, 4$, expressed in the local cartesian coordinate system (Fig. 3.5).

2 Prove that the determinant of the defining coefficient matrices, Table 3.1, yields twice the area and six times the volume of the triangle and tetrahedron finite elements respectively.

3 Prove the general integration formula analogous to (3.43) for three-dimensional space.

3.5 MATRIX STRUCTURE FOR MULTIDIMENSIONAL POTENTIAL FLOW

The theoretical and formulational aspects of the finite-element potential flow algorithm are complete at a base level of sophistication. Equation (3.17) or (3.20) can now be evaluated for the simplest family of finite-element geometries. The concise matrix structure for each (dimensional) specification is developed in this section. For compactness, Eqs. (3.17) and (3.20) are of the form

$$S_e[[M1(k)]_e\{Q\}_e + [M2(k)]_e\{UP\}_e] \equiv \{0\} \tag{3.44}$$

where $[M1]_e$ is the elemental diffusion matrix, $[M2]_e$ is the boundary condition matrix, and both depend upon the degree k of the interpolation cardinal basis $\{N_k\}$ and the form of the differential elements $d\tau$ and $d\sigma$. (Of course, the elements of $\{UP\}_e$ are the nodal boundary values of u^1 or u''.) A given specification for k, $d\tau$ and $d\sigma$ produces a corresponding elemental matrix, and the attendant details can obscure the intrinsic simplicity. Therefore, a convenient descriptive shorthand notation is required for element matrices. Define any matrix by a six-digit code as

$$[M] \equiv [abccc\ldots d] \qquad \{M\} \equiv \{abcd\} \tag{3.45}$$

where $a \equiv \begin{Bmatrix} A \\ B \\ C \end{Bmatrix}$ for $n = \begin{Bmatrix} 1 \\ 2 \\ 3 \end{Bmatrix}$

$b \equiv$ an integer corresponding to the number of cardinal bases $\{N_k\}$ appearing in the matrix definition

$c \equiv \begin{Bmatrix} 0 \\ 1 \end{Bmatrix}$ boolean counters for each $\{N_k\}\begin{Bmatrix} \text{not differentiated} \\ \text{differentiated} \end{Bmatrix}$

$d \equiv$ an additional position for identifying nomenclature

Therefore, for example, the three-dimensional problem statement (3.44) becomes

Boundary data
Neither $\{N_k\}$ differentiated
Two $\{N_k\}$
Two-dimensional matrix
Measure of three-dimensional element face, which is a two-dimensional element

$$S_e[\Delta_e[C211]_e\{Q\}_e + \Delta_e[B200]\{UP\}_e] \equiv \{0\} \tag{3.46}$$

Unknown
Both $\{N_k\}$ differentiated
Two $\{N_k\}$
Three-dimensional matrix
Measure for three-dimensional element
Assembly operator

Correspondingly, the three-dimensional axisymmetric problem statement becomes

$$S_e[\Delta_e\{R\}_e^T[B3011]_e\{Q\}_e + \Delta_e[B200]\{UP\}_e] \equiv \{0\} \tag{3.47}$$

where the elements of $\{R\}_e$ are nodal radii, and $[B3\ldots]$ is a hypermatrix of degree one (see Sec. 2.6).

We may now proceed with the various constructions. For reference, Table 3.2 lists the elements of the $\{N_k\}$ for $1 \leqslant n \leqslant 3$ and $1 \leqslant k \leqslant 2$. The following is detailed for $k = 1$.

Table 3.2 Finite-element interpolation functions for *n*-dimensional space in terms of natural coordinates $\{\zeta\}$

Degree	Function	One-dimensional	Two-dimensional	Three-dimensional
Linear	$\{N_1(\zeta)\}$	ζ_1 ζ_2	ζ_1 ζ_2 ζ_3	ζ_1 ζ_2 ζ_3 ζ_4
Quadratic	$\{N_2(\zeta)\}$	$\zeta_1(2\zeta_1 - 1)$ $\zeta_2(2\zeta_2 - 1)$ $4\zeta_1\zeta_2$	$\zeta_1(2\zeta_1 - 1)$ $\zeta_2(2\zeta_2 - 1)$ $\zeta_3(2\zeta_3 - 1)$ $4\zeta_1\zeta_2$ $4\zeta_2\zeta_3$ $4\zeta_3\zeta_1$	$\zeta_1(2\zeta_1 - 1)$ $\zeta_2(2\zeta_2 - 1)$ $\zeta_3(2\zeta_3 - 1)$ $\zeta_4(2\zeta_4 - 1)$ $4\zeta_1\zeta_2$ $4\zeta_2\zeta_3$ $4\zeta_3\zeta_1$ $4\zeta_4\zeta_1$ $4\zeta_4\zeta_2$ $4\zeta_4\zeta_3$

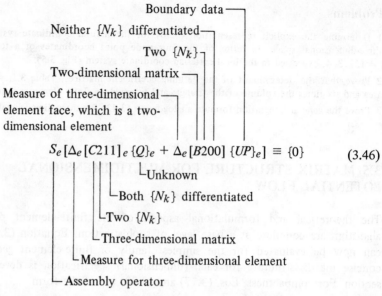

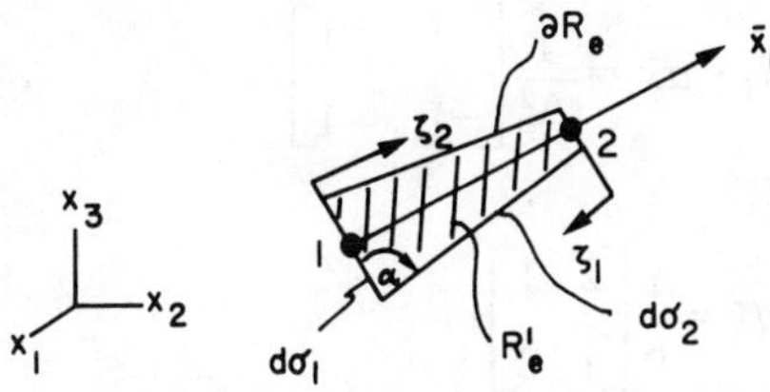

Figure 3.7 Generalized one-dimensional finite element.

3.5.1 One-Dimensional Element

The tapered one-dimensional element illustrated in Fig. 3.7 is of general usefulness for the scalar potential function description. Assume the thickness distribution t_e varies linearly on R_e^1,

$$t_e(\bar{x}) = \{N_1(\zeta)\}^T \{T\}_e \tag{3.48}$$

where the elements of $\{T\}_e$ correspond to element thickness at nodes 1 and 2 respectively. The differential elements for (3.17) and/or (3.20) are

$$d\tau = t_e \, d\bar{x} \qquad \int d\sigma_1 = T1 \qquad d\sigma_2 = d\bar{x} \tag{3.49}$$

where $d\sigma_1$ corresponds to flow into the end of the element at node 1, while $d\sigma_2$ assumes flow over the element surface, oriented parallel to $\bar{x}^1$ (that is, $\sin\alpha \approx 1$; Fig. 3.7). With scalar rearrangements, the diffusion term in (3.17) or (3.20) becomes

$$\begin{aligned}
\int_{R_e^1} \nabla\{N_1\}\cdot\nabla\{N_1\}^T \{Q\}_e \, d\tau &= \{T\}_e^T \int_{R_e^1} \{N_1\} \frac{d}{dx_1}\{N_1\}\cdot\frac{d}{dx_1}\{N_1\}^T \, d\bar{x}\, \{Q\}_e \\
&= \frac{1}{2\,\Delta_e}\left(\{T\}_e^T \begin{bmatrix} \begin{Bmatrix}1\\1\end{Bmatrix} & -\begin{Bmatrix}1\\1\end{Bmatrix} \\ -\begin{Bmatrix}1\\1\end{Bmatrix} & \begin{Bmatrix}1\\1\end{Bmatrix}\end{bmatrix}\right)\{Q\}_e \\
&= \Delta_e \{T\}_e^T [A3011]\, \{Q\}_e \\
&= \Delta_e \{T\}_e^T \{A10\}\, [A211]\, \{Q\}_e
\end{aligned} \tag{3.50}$$

The third line of (3.50) involves the basic hypermatrix definition, while the latter explicitly expresses the element independence of $[A211]$ when formed for $k = 1$. By definition then, for $k = 1$

$$[A3011] \equiv \frac{1}{\Delta_e}\int_{R_e^1} \{N_1\}\nabla\{N_1\}\cdot\nabla\{N_1\}^T \, d\bar{x} = \frac{1}{2\,\Delta_e^2}\begin{bmatrix} \begin{Bmatrix}1\\1\end{Bmatrix} & -\begin{Bmatrix}1\\1\end{Bmatrix} \\ -\begin{Bmatrix}1\\1\end{Bmatrix} & \begin{Bmatrix}1\\1\end{Bmatrix}\end{bmatrix} \tag{3.51}$$

$$[A211] \equiv \frac{1}{\Delta_e}\int_{R_e^1} \nabla\{N_1\}\cdot\nabla\{N_1\}\, d\bar{x} = \frac{1}{\Delta_e^2}\begin{bmatrix} 1 & -1 \\ -1 & 1 \end{bmatrix}$$

$$[A200] \equiv \frac{1}{\Delta_e}\int_{R_e^1} \{N_1\}\{N_1\}^T\, d\bar{x} = \frac{1}{6}\begin{bmatrix} 2 & 1 \\ 1 & 2 \end{bmatrix}$$

$$\{A10\} \equiv \frac{1}{\Delta_e}\int_{R_e^1} \{N_1\}\, d\bar{x} = \frac{1}{2}\begin{Bmatrix} 1 \\ 1 \end{Bmatrix} \tag{3.51 (Cont.)}$$

The boundary condition terms in (3.17) are

$$\int_{\partial R_e \cap \partial R} \{N_1\}\{N_1\}^T \{UP\}_e\, d\sigma_1 = T1 \cdot UP1 \tag{3.52}$$

$$\int_{\partial R_e} \{N_1\}\{N_1\}^T \{UP\}_e\, d\sigma_2 = \frac{\Delta_e}{6}\begin{bmatrix} 2 & 1 \\ 1 & 2 \end{bmatrix}\{UP\}_e = \Delta_e [A200]\,\{UP\}_e \tag{3.53}$$

where (3.52) corresponds to mass flux across the left end of the finite element with thickness $T1_e$, while in (3.53) the flux crosses the elemental surface. Therefore, for potential flow through a tapered one-dimensional channel with thickness distribution $t(x)$, the finite-element solution statement for (3.17) is

$$S_e\left[\Delta_e \{T\}_e^T [A3011]\,\{PHI\}_e + T1\cdot UP1 + \Delta_e [A200]\,\{UP\}_e\right] = \{0\} \tag{3.54}$$

The form of (3.54) is valid for all k, since the named matrices are generally interpreted. For example, adding a subscript L to $[A3011]$, as formed using $\{N_1\}$ produces

$$[A3011L] = \frac{1}{2\,\Delta_e^2}\begin{bmatrix} \begin{Bmatrix} 1 \\ 1 \end{Bmatrix} & -\begin{Bmatrix} 1 \\ 1 \end{Bmatrix} \\ -\begin{Bmatrix} 1 \\ 1 \end{Bmatrix} & \begin{Bmatrix} 1 \\ 1 \end{Bmatrix} \end{bmatrix} \tag{3.55}$$

The equivalent matrix established using $\{N_2(x)\}$ for ϕ_e and $\{N_1\}$ for t was presented as (2.140), i.e.,

$$[A3011Q] = \frac{1}{\Delta_e^2}\begin{bmatrix} \begin{Bmatrix} 11 \\ 3 \end{Bmatrix} & \begin{Bmatrix} -12 \\ -4 \end{Bmatrix} & \begin{Bmatrix} 1 \\ 1 \end{Bmatrix} \\ & \begin{Bmatrix} 16 \\ 16 \end{Bmatrix} & \begin{Bmatrix} -4 \\ -12 \end{Bmatrix} \\ (\text{sym}) & & \begin{Bmatrix} 3 \\ 11 \end{Bmatrix} \end{bmatrix} \tag{3.56}$$

A quadratic interpolation for t would increase the order of the elements of the hypermatrix (3.56) to three. The cubic form is given as (2.156) for derivative degrees of freedom, and as (2.166) for cubic with interior nodes.

3.5.2 Two-Dimensional Element

Generalize the two-dimensional triangle to include a thickness distribution, assumed a linear function of the coordinate system spanning the triangle:

$$t_e(x_i) = \{N_1(\zeta)\}^T \{T\}_e \tag{3.57}$$

The node coordinates for the triangle are now assumed to lie in the midplane (see Fig. 3.8). The differential elements for (3.17) and/or (3.20) are

$$d\tau = t_e\, d\bar{x}_1\, d\bar{x}_2 = t_e\, d\bar{x}_i \qquad d\sigma_1 = t_e\, d\bar{x}_1 \qquad d\sigma_2 = d\bar{x}_1\, d\bar{x}_2 = d\bar{x}_i \tag{3.58}$$

The algorithm statement of (3.17) or (3.20) is then

$$S_e[\Delta_e \{T\}_e^T [B3011]_e \{Q\}_e + \Delta_e \{T\}_e^T [A3000]\, \{UP\}_e + \Delta_e [B200]\, \{UP\}_e] \equiv \{Q\} \tag{3.59}$$

The Δ_e correlates with the dimension of the corresponding matrix; that is, $\Delta_e(B)$ is one-half the triangular area, while $\Delta_e(A)$ is the length of the element side, and the elements of $\{T\}_e$ are element thickness at the vertex nodes.

Using the linear basis for illustration, the middle term in (3.59) defines

$$[A3000] \equiv \frac{1}{\Delta_e}\int_{R_e^1} \{N_1\}\{N_1\}\{N_1\}^T\, d\bar{x}_1 = \frac{1}{12}\begin{bmatrix} \begin{Bmatrix} 3 \\ 1 \end{Bmatrix} & \begin{Bmatrix} 1 \\ 1 \end{Bmatrix} \\ \begin{Bmatrix} 1 \\ 1 \end{Bmatrix} & \begin{Bmatrix} 1 \\ 3 \end{Bmatrix} \end{bmatrix} \tag{3.60}$$

For the first term, as occurred in the one-dimensional example [see (3.50)], $[B3011L]_e \rightarrow \{B10\}[B211L]_e$, and

$$\begin{aligned} [B211L] &\equiv \frac{1}{\Delta_e}\int_{R_e^2} \nabla\{N_1\}\cdot\nabla\{N_1\}^T\, d\bar{x}_1\, d\bar{x}_2 \\ &= \frac{1}{(\bar{X}1_2)^2}\begin{Bmatrix} -1 \\ 1 \\ 0 \end{Bmatrix}\{-1,\ \ 1,\ \ 0\} \\ &\quad + \frac{1}{(\bar{X}1_2\bar{X}2_3)^2}\begin{Bmatrix} \bar{X}1_3 - \bar{X}1_2 \\ -\bar{X}1_3 \\ \bar{X}1_2 \end{Bmatrix}\{\bar{X}1_3 - \bar{X}1_2,\ \ -\bar{X}1_3,\ \ \bar{X}1_2\} \end{aligned} \tag{3.61}$$

$$[B211L] = \frac{1}{(\bar{X}1_2)^2}\begin{bmatrix} 1 & -1 & 0 \\ & 1 & 0 \\ (\text{sym}) & & 0 \end{bmatrix}$$

$$+ \frac{1}{(\bar{X}2_3)^2}\begin{bmatrix} \left(\frac{\bar{X}1_3}{\bar{X}1_2}-1\right)^2, & \frac{\bar{X}1_3}{\bar{X}1_2}\left(\frac{\bar{X}1_3}{\bar{X}1_2}-1\right), & \left(\frac{\bar{X}1_3}{\bar{X}1_2}-1\right) \\ & \left(\frac{\bar{X}1_3}{\bar{X}1_2}\right)^2, & -\left(\frac{\bar{X}1_3}{\bar{X}1_2}\right) \\ (\text{sym}) & , & 1 \end{bmatrix} \quad (3.61) \text{ (Cont.)}$$

Note that the first contribution to $[B211L]$ is identical to $[A211L]$, with a row and column of zeroes added to bring the matrix order to three. The various two-dimensional matrices constructed from products of $\{N_1\}$ are

$$\{B10\} \equiv \frac{1}{\Delta_e}\int_{R_e^2} \{N_1\}\, d\bar{x}_1\, d\bar{x}_2 = \frac{1}{3}\begin{Bmatrix} 1 \\ 1 \\ 1 \end{Bmatrix}$$

$$[B200] \equiv \frac{1}{\Delta_e}\int_{R_e^2} \{N_1\}\{N_1\}^T\, d\bar{x}_1\, d\bar{x}_2 = \frac{1}{12}\begin{bmatrix} 2 & 1 & 1 \\ & 2 & 1 \\ (\text{sym}) & & 2 \end{bmatrix}$$

$$[B3000] \equiv \frac{1}{\Delta_e}\int_{R_e^2} \{N_1\}\{N_1\}\{N_1\}^T\, d\bar{x}_1\, d\bar{x}_2 = \frac{1}{60}\begin{bmatrix} \begin{Bmatrix} 6 \\ 2 \\ 2 \end{Bmatrix} & \begin{Bmatrix} 2 \\ 2 \\ 1 \end{Bmatrix} & \begin{Bmatrix} 2 \\ 1 \\ 2 \end{Bmatrix} \\ & \begin{Bmatrix} 2 \\ 6 \\ 2 \end{Bmatrix} & \begin{Bmatrix} 1 \\ 2 \\ 2 \end{Bmatrix} \\ (\text{sym}) & & \begin{Bmatrix} 2 \\ 2 \\ 6 \end{Bmatrix} \end{bmatrix} \quad (3.62)$$

It is left as an exercise (for the hardy!) to verify the construction of the diffusion matrix, using the quadratic basis $\{N_2\}$, as

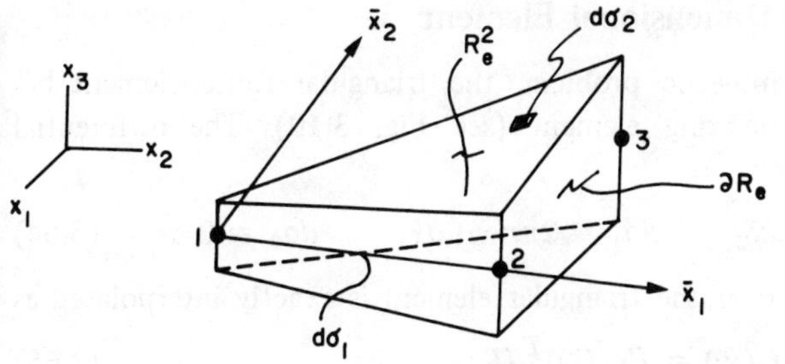

Figure 3.8 Generalized two-dimensional finite element.

$$[B211Q]_e \equiv \frac{1}{\Delta_e}\int_{R_e^2} \nabla\{N_2\}\cdot\nabla\{N_2\}\; d\bar{x}_1\, d\bar{x}_2$$

$$= \frac{1}{12(\bar{X}1_2)^2}\begin{bmatrix} 3 & 1 & 0 & -4 & 0 & 0 \\ & 3 & 0 & -4 & 0 & 0 \\ & & 0 & 0 & 0 & 0 \\ & & & 8 & 0 & 0 \\ & & & & 8 & -8 \\ (\text{sym}) & & & & & 8 \end{bmatrix}$$

$$+ \frac{1}{12(\bar{X}2_3)^2}\begin{bmatrix} 3\alpha^2, & \alpha\beta, & -\alpha\beta, & 4\alpha\beta & , & 0, & 4\alpha\beta \\ & 3\beta^2, & \beta, & -4\alpha\beta & , & -4\beta, & 0 \\ & & 3, & 0 & , & -4\beta, & 4\alpha \\ & & & 8\beta(2\beta-1), & & 8\alpha\beta, & -8\beta \\ & & & & & 4\alpha^2, & 8\alpha \\ (\text{sym}) & & & & & , & 8\alpha \end{bmatrix} \tag{3.63}$$

where $\alpha \equiv \bar{X}1_3/\bar{X}1_2 - 1$ and $\beta \equiv \bar{X}1_3/\bar{X}1_2$. The conventional node numbering for matrices constructed using $\{N_2\}$ is shown in Fig. 3.9.

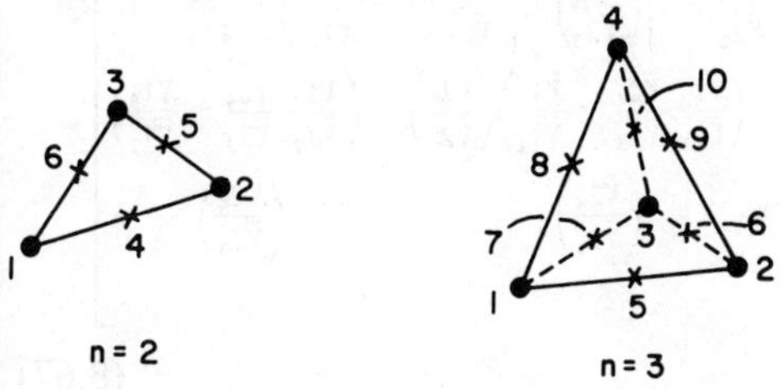

Figure 3.9 Node numbering for linear and quadratic finite element bases $\{N_{k(\zeta)}\}$ spanning two- and three-dimensional space.

3.5.3 Axisymmetric Three-Dimensional Element

For a three-dimensional axisymmetric problem, the triangular finite element becomes a triangular cross-section ring element (see Fig. 3.10). The differential elements in (3.17) and (3.20) are

$$d\tau = 2\pi r(x_i)\, d\bar{x}_1\, d\bar{x}_2 \qquad d\sigma_1 = 2\pi r(x_i)\, d\bar{x}_1 \qquad d\sigma_2 = 0 \tag{3.64}$$

The distribution of the radius over the triangular element is exactly interpolated as

$$r_e(x_i) = \{N_1(\zeta)\}^T \{R\}_e \tag{3.65}$$

where the elements of $\{R\}_e$ are the global radii of the vertex nodes of the triangular ring element. Therefore, (3.59) is the algorithm statement with replacement of $\{T\}_e$ by $\{R\}_e$ and deletion of the boundary condition matrix involving $[B200]$.

3.5.4 Three-Dimensional Element

The three-dimensional algorithm statement was given in (3.46), as obtained using (see Fig. 3.11)

$$d\tau = d\bar{x}_1\, d\bar{x}_2\, d\bar{x}_3 \qquad d\sigma_1 = d\bar{x}_1\, d\bar{x}_2 \tag{3.66}$$

The linear-element diffusion matrix for the three-dimensional domain is

$$
\begin{aligned}
[C211L] &\equiv \frac{1}{\Delta_e}\int_{R_e^3} \nabla\{N_1\}\cdot\nabla\{N_1\}^T\, d\bar{x}_1\, d\bar{x}_2\, d\bar{x}_3 \\
&= \frac{1}{(\bar{X}1_2)^2}\begin{bmatrix} 1 & -1 & 0 & 0 \\ & 1 & 0 & 0 \\ & & 0 & 0 \\ \text{(sym)} & & & 0 \end{bmatrix} \\
&+ \frac{1}{(\bar{X}2_3)^2}\begin{bmatrix} \left(\dfrac{\bar{X}1_3}{\bar{X}1_2}-1\right)^2, & -\dfrac{\bar{X}1_3}{\bar{X}1_2}\left(\dfrac{\bar{X}1_3}{\bar{X}1_2}-1\right), & \left(\dfrac{\bar{X}1_3}{\bar{X}1_2}-1\right), & 0 \\ & \left(\dfrac{\bar{X}1_3}{\bar{X}1_2}\right)^2, & -\dfrac{\bar{X}1_3}{\bar{X}1_2}, & 0 \\ & , & 1, & 0 \\ \text{(sym)} & & , & 0 \end{bmatrix} \\
&+ \frac{1}{(\bar{X}3_4)^2}\begin{bmatrix} \left[\dfrac{\bar{X}2_4}{\bar{X}2_3}\left(1-\dfrac{\bar{X}1_3}{\bar{X}1_2}\right)+\dfrac{\bar{X}1_4}{\bar{X}1_2}-1\right]^2, & \left[\dfrac{\bar{X}2_4}{\bar{X}2_3}\left(1-\dfrac{\bar{X}1_3}{\bar{X}1_2}\right)+\dfrac{\bar{X}1_4}{\bar{X}1_2}-1\right]\left(\dfrac{\bar{X}1_3}{\bar{X}1_2}\dfrac{\bar{X}2_4}{\bar{X}2_3}-\dfrac{\bar{X}1_4}{\bar{X}1_2}\right), & -\left[\dfrac{\bar{X}2_4}{\bar{X}2_3}\left(1-\dfrac{\bar{X}1_3}{\bar{X}1_2}\right)+\dfrac{\bar{X}1_4}{\bar{X}2_2}-1\right]\left(\dfrac{\bar{X}2_4}{\bar{X}2_3}\right), & \left[\dfrac{\bar{X}2_4}{\bar{X}2_3}\left(1-\dfrac{\bar{X}1_3}{\bar{X}1_2}\right)+\dfrac{\bar{X}1_4}{\bar{X}1_2}-1\right] \\ , & \left(\dfrac{\bar{X}1_3}{\bar{X}1_2}\dfrac{\bar{X}2_4}{\bar{X}2_3}-\dfrac{\bar{X}1_4}{\bar{X}1_2}\right)^2, & -\left(\dfrac{\bar{X}1_3}{\bar{X}1_2}\dfrac{\bar{X}2_4}{\bar{X}2_3}-\dfrac{\bar{X}1_4}{\bar{X}1_2}\right)\left(\dfrac{\bar{X}2_4}{\bar{X}2_3}\right), & \left(\dfrac{\bar{X}1_3}{\bar{X}1_2}\dfrac{\bar{X}2_4}{\bar{X}2_3}-\dfrac{\bar{X}1_4}{\bar{X}1_2}\right) \\ , & , & \left(\dfrac{\bar{X}2_4}{\bar{X}2_3}\right)^2, & \left(\dfrac{\bar{X}2_4}{\bar{X}2_3}\right) \\ \text{(sym)}, & , & , & 1 \end{bmatrix}
\end{aligned}
\tag{3.67}
$$

Comparing (3.67) to (3.51) and (3.61), after addition of appropriate null rows and columns, the first term in $[C211L]$ is $[A211L]$, while the sum of the first and second terms constitutes $[B211L]$. Additional three-dimensional matrices constructed on $\{N_1\}$ are

$$\{C10\} \equiv \frac{1}{\Delta_e}\int_{R_e^3} \{N_1\}\, d\bar{x}^1\, d\bar{x}^2\, d\bar{x}^3 = \frac{1}{4}\begin{Bmatrix}1\\1\\1\\1\end{Bmatrix}$$

$$[C200] \equiv \frac{1}{\Delta_e}\int_{R_e^3} \{N_1\}\{N_1\}^T\, d\bar{x}^1\, d\bar{x}^2\, d\bar{x}^3 = \frac{1}{20}\begin{bmatrix}2 & 1 & 1 & 1\\ & 2 & 1 & 1\\ & & 2 & 1\\ \text{(sym)} & & & 2\end{bmatrix}$$

$$[C3000] \equiv \frac{1}{\Delta_e}\int_{R_e^3} \{N_1\}\{N_1\}\{N_1\}^T\, d\bar{x}^1\, d\bar{x}^2\, d\bar{x}^3$$

$$= \frac{1}{120}\begin{bmatrix}\begin{Bmatrix}6\\2\\2\\2\end{Bmatrix} & \begin{Bmatrix}2\\2\\1\\1\end{Bmatrix} & \begin{Bmatrix}2\\1\\2\\1\end{Bmatrix} & \begin{Bmatrix}2\\1\\1\\2\end{Bmatrix}\\ & \begin{Bmatrix}2\\6\\2\\2\end{Bmatrix} & \begin{Bmatrix}1\\2\\2\\1\end{Bmatrix} & \begin{Bmatrix}1\\2\\1\\2\end{Bmatrix}\\ & & \begin{Bmatrix}2\\2\\6\\2\end{Bmatrix} & \begin{Bmatrix}1\\1\\2\\2\end{Bmatrix}\\ \text{(sym)} & & & \begin{Bmatrix}2\\2\\2\\6\end{Bmatrix}\end{bmatrix} \tag{3.68}$$

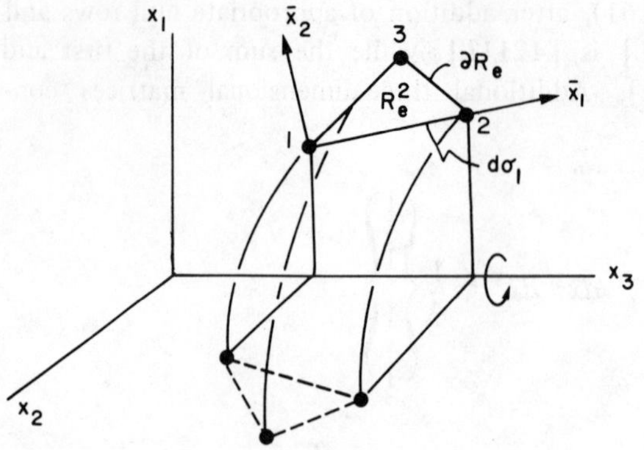

Figure 3.10 Triangular cross-sectional ring axisymmetric finite element.

This completes the development for the natural coordinate finite-element cardinal bases for potential flow analysis on R^n. The progression to $k > 1$ for $n > 1$ introduces considerable extra algebra, but involves no new theoretical or pragmatic concepts.

Problems

1 Verify the form (3.61) for $[B211L]$.

2 Verify the standard two-dimensional matrices (3.62).

3 Confirm the form (3.63) for $[B211Q]$.

3.6 TENSOR PRODUCT FINITE-ELEMENT BASIS

The n-dimensional natural coordinate finite-element domains of the previous section are probably most familiar. For $2 \leqslant n \leqslant 3$, the triangular slab and tetrahedron facilitate construction of nonuniform computational meshes that can fit any nonregular geometry. Furthermore, a symmetric disposition of nodal coordinates readily admits construction of required cardinal basis $\{N_k\}$, using interpolation polynomials complete to degree $1 \leqslant k \leqslant 3$.

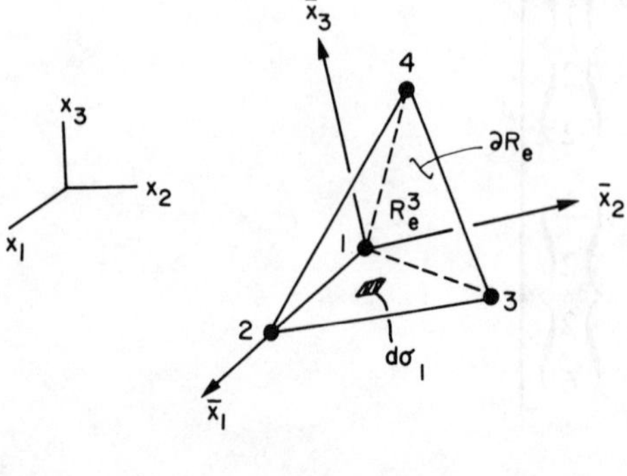

Figure 3.11 Three-dimensional finite element.

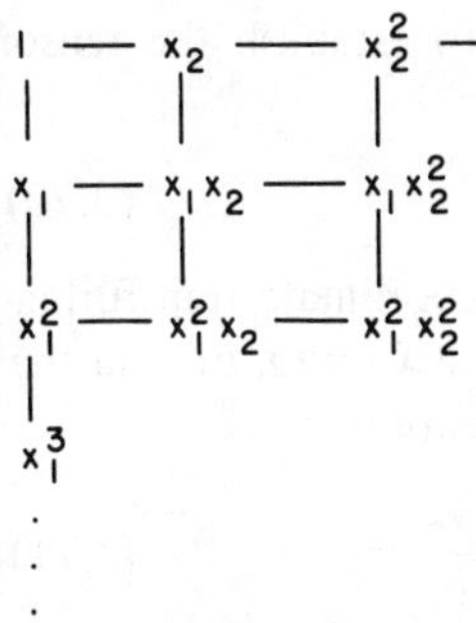

Figure 3.12 Two-dimensional tensor product basis construction.

A second family of finite-element cardinal basis and corresponding domain geometries can be constructed using outer (tensor) products of the one-dimensional basis developed in Chap. 2. For example, the linear interpolation of a function of x_1 is $a_1 + a_2x_1$, the form of which holds for $x_1 \Rightarrow x_i$. The resultant geometric construction of the cardinal basis, similar to Pascal's triangle for two-dimensional space, is shown in Fig. 3.12. The extension to three dimensions is obvious, and the finite-element domain geometries appear analagous to the unit square and unit cube. This feature, unaltered, would severely limit the utility of the tensor product basis to uniform geometries. However, geometric flexibility will return through the concept of "isoparametrism," as developed in this section.

The developments are easily illustrated using linear interpolants on two-dimensional space. Figure 3.13 shows the corresponding finite element, assumed rectangular with side measures $2a$ and $2b$, and correlated to the global coordinate system x_i through the affine (constant) coordinate transformation $\bar{x}_i = \bar{x}_i(x_j)$. The η_i natural coordinate system spanning the rectangle has its origin at the centroid $\bar{x}_c$ of the element. Referring to Fig. 3.12, the lowest degree interpolation for $q_e(x_i)$ on R_e^2 is the tensor product of $a_1 + a_2x_i$. The corresponding Taylor series must be

$$q_e(x_i) \equiv a_1 + a_2x_1 + a_3x_2 + a_4x_1x_2 \equiv \{1, x_1, x_2, x_1x_2\}\{a\}_e \tag{3.69}$$

which is termed a "bilinear" expansion due to the appearance of the mixed product. As previously illustrated, the basic step is to solve for the coefficient

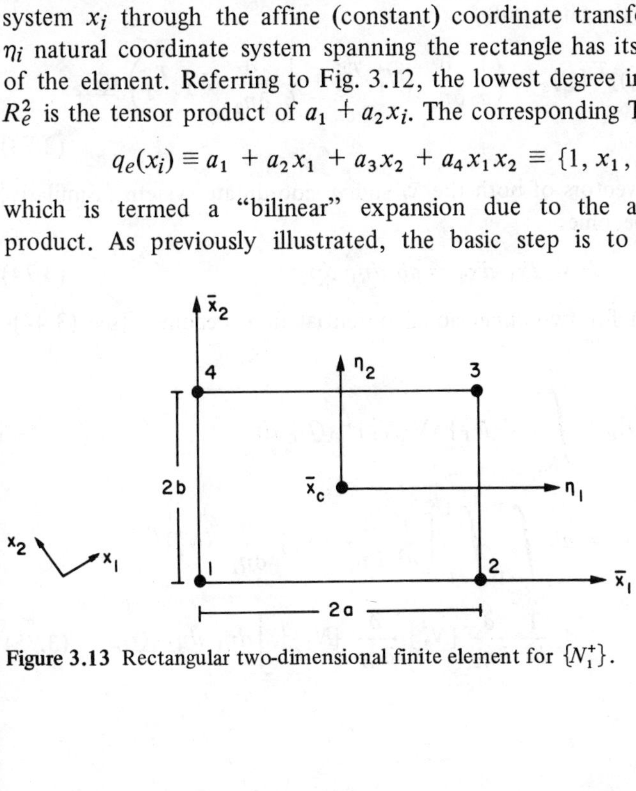

Figure 3.13 Rectangular two-dimensional finite element for $\{N_1^+\}$.

matrix $\{a\}$ in terms of the element nodal coordinates $x^i(l)$ to establish the tensor product linear cardinal basis $\{N_1^+(\eta_i)\}$. Hence,

$$q_e(x_i) \equiv \{N_1^+(\eta_i)\}^T \{Q\}_e \tag{3.70}$$

and the elements of $\{Q\}_e$ are the nodal values of $q_e(x_i)$. The coordinate transformation to $\bar{x}_i$ is given as (3.37), the coordinates of the centroid are $\bar{x}_c = (a, b)$, and the normalized natural coordinate system η_i is determined by inspection as

$$\eta_1 = \frac{\bar{x}_1 - a}{a} = \frac{\bar{x}_1}{a} - 1 \qquad \eta_2 = \frac{\bar{x}_2 - b}{b} = \frac{\bar{x}_2}{b} - 1 \tag{3.71}$$

The matrix elements of $\{N_1^+(\eta_i)\}$ are linearly dependent upon η_i, and the product $\eta_1\eta_2$, as observed by substitution of (3.71) into (3.69). The coefficient matrix $\{a\}_e$ could be solved using the procedures of Chap. 2. However, the elements of $\{N_1^+\}$ are readily determined by inspection as

$$\{N_1^+(\eta_i)\} = \frac{1}{4}\begin{Bmatrix} (1-\eta_1)(1-\eta_2) \\ (1+\eta_1)(1-\eta_2) \\ (1+\eta_1)(1+\eta_2) \\ (1-\eta_1)(1+\eta_2) \end{Bmatrix} \tag{3.72}$$

for the counterclockwise node numbering convention given in Fig. 3.13.

The calculus operations required to construct the finite-element matrices for potential flow [see (3.17) and (3.20)] must be transformed to the η_i coordinate system. Using (3.71) and the chain rule,

$$\nabla q_e(x_i) = \nabla\{N_1^+(\eta_i)\}^T \{Q\}_e = \left(\frac{1}{a}\frac{\partial}{\partial\eta_1}\{N_1^+\}^T\hat{\mathrm{i}} + \frac{1}{b}\frac{\partial}{\partial\eta_2}\{N_1^+\}^T\hat{\mathrm{j}}\right)\{Q\}_e \tag{3.73}$$

where $(\hat{\mathrm{i}}, \hat{\mathrm{j}})$ are the unit vectors of both the $\bar{x}_i$ and η_i coordinate systems. Similarly, the differential element becomes

$$d\tau = d\bar{x}_1\, d\bar{x}_2 = ab\, d\eta_1\, d\eta_2 \tag{3.74}$$

Then, the diffusion term for two-dimensional potential flow becomes [see (3.44)–(3.47)]

$$\begin{aligned}\Delta_e[B211L^+]\{Q\}_e &\equiv \int_{R_e^2} \nabla\{N_1^+\}\cdot\nabla\{N_1^+\}^T\{Q\}_e\, d\tau \\ &= ab\int_{-1}^{1}\int_{-1}^{1}\left[\frac{1}{a^2}\frac{\partial}{\partial\eta_1}\{N_1^+\}\frac{\partial}{\partial\eta_1}\{N_1^+\}^T\right. \\ &\quad \left. + \frac{1}{b^2}\frac{\partial}{\partial\eta_2}\{N_1^+\}\frac{\partial}{\partial\eta_2}\{N_1^+\}^T\right] d\eta_1\, d\eta_2\,\{Q\}_e\end{aligned} \tag{3.75}$$

Defining the measure of R_e^2 as $\Delta_e \equiv ab$ (one-fourth the plane area), it is left as an exercise to show that

$$[B211L^{+}]_e = \frac{1}{6a^2}\begin{bmatrix} 2 & -2 & -1 & 1 \\ & 2 & 1 & -1 \\ & & 2 & -2 \\ (\text{sym}) & & & 2 \end{bmatrix} + \frac{1}{6b^2}\begin{bmatrix} 2 & 1 & -1 & -2 \\ & 2 & -2 & -1 \\ & & 2 & 1 \\ (\text{sym}) & & & 2 \end{bmatrix} \tag{3.76}$$

In the instance of a square domain ($a = b$), (3.76) takes the elementary form

$$[B211L^{+}]_e = \frac{1}{6a^2}\begin{bmatrix} 4 & -1 & -2 & -1 \\ & 4 & -1 & -2 \\ & & 4 & -1 \\ (\text{sym}) & & & 4 \end{bmatrix} \tag{3.77}$$

Establishment of $[B200L^{+}]$ is left as Problem 3 at the end of this section.

Viewing Fig. 3.13, the linear tensor product basis must exhibit close similarities to conventional second-order accurate finite-difference methods. On a uniform discretization, assembly of (3.77) at a common node yields the equivalent finite difference "star." Problem 4 suggests confirming that assembly of (3.77) at node (i, j) yields

$$\nabla^2 Q_{ij} \approx \mathop{S}_{e=1}^{4} [B211L^{+}]\{Q\}_e$$

$$\Rightarrow \frac{1}{6a^2}\begin{bmatrix} -2Q_{i-1,j+1} & -2Q_{i,j+1} & -2Q_{i+1,j+1} \\ -2Q_{i-1,j} & 16Q_{i,j} & -2Q_{i+1,j} \\ -2Q_{i-1,j-1} & -2Q_{i,j-1} & -2Q_{i+1,j-1} \end{bmatrix} \tag{3.78}$$

Normalizing (3.78) by $3a^2$, the "difference star" equivalent of (3.78) is

$$\begin{bmatrix} -1 & -1 & -1 \\ -1 & 8 & -1 \\ -1 & -1 & -1 \end{bmatrix}$$

By replacing the four outrigger elements ($i \pm 1$, $j \pm 1$) by the appropriate algebraic average, this star reduces to the familiar form

$$\begin{bmatrix} & -1 & \\ -1 & 4 & -1 \\ & -1 & \end{bmatrix}$$

$$\begin{bmatrix} & 1 & \\ 1 & -4 & 1 \\ & 1 & \end{bmatrix} \qquad \frac{1}{4}\begin{bmatrix} 1 & 2 & 1 \\ 2 & -12 & 2 \\ 1 & 2 & 1 \end{bmatrix}$$

(*a*) (*c*)

$$\frac{1}{2}\begin{bmatrix} 1 & & 1 \\ & -4 & \\ 1 & & 1 \end{bmatrix} \qquad \frac{1}{6}\begin{bmatrix} 1 & 4 & 1 \\ 4 & -20 & 4 \\ 1 & 4 & 1 \end{bmatrix}$$

(*b*) (*d*)

Figure 3.14 Schematic of finite-difference analogs of ∇^2 on a square mesh. (*a*) Basic unit square; (*b*) diagonal unit square; (*c*) the "12" formula; (*d*) the "20" formula.

which is the basic second-order accurate central difference equivalent of the laplacian. Roache (1972, p. 135) summarizes several difference analogues of ∇^2, as shown in Fig. 3.14, which may be selectively higher-order accurate representations of ∇^2 under special circumstances. An interesting exercise would seek construction of cardinal bases $\{N_1^+\}$ yielding these various representations.

The biquadratic cardinal basis $\{N_2^+(\eta_i)\}$ can also be identified by inspection. From Fig. 3.12, nine nodal locations are required, with the extras coinciding with the centroid and the midcoordinates of each side (see Fig. 3.15). With nine nodes, the appropriate biquadratic expansion for q_e is

$$q_e(x_i) = \{1, x_1, x_2, x_1x_2, x_1^2, x_2^2, x_1x_2^2, x_1^2x_2, x_1^2x_2^2\}\{a\}_e \tag{3.79}$$

The finite-element cardinal basis specification is

$$q_e(x_i) \equiv \{N_2^+(\eta_i)\}^T\{Q\}_e \tag{3.80}$$

Solution of the elements of $\{a\}$ in terms of $\{Q\}_e$, for the nodal numbering scheme illustrated, yields

$$\{N_2^+(\eta_i)\} = \frac{1}{4}\begin{Bmatrix} (1-\eta_1)(1-\eta_2)(-\eta_1-\eta_2-1) \\ (1+\eta_1)(1-\eta_2)(\ \eta_1-\eta_2-1) \\ (1+\eta_1)(1+\eta_2)(\ \eta_1+\eta_2-1) \\ (1-\eta_1)(1+\eta_2)(-\eta_1+\eta_2-1) \\ 2(1-\eta_1^2)(1-\eta_2) \\ 2(1+\eta_1)(1-\eta_2^2) \\ 2(1-\eta_1^2)(1+\eta_2) \\ 2(1-\eta_1)(1+\eta_2^2) \\ 4(1-\eta_1^2)(1-\eta_2^2) \end{Bmatrix} \tag{3.81}$$

Compared to the tedium involved in establishing the quadratic and cubic one-dimensional diffusion matrices, formulation of $[B211Q^+]$ is straightforward but certainly time-consuming. In actual practice, (3.80)–(3.81) are of small value since their use is restricted to rectangular domains. It is sufficient to note that (3.81) is indeed biquadratic in the natural coordinate system η_i.

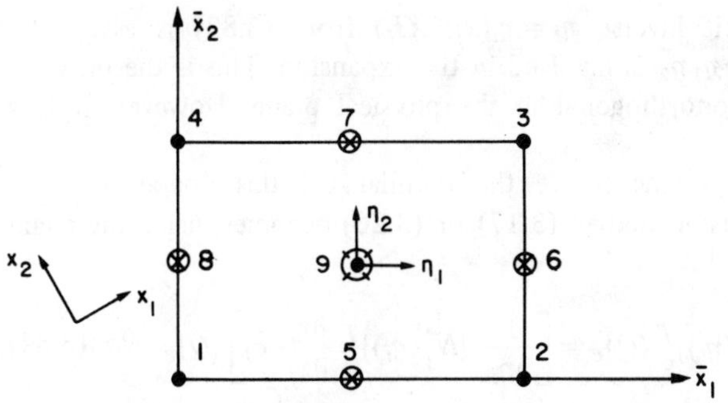

Figure 3.15 Rectangular two-dimensional finite-element domain for $\{N_2^+\}$.

The fundamental requirement is extension of the tensor product basis to nonrectangular domains possessing curved boundaries. As an introduction, consider the straight-sided general quadrilateral finite-element domain shown in Fig. 3.16. The origin of the η_i coordinate system is defined at the centroid, and the coordinate curves remain straight lines. However, the η_i system is not orthogonal in the $\bar{x}_i$ plane, yet remains defined as orthogonal and normalized in the transform plane. A coordinate transformation is required, and the tool for determination is at hand in $\{N_1^+(\eta_i)\}$. Just as a dependent variable $q(x_i)$ is interpolated on R_e^2, using the bilinear cardinal basis, the corresponding interpolation of the cartesian coordinate system x_i is

$$x_1 = \{N_1^+(\eta_i)\}^T \{X1\}_e \qquad x_2 = \{N_1^+(\eta_i)\}^T \{X2\}_e \tag{3.82}$$

Equation (3.82) expresses interpolation of the variables x_i on R_e^2 in terms of nodal values (global coordinates) and the natural coordinate system η_i. This is conceptually identical to interpolation of the radius r in terms of $\{N_1(\xi_i)\}$, as used in Chap. 2. Recalling the notation XI_j for nodal coordinates, the expansion of (3.82) using (3.72) is

$$\begin{aligned} x_1 &= [(1-\eta_1)(1-\eta_2)X1_1 + (1+\eta_1)(1-\eta_2)X1_2 \\ &\quad + (1+\eta_1)(1+\eta_2)X1_3 + (1-\eta_1)(1+\eta_2)X1_4]/4 \\ x_2 &= [(1-\eta_1)(1-\eta_2)X2_1 + (1+\eta_1)(1-\eta_2)X2_2 \\ &\quad + (1+\eta_1)(1+\eta_2)X2_3 + (1-\eta_1)(1+\eta_2)X2_4]/4 \end{aligned} \tag{3.83}$$

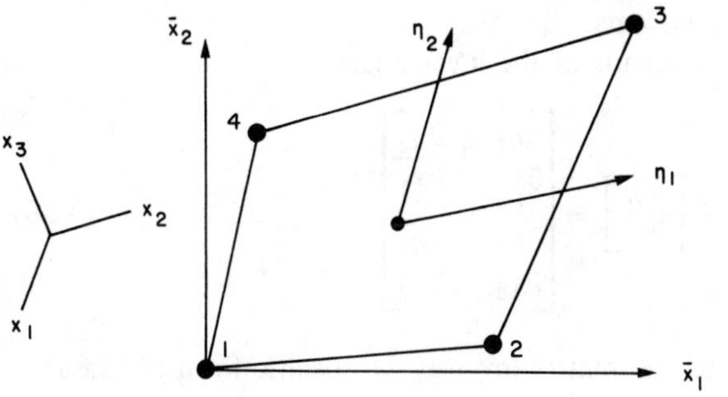

Figure 3.16 Quadrilateral two-dimensional finite-element for $\{N_1^+\}$.

Determination of the explicit inverse $\eta_i = \eta_i(x_i, XI_j)$ from (3.83) is essentially impossible, since the product $\eta_1 \eta_2$ is involved in the expansion. This is the outward manifestation of η_i being nonorthogonal in the physical plane. However, it is a detail easily circumvented.

The basic algorithm requirements are the familiar calculus operations. The gradient operator in the diffusion matrix (3.17) or (3.20) becomes, using the chain rule,

$$\nabla q_e(x_i) = \nabla \{N_1^+(\eta_i)\}^T \{Q\}_e = \left[\frac{\partial}{\partial \eta_i} \{N_1^+(\eta_i)\}^T \frac{\partial \eta_i}{\partial x_j} \hat{\epsilon}_j\right] \{Q\}_e \tag{3.84}$$

where $\hat{\epsilon}_j$ are the unit vectors of the x_j coordinate system. The elements of $\{N_1^+(\eta_i)\}$ are readily differentiated by η_i, but the inverse transformation $\eta_i = \eta_i(x_j)$ is not yet available. However, see (3.83), the operations $\partial x_j / \partial \eta_i$ define the elements of the forward jacobian $[J]$

$$[J] \equiv \left[\frac{\partial x_i}{\partial \eta_j}\right] = \begin{bmatrix} \dfrac{\partial x_1}{\partial \eta_1} & \dfrac{\partial x_2}{\partial \eta_1} \\[2ex] \dfrac{\partial x_1}{\partial \eta_2} & \dfrac{\partial x_2}{\partial \eta_2} \end{bmatrix} \tag{3.85}$$

which are easy to form. For example, using (3.82) [see (3.83)],

$$\begin{aligned} \frac{\partial x_1}{\partial \eta_1} &= \frac{\partial x_1}{\partial N_1}\frac{\partial N_1}{\partial \eta_1} + \frac{\partial x_1}{\partial N_2}\frac{\partial N_2}{\partial \eta_1} + \frac{\partial x_1}{\partial N_3}\frac{\partial N_3}{\partial \eta_1} + \frac{\partial x_1}{\partial N_4}\frac{\partial N_4}{\partial \eta_1} \\ &= \tfrac{1}{4}[-X1_1(1-\eta_2) + X1_2(1-\eta_2) + X1_3(1+\eta_2) - X1_4(1+\eta_2)] \\ &\equiv a(1-\eta_2) + b(1+\eta_2) \end{aligned} \tag{3.86}$$

Hence, all matrix elements of (3.85) are linear polynomials in η_i with coefficients an elementary function of the global coordinates of the finite-element domain nodes. Therefore, the specific form of (3.85) is

$$[J] = \begin{bmatrix} a(1-\eta_2) + b(1+\eta_2), & c(1-\eta_2) + d(1+\eta_2) \\ \alpha(1-\eta_1) + \beta(1+\eta_1), & \gamma(1-\eta_1) + \delta(1+\eta_1) \end{bmatrix} \tag{3.87}$$

where a–d and α–δ are specified constants.

Equation (3.84) requires the elements of the inverse jacobian:

$$[J]^{-1} \equiv \left[\frac{\partial \eta_i}{\partial x_j}\right] = \begin{bmatrix} \dfrac{\partial \eta_1}{\partial x_1} & \dfrac{\partial \eta_2}{\partial x_1} \\[2ex] \dfrac{\partial \eta_1}{\partial x_2} & \dfrac{\partial \eta_2}{\partial x_2} \end{bmatrix} \tag{3.88}$$

From (3.87) and the definition of the matrix inverse, the specific form of (3.88) is

$$[J]^{-1} = \frac{1}{\det\,[J]}\begin{bmatrix} \gamma(1-\eta_1)+\delta(1+\eta_1), & -c(1-\eta_2)-d(1+\eta_2) \\ -\alpha(1-\eta_1)-\beta(1+\eta_1), & a(1-\eta_2)+b(1+\eta_2) \end{bmatrix} \tag{3.89}$$

where det $[J]$ is the determinant of (3.85), hence dependent upon η_i.

Therefore, (3.84) becomes formally expressed as

$$\nabla q_e(x_i) = \frac{\partial}{\partial \eta_i}\{N_1^+(\eta)\}^T [J]^{-1}\hat{\epsilon}_j\,\{Q\}_e \tag{3.90}$$

The differential element for (3.17) or (3.20) is

$$d\tau = dx_1\,dx_2 = \det\,[J]\,d\eta_1\,d\eta_2 \tag{3.91}$$

Note that (3.73) is the special case of (3.90), where $[J]^{-1}$ is the diagonal matrix

$$\begin{bmatrix} \frac{1}{a} & 0 \\ 0 & \frac{1}{b} \end{bmatrix}$$

and det $[J] = ab$ for the rectangular element [see (3.74) and (3.71)].

The forms necessary for construction of the potential flow diffusion matrix for a straight-sided quadrilateral element domain shape are (3.84) and (3.91). Hence,

$$\begin{aligned}
\Delta_e\,[B211L^+]\,\{Q\}_e &\equiv \int_{R_e^2} \nabla\{N_1^+\}\cdot\nabla\{N_1^+\}^T\{Q\}_e\,d\tau \\
&= \int_{-1}^{+1}\int_{-1}^{+1} [J]^{-1}\frac{\partial}{\partial\eta_i}\{N_1^+\}\cdot\frac{\partial}{\partial\eta_i}\{N_1^+\}^T[J]^{-1}\det\,[J]\,d\eta_1\,d\eta_2\,\{Q\}_e \\
&= \int_{-1}^{+1}\int_{-1}^{+1}\Bigg[\left(\frac{\partial\eta_1}{\partial x_1}\right)^2\frac{\partial\{N_1^+\}}{\partial\eta_1}\frac{\partial\{N_1^+\}^T}{\partial\eta_1} + \frac{\partial\eta_1}{\partial x_1}\frac{\partial\eta_2}{\partial x_1}\left(\frac{\partial\{N_1^+\}}{\partial\eta_1}\frac{\partial\{N_1^+\}^T}{\partial\eta_2}\right. \\
&\quad \left. + \frac{\partial\{N_1^+\}}{\partial\eta_2}\frac{\partial\{N_1^+\}^T}{\partial\eta_1}\right) + \left(\frac{\partial\eta_2}{\partial x_1}\right)^2\frac{\partial\{N_1^+\}}{\partial\eta_2}\frac{\partial\{N_1^+\}^T}{\partial\eta_2} \\
&\quad + (\text{same terms with } x_1 \text{ replaced by } x_2)\Bigg]\det\,[J]\,d\eta_1\,d\eta_2\,\{Q\}_e
\end{aligned} \tag{3.92}$$

Since the x_i coordinates are cartesian, no mixed derivatives on x_i occur in the vector dot product. However, even though the integration limits in (3.92) are convenient, the integrand has become complicated, especially since each term involving $\partial\eta_i/\partial x_j$ contains det $[J]$ in the denominator. Therefore, the matrix elements of $[B211L^+]$ cannot in general be determined using analytical procedures.

The method appropriate for determination of the coefficients is numerical integration, and gaussian quadrature is probably preferred (see Zienkiewicz, 1977, Chap. 8). Considering one dimension for the moment, numerical quadrature replaces an integral by a discrete sum.

$$I \equiv \int_{-1}^{+1} f(\eta)\, d\eta = \sum_{i=1}^{k} H_i f(\eta_i) \tag{3.93}$$

The coordinate locations η_i for evaluating the integrand are determined by requiring that (3.93) yield the exact integral for a polynomial of degree $k \geqslant 1$. Table 3.3 lists

Table 3.3 Abscissas and weight coefficients of the gaussian quadrature formula $\int_{-1}^{+1} f(\eta)\, d\eta = \Sigma_{j=1}^{k} H_j f(\eta_j)$

Degree, k	Coordinates, $\pm\eta_j$			Weights, H_j		
2	0.57735	02691	89626	1.00000	00000	00000
3	0.77459	66692	41483	0.55555	55555	55556
	0.00000	00000	00000	0.88888	88888	88889
4	0.86113	63115	94053	0.34785	48451	37454
	0.33998	10435	84856	0.65214	51548	62546
5	0.90617	98459	38664	0.23692	68850	56189
	0.53846	93101	05683	0.47862	86704	99366
	0.00000	00000	00000	0.56888	88888	88889
6	0.93246	95142	03152	0.17132	44923	79170
	0.66120	93864	66265	0.36076	15730	48139
	0.23861	91860	83197	0.46791	39345	72691
7	0.94910	79123	42759	0.12948	49661	68870
	0.74153	11855	99394	0.27970	53914	89277
	0.40584	51513	77397	0.38183	00505	05119
	0.00000	00000	00000	0.41795	91836	73469
8	0.96028	98564	97536	0.10122	85362	90376
	0.79666	64774	13627	0.22238	10344	53374
	0.52553	24099	16329	0.31370	66458	77887
	0.18343	46424	95650	0.36268	37833	78362
9	0.96816	02395	07626	0.08127	43883	61574
	0.83603	11073	26636	0.18064	81606	94857
	0.61337	14327	00590	0.26061	06964	02935
	0.32425	34234	03809	0.31234	70770	40003
	0.00000	00000	00000	0.33023	93550	01260
10	0.97390	65285	17172	0.06667	13443	08688
	0.86506	33666	88985	0.14945	13491	50581
	0.67940	95682	99024	0.21908	63625	15982
	0.43339	53941	29427	0.26926	67193	09996
	0.14887	43389	81631	0.29552	42247	14753

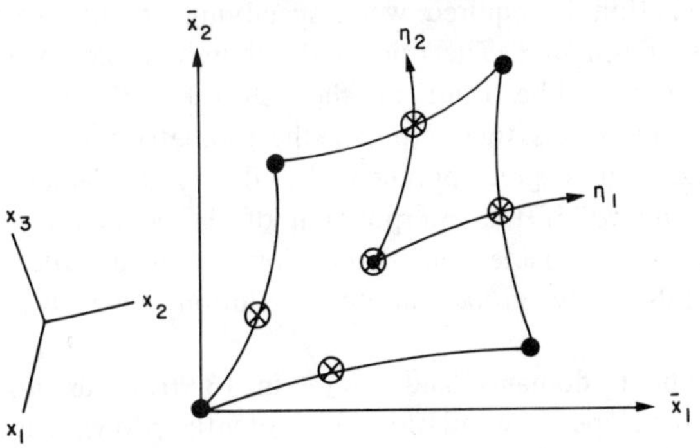

Figure 3.17 Generalized quadrilateral two-dimensional finite-element for $\{N_2^+\}$.

the abscissas and weight functions H_i for (3.93), for $2 \leqslant k \leqslant 10$, assuming specification of Legendre polynomials. The error in the discrete evaluation is $0(\Delta_e)^{2k}$; hence, the formula for $k = 2$ would be completely adequate for the bilinear tensor product basis $\{N_1^+\}$.

The requirement in (3.92) is to evaluate the two-dimensional integral

$$I \equiv \int_{-1}^{+1} \int_{-1}^{+1} f(\eta_1, \eta_2)\, d\eta_1\, d\eta_2 \tag{3.94}$$

Building on (3.93), hold η_2 constant and replace the first integration as

$$\int_{-1}^{+1} f(\eta_1, \eta_2)\, d\eta_1 = \sum_{i=1}^{k} H_i f(\eta_1, \eta_2) = \psi(\eta_2)$$

Integrating over $d\eta_2$, each term in (3.94) becomes the double summation

$$I = \int_{-1}^{+1} \psi(\eta_2)\, d\eta_2 = \sum_{i=1}^{k} H_i \psi(\eta_i) = \sum_{i=1}^{k} \sum_{j=1}^{k} H_i H_j f(\eta_i, \eta_j) \tag{3.95}$$

Extension to a three-dimensional problem definition is direct. Obviously, different order quadrature could be employed in respective coordinate directions if desired.

The final step is recovery of geometric versatility, which accrues to replacement of the straight-sided quadrilateral boundary with curved sides (see Fig. 3.17). Assuming the element domain boundaries adequately interpolated by a quadratic, the extension of (3.82) is

$$x_1 = \{N_2^+(\eta_i)\}^T \{X1\}_e \qquad x_2 = \{N_2^+(\eta_i)\}^T \{X2\}_e \tag{3.96}$$

The cardinal basis $\{N_2^+\}$ is given in (3.81). Referring to Fig. 3.15, the nodal disposition in the transform plane is uniform and η_i is cartesian. In the physical plane, the element is curved-sided, and the nodal disposition may be made nonuniform by defining nonvertex nodes $\otimes$ other than midway between vertex nodes. [As a matter of practice, (3.96) is the heart of a convenient methodology for generating smoothly nonuniform discretizations on macroelement discretizations of the physical domain.] However, caution is required when specifying nonuniform nodal dispositions to ensure $[J]$ is nonsingular. The rule of the thumb is that each nonvertex node must lie within the middle third of the interval defined by corresponding vertex node pairs. If one elects to interpolate the geometry and the dependent variable using identical kth degree polynomials, the finite-element description has been called *isoparametric*. If the interpolation of the geometry is more general than for the dependent variable, the description is called *superparametric*. The converse corresponds to the *subparametric* description, which was employed throughout Chap. 2.

The use of curved-sided element domains and $\{N_2^+\}$ in (3.96) adds no theoretical complications to the developed formulation for potential flow. The elements of the jacobian $[J]$ (3.85) are easy to form, although nine terms now result in (3.86). However, the rank of $[J]$ remains equal to two, the dimension of R^2. The expression for ∇q_e is

$$\nabla q_e(x_i) = \frac{\partial}{\partial \eta_i} \{N_2^+(\eta)\}^T [J]^{-1} \{Q\}_e \hat{\mathbf{e}}_j \tag{3.97}$$

and the number of matrix elements in $\{Q\}_e$ now equals nine. The element diffusion matrix is of the form

$$\Delta_e [B211Q^+] \{Q\}_e \equiv \int_{R_e^2} \nabla \{N_2^+\} \cdot \nabla \{N_2^+\}^T \{Q\}_e \, d\tau \tag{3.98}$$

The order of $[B211Q^+]$ also equals nine and gaussian quadrature ($k \geqslant 2$) is employed to evaluate the entries.

Problems

1 By substituting (3.71) into (3.69), solve the resultant expression to verify the matrix elements of $\{N_1^+(\eta_i)\}$ given in (3.72).

2 Evaluate the expression (3.75) to determine the form for $[B211L^+]$ given in (3.76).

3 Using (3.72), show that

$$[B200L^+] = \frac{1}{36} \begin{bmatrix} 4 & 2 & 1 & 2 \\ & 4 & 2 & 1 \\ & & 4 & 2 \\ (\text{sym}) & & & 4 \end{bmatrix}$$

4 By assembling $[B211L^+]$ for four adjacent elements sharing node coordinate (i, j), construct the recursion relationship (3.78).

5 Determine what modifications to the tensor product bilinear cardinal basis $\{N_1^+\}$ can reproduce the various finite-difference stars shown in Fig. 3.14.

6 Complete the formulation of (3.92).

3.7 FLOW OVER A WAVE-SHAPED WALL, ACCURACY AND CONVERGENCE

An informative problem is two-dimensional incompressible potential flow over a wave-shaped wall (see Fig. 3.18*a*). For small aspect ratio, $\epsilon/\lambda \ll 1$, the flow tangency wall boundary condition (3.6) can be linearized, yielding an analytical solution for comparison. For a sine-wave wall,

$$y_w(x) = \epsilon \sin \frac{2\pi x}{\lambda} \tag{3.99}$$

the infinite series solution degenerates to one nonzero term (Shames, 1962, p. 458), and

$$\Phi(x, y) = U_\infty\left[-x + \epsilon \cos \frac{2\pi x}{\lambda} \exp\left(-\frac{2\pi y}{\lambda}\right)\right] \tag{3.100}$$

The finite-element solution algorithm for the planar two-dimensional problem specification is established from (3.59) with uniform element thickness and no mass flux across the element face. For

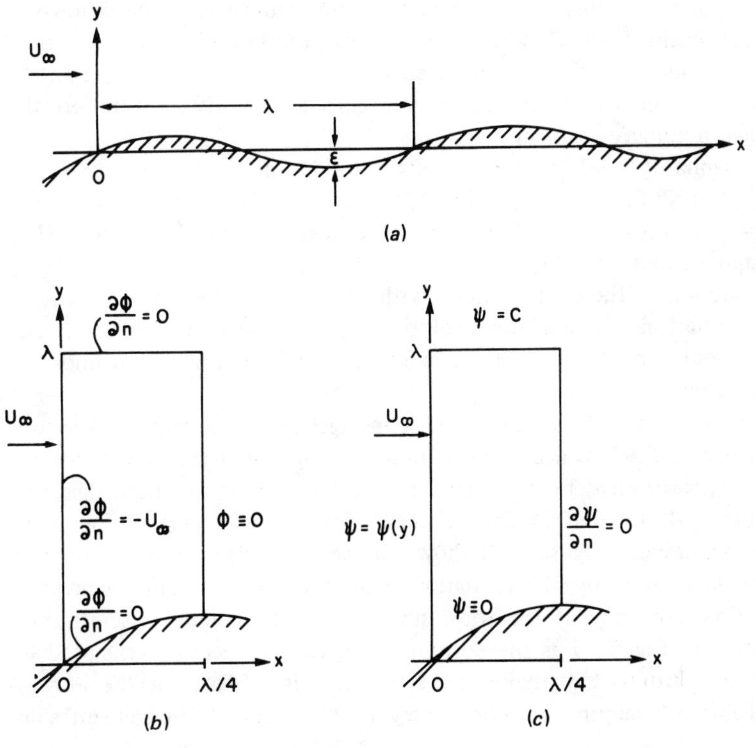

Figure 3.18 Flow over a wave-shaped wall. (*a*) Geometry; (*b*) solution domain for scalar potential; (*c*) solution domain for vector potential.

$$\Phi_e(x, y) \equiv \{N_k(\zeta)\}^T \{PHI\}_e \tag{3.101}$$

the algorithmic solution statement is

$$S_e[A_e[B211]_e\{PHI\}_e + L_e[A200]\{UPERP\}_e] = \{0\} \tag{3.102}$$

Similarly, for

$$\psi_e(x, y) \equiv \{N_k(\zeta)\}^T \{PSI\}_e$$

the finite-element solution form is

$$S_e[A_e[B211]_e\{PSI\}_e + L_e[A200]\{UPARA\}_e] = \{0\} \tag{3.103}$$

As observed, the sole difference between a Φ and ψ solution is specification of the boundary conditions; hence, the diffusion matrix is identical. Selection of the solution domain boundary is therefore of paramount importance. Shown in Fig. 3.18*b* is an optimal, i.e., minimum-sized, solution domain for determination of scalar potential Φ. At the inflow boundary $x = 0$, the imposed freestream velocity U_∞ becomes a gradient boundary condition on Φ as noted. The normal gradient of Φ vanishes at both the top and bottom of the domain, since $y = \lambda$ is assumed a good approximation to a farfield streamline and the wall is impervious, respectively. The downstream boundary is defined at $x = \lambda/4$, since from geometrical considerations, the scalar potential must be a constant on this symmetry plane. Shown in Fig. 3.18*c* is the optimal solution domain for computation of stream function, which happens to coincide with that for potential function. Note however, that the specification of the boundary conditions on ψ is considerably different but equally facilitated on each boundary segment.

Baker and Manhardt (1975) report results for solutions of the sine-wave wall for the case $U_\infty = 100$ f/s (32 m/s), $\epsilon/\lambda = 0.025$, $\lambda = 2\pi$. The computational grid consisted of 240 straight-sided triangular finite elements spanned by $\{N_1\}$ (Fig. 3.19*a*). The computed equipotential distribution is shown in Fig. 3.19*b*. Noteworthy is the normal intersection of the equipotentials with the wall and the upper freestream boundary. The numerical and analytical solutions are compared in Table 3.4. The average error is about 1 percent with the maximum error located at about midspan. No energy measure was reported.

The companion study of accuracy and convergence for potential flow was completed by Lawkins (1977), using tensor product isoparametric two-dimensional quadrilateral elements spanned by both bilinear and biquadratic functions. Discretizations containing 1, 4, 16, and 64 finite elements spanning the solution domain of Fig. 3.18*b* were employed. Figure 3.20 shows the velocity distributions computed from the bilinear Φ solution by differentiation at the Gauss points. Improvement in the fidelity of flow tangency at the wave surface is evident under discretization refinement. Shown in Fig. 3.21 is the corresponding velocity vectors generated by the biquadratic Φ solution. Essentially exact tangency is evident for the $M = 64$ discretization. Table 3.5 summarizes the energy (3.22) in the finite-element solutions.

The approximation to the energy in the solution error [see (3.24)], as obtained

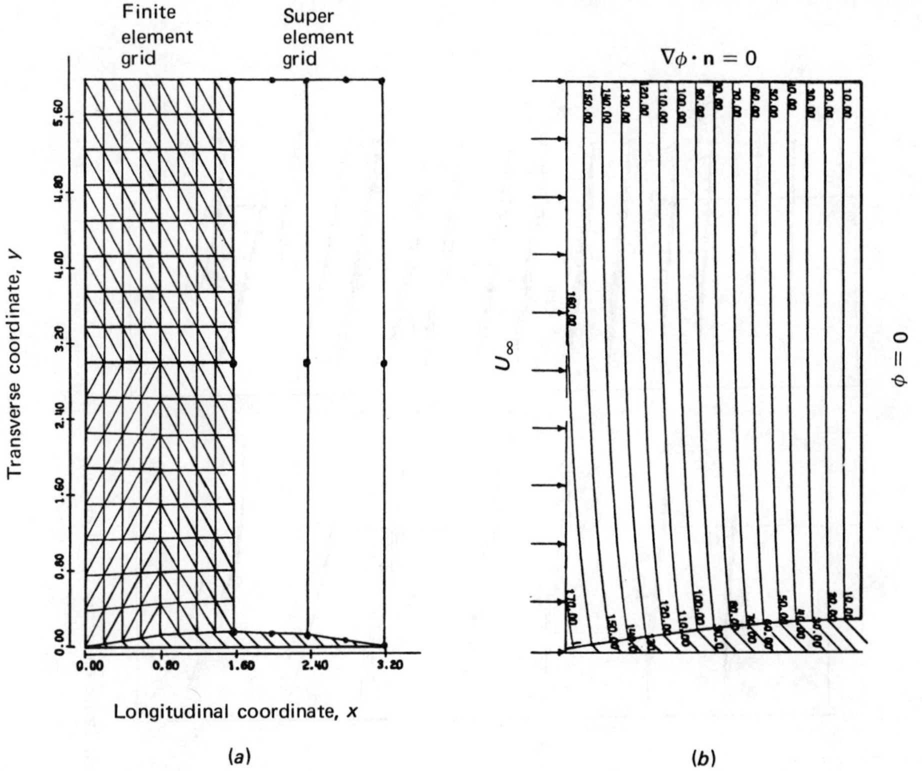

Figure 3.19 Wave-shaped wall solution domain discretization and computed equipotential distribution. (*a*) Discretization; (*b*) equipotential distribution.

Table 3.4 Computed potential distribution for flow over a wave-shaped wall

Wall potential function, $\Phi(x, y_W)$		
Analytical	Finite element	Error, %[a]
166.2	166.7	0.5
153.2	153.8	0.6
140.0	140.7	0.7
126.5	127.4	0.9
112.9	113.9	1.0
99.1	100.2	1.1
85.2	86.4	1.2
71.1	72.3	1.2
57.0	58.1	1.1
42.8	43.7	0.9
28.6	29.2	0.6
14.3	14.6	0.3
0	0	0

[a] Evaluated at the wall and normalized by U_∞.

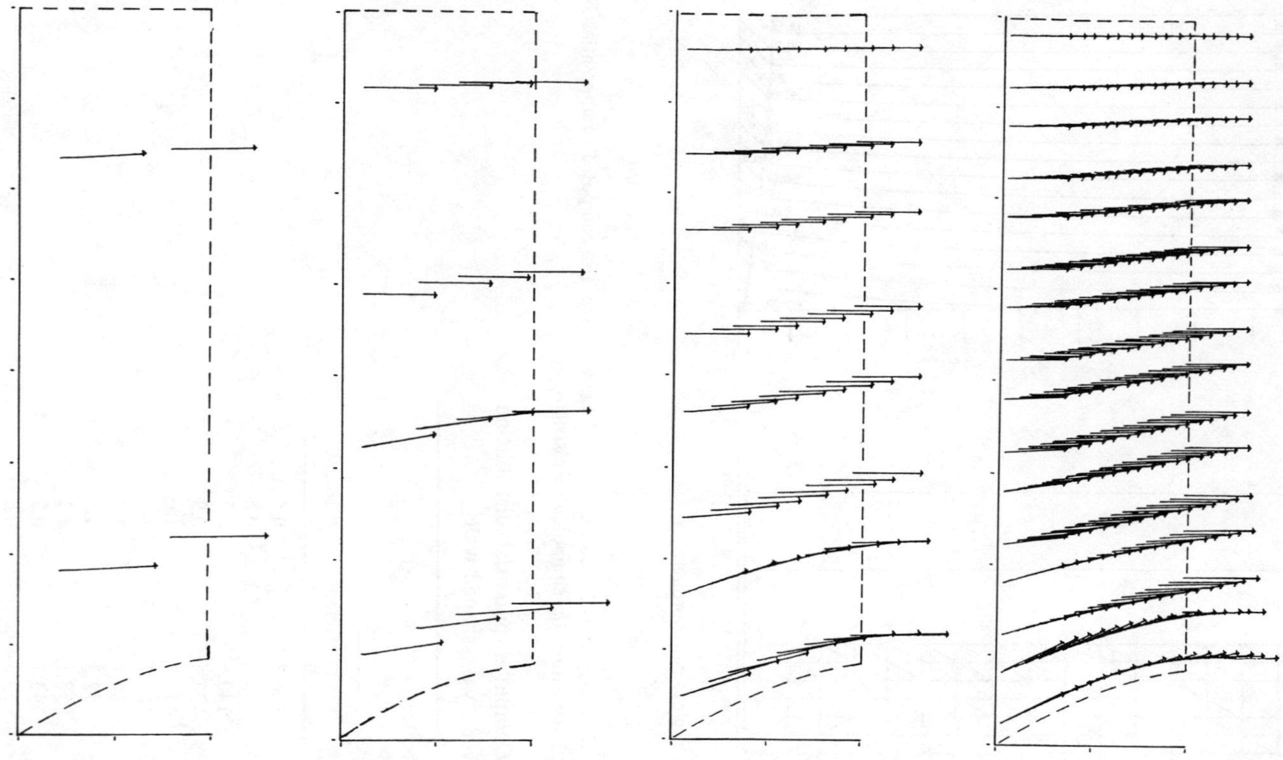

Figure 3.20 Computed velocity vector distributions using bilinear finite elements for flow over wave-shaped wall.

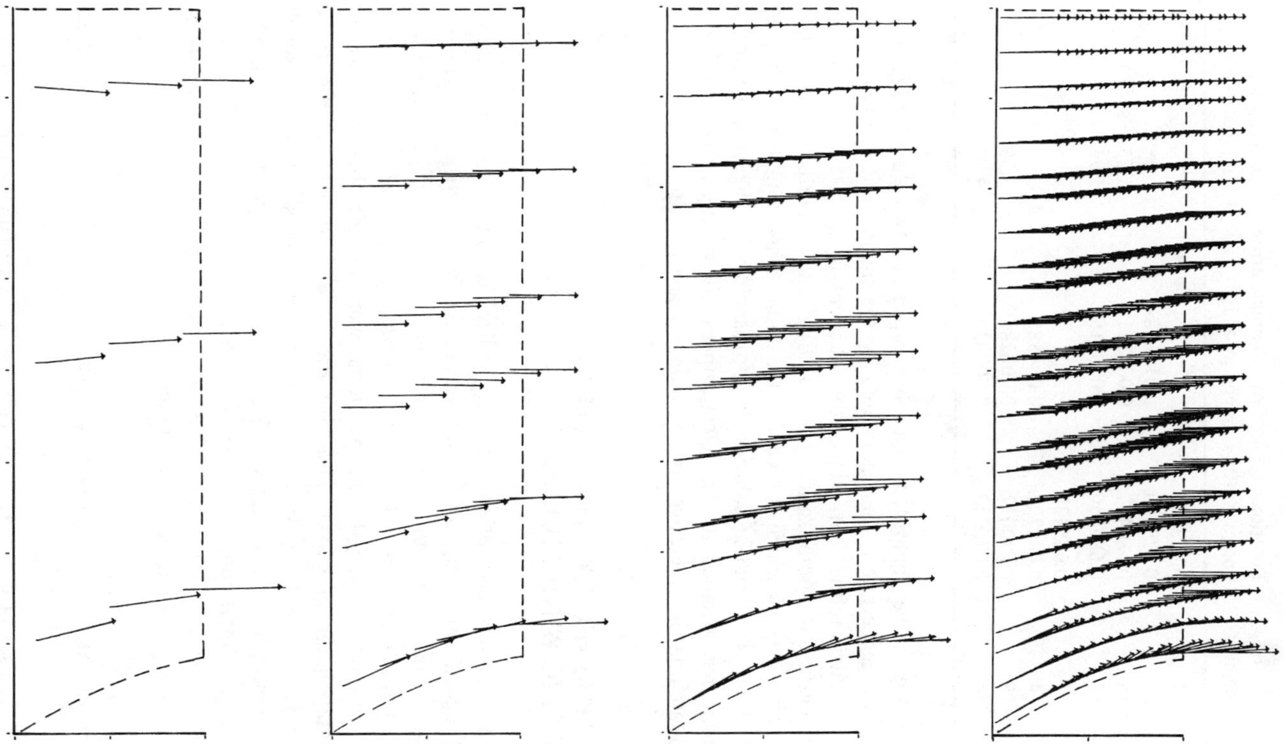

Figure 3.21 Computed velocity vector distributions using biquadratic finite elements for flow over wave-shaped wall.

Table 3.5 Computed convergence for flow over sine-wave wall

Functional	No. of elements	Solution energy × 10^5	Approximate error energy × 10^5	Convergence rate (approximate)
Bilinear	1	0.662564		
	4	0.678380	0.011668	
	16	0.686477	0.003571	1.63
	64	0.689130	0.000918	1.94
Biquadratic	1	0.685139		
	4	0.689724	0.004585	
	16	0.690012	0.000288	3.99
	64	0.690030	0.000018	4.00

by the difference in the computed solution energies for two discretizations, is also listed. The convergence rate is then estimated by the square root of the reduction in error energy under refinement, since the element spans were halved in each direction for each new discretization [see (3.26)]. The theoretical convergence rate is equal to $2(k + 1 - m)$ which is two for the bilinear and four for the biquadratic element solutions. The bilinear solution is approaching the theoretical value, while the biquadratic has attained it. The clear superiority of the curved-sided element solution in matching the sine-wave wall boundary shape is quite evident.

3.8 CONSTRAINED EXTREMIZATION, ATMOSPHERIC WIND FIELDS

The potential function description has been utilized in the atmospheric sciences to establish a procedure to compute three-dimensional, divergence-free wind fields from sparse boundary data. The theoretical statement is based on extremization of a constrained energy functional, originally formulated by Sasaki (1970).

The first estimate of the three-dimensional wind field is obtained by interpolation and extrapolation of known data over the node coordinates of the discretization of R^3. The estimate is denoted as $\mathbf{u}_0(x_i)$, and an adjustment is sought to produce the windfield $\mathbf{u}_\alpha(x_i)$ that satisfies the continuity equation (3.1), which is divergence-free or "mass-consistent." Using satisfaction of (3.1) as the differential constraint, the Lawrence Livermore National Laboratory (LLNL) procedure (Sherman, 1976) defines for extremization, the energy functional

$$E(\mathbf{u}, \mathbf{u}_0, \lambda) \equiv \tfrac{1}{2} \int_{R^3} \beta_\alpha^2 (\mathbf{u}_\alpha - \mathbf{u}_0) \cdot (\mathbf{u}_\alpha - \mathbf{u}_0)\, d\tau + \lambda \int \nabla \cdot \mathbf{u}_\alpha \, d\tau \qquad (3.104)$$

In (3.104), β_α is a set $(1 \leqslant \alpha \leqslant 3)$ of model coefficients available for computed field adjustment, e.g., empirical considerations of atmospheric stability, and $\lambda(x_i)$ is the Lagrange multiplier. The associated Euler-Lagrange equation system, established in the usual manner from (3.104), is

$$\beta_\alpha^2(\mathbf{u}_\alpha - \mathbf{u}_0) - \nabla\lambda = 0 \tag{3.105}$$

The governing equation for λ is obtained by inserting (3.105) in (3.1), written on $\mathbf{u}_\alpha$, yielding,

$$\frac{1}{\beta_\alpha^2}\nabla\cdot\nabla\lambda + \nabla\cdot\mathbf{u}_0 = 0 \tag{3.106}$$

where the subscript α is now associated with each coordinate direction. The expanded form for (3.106), in a rectangular cartesian coordinate system, is

$$L(\lambda) \equiv \frac{1}{\beta_1^2}\frac{\partial^2\lambda}{\partial x_1^2} + \frac{1}{\beta_2^2}\frac{\partial^2\lambda}{\partial x_2^2} + \frac{1}{\beta_3^2}\frac{\partial^2\lambda}{\partial x_3^2} + \left(\frac{\partial u_0}{\partial x} + \frac{\partial v_0}{\partial y} + \frac{\partial w_0}{\partial z}\right) = 0 \tag{3.107}$$

Making the identification $\Phi \equiv \lambda$, (3.107) and (3.105) become

$$L(\phi) \equiv \frac{1}{\beta_\alpha^2}\nabla^2\Phi + \nabla\cdot\mathbf{u}_0 = 0 \tag{3.108}$$

$$\mathbf{u}_\alpha \equiv \mathbf{u}_0 + \frac{1}{\beta_\alpha^2}\nabla\Phi \tag{3.109}$$

From (3.109), $\nabla\Phi$ defines a potential flow velocity distribution that "corrects" the initial estimated velocity field $\mathbf{u}_0$ to produce one that satisfies the continuity equation (3.1). The differential equation statement (3.108) is a Poisson equation that yields the distribution of Φ based upon the distribution of the continuity error in the guessed field $\mathbf{u}_0$. The boundary conditions for the solution of Φ are of the form (3.5), i.e.,

$$l(\Phi) \equiv a\Phi + b\,\nabla\Phi\cdot\hat{\mathbf{n}} = 0 \tag{3.110}$$

From (3.109), $a \equiv 1$ and $b \equiv 0$ for flow-through boundaries, that is, $\mathbf{u}_\alpha(\underline{x}) \equiv \mathbf{u}_0(\underline{x})$, the known input data. For an impervious boundary, $a \equiv 0$ and $b \equiv 1$ induces flow tangency.

The finite-element algorithm statement for (3.108)-(3.110) is identically (3.110), with the addition of the nonhomogeneity, i.e.,

$$S_e \frac{\partial I^h}{\partial\{Q\}} = S_e\left[\int_{R_e^n} \frac{1}{\beta_\alpha^2}\nabla\{N_k\}\cdot\nabla\{N_k\}^T\{PHI\}_e\,d\tau - \int_{R_e^n}\{N_k\}\,\nabla\{N_k\}^T\cdot\{UIO\}\,\hat{\mathbf{e}}\,d\tau\right] = \{0\} \tag{3.111}$$

Here, subscript α is associated with the scalar component of ∇, and the initial estimated velocity field $\mathbf{u}_0$ is interpolated on R_e^n as

$$\mathbf{u}_0(x_i) = \{N_k\}^T(\{UO\}\hat{\mathbf{i}} + \{VO\}\hat{\mathbf{j}} + \{WO\}\hat{\mathbf{k}}) \equiv \{N_k\}^T\{UIO\}\hat{\mathbf{e}} \tag{3.112}$$

where $\hat{\mathbf{e}}$ is the unit vector triad for scalar components $\{UIO\}$. Note that the coefficients (a, b) in (3.110) do not appear in (3.111) since the sole Neumann constraint is homogeneous.

B. COMPRESSIBLE FLOW

3.9 POTENTIAL FLOW OF A COMPRESSIBLE FLUID

Up to this point we have considered the potential flow of an incompressible fluid in terms of the scalar and vector potential functions Φ and ψ. An alternative description is employed for the general aerodynamics problem class including flows over airfoils, turbine cascades and the like, and including the extension to variable density and nonzero Mach number. The geometry of these aerodynamic configurations is such that the local flow field is assumed to be a variation about the freestream flow. This prompts definition of a perturbation potential function ϕ, the gradient of which yields the components of the perturbed velocity field.

This section develops the appropriate differential equation systems. Since these equations display tensor character, it is necessary to expand the flexibility of the vector and differential notation somewhat. In particular, the velocity vector $\mathbf{u}$ is expressed in terms of scalar components parallel to a coordinate system as, for example

$$\mathbf{u} = u\hat{\mathbf{i}} + v\hat{\mathbf{j}} + w\hat{\mathbf{k}} \tag{3.113}$$

In (3.113), u, v, and w could as well be replaced by a subscript notation u_i denoting these scalar components, i.e.,

$$\mathbf{u} = u_1\hat{\mathbf{i}} + u_2\hat{\mathbf{j}} + u_3\hat{\mathbf{k}} \tag{3.114}$$

Of course, the u_i could represent the components of $\mathbf{u}$ in any other coordinate system. Therefore, making the correlation

$$\mathbf{u} \Leftrightarrow u_i \tag{3.115}$$

then $\mathbf{u}$ and u_i both define a vector that can be resolved into scalar components parallel to any convenient coordinate system.

The gradient differential operator, in similar fashion, is usually considered in terms of its scalar components, for example

$$\nabla \equiv \hat{\mathbf{i}}\frac{\partial}{\partial x} + \hat{\mathbf{j}}\frac{\partial}{\partial y} + \hat{\mathbf{k}}\frac{\partial}{\partial z} \tag{3.116}$$

In (3.116), if x, y, and z were replaced by a subscript notation x_i, then ∇ becomes

$$\nabla \equiv \hat{\mathbf{i}}\frac{\partial}{\partial x_1} + \hat{\mathbf{j}}\frac{\partial}{\partial x_2} + \hat{\mathbf{k}}\frac{\partial}{\partial x_3} \tag{3.117}$$

Here again, $\partial/\partial x_i$ represents the scalar components of ∇ in any coordinate system to make the correlation

$$\nabla \Leftrightarrow \frac{\partial}{\partial x_i} \tag{3.118}$$

with the understanding that each form is readily resolved into scalar components in any coordinate system.

The unknowns in potential flow remain the velocity vector $u_i(\mathbf{u})$ and pressure p. The eulerian equations describing conservation of mass and momentum, as simplified for steady, compressible, inviscid flows are, respectively,

$$L(\rho) = \frac{\partial}{\partial x_j}(\rho u_j) = 0 \tag{3.119}$$

$$L(\rho u_j) = \frac{\partial}{\partial x_j}(\rho u_i u_j + p\delta_{ij}) = 0 \tag{3.120}$$

These four equations can be combined into a single equation using the definition of isentropic sound speed (Shames, 1982).

$$c^2 \equiv \left(\frac{\partial p}{\partial \rho}\right)_s \tag{3.121}$$

Expanding (3.119) and replacing the resultant density derivative with (3.121) yields

$$L(u_j) = (\delta_{ij} - c^{-2}u_i u_j)\frac{\partial u_j}{\partial x_i} = 0 \tag{3.122}$$

The local sound speed is referenced to the stagnation state using the energy equation

$$c^2 = c_0^2 - \frac{\gamma - 1}{2} u_j u_j \tag{3.123}$$

where γ is the ratio of specific heats, and δ_{ij} is the Kronecker delta.

Equation (3.122) is a highly nonlinear, first-order partial differential equation valid for all Mach numbers. As a function of M, it can display elliptic, parabolic, and/or hyperbolic differential character. The class of interest corresponds to an irrotational (or rotation preserving) velocity field. Since the curl thus vanishes to within an arbitrary constant, in the current notation

$$u_j \equiv -\frac{\partial \Phi}{\partial x_j} \tag{3.124}$$

where Φ is the familiar velocity (total) potential function. By direct substitution, (3.122) becomes

$$L(\Phi) = \left(\delta_{ij} - c^{-2}\frac{\partial \Phi}{\partial x_i}\frac{\partial \Phi}{\partial x_j}\right)\frac{\partial^2 \Phi}{\partial x_i\,\partial x_j} = 0 \tag{3.125}$$

Equation (3.125), a second-order partial differential equation, preserves the mixed differential character cited. For subsonic flow at zero Mach number, (3.125) simplifies to the linear laplacian

$$L(\Phi) \approx \frac{\partial^2 \Phi}{\partial x_i\,\partial x_i} = 0 \tag{3.126}$$

which is formally identical to (3.4). Boundary condition specification remains enforcement of flow tangency to given surfaces. Assuming $\hat{\mathbf{n}}_j$ the unit outward pointing surface normal vector, the boundary constraint is

$$u_j \hat{\mathbf{n}}_j \equiv u_n = \frac{\partial \Phi}{\partial x_j} \hat{\mathbf{n}}_j \tag{3.127}$$

which is identical to (3.5).

Total potential has been evaluated; the alternative perturbation function definition ϕ is common to aerodynamics. Herein, the local velocity field u_j is referenced to the freestream and the perturbation as

$$u_j \equiv U_\infty\left(\hat{\epsilon}_j - \frac{\partial \Phi}{\partial x_j}\right) \tag{3.128}$$

where $\hat{\epsilon}_j$ is the freestream flow unit vector. Substituting (3.128) into (3.122) and dividing by the freestream sound speed yields

$$L(\phi) \equiv \left[\delta_{ij} - M_\infty^2 \hat{\epsilon}_i \hat{\epsilon}_j + (\gamma - 1)M_\infty^2 \delta_{ij}\left(\hat{\epsilon}_k \frac{\partial \phi}{\partial x_k} - \frac{1}{2}\frac{\partial \phi}{\partial x_k}\frac{\partial \phi}{\partial x_k}\right)\right.$$

$$\left. + M_\infty^2\left(\hat{\epsilon}_i \frac{\partial \phi}{\partial x_j} + \hat{\epsilon}_j \frac{\partial \phi}{\partial x_i} - \frac{\partial \phi}{\partial x_i}\frac{\partial \phi}{\partial x_j}\right)\right] \frac{\partial^2 \phi}{\partial x_i \, \partial x_j} = 0 \tag{3.129}$$

Equation (3.123) is now conveniently referenced to freestream conditions as

$$c^2 = c_\infty^2 + \frac{(\gamma - 1)}{2} U_\infty^2 \left(2\hat{\epsilon}_j \frac{\partial \phi}{\partial x_j} - \frac{\partial \phi}{\partial x_j}\frac{\partial \phi}{\partial x_j}\right) \tag{3.123a}$$

Sufficiently remote from the airfoil $u_j = U_\infty \hat{\epsilon}_j$; therefore, an appropriate freestream boundary condition is ϕ any constant. However, the Kutta condition for angle of attack modifies the interpretation to allow a jump in ϕ across the wake trajectory. Hence, a farfield constraint valid for all cases is vanishing of the efflux perturbation velocity component as

$$\frac{\partial \phi}{\partial x_i} \hat{\mathbf{n}}_i = 0 \tag{3.130}$$

where $\hat{\mathbf{n}}_j$ is the outward-pointing unit normal vector. At any streamline surface, since $u_j \hat{\mathbf{n}}_j$ vanishes identically, the boundary condition on ϕ from (3.128) is

$$\frac{\partial \phi}{\partial x_j} \hat{\mathbf{n}}_j = \hat{\epsilon}_j \hat{\mathbf{n}}_j \tag{3.131}$$

Hence, angle of attack and local surface contour (unit normal) are applied directly as a boundary condition.

Equations (3.128)–(3.131) are also valid for all Mach numbers and display the mixed differential behavior. The small disturbance approximation can significantly simplify (3.129) by the neglect of all products in perturbation velocity and the assumption that $\hat{\epsilon}_j$ is aligned with a principal coordinate direction say x_1, that is,

$$\hat{\epsilon}_j = \delta_{j1} \tag{3.132}$$

Equation (3.129) then takes the form

$$L(\phi) \approx \left[\delta_{ij} - M_\infty^2 \delta_{i1}\delta_{j1} + (\gamma - 1)M_\infty^2 \frac{\partial \phi}{\partial x_1} \delta_{ij} \right.$$

$$\left. + M_\infty^2 \left(\delta_{i1} \frac{\partial \phi}{\partial x_j} + \delta_{j1} \frac{\partial \phi}{\partial x_i} \right) \right] \frac{\partial^2 \phi}{\partial x_i \, \partial x_j} = 0 \tag{3.133}$$

In expanded form for two-dimensional flow, (3.133) becomes

$$L(\phi) \approx \left[1 - M_\infty^2 + (\gamma + 1)M_\infty^2 \frac{\partial \phi}{\partial x_1} \right] \frac{\partial^2 \phi}{\partial x_1^2}$$

$$+ 2M_\infty^2 \frac{\partial \phi}{\partial x_2} \frac{\partial^2 \phi}{\partial x_1 \, \partial x_2} + \left[1 + (\gamma - 1)M_\infty^2 \frac{\partial^2 \phi}{\partial x_1} \right] \frac{\partial^2 \phi}{\partial x_2^2} = 0 \tag{3.134}$$

For flow velocities uniformly below transonic, (3.133) or (3.134) can be linearized by retention of only $(1 - M_\infty^2)$ on the lead term. The Goethert transformation $\bar{x}_1 = x_1/\sqrt{1 - M_\infty^2}$ then eliminates explicit appearance of M_∞. Hence, for all subsonic flows about slender bodies, (3.133) becomes the laplacian.

$$L(\phi) \approx \frac{\partial^2 \phi}{\partial \bar{x}_i \, \partial \bar{x}_i} = 0 \tag{3.135}$$

Therefore, (3.135) and (3.131) define the subsonic potential flow problem in terms of perturbation potential function.

The desired output from the potential flow solution is the pressure distribution on any surface, defined as

$$C_p \equiv 1 - \frac{\rho u_i u_i}{\rho_\infty U_\infty^2} \tag{3.136}$$

Substituting (3.128) yields

$$C_p = 2 \frac{\partial \phi}{\partial x_j} \hat{\epsilon}_j - \frac{\partial \phi}{\partial x_j} \frac{\partial \phi}{\partial x_j} \tag{3.137}$$

Evaluation of (3.137) is accomplished by resolution of the velocity vector into scalar components locally parallel and perpendicular to the surface. Letting $\hat{\mathbf{t}}_j$ denote the unit tangent vector, and (n, s) the corresponding surface-oriented coordinate system,

$$\frac{\partial \phi}{\partial x_j} = \frac{\partial \phi}{\partial n} \hat{\mathbf{n}}_j + \frac{\partial \phi}{\partial s} \hat{\mathbf{t}}_j = (\hat{\epsilon}_k \hat{\mathbf{n}}_k)\hat{\mathbf{n}}_j + \frac{\partial \phi}{\partial s} \hat{\mathbf{t}}_j \tag{3.138}$$

The last form was obtained using (3.131). Substituting (3.138) into (3.137) yields

$$C_p = (\hat{\epsilon}_j \hat{\mathbf{n}}_j)^2 + 2 \frac{\partial \phi}{\partial s} \hat{\epsilon}_j \hat{\mathbf{t}}_j - \frac{\partial \phi}{\partial s} \frac{\partial \phi}{\partial s} \tag{3.139}$$

Recall that $\hat{\epsilon}_j$ is the (constant) unit vector for u_∞; the remaining terms in (3.139) are all a function of the surface coordinate s. The decomposition in (3.138) has yielded C_p in a form directly dependent upon surface geometry. Hence, $\hat{\mathbf{n}}_j$ and $\hat{\mathbf{t}}_j$ are available to any required degree of accuracy.

An extremely important aerodynamics problem class, amenable to quantization in terms of perturbation potential, is transonic flow. This occurs when a subsonic freestream flow is accelerated to locally supersonic speeds by an aerodynamic surface (airfoil). The zone of supersonic flow is usually terminated by a shock to subsonic flow, unless the airfoil is specifically designed to be shock-free. Equations (3.133) and (3.131) govern the most general case, and (3.133) is extremely nonlinear. An important simplification accrues to the slender-body assumption, whereupon most of the nonlinear terms are negligibly small. For the two-dimensional transonic slender-body assumption, (3.134) takes the form

$$L(\phi) \approx \left[1 - M_\infty^2 + (\gamma + 1)M_\infty^2 \frac{\partial \phi}{\partial x_1}\right] \frac{\partial^2 \phi}{\partial x_1^2} + \frac{\partial^2 \phi}{\partial x_2^2} = 0 \tag{3.140}$$

Since $M_\infty \approx 1.0$, $1 - M_\infty^2$ can be dominated by the retained term in brackets, introducing the important nonlinearity. Equation (3.131) remains the boundary-condition specification, and (3.139) yields the pressure coefficient distribution.

Problems

1 Derive (3.122) from (3.119)–(3.121).
2 Derive (3.129) from (3.125) using (3.128) and (3.123*a*).
3 Derive (3.133) from (3.129).
4 Simplify (3.133) to yield (3.134).

3.10 ACCURACY AND CONVERGENCE, SUBSONIC FLOW

For all subsonic compressible flows, the Goethert transformation yields (3.135) and (3.131) as the perturbation potential flow differential equation system. Equation (3.33) remains the statement of convergence and accuracy, and the dominant utility of the solution is determination of surface pressure distribution C_p, see (3.137). An informative geometry for solution comparison is two-dimensional flow about a circular cylinder. The analytical solution for perturbation potential $\phi(x_i)$, for a cylinder of radius $r = a$ (Kuethe and Chow, 1976, Chap. 4.6), is

$$\phi(x_i) = -\frac{a^2}{r} \cos \theta \tag{3.141}$$

The finite-element algorithm statement for (3.135) and (3.131) is

$$S_e[A_e[B211]\{PHI\}_e - L_e[A200]\{EDOTN\}_e] \equiv \{0\} \tag{3.142}$$

The elements of $\{EDOTN\}_e$ are nodal evaluations of $\hat{\mathbf{e}}_j \cdot \hat{\mathbf{n}}_j$; hence, (3.131) is interpolated over ∂R_e.

The numerical solution is generated using the bilinear tensor product basis $\{N_1^+(\eta_i)\}$ and the finite-element solution algorithm (3.44), yielding (3.92). The selected upper-half solution domain is illustrated in Fig. 3.22*a*, for the $M = 4 \times 4 = 16$ element uniform discretization, and Fig. 3.22*b* for the $M = 32 \times 32$ nonuniform discretization, with grid clustering in the radial direction near the cylinder surface. The Neumann boundary condition (3.131) was specified everywhere on the domain boundary, except $\phi \equiv 0$ at the extremum node of the ray $\theta = 90°$.

Figure 3.23 is the plot of the computed ϕ solution for the finest grid, $M = 32 \times 32$, which illustrates the importance of the gradient boundary condition constraint on the cylinder. Figure 3.24 is the plot of normalized energy in the error $E(\epsilon^h, \epsilon^h)$ for the range of uniform and nonuniform grids evaluated. The convergence rate is quadratic, for the finer uniform grid solutions, in agreement with the extremum theoretical estimate $\lambda \leqslant 2(k + 1 - m) \Rightarrow 2$, see (3.33). In all cases evaluated (Fig. 3.24), the radially nonuniform grid with clustering near the cylinder produces a smaller energy error than the corresponding uniform grid solution. These data, plotted at abscissas corresponding to $M^{-1/2}$ (uniform grid), indicate the significant accuracy improvement attainable using "finely tuned" grids.

As stated, the principal solution accuracy requirement is prediction of surface pressure C_p. Table 3.6 summarizes the finite-element solution for $\phi^h(r = a, \theta)$, in comparison to the analytical solution (3.141) for $4^2 \leqslant M \leqslant 32^2$ nonuniform grid. The finest grid and exact solutions agree to one in the fourth significant digit, which would produce similar accuracy in the determination of C_p.

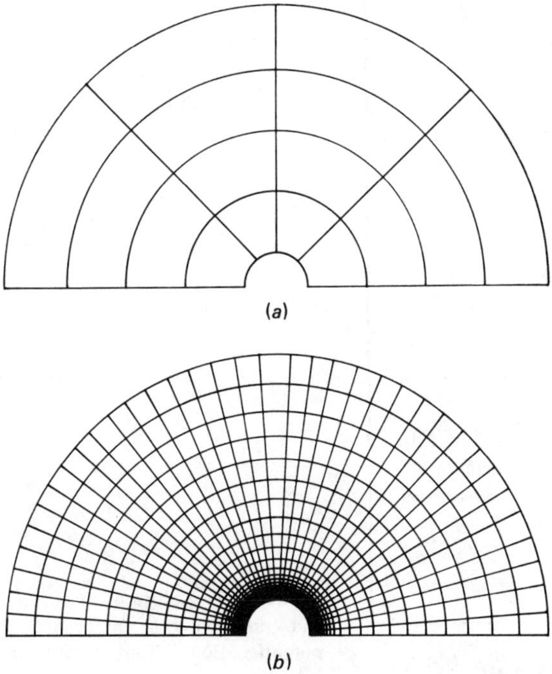

Figure 3.22 Finite-element discretization of solution domain for potential flow about a circular cylinder. (*a*) $\{N_1^+\}$, $M = 4 \times 4$, uniform; (*b*) $\{N_1^+\}$, $M = 32 \times 32$, nonuniform.

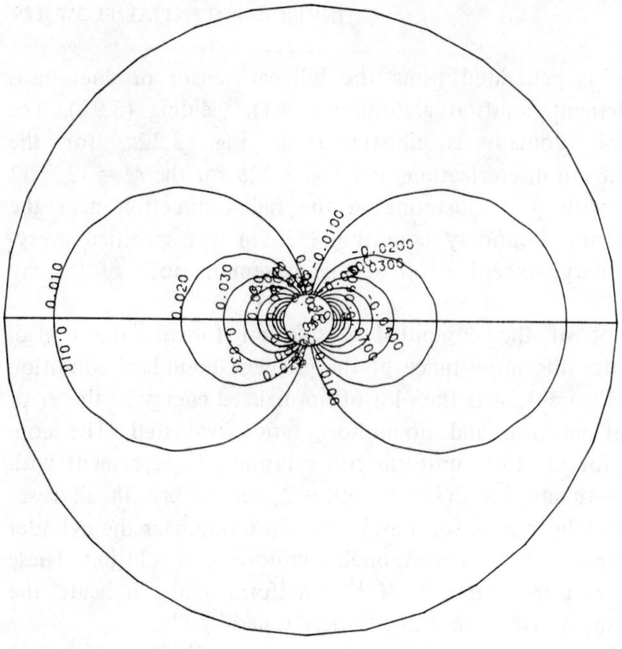

Figure 3.23 Finite-element computed perturbation potential solution, $M = 32 \times 32$, $\{N_1^+\}$.

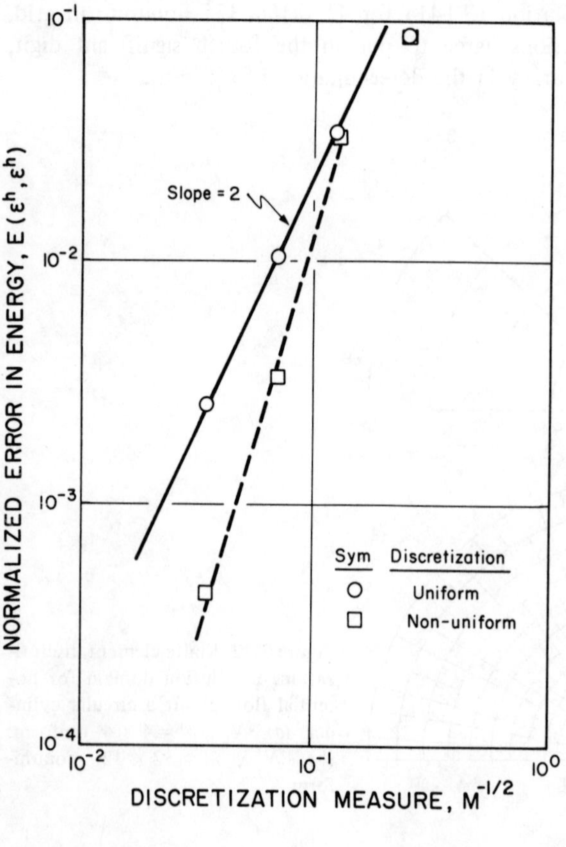

Figure 3.24 Solution accuracy and convergence in energy norm, potential flow about a circular cylinder.

Table 3.6 Perturbation potential distribution on cylinder, finite-element solution $\{N_1^+\}$, nonuniform grid

θ, degrees	Exact	$M = 32^2$	$M = 16^2$	$M = 8^2$	$M = 4^2$
180.0	1.0000	0.9999	0.9893	0.8259	0.5475
174.38	0.9952	0.9951			
168.75	0.9808	0.9807	0.9715		
163.13	0.9569	0.9569			
157.50	0.9239	0.9238	0.9152	0.7826	
151.88	0.8819	0.8818			
146.25	0.8315	0.8314	0.8238		
140.63	0.7730	0.7729			
135.00	0.7071	0.7070	0.7007	0.6051	0.4477
129.38	0.6344	0.6344			
123.75	0.5556	0.5555	0.5505		
118.13	0.4714	0.4714			
112.50	0.3827	0.3826	0.3792	0.3289	
106.88	0.2903	0.2902			
101.25	0.1951	0.1951	0.1933		
98.62	0.0979	0.0980			
90.0	0.0000	0.0000	0.0000	0.0000	0.0001

3.11 TWO-DIMENSIONAL SUBSONIC AIRFOIL ANALYSIS

The key elements of a potential flow finite-element analysis of an isolated two-dimensional airfoil are location of the farfield infinity boundary and application of the Kutta condition at the trailing edge. The results of detailed numerical evaluations (Baker and Manhardt, 1977) indicated the minimum displacement of the infinity boundary to be on the order of one chord length (C), except for upstream, where the minimum acceptable displacement was 1.5 C. A performance study of the finite-element solution algorithm, as embodied using $\{N_1\}$ natural coordinate triangular domains, was completed on a solution domain with farfield boundary lying 1.5-2.0 C distant from the airfoil. A symmetric Joukowski profile was used, with thickness ratio $t/C = 0.12$ and $M_\infty = 0$.

As concluded in the previous section, a smoothly varying nonuniform discretization can notably enhance solution accuracy in comparison to a uniform grid containing the same number of elements. In the cited reference, the authors (Baker and Manhardt, 1977) employed the isoparametric coordinate transformation $\{N_2^+\}$ on a macroelement discretization of the solution domain to generate the nodal coordinate distribution of a suitable discretization. Figure 3.25a illustrates this macroelement discretization and the locations of the vertex and nonvertex nodes for $\{N_2^+\}$ for each domain. By interrogating the resultant coordinate transformation (3.96) at select (uniform) coordinates η_i, the global nodal coordinates of the refined

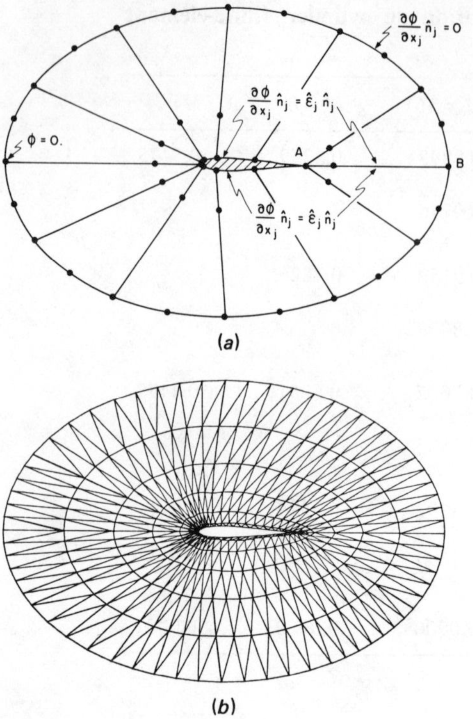

Figure 3.25 Discretizations for subsonic flow about an isolated airfoil. (*a*) Macroelement discretization, $\{N_2^+\}$; (*b*) finite-element discretization, $\{N_1\}$.

finite-element grid shown in Fig. 3.25*b* were computed and connected to form $\cup R_e^2$, suitable for use with $\{N_1\}$ spanning triangles. The $M = 12$ macroelement discretization thereby generated automatically the smoothly varying $M = 648$ nonuniform finite element discretization shown.

The boundary condition specification for an isolated airfoil analysis is also illustrated in Fig. 3.25*a*. The single (required) Dirichlet constraint is located on the farfield upstream boundary. Everywhere else, the nonhomogeneous Neumann constraint (3.131) enforces flow tangency in terms of the unit outward pointing normal $\hat{\eta}_j$ and the angle of attack $\hat{\epsilon}_j$. The illustrated multiply connected domain was rendered simply connected by enforcing the Kutta condition at the trailing edge, i.e., each of the to-be-computed upper and lower surface velocities at the trailing edge must be parallel to the bisector of the airfoil trailing edge. This is directly enforced by identifying unique numbers to nodes lying on the segment *A–B* (Fig. 3.25*a*), for element connections above and below this line segment, and enforcing the flow tangency Neumann boundary condition thereon. As a consequence, the circulation (hence, lift) of the analysis is a computed output, and comparable to the theoretical determination as a measure of accuracy.

Perturbation potential function distributions were computed for the symmetric 12-percent thick Joukowski airfoil at five angles of attack, $0° \leqslant \alpha \leqslant 8°$, specified through rotation of the freestream in the gradient boundary condition statement (3.131). The associated isopleth distributions for the finite-element solutions are shown in Fig. 3.26. Note the near exact solution symmetry for zero angle of attack, even though the discretization is not symmetric. The solution extremum for ϕ is located at the stagnation point for $\alpha = 0°$ and $2°$. As angle of attack is increased, the extremum moves into the lower half plane and becomes distributed along the trailing edge branch cut. The discontinuity in ϕ across the wake trajectory is also graphically evident for $\alpha \neq 0°$. For all cases, the fidelity with which the finite-

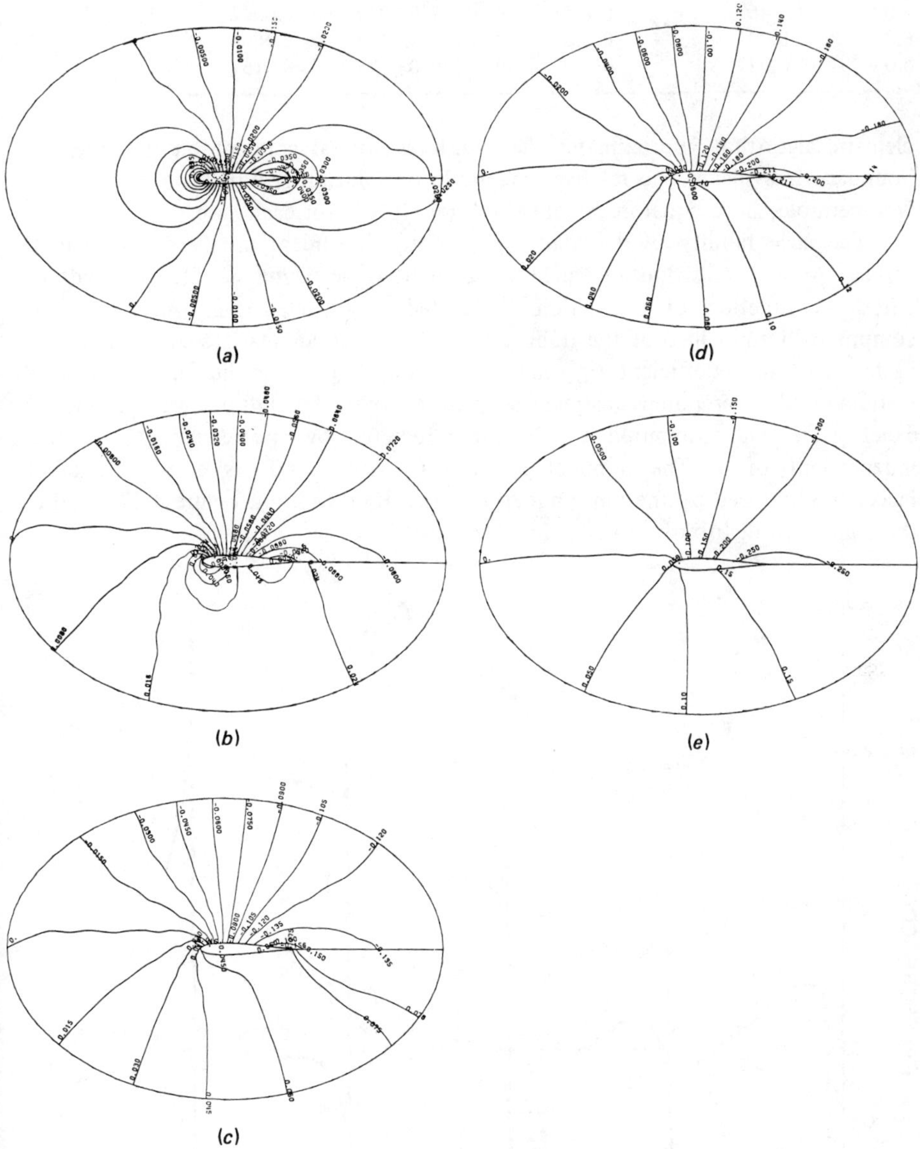

Figure 3.26 Computed potential distributions for Joukowski airfoil, $t/C = 0.12$, $M_\infty = 0$. Angle of attack, $\alpha =$ (*a*) 0°; (*b*) 2°; (*c*) 4°; (*d*) 6°; (*e*) 8°.

Table 3.7 Aerodynamic parameters for Joukowski airfoil

Angle of attack, α	Lift coefficient C_L		Stagnation point, x_S/C	
	Finite element	Exact	Finite element	Exact
0.0	0.001	0.0	0.000	0.0
2.0	0.232	0.237	0.00000–0.00117	0.0011
4.0	0.462	0.478	0.00117–0.00779	0.0042
6.0	0.694	0.716	0.00779–0.01987	0.0094
8.0	0.924	0.954	0.00779–0.01987	0.0167

element algorithm approximates the vanishing normal gradient on the freestream boundary is evident. The relative magnitude of solution perturbation velocity levels is discernible, since equal increments in ϕ are plotted for each case.

The acceptability of the solution is strictly dependent on the accuracy of the surface pressure distribution and the computed aerodynamic lift. The latter is strictly a function of circulation Γ, related in an elementary manner to the computed "jump" in ϕ at the trailing edge. Table 3.7 summarizes solution accuracy in terms of lift coefficient C_L, and the coordinate pair for the finite element R_e^2 containing the computed upstream stagnation point. The latter always bounds the exact value; the computed C_L is underpredicted by approximately 3 percent, independent of α. The nominal nonzero C_L for $\alpha = 0°$ is a measure of the inaccuracy induced by the nonsymmetry of the discretization. Figure 3.27 illustrates the computed distributions of C_p for $0° \leqslant \alpha \leqslant 8°$.

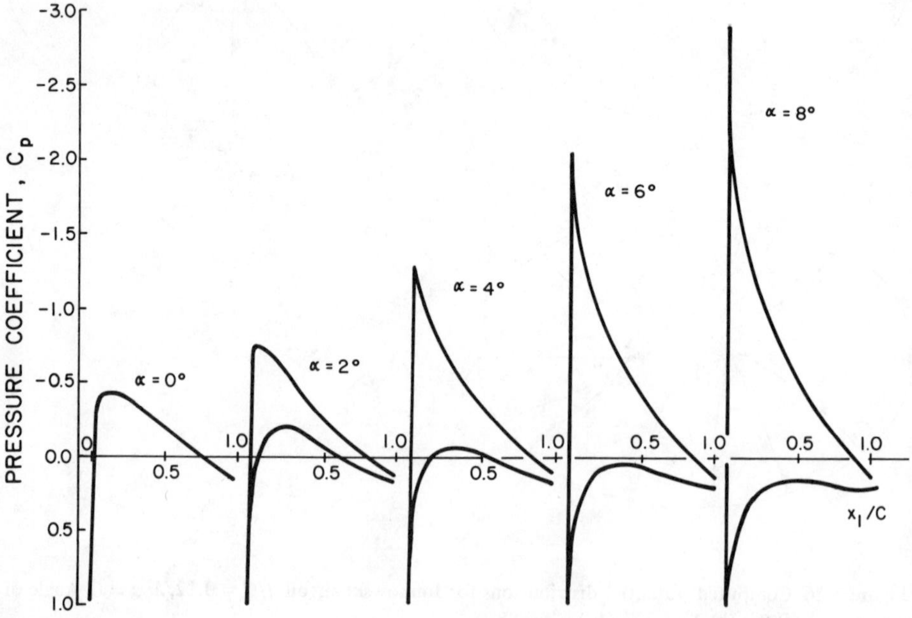

Figure 3.27 Computed pressure coefficient distributions on Joukowski airfoil, $t/C = 0.12$, $0° \leqslant \alpha \leqslant 8°$.

3.12 CIRCULATION CONSTRAINED SUBSONIC CASCADE ANALYSIS

Baskharone and Hamed (1981) evaluate an alternative theoretical formulation for two-dimensional potential flow analysis of airfoils and cascades, which employs a constraint on the equivalent energy functional to enforce the Kutta condition. Figure 3.28*a* shows the basic isolated airfoil solution domain, with branch cut ("splitting boundary") denoted *e–f* and *g–h*. Figures 3.28*b–c* show two solution domains appropriate for analysis of blade-to-blade cascade potential flows: the branch cut sides remain *e–f* and *g–h*, in each instance.

The domain of Fig. 3.28*c* was selected with application of periodic boundary conditions on boundary segments *a–b* and *c–d*. On the branch cut *e–f* and *g–h*, the nodal values of the expansion coefficients $\{PHI\}_e$, in adjacent elemental domains, R_r^2 and R_s^2 are linearly related through the circulation Γ. Specifically, using the natural coordinate basis $\{N_1\}$, for example,

$$\phi_r(x_i) \equiv \{N_1\}^T \{PHI\}_r \qquad \phi_s(x_i) \equiv \{N_1\}^T \{PHI\}_s \tag{3.143}$$

and

$$\{PHI\}_s = \begin{Bmatrix} PHI(1)_s \\ PHI(2)_s \\ PHI(3)_s \end{Bmatrix} = \begin{Bmatrix} PHI(1)_s \\ PHI(3)_r + \Gamma \\ PHI(2)_r + \Gamma \end{Bmatrix} \tag{3.144}$$

where nodes 2 and 3 are assumed to lie on *e–f* and *g–h*, using the standard

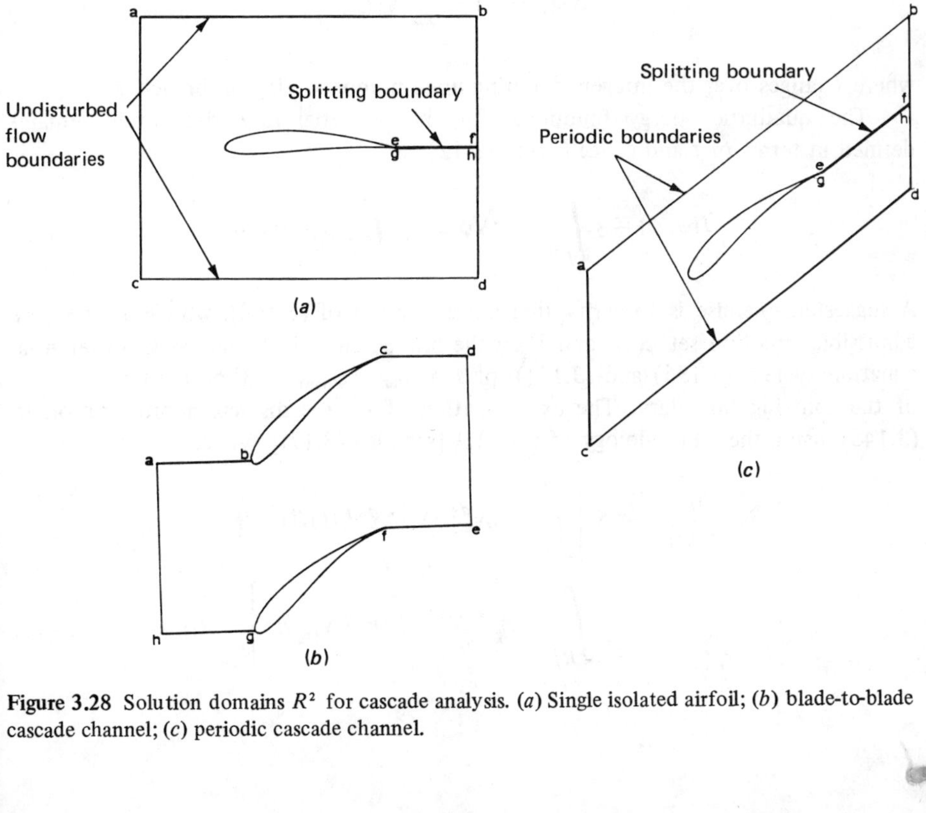

Figure 3.28 Solution domains R^2 for cascade analysis. (*a*) Single isolated airfoil; (*b*) blade-to-blade cascade channel; (*c*) periodic cascade channel.

counterclockwise numbering procedure. [Equations of the form (3.143) and (3.144) could easily be established using any other cardinal basis $\{N_k(\eta_j)\}$, and $\Gamma \equiv$ constant is an explicit assumption.] Therefore, for all finite-element domains R_e^2 possessing nodal coordinates on the branch *g–h*, define the augmented cardinal basis

$$\{N_\Gamma^a\} \equiv \begin{Bmatrix} N_1(1) \\ N_1(2) \\ N_1(3) \\ N_1(4) \end{Bmatrix} \tag{3.145}$$

where, for example, $N_1^a(4) \equiv N_1(2) + N_1(3)$ for element R_s^2 (Fig. 3.28*c*). Hence, for all finite elements R_s^2

$$\phi_s \equiv \{N_1^a\}^T \{PHI\}_s = \{N_1^a\}^T \begin{Bmatrix} PHI(1)_s \\ PHI(3)_r \\ PHI(2)_r \\ \Gamma \end{Bmatrix} \tag{3.146}$$

For the general case, for R_s^n possessing p nodes, the cardinal base associated with Γ, denoted $N_k^a(p+1)$ is

$$N_k^a(p+1) \equiv \sum_J N_k(J) \tag{3.147}$$

where J ranges over the integers denoting node numbers lying on branch *g–h*.

The quadratic energy functional for the potential flow description remains defined in terms of f and g, see (3.11)-(3.12), as

$$I(\phi, \phi) \equiv \tfrac{1}{2} \int_{R^n} \nabla\phi \cdot \nabla\phi \, d\tau - \int_{\partial R} \phi \, \nabla\phi \cdot n \, d\sigma \tag{3.148}$$

A suggested exercise is to verify that extremization of (3.148), with respect to the admissible function set $\phi(x_i)$ and Γ on the branch cut, yields the partial differential equation system (3.135) and (3.131), plus $\phi_{\text{lower}} = \phi_{\text{upper}} + \Gamma$ on the lower branch of the splitting boundary. The extremization of I^h, the discrete approximation to (3.148), using the methodology of Sec. 2.9 [see also (3.17)], yields

$$S_e \frac{\partial I^h}{\partial \{Q\}_e} = S_e \left[\int_{R_e^2} \nabla \{N_k^a\} \cdot \nabla \{N_k^a\}^T \{PHI\}_e \, d\tau + \int_{R_e^2} \{N_k^a\} \{N\}^T \{EDOTN\}_e \, d\tau \right] \equiv \{0\} \tag{3.149}$$

For all elements not containing nodal coordinates lying on the lower branch g-h of the splitting boundary, $\{N_k^a\}$ is coincident with $\{N_k\}$. For domain R_s^2 with nodes on boundary g-h, the element dependent variable is given by the form (3.146), and $\{N_k^a\}$ by the generalization of (3.145)-(3.146) using (3.147).

The matrix statement of the finite-element algorithm (3.149) remains of the form (3.142), i.e.,

$$S_e[A_e[B211A]_e\{PHI\}_e - L_e[A200A]\{EDOTN\}_e] \equiv \{0\} \qquad (3.150)$$

Now, the postscript A in the matrix name indicates the augmented matrix, in agreement with the definition of the cardinal basis (3.145). For example, assume $k \equiv 1$ in (3.149) and that $\{N_1^a\}$ spans a triangular element domain R_e^2. For all elements of the discretization not possessing one (or two) nodes on branch g-h, $[B211A]_e \Rightarrow [B211L]_e$, as given in (3.61), a square matrix of order three. For the element R_s^2 having nodes 2 and 3 on the branch g-h, $[B211A]$ is a square matrix of order four, and $[B211L]$ constitutes the upper left 3 X 3 partition, i.e.,

$$[B211A] = \left[\begin{array}{c|c} & b_{14} \\ [B211L] & b_{24} \\ & b_{34} \\ \hline (\text{sym}) & b_{44} \end{array}\right] \qquad (3.151)$$

The matrix elements b_{j4} in (3.151) are the sums of the various elements of $[B211L]$, as formed by the integral of the definition $N_1(4) \equiv N_1(2) + N_1(3)$ (see Table 3.2). The corresponding element dependent variable matrix is given in (3.146).

The element matrix $[A200A]$ in (3.150) is square of order two [see (3.51)] for all R_e not possessing a boundary segment on branch g-h. For R_s^2 $[A200A]$ is a 2 X 3 matrix, where $[A200]$ forms the upper partition, i.e.,

$$[A200A] = \left[\begin{array}{cc} \multicolumn{2}{c}{[A200]} \\ \hline a_{31} & a_{32} \end{array}\right] \qquad (3.152)$$

and the elements a_{3j} are evaluated in the standard manner. Finally, note that since $\{PHI\}_s$ contains Γ as a matrix element, the algebraic solution statement (3.150) also contains Γ as a nodeless degree of freedom. It is determined during the matrix solution of (3.150).

Baskharone and Hamed (1981) report results on application of the circulation-constrained finite-element algorithm to the cascade geometry of Gastelow (1965). Figure 3.29*a* shows the $M = 624$ finite-element discretization for the $\{N_1\}$ basis algorithm form. The agreement between computed and analytical C_p is generally good (Fig. 3.29*b*). The detailed inaccuracy can be correlated with regions of coarse and nonsmooth discretization on the airfoil underside. Figure 3.30 illustrates these comparisons for the algorithm implemented using the $\{N_2^+\}$ isoparametric cardinal basis. The detailed disagreement in C_p has been shifted upstream.

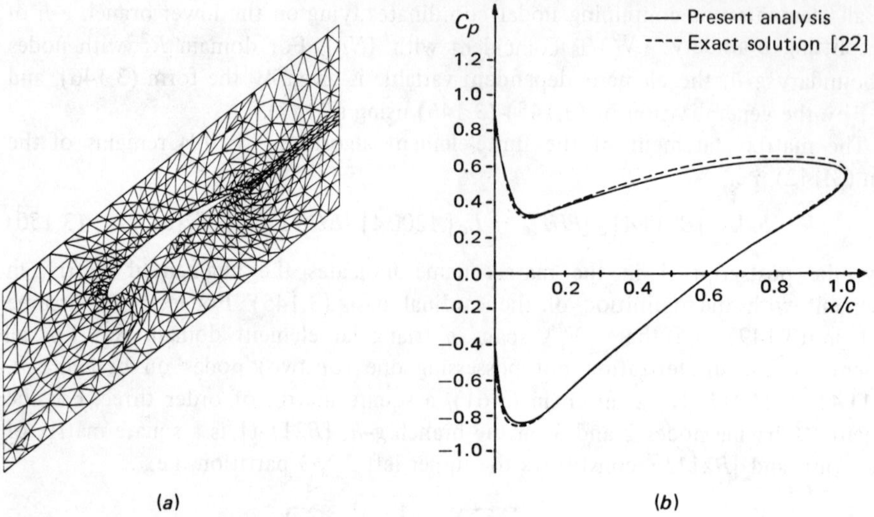

Figure 3.29 Circulation-constrained finite-element solution, $\{N_1\}$. (*a*) Discretization, $M = 624$; (*b*) pressure coefficient. *[From Baskharone and Hamed (1981).]*

Overall, the accuracy is comparable using $\{N_1\}$ and $\{N_2^+\}$. However, both solutions suffer from coarse grid inaccuracy, compounded by use of nonsmooth grid nonuniformity. Nevertheless, these results do confirm the viability of the circulation-constraint algorithm. Table 3.8, summarized from the cited reference, indicates and confirms a serious problem with use of the $\{N_2^+\}$ basis. For the same

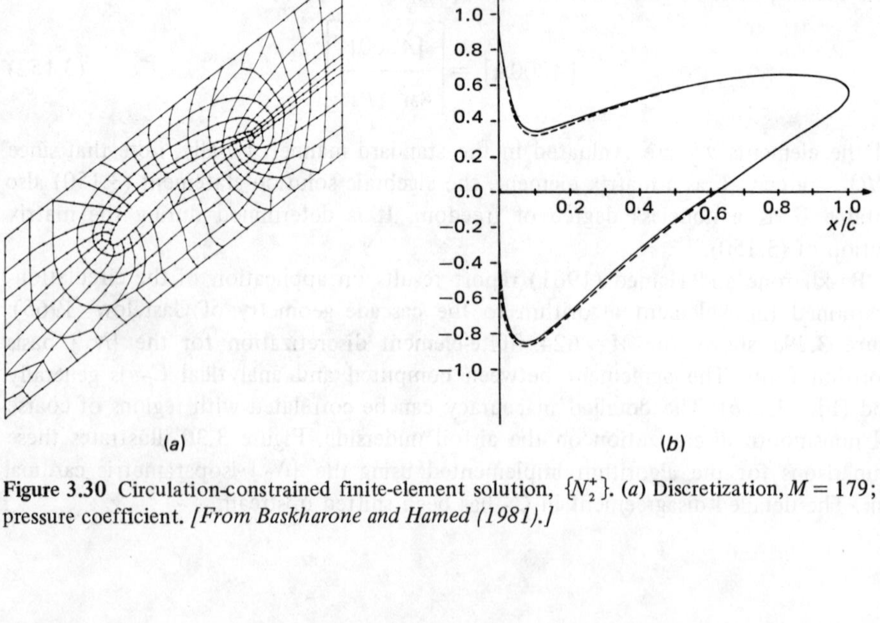

Figure 3.30 Circulation-constrained finite-element solution, $\{N_2^+\}$. (*a*) Discretization, $M = 179$; (*b*) pressure coefficient. *[From Baskharone and Hamed (1981).]*

Table 3.8 Efficiency comparison of potential solutions[a]

Finite element basis	Number of nodes	Number of elements	Computer core (Kbyte)	Computer *CPU* (sec)
$\{N_1\}$	624	1074	457[b]	16
$\{N_2^+\}$	624	179	779	628

[a]From Baskharone and Hamed (1981).
[b]Using double precision arithmetic.

number of nodes (hence, rank of the matrix solution statement), the $\{N_2^+\}$ solution required approximately twice the computer core and 40 times the computer *CPU* to generate a solution of negligibly superior accuracy. This foretells a near fatal criticism of use of direct matrix solution procedures with higher degree interpolation in aerodynamics. The alternative is addressed in the remaining sections of this chapter.

Problems

1 Extremize the energy functional $I(\phi, \phi)$ in (3.148), with respect to the set of admissible functions, ϕ and Γ, to produce the equivalent differential equation and wake jump conditions.

2 Using $\{N_1\}$ on a triangle, compute the matrix elements b_{j_4} of the augmented diffusion matrix $[B211A]$.

3 Repeat the evaluation in (3.144) for the elements a_{3j} of $[A200A]$.

3.13 THE MULTIGRID ALGORITHM

Table 3.8 highlights a significant practical problem associated with direct use of more complete finite-element basis $\{N_k\}$, $k > 1$, for potential flow simulations. The finite-element algorithm statement (3.149) produces the elementary linear algebra requirement: solve $Ax = b$ (recall the discussion in Sec. 1.6). Since A is independent of x, any direct solution procedure is usable. For the cascade problem (Table 3.8) the rank of A for both the $\{N_1\}$ and $\{N_2^+\}$ formulations is of the order 600, the number of nodes. The reduced number of R_e^2 for $\{N_2^+\}$ does not affect the rank. Assuming an efficient node numbering scheme was used, A is a sparse matrix with many null elements for which direct solvers have been designed, e.g., Cholesky factorization. However, the A formed using $\{N_2^+\}$ is considerably less sparse than A from $\{N_1\}$, since the quadratic elements connect nodes over a larger stencil of $\cup R_e^2$, that is, the bandwidth is significantly larger. While some of the disparity in computer *CPU* can be traced to numerical quadrature operations for A from $\{N_2^+\}$, the large portion of the factor of 40 increase, and the 50 percent increase in computer core, is attributable to the significantly increased "size" of A. Furthermore, due in part to the mesh measure of the $\{N_2^+\}$ discretization being twice that of the $\{N_1\}$ grid, no improvement in accuracy was achieved.

This computer efficiency comparison becomes outrageous for a three-dimensional solution, as required for a truly practical analysis. Is the potential for enhanced accuracy embedded within $\{N_k\}$, $k > 1$, [see (3.33)] thus strictly limited, of academic value only? The answer is no; these data simply confirm that additional thought need be given to matrix solution techniques utilized. Replacing direct solution procedures with matrix iterative methods is well established, e.g., Picard, Gauss-Seidel, successive over-relaxation (Varga, 1962). In certain instances, the direct fast Fourier transform (FFT) solution could also be utilized (Ames, 1977).

The primary detraction of any matrix iterative solution for $Ax = b$ is the slow rate of convergence of the sequence of iterates $\{\delta Q\}$ to the solution. The heart of the multigrid concept (Brandt, 1977, 1979; Nicolaides, 1978) is the recognition that the high frequency (short wavelength) components of error resolved on the fine mesh cause the slow convergence. The basic idea is to employ a sequence of coarser grids to smooth these error components, hence remarkably improve the convergence rate of the matrix iterative solution algorithm in use. Thus, discretization refinement becomes embedded within the matrix solution process, yielding a highly efficient procedure for producing the sequence of solutions ϕ^h on progressively refined grids.

The finite-element algorithm (3.17) yields the matrix statement

$$S_e \frac{\partial I^h}{\partial \{Q\}_e} \equiv \{F^h\} \equiv \{0\} \tag{3.153}$$

With the bracket notation deleted for convenience, F^h is the homogeneous form of the matrix statement $Ax = b$;

$$F^h = A^h \phi^h - b^h = 0 \tag{3.154}$$

Comparing (3.154) and (3.149) for example,

$$A^h \equiv S_e[A_e[B211A]_e] \tag{3.155}$$

$$b^h \equiv S_e[L_e[A200A]\,\{EDOTN\}_e] \tag{3.156}$$

The superscript h in (3.154)-(3.156) emphasizes that the computational mesh of measure h lies on R^n, which in combination with $\{N_k(x_i)\}$ yields the approximation I^h to I.

In accordance with Brandt (1979), let x^h denote the nodes of the (uniform) discretization R^h of R^n. Noting that ϕ^h is the exact solution to (3.154), let Q^h denote the approximation to ϕ^h on R^h as produced by any nondirect solution of (3.154). Let x^H denote nodes of a coarser discretization R^H of R^n, and Q^H the associated approximation to the exact solution ϕ^H on R^H. Hence, the solution ϕ^H of

$$F^H \equiv A^H \phi^H - b^H = 0 \tag{3.157}$$

is approximated by Q^H. Let I_H^h denote a projection operator from R^H to R^h, which could be simple linear interpolation (or use of $\{N_2^+\}$ over the nodal values of a $\{N_1^+\}$ discretization solution). Then, existence of Q^H yields the approximation to Q^h

$$Q^h = I_H^h Q^H \tag{3.158}$$

Finally, denote V^h as the (unknown) error in the approximation Q^h to ϕ^h,

$$\phi^h \equiv Q^h + V^h \approx I_H^h Q^H + V^h \tag{3.159}$$

If Q^H is at all a decent approximation to ϕ^h, then V^h must be a highly oscillatory distribution on R^h, hence not visible on R^H. Therefore, the smoothing of V^h must be done on R^h.

An efficient smoothing is produced by using relaxation sweeps on R^h using, for example, the Gauss-Seidel algorithm. Here, the nodes x^h of R^h are scanned in some prescribed order, and each value of Q^h is replaced by a new value, as obtained by the approximate solution of (3.154). Completing one such sweep, Q^h is not yet coincident with ϕ^h since the matrix A^h has been consequentially approximated to produce the localized Gauss-Seidel solution. However, the relaxation sweep is fast, uses little computer core, and is very efficient in smoothing the high-frequency components [those of wavelength $0(h)$] of V^h.

Therefore, the multigrid algorithm solution of (3.154) proceeds as follows. On the finest grid R^h, perform two or three (Gauss-Seidel) relaxation sweeps [approximate solutions to (3.154)] to smooth the finest grid error V^h associated with Q^h. Once smoothed, approximate this error by V^H using a solution on the next coarser grid R^H. The associated matrix statement is constructed from (3.154) by subtracting $A^h\phi^h$ from both sides, yielding

$$A^h(Q^h + V^h) - A^h\phi^h = b^h - A^h\phi^h \equiv r^h \tag{3.160}$$

This defines the residual error r^h, the deviation from $F^h = 0$, the exact solution to (3.154). The fine grid equation (3.160) is approximated on the coarse grid R^H as

$$A^H(I_h^H Q^h + V^H) - A^H(I_h^H Q^h) = \bar{I}_h^H r^h \tag{3.161}$$

defining the interpolation operators I_h^H and $\bar{I}_h^H$ from R^h to R^H. To avoid complicated linearization in (3.161), define the new dependent variable $\bar{Q}^H \equiv I_h^H Q^h + V^H$ to replace V^H on R^H. Then, (3.161) becomes

$$A^H\bar{Q}^H = A^H(I_h^H Q^h) + \bar{I}_h^H r^h \tag{3.162}$$

The right-hand side is known from (3.160), and the form of A^H is identical to A^h, see (3.155). Equation (3.162) is then solved in the identical manner [(3.160)-(3.161)] using a combination of relaxation sweeps and coarse grid corrections on discretizations still coarser than R^H.

Once (3.162) is solved (or approximately solved), $\bar{Q}^H$ is employed to correct the basic approximation Q^h, bearing in mind that

$$V^H \equiv \bar{Q}^H - I_h^H Q^h \tag{3.163}$$

and that V^H, not $\bar{Q}^H$, is the function that approximates V^h on the fine grid R^h, Hence, letting subscript p denote sequence step within the iteration cycle, from (3.159),

$$Q_{p+1}^h = Q_p^h + I_H^h\left[\bar{Q}_{p+1}^H + I_h^H Q_p^h\right] \tag{3.164}$$

defines the corrected approximation of the solution ϕ^h to (3.154).

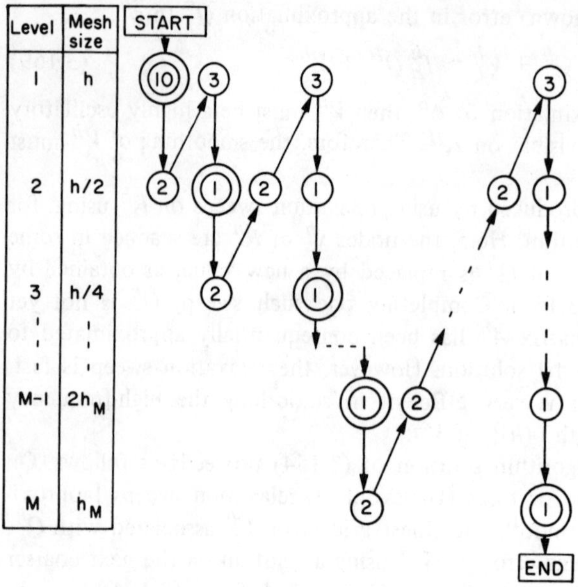

Figure 3.31 Visualization of multigrid algorithm. *[From Brandt (1979).]*

The complete multigrid algorithm for the potential flow description is simply repetitive operations of the solution steps presented in (3.160)-(3.164). Figure 3.31 (Brandt, 1979) is a graphic summary of the complete multigrid solution sequence. Shown in each circle is the number of relaxation sweeps performed on R^h at that stage. A double circle indicates the solution stage for which the error V^h on that level is guaranteed to be less than the truncation error. The first transfer down (↓) is the first approximation interpolation (3.158). The transfer to the right (↗) returns the computation to the next coarser grid and solution of (3.162) for $\bar{Q}^H$. The following transfers down correspond to the correction interpolation (3.164).

The efficiency of the multigrid algorithm can be estimated from Fig. 3.31 for the potential flow problem description. Let the basic unit of work correspond to one relaxation sweep on the finest grid R^h, corresponding to level M in the figure. One sweep over level $k < M$ costs roughly $2^{-n(M-k)}$ units. Hence, the total work of all relaxation steps in Fig. 3.31 is roughly

$$3(1 \cdot 1 + 2 \cdot 2^{-n} + 3 \cdot 2^{-3n} + \cdots) = \frac{3}{(1 - 2^{-n})^2} \tag{3.165}$$

work units. The work unit cost of the interpolations and residual transfers (3.164) is small compared to (3.165). Hence, the overall work should not exceed seven to eight work units for a two-dimensional problem ($n = 2$), and four to five units in three dimensions.

In the multigrid algorithm, it must be emphasized that the role of the relaxation sweeps is not to reduce the error V^h, but to smooth it, i.e., to reduce the magnitude of the high-frequency components [wavelengths of $0(h)$]. Since this smoothing is basically a local process, a Fourier modal analysis can assess the efficiency of the relaxation process. Anticipating the need to analyze high-speed compressible flows, consider (3.140) written in the simplified form

$$L(\phi) = a\frac{\partial^2 \phi}{\partial x^2} + c\frac{\partial^2 \phi}{\partial y^2} = 0 \tag{3.166}$$

For present purposes, $a \leqslant c$ and c may be assumed to be constants. Brandt (1977) documents the local mode analysis for (3.166) approximated by the basic unit square finite-difference stencil (Fig. 3.14*a*). The corresponding finite-difference recursion relation form for (3.154) is

$$F^h \Rightarrow a\frac{\phi^h_{j+1,k} - 2\phi^h_{j,k} + \phi^h_{j-1,k}}{h^2} + c\frac{\phi^h_{j,k+1} - 2\phi^h_{j,k} + \phi^h_{j,k-1}}{h^2} \tag{3.167}$$

where (j, k) are integers denoting x^h of R^h, assumed to be uniformly distributed.

A most elementary relaxation procedure is Gauss-Seidel point relaxation, wherein x^h of R^h are scanned in a prescribed (lexicographic) order, and $\phi^h_{j,k} \Rightarrow Q^h_{j,k}$ are updated to $\bar{Q}^h_{j,k}$ for (j, k) in (say) ascending order, e.g.,

$$\frac{a}{h^2}(Q^h_{j+1,k} - 2\bar{Q}^h_{j,k} + \bar{Q}^h_{j-1,k}) + \frac{c}{h^2}(Q^h_{j,k+1} - 2\bar{Q}^h_{j,k} + \bar{Q}^h_{j,k-1}) = r^h_{j,k} \tag{3.168}$$

Define the error functions $V^h_{j,k}$ and $\bar{V}^h_{j,k}$ in terms of the Fourier normal mode expansions,

$$V^h_{j,k} \equiv A_\theta e^{i(j\theta_1 + k\theta_2)} \qquad \bar{V}^h_{j,k} \equiv \bar{A}_\theta e^{i(j\theta_1 + k\theta_2)} \tag{3.169}$$

where $i \equiv \sqrt{-1}$ and A_θ represents the normal mode magnitude. Subtracting (3.167), written for $Q^h_{j,k}$, from (3.168) and using (3.169), it is left as an exercise to show that

$$A_\theta(ae^{i\theta_1} + ce^{i\theta_2}) + \bar{A}_\theta(ae^{-i\theta_1} + ce^{-i\theta_2} - 2a - 2c) = 0 \tag{3.170}$$

The amplification (convergence) factor $\mu(\theta = \theta_1, \theta_2)$ is

$$\mu(\theta) \equiv \frac{\bar{A}_\theta}{A_\theta} = \frac{ae^{-i\theta_1} + ce^{-i\theta_2} - 2a - 2c}{ae^{i\theta_1} + ce^{i\theta_2}} \tag{3.171}$$

The corresponding smoothing factor $\bar{\mu}$ is defined as

$$\bar{\mu} \equiv \max_{\bar{\rho}\pi \leqslant |\theta| \leqslant \pi} \mu(\theta) \tag{3.172}$$

where $\bar{\rho}$ is the mesh size ratio, and $\bar{\rho}\pi \leqslant |\theta| \leqslant \pi$ is a suitable range of high-frequency components that are not resolved on R^H, since $\bar{\rho}H = h$.

For the laplacian $(a = c)$, assuming $\bar{\rho} = \frac{1}{2}$, the typical value is

$$\bar{\mu} = \mu\left(\frac{\pi}{2}, \cos^{-1}\frac{4}{5}\right) = 0.5 \tag{3.173}$$

Hence, three Gauss-Seidel relaxation sweeps can reduce the high-frequency components of V^h by almost an order of magnitude. Equation (3.173) is representative for general a and c, provided a/c is of moderate size. For $a \ll c$, as would occur in regions of transonic flow, $\bar{\mu}$ approaches unity, e.g.,

$$\mu\left(\frac{\pi}{2}, 0\right) = \left[\frac{a^2 + c^2}{a^2 + (c + 2a)^2}\right]^{1/2} \tag{3.174}$$

The fact that Gauss-Seidel relaxation could become unsuitable is not surprising, bearing in mind its ultimate simplicity, i.e., it utilizes an extremely simplified approximation to A^h, (3.154). An improved approach, called line relaxation, factors A^h into strips parallel to the rows and columns of x^h. For the finite-difference stencil (3.168), this amounts to replacement of $Q^h_{j,k+1}$ by $\bar{Q}^h_{j,k+1}$ (or $Q^h_{j+1,k}$ by $\bar{Q}^h_{j+1,k}$, for the alternate sweep). Completing the associated Fourier modal analysis,

$$\mu(\theta) = \left[\frac{a}{2(a + c - c\cos\theta_2) - ae^{-i\theta_1}}\right] \tag{3.175}$$

The associated smoothing factor is

$$\bar{\mu} = \max\left\{5^{-1/2}, \frac{a}{a + 2c}\right\} \tag{3.176}$$

which is highly satisfactory even for $a \ll c$.

Problems

1 Derive (3.170).

2 Describe the psychology for definition (3.172) and generate (3.173)–(3.174).

3 Derive (3.175) and (3.176).

3.14 FINITE-ELEMENT MULTIGRID SOLUTION ALGORITHM

The multigrid algorithm is directly applicable to a finite-element solution for potential flow, upon definition of a suitable decomposition of the matrix A^h, (3.154), which is termed the jacobian of F^h, that is,

$$[J] \equiv \frac{\partial \{F^h\}}{\partial \{\phi^h\}} = [A^h] \tag{3.177}$$

Implementation of multigrid (or any other iterative solution procedure) simply requires definition of a suitable approximation to $[J]$. Viewing the finite-difference laplacian stencils illustrated in Sec. 3.6 [see (3.78)], a symbol representation of the Gauss-Seidel iteration is [see (3.168)]

$$[J]_{j,k} = \begin{bmatrix} & -1 & \\ -1 & 4 & -1 \\ & -1 & \end{bmatrix} \approx\!> [0 \quad 2 \quad -1], \begin{bmatrix} 0 \\ 2 \\ -1 \end{bmatrix} \tag{3.178}$$

Equation (3.178) symbolizes that $(\cdot)_{j+1}$ is (implicitly) absent for the j-grid sweep $[0 \quad 2 \quad -1]$, and that $(\cdot)_{k+1}$ is implicitly absent during the k sweep, $[0 \quad 2 \quad -1]^T$. Correspondingly, the more robust line relaxation algorithm can be symbolized as

$$[J]_{j,k} = \begin{bmatrix} & -1 & \\ -1 & 4 & -1 \\ & -1 & \end{bmatrix} \approx\!> [-1, \quad 2, \quad -1], \begin{bmatrix} -1 \\ 2 \\ -1 \end{bmatrix} \tag{3.179}$$

that is, $(\cdot)_{j+1}$ and $(\cdot)_{k+1}$ are present (implicitly) in each respective sweep, requiring a tridiagonal matrix inversion (the Thomas algorithm, see Roache, 1972).

The methodology for constructing a suitable approximation to $[J]$, from the elemental diffusion matrix $[M1(k)]_e$, see (3.44), is illustrated by proceeding through (3.75)-(3.78) in reverse order. For $\{N_1^+\}$ on a square domain,

$$[J]_{j,k} = \begin{bmatrix} -2 & -2 & -2 \\ -2 & 16 & -2 \\ -2 & -2 & -2 \end{bmatrix} \approx\!> [-4 \quad 8 \quad -4], \begin{bmatrix} -4 \\ 8 \\ -4 \end{bmatrix} \tag{3.180}$$

for the line-relaxation equivalent expression. Since (3.78) is the assembly of (3.77), which is the sum of terms in (3.76) for a square domain, the entries in the symbol (3.180) can be traced to each elemental domain sharing node (j, k). For the j direction (assumed parallel to the x_1 axis, that is, η_1), the entries in the first term (3.76) that correspond to this direction are $+2$ and -2. Figure 3.32*a* illustrates the entries at location, and the circled number denotes the matrix row from which the numbers were taken. Figure 3.32*b* shows the corresponding formation for the k direction (η_2). The assembly of these directional terms yields the symbol (3.180), to within the scalar multipliers $1/6\, a^2$ and $1/6\, b^2$. Therefore, on a discretization formed as the union of rectangles, the jacobian construction for line-relaxation multigrid is a programming detail, requiring assembly of select elements of $\Delta_e[B211L^+]_e$ into a tridiagonal matrix. Since the directional matrices differ only by the appropriate element measure, the implementation is quite staightforward.

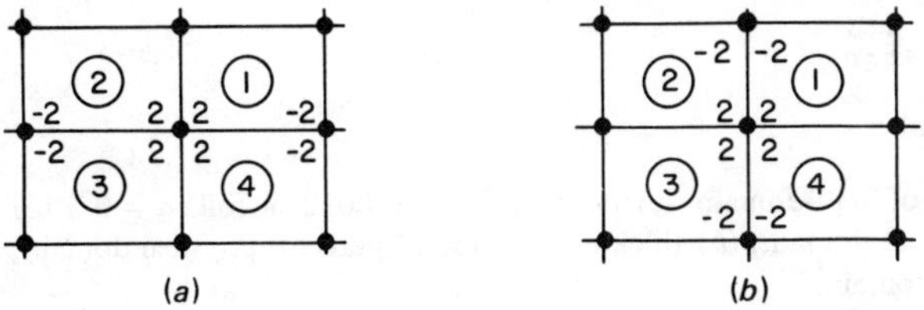

Figure 3.32 Illustration of the jacobian stencil assembly. (*a*) η_1 Direction; (*b*) η_2 direction.

Of course, few practical problems in aerodynamics can be discretized by the union of rectangles. Extending the elementary concept to curvilinear discretizations of domains surrounding aerodynamic shapes (see Fig. 3.33) is straightforward. Using multigrid, the $M = 16^2$ grids shown represent an intermediate refinement, a substantial improvement over those of Figs. 3.29–3.30. The line relaxation jacobian stencil is constructed, in this instance, in the transform space spanned by η_i. Recall in Sec. 3.6, that $\{N_k^+\}$ generates the required transformation, and that η_i is an orthonormal coordinate system. The evaluation of $\Delta_e[B211]$ is accomplished in the transform space; see (3.92) for $\{N_1^+\}$ and (3.98) for $\{N_2^+\}$. In particular, for $\{N_1^+\}$, (3.92) provides the detailed expansion of the terms forming contributions to the 4×4 element matrix. However, it is not easy to reconstruct the components of the vector (gradient) from this scalar expression.

The required construction is direct using the one-dimensional basis $\{N_k(\bar{x})\}$, however. Realizing the two-dimensional element measure (ab) is one-fourth the plane area, the directional jacobian is simply the matrix $l_e[A211]$, where for $\{N_1\}$ for example, is

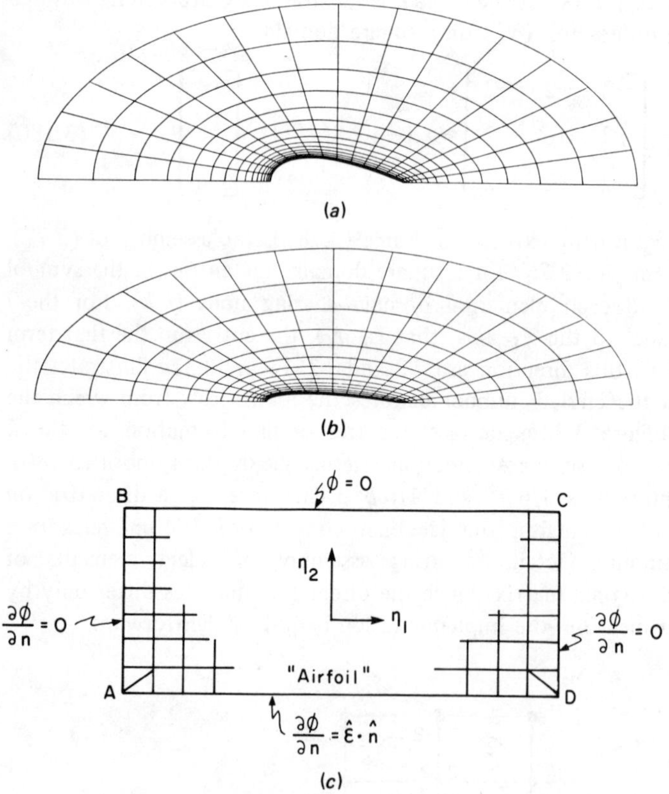

Figure 3.33 $M = 64$ discretization of half-domain surrounding NACA 0012 airfoil, $\alpha = 0°$. (*a*) Thickness ratio = 35 percent, physical domain; (*b*) thickness ratio = 12 percent, physical domain; (*c*) any airfoil section, transformed domain.

$$[A211] = \frac{1}{l_e^2}\begin{bmatrix} 1 & -1 \\ -1 & 1 \end{bmatrix} \tag{3.181}$$

and l_e is the appropriate length of the element a or b. This measure is easily computed from the coordinate pairs defining R_e^n. Therefore, implementation of the multigrid algorithm in a generalized coordinate problem specification is direct.

The results presented in Sec. 3.10 for potential flow about a cylinder were generated using the multigrid algorithm and the line relaxation approximation to the jacobian. In the transform space, the two-dimensional solution domains appear as the unit square. The airfoils shown in Fig. 3.33, from the standpoint of the line relaxation algorithm, appear as illustrated in Fig. 3.33*c*. The vertices *A–D* are noted for comparison, and the appropriate boundary conditions are shown. Since $\phi \equiv 0$ on segment *B–C*, these nodes serve as the sole Dirichlet specification. Segments with distinct gradient boundary conditions intersect at vertices *A* and *D*. For stability, the respective corner elements R_e^2 must be subdivided into triangles by a bisector to the corner, as shown. This rezone separates the gradient constraints during the line relaxation. The corresponding construction for R_e^3 is resolution into five tetrahedrons with each surface face bisected.

3.15 ARTIFICIAL DENSITY FORMULATION FOR TRANSONIC FLOW

The methodology is in place to construct the finite-element algorithm for steady transonic flow. The differential equation and algorithm formulation is given by Hafez et al. (1978). The transonic flow potential equation (3.129) can be rewritten, for a two-dimensional problem, in the form

$$L(\phi) = \frac{\partial}{\partial x_i}\left(\rho \frac{\partial \phi}{\partial x_i}\right) = 0 \tag{3.182}$$

where $\rho = (M_\infty^2 c^2)^{1/(\gamma-1)} = \left(1 - \frac{\gamma-1}{2} M_\infty^2 \left[\left(\frac{\partial \phi}{\partial x_1}\right)^2 + \left(\frac{\partial \phi}{\partial x_2}\right)^2 - 1\right]\right)^{1/(\gamma-1)}$

$$\tag{3.183}$$

Equations (3.182) and (3.183) will admit expansion as well as compression shocks. To capture only the physically realizable compression shocks requires inclusion of viscosity effects. Following examination of several alternatives, the authors establish the modified (artificial) density form

$$\bar{\rho} = \left(1 - \frac{\gamma-1}{2} M_\infty^2 \left[\left(\frac{\partial \phi}{\partial x}\right)^2 + \left(\frac{\partial \phi}{\partial y}\right)^2 - \epsilon(uf_x + vg_y) - 1\right]\right)^{1/(\gamma-1)} \tag{3.184}$$

The term $uf_x + vg_y$ is the modification due to viscosity effects, where u and v are scalar components of u_i, and ρ is replaced by $\bar{\rho}$ in (3.182). The artificial compressibility method is based on (3.184), where the density is modified according to an artificial viscosity term, not necessarily the physical one given in (3.184).

Hafez et al. (1978) examine several artificial viscosity formulations for transonic flow prediction and select

$$-\frac{\partial}{\partial x_i}\left(\mu u_i \frac{\partial \rho}{\partial s} \Delta s\right) \tag{3.185}$$

as the form for the artificial viscosity term. In (3.185), μ is a coefficient that vanishes in regions of subsonic flow and

$$\frac{\partial \rho}{\partial s} \Delta s \equiv \frac{u}{q}\frac{\partial \rho}{\partial x} \Delta x + \frac{v}{q}\frac{\partial \rho}{\partial y} \Delta y \tag{3.186}$$

where Δx, Δy are measures of the mesh and $q^2 = u_i u_i$. Therefore, the modified density is defined as

$$\bar{\rho} = \rho - \mu \frac{\partial \rho}{\partial s} \Delta s \tag{3.187}$$

where ρ is given by (3.183). The boundary condition (3.131) completes the problem specification.

While there is no variational principle for (3.182), (3.183), and (3.187), the divergence form of (3.182) suggests that the extremization of the energy functional, if it existed, would be of the form (3.17), modified for a "variable density," i.e.,

$$S_e \frac{\partial I^h}{\partial \{Q\}_e} = S_e \left[\int_{R_e^2} \nabla \{N_k\} \cdot \bar{\rho}_e(x_i)\, \nabla \{N_k\}^T \{PHI\}_e \, d\tau \right.$$
$$\left. + \int_{\partial R_e \cap \partial R} \{N_k\}\{N_k\}^T \{EDOTN\}_e \, d\sigma \right] \equiv \{0\} \tag{3.188}$$

Recall the elements of $\{EDOTN\}_e$ are nodal evaluations of $\hat{\epsilon}_j \cdot \hat{n}_j$. The artificial density $\bar{\rho}(x_i)$ is evaluated in terms of its nodal distribution according to (3.187) in two parts. For $\rho_e(x_i)$, from (3.183)

$$\rho_e(x_i) = \left[1 - \frac{\gamma - 1}{2} M_\infty^2 (u_e^2 + v_e^2 - 1)\right]^{1/(\gamma-1)} \tag{3.189}$$

The sum of the elemental velocities (squared) is q_e^2, evaluated as

$$q_e^2(x_i) = \{PHI\}_e^T \, \nabla \{N_k\} \cdot \nabla \{N_k\}^T \{PHI\}_e \tag{3.190}$$

For the $k = 1$ basis, (3.190) can be evaluated as the element scalar

$$q_e^2 \{x_i\} = \{PHI\}_e^T [B211] \{PHI\}_e \tag{3.191}$$

Hence, (3.189) is evaluable including exponentiation as a scalar. Such an elementary construction is not possible for $k > 1$. In this instance, evaluating (3.190) at the nodes of R_e^2, the resultant determination for ρ_e can be interpolated on R_e^2 as

$$\rho_e(x_i) = \{N_k\}^T \{RHOEXP\}_e \tag{3.192}$$

where the elements of $\{RHOEXP\}_e$ are (3.189) evaluated at the nodes of R_e^2.

The second term in $\bar{\rho}$, (3.187), requires the directional derivative of ρ, see (3.186). The experience with finite-difference methods indicates the requirement to weight these derivatives with reference to the sign of the local velocity vector scalar components (called "upwinding"). To accomplish this in a general framework requires techniques discussed in Chap. 8. However, restricting the application to a rectangular discretization, and using the one-dimensional basis $\{N_1(\bar{x})\}$,

$$S_e\left[\frac{\partial \rho}{\partial x}\,\Delta x\right] = S_e[\tfrac{1}{2}[A201]^T\{RHO\}_e + \tfrac{1}{2}E_x[A211]\{RHO\}_e] \tag{3.193}$$

In (3.193), S_e is the assembly operator and $E_x = \text{sign}\ (u_e)$. In particular, for elements sharing node (i, j), the difference recursion relation equivalent to (3.193) is

$$\left.\frac{\partial \rho}{\partial x}\right|_{ij} \Delta x = \tfrac{1}{2}(\rho_{i+1,j} - \rho_{i-1,j}) - \tfrac{1}{2}E_x(\rho_{i+1,j} - 2\rho_{i,j} + \rho_{i-1,j}) \tag{3.194}$$

A similar expression (3.193) exists for $(\partial \rho/\partial y)\,\Delta y$, following definition of $\{N_1(\bar{x})\}$ parallel to the x_2 coordinate. Finally, the coefficient of artificial viscosity is defined on a nodal basis as

$$\mu \equiv \max\left(0,\ \frac{1 - c^2}{q^2}\right) \tag{3.195}$$

Equations (3.192)–(3.195) complete the expression for $\bar{\rho}_e(x_i)$ in (3.188). Thereupon, (3.188) can be written in a compact notation, in the form of (3.153), as

$$S_e\ \frac{\partial I^h}{\partial\{Q\}_e} \equiv \{F^h\} = S_e[\Delta_e\{RHO\}_e^T[B3011]_e\{PHI\}_e$$
$$+ l_e[A200]\{EDOTN\}_e] = \{0\} \tag{3.196}$$

Equation (3.196) is a nonlinear algebraic equation. The jacobian of (3.196), see (3.177), is

$$[J] = S_e[\Delta_e\{RHO\}_e^T[B3011]] \tag{3.197}$$

The multigrid solution of this problem statement has not been published. However, Eberle (1977) does report the finite-element implementation.

3.16 CLOSURE

Chapter 3 has derived and documented application of finite-element solution techniques to inviscid potential flows. The governing linear laplacian differential operator has been established in several instances, and numerical experiments have confirmed theoretical convergence rates. The example problems have illustrated the distinct features of the finite-element solution procedure with respect to boundary condition flexibility and use of nonuniform discretizations on nonregular shaped solution domains. The concepts of the multigrid solution algorithm and matrix iteration techniques have been introduced, including the extension to transonic potential flow. Our attention now turns to extension of the finite-element concept and methodology to the initial-value and nonlinear problem classes in fluid dynamics.

REFERENCES

Ames, W. F. (1977). *Numerical Methods for Partial Differential Equations,* Academic Press, New York.

Baker, A. J. and Manhardt, P. D. (1975). The Finite Element Method in Low Speed Aerodynamics, Old Dominion Univ. Tech. Report No. 75-T5.

Baker, A. J. and Manhardt, P. D. (1977). Finite Element Analysis of Low Speed Viscous and Invsicid Aerodynamic Flows, NASA CR-2908.

Baskharone, E. and Hamed, A. (1981). A New Approach in Cascade Flow Analysis Using the Finite Element Method, *AIAA J.,* vol. 19, no. 1, pp. 65–71.

Brandt, A. (1977). Multi-Level Adaptive Solution to Boundary-Value Problems, *Math. Comp.,* vol. 31, no. 138, pp. 333–390.

Brandt, A. (1979). Multi-Level Adaptive Computations in Fluid Dynamics, *AIAA* paper no. 79-1455.

Bratanow, T. and Ecer, A. (1974). On the Applications of the Finite Element Method in Unsteady Aerodynamics, *AIAA J.,* vol. 12, no. 4, pp. 503–510.

DeVries, G. and Norrie, D. A. (1971). The Application of the Finite Element Technique to Potential Flow Problems, *Trans. ASME, J. Appl. Mech.,* pp. 798–802.

Eberle, A. (1977). Eine Method Finiter Elements Berechnung der Transsonicken Potential-Strinung im Profile, *Messerschmitt-Bölkow-Blohm* 1352(0).

Eisenberg, M. A. and Malvern, L. E. (1973). On Finite Element Integration in Natural Co-ordinates, *Int. J. Numer. Methods Eng.,* vol. 6.

Gastelow, J. P. (1965). Potential Flow through Cascades–A Comparison between Exact and Approximate Solution, *A.R.C.* Rept. CP No. 807.

Hafez, M., South, J., and Murman, E. (1978). Artificial Compressibility Methods for Numerical Solutions of Transonic Full Potential Equation, *AIAA J.,* vol. 17, no. 8, pp. 838–844.

Hirsch, C. and Warzee, G. (1974). A Finite Element Method for Flow Calculations in Turbo-Machines, Free University of Brussels Report V.U.B.-Str.-5.

Isaacs, L. T. (1973). A Curved Cubic Triangular Finite Element for Potential Flow Problems, *Int. J. Numer. Methods Eng.,* vol. 7, pp. 337–344.

Kuethe, A. M. and Chow, C.-Y. (1976). *Foundations of Aerodynamics,* Wiley, New York.

Lawkins, W. R. (1977). Accuracy and Convergence of the Finite Element Solution of Flow Over a Wave-Shaped Wall, Dept. Engineering Science and Mechanics ESM 6910 Term Rept., University of Tennessee, Knoxville.

Meissner, U. (1973). A Mixed Finite Element Model for Use in Potential Flow Problems, *Int. J. Numer. Methods Eng.*, vol. 6, pp. 467–473.

Nicolaides, R. A. (1978). On Finite Element Multi-Grid Algorithms and Their Use, ICASE Rept. 78-8, NASA Langley Research Center, Hampton, Va.

Oden, J. T. and Reddy, J. N. (1976). *An Introduction to the Mathematical Theory of Finite Elements,* Wiley, New York.

Roache, P. J. (1972). *Computational Fluid Dynamics,* Hermosa, Albuquerque, New Mexico.

Sarpkaya, T. and Hiriart, H. G. (1975). On the Analysis of Target-Type Thrust Reversers, *AIAA J.*, vol. 13, no. 2, pp. 185–192.

Sasaki, Y. (1970). Some Basic Formalisms in Numerical Variational Analysis, *Mon. Weather Rev.*, vol. 98, p. 875.

Shames, I. H. (1962). *Mechanics of Fluids,* McGraw-Hill, New York.

Sherman, C. A. (1976). A Mass-Consistent Model for Wind Fields Over Complex Terrain, unpublished report of Lawrence Livermore Laboratory, UCRL-76171.

Thompson, D. S. (1973). Finite Element Analysis of the Flow through a Cascade of Aerofoils, Cambridge Univ. Report CUED/A Torbo/TR45.

Varga, R. S. (1962). *Matrix Iterative Analysis,* Prentice-Hall, New Jersey.

Vooren, J. V. D. and Laburjere, Th. E. (1973). Finite Element Solution of the Incompressible Flow Over an Airfoil in a Nonuniform Stream, *Proc. Int. Conf. Numer. Methods in Fluid Dynamics,* Southampton, England.

Zienkiewicz, O. C. (1977). *The Finite Element Method,* McGraw-Hill, London.

CHAPTER

FOUR

INITIAL-VALUE PROBLEMS, CONVECTION/DIFFUSION

4.1 INTRODUCTION

Chapters 2 and 3 developed the essence of the finite-element solution algorithm for linear field problems in fluid mechanics. Linearity permitted use of variational calculus to establish an equivalent energy functional for extremization. While certain extensions exist (Gurtin, 1964), constraint of linearity is much too restrictive for the vast majority of problem classes in fluid mechanics and heat transfer. For the finite-element algorithm to exhibit wide-ranging applicability, it is imperative that an alternative theoretical structure be established. As indicated in Chap. 1, the method of weighted residuals (MWR) is the theoretical vehicle required.

This chapter begins by reestablishing the basis for the finite-element algorithm for convective energy conservation in terms of MWR. The problem scope is then expanded to include the transient description and explicit appearance of nonlinearity. The MWR basis is constructed by requiring the general theory to exactly reproduce the algorithm as established by the variational principle for the linear problem. The requirements for this identity expose many theoretical issues of fundamental impact. Upon completion, the requirement emerges to solve either nonlinear algebraic or ordinary differential equation systems. This chapter presents the essence of equation solving, iteration, and convergence, and then proceeds with evaluation of the transient solution of sample one-dimensional conservation problems initiated in Chap. 2. These concepts are then extended to full dimensionality, using the procedure of time splitting, for the general convection-diffusion equation.

4.2 METHOD OF WEIGHTED RESIDUALS

As indicated, an expanded theoretical framework is required for applying the finite-element algorithm to general problem classes in computational fluid dynamics. Many alternatives exist under the general concept of "pseudovariational" procedures. However, the straightforward approach is to employ the general concept of MWR, first introduced by Galerkin (1915) for a problem class in elasticity. Finlayson and Scriven (1966, 1967) have thoroughly documented the parallelisms existent among the various pseudovariational structures and MWR.

The fundamental concept in MWR is to deal directly with the governing differential equation $L(q)$ and the boundary condition $l(q)$. Any approximate solution, say q^h, is hypothesized to exist; upon direct substitution, $L(q^h)$ and $l(q^h)$ are statements of the error in the solution approximation. Defining any set of weighting functions, say $\{W(\mathbf{x})\}$, the generated error is required to be orthogonal on R^n and on ∂R in the sense that

$$\int_{R^n} \{W(\mathbf{x})\} L(q^h)\, d\tau - \lambda \int_{\partial R} \{W(\mathbf{x})\} l(q^h)\, d\sigma \equiv \{0\} \tag{4.1}$$

In (4.1), λ is an arbitrary multiplier that can take on a convenient value, and there are as many (scalar) equations as members w_k of the weight set $\{W(\mathbf{x})\}$, $1 \leqslant k \leqslant K$. The essential step is restatement of (4.1) onto the assembly of operations performed on a finite-element domain basis. The required matrix operator is S_e (see Sec. 2.9); hence, (4.1) takes the form

$$S_e \left[\int_{R_e^n} \{W(\mathbf{x})\} L(q_e)\, d\tau - \lambda \int_{\partial R_e \cap \partial R} \{W(\mathbf{x})\} l(q_e)\, d\sigma \right] \equiv \{0\} \tag{4.2}$$

where $q_e(\mathbf{x})$ is the elemental contribution to the approximate solution q^h:

$$q^h(\mathbf{x}) \equiv \sum_{e=1}^{M} q_e(\mathbf{x}) = \sum_{e=1}^{M} \{N_k(\mathbf{x})\}^T \{Q\}_e \tag{4.3}$$

Equation (4.2) is sufficiently general to encompass the theoretical statement of practically all discrete approximation algorithms in the Eulerian description of fluid dynamics, including finite differences, finite volume, control volume, and discrete element procedures. The basic distinction between these methods and a finite-element algorithm is selection of the weight function basis $\{W(\mathbf{x})\}$. The psychology of the finite-element definition is simply to faithfully reproduce the energy functional extremization

$$S_e \left[\frac{\partial I^h}{\partial \{Q\}_e} \right] \equiv \{0\}$$

for the linear, steady-state heat-conduction problem statement, since in this instance the theoretical structure guarantees an optimally accurate approximation (in the energy norm).

With reference to (2.26)-(2.27), the differential equation statement for the steady-state heat conduction problem is

$$L(T) = \nabla \cdot k \, \nabla T + \rho \dot{q} = 0 \tag{4.4}$$

$$l(T) = k \, \nabla T \cdot \hat{\mathbf{n}} + h(T - T_r) = 0 \tag{4.5}$$

Direct substitution of (4.4)-(4.5) in (4.2) yields

$$S_e \left[\int_{R_e^n} \{W\}(\nabla \cdot k \, \nabla T_e + \rho \dot{q}_e) \, d\tau - \lambda \int_{\partial R_e \cap \partial R} \{W\}[k \, \nabla T_e \cdot \hat{\mathbf{n}} + h(T_e - T_r)] \, d\sigma \right] \equiv \{0\} \tag{4.6}$$

Correspondingly, see (2.195), the extremization of elemental contributions to the energy functional, for the variational statement equivalent to (4.4)-(4.5) is

$$S_e \left[\int_{R_e^n} [k \, \nabla\{N_k\} \cdot \nabla\{N_k\}^T \{Q\}_e - \{N_k\} \rho \dot{q}] \, d\tau + \int_{\partial R_e \cap \partial R} \{N_k\} h [\{N_k\}^T \{Q\}_e - T_r] \, d\sigma \right] = \{0\} \tag{4.7}$$

Direct comparison of (4.6) and (4.7) can be established, following substitution of the functional form for $T_e \equiv \{N_k\}^T \{Q\}_e$. Before that, however, the most apparent distinction is the difference in the sign of the term involving the heat generation term $\rho \dot{q}$. This leads to the singularly significant step to achieve the comparison, which is to apply the divergence theorem (actually, Green's first identity, the multidimensional equivalent of integration by parts) to the first term in (4.6). Hence,

$$\int_{R_e^n} \{W\} \nabla \cdot k \, \nabla T_e \, d\tau = \oint_{\partial R_e} \{W\} k \, \nabla T_e \cdot \hat{\mathbf{n}} \, d\sigma - \int_{R_e^n} \nabla \{W\} \cdot k \, \nabla T_e \, d\tau \tag{4.8}$$

where $\oint$ indicates the closed (complete) surface integral over ∂R_e. Substituting (4.8) into (4.6), multiplying through by -1, and using the finite element approximation form for T_e yields

$$S_e \left[\int_{R_e^n} (\nabla\{W\} \cdot k \, \nabla\{N_k\}^T \{Q\}_e - \{W\} \rho \dot{q}) \, d\tau + \lambda \int_{\partial R_e \cap \partial R} \{W\}(k \, \nabla\{N_k\}^T \{Q\}_e \cdot \hat{\mathbf{n}} + h[\{N_k\}^T \{Q\}_e - T_r]) \, d\sigma - \oint_{\partial R_e} \{W\} k \, \nabla\{N_k\}^T \{Q\}_e \cdot \hat{\mathbf{n}} \, d\sigma \right] \equiv \{0\} \tag{4.9}$$

Comparing (4.7)-(4.9), for the weighted residual formalism to correspond exactly to the variational statement, with its attendant theoretical structure, the weighting functions $\{W(\mathbf{x})\}$ must correspond identically with the cardinal basis $\{N_k(\mathbf{x})\}$ for T_e. Henceforth, by definition in this text, the finite element embodiment of the weighted residuals formalism shall specify

$$\{W(\mathbf{x})\} \equiv \{N_k(\mathbf{x})\} \tag{4.10}$$

Since (4.10) is a matrix equation, the identity holds by elements. For defined non-finite element applications of the weighted residual theory (4.2), alternative weighting functions that do not satisfy (4.10) may be defined. In particular, several familiar finite difference algorithms can be developed by avoiding the definition (4.10).

The second observation, comparing (4.7)-(4.9), is that a partial cancellation of surface integrals in (4.9) is achieved by defining $\lambda \equiv +1$. Thereupon, the MWR finite-element algorithm for (4.4)-(4.5) becomes

$$S_e\left[\int_{R_e^n} (\nabla\{N_k\}\cdot k\,\nabla\{N_k\}^T\{Q\}_e - \rho\dot{q}\{N_k\})\,d\tau + \int_{\partial R_e \cap \partial R} \{N_k\}h(\{N_k\}^T\{Q\}_e - T_r)\,d\sigma - \oint_{\partial R_e:\,\partial R_e \cap \partial R = 0} \{N_k\}k\,\nabla\{N_k\}^T\{Q\}_e\cdot\hat{\mathbf{n}}\,d\sigma\right] \equiv \{0\} \tag{4.11}$$

Comparing (4.11) and (4.7), the correspondence for the dual derivations is one-to-one for the first two integrals. The third integral in (4.11) is a closed surface integral over the boundary ∂R_e of each finite-element domain, provided that ∂R_e does not coincide with a segment of the global domain boundary ∂R (reads ∂R_e: $\partial R_e \cap \partial R = 0$) whereupon the gradient boundary condition (4.5) is applied. Therefore, for the weighted residual formalism to coincide exactly with the variational statement this integral must vanish. This is accomplished following the general problem class algorithm statement.

4.3 FINITE-ELEMENT ALGORITHM FOR UNSTEADY CONVECTION/DIFFUSION

The MWR algorithm statement (4.2), (4.8), and (4.10), for the finite-element algorithm, renders the developed concept extensible to all problem classes in fluid mechanics. The convection/diffusion equation for a scalar variable is representative of the Eulerian transport description in fluid mechanics. Consider the energy equation, written for a compressible fluid with variable properties, and influenced by the convective velocity field $\mathbf{u}(\mathbf{x}, t)$. The partial differential equation system governing the multidimensional temperature distribution $T(\mathbf{x}, t)$ is on R^n: $$L(T(\mathbf{x}, t)) = \rho c \frac{\partial T}{\partial t} + \rho \mathbf{u} \cdot \nabla T - \nabla \cdot k \nabla T - \rho \dot{q} = 0 \tag{4.12}$$

on ∂R_1: $$l(T(\mathbf{x}, t)) = k \nabla T \cdot \hat{\mathbf{n}} + h(T - T_r) = 0 \tag{4.13}$$

on ∂R_2: $$T(\mathbf{x}, t) = T_b(t) \tag{4.14}$$

at $t = 0$: $$T(\mathbf{x}, 0) = T_0(\mathbf{x}) \tag{4.15}$$

In (4.12)-(4.15), ρ is the fluid density; the specific heat c and thermal conductivity k could be variable with temperature; and the solution parameters $\mathbf{u}$, $\dot{q}$, and h are arbitrarily specifiable. The student of fluid mechanics recognizes that (4.12)-(4.15) is Reynold's transport theorem for energy conservation, and that all other conservation laws in mechanics in the Eulerian description have a similar appearance. Therefore, the variable T could represent any scalar field as, for example, the concentration of a species (nuclear or chemical) in a fluid system.

Generalize the finite-element approximation (4.3), for the transient problem specification, to the semidiscrete form

$$T_e(\mathbf{x}, t) \equiv \{N_k(\mathbf{x})\}^T \{Q(t)\}_e \tag{4.16}$$

The matrix elements of $\{N_k(\mathbf{x})\}$ remain the multidimensional cardinal basis constructed in Chap. 3, while the elements of $\{Q(t)\}_e$ are interpreted as the time-varying temperatures at the nodes of the finite-element discretization of the solution domain. The MWR finite-element algorithm (4.2) requires establishment of the time derivative. Using the chain rule,

$$\frac{\partial T_e(\mathbf{x}, t)}{\partial t} = \{N_k(\mathbf{x})\}^T \frac{d}{dt} \{Q(t)\}_e \equiv \{N_k(\mathbf{x})\}^T \{Q(t)\}_e' \tag{4.17}$$

where prime (′) denotes the ordinary derivative of the column matrix $\{Q(t)\}_e$. The MWR finite-element algorithm statement for (4.12)-(4.15) thus becomes

$$\begin{aligned} S_e \Bigg[& \int_{R_e^n} \{N_k\} \rho c_e \{N_k\}^T \{Q\}_e' \, d\tau + \int_{R_e^n} \rho \{N_k\} \mathbf{u}_e \cdot \nabla \{N_k\}^T \{Q\}_e \, d\tau \\ & + \int_{R_e^n} \nabla \{N_k\} \cdot k_e \nabla \{N_k\}^T \{Q\}_e \, d\tau - \int_{R_e^n} \{N_k\} \rho \dot{q}_e \, d\tau \\ & + \int_{\partial R_e \cap \partial R_1} \{N_k\} h_e (\{N_k\}^T \{Q\}_e - T_r) \, d\sigma \\ & - \oint_{\partial R_e :\, \partial R_e \cap \partial R = 0} \{N_k\} k_e \nabla \{N_k\}^T \{Q\} \cdot \hat{\mathbf{n}} \, d\sigma \Bigg] \equiv \{0\} \end{aligned} \tag{4.18}$$

In (4.18), solution parameters are assumed variable, as noted with subscript e. For example, if the thermal conductivity varies as the square root of temperature, the numerical solution could be established using the quadratic approximation $\{N_2\}$ for temperature and $\{N_1\}$ for thermal conductivity. Then,

$$k_e(\mathbf{x}, t) = \{N_1(\mathbf{x})\}^T\{K(Q(t))\}_e \tag{4.19}$$

and $\{K(Q)\}$ are the time-dependent node point values of thermal conductivity as determined from the temperature dependence. In this case, finite-element boundaries should coincide with the interfaces separating dissimilar materials. No special assembly logic is required, and no need to interpolate a step function exists, since node points occur naturally on the interfacial boundaries. Finally, note that (4.18) is a system of ordinary differential equations, written on the temporal evolution of node point temperatures. In the event a direct steady-state solution is required, the first term vanishes, and (4.18) becomes a nonlinear algebraic system for the steady-state temperature distribution.

The newly created requirements are to establish matrix solution procedures for large order ordinary differential and/or nonlinear algebraic equations, as well as elimination of the extraneous closed surface integrals. This is accomplished in the next section, and the following two sections present a general overview of the required solution procedures.

4.4 ELIMINATION OF EXTRANEOUS SURFACE INTEGRALS

The MWR finite-element algorithm statement (4.18) [see (4.11)] is identical to the variational statement (4.7) for a linear problem to within the extraneous closed surface integrals on ∂R_e. Equation (4.11) was generated using Green's theorem (4.8) at the element level, i.e.,

$$\int_{R_e^n} \{N_k\}\nabla\cdot k\nabla T_e\, d\tau = \oint_{\partial R_e} \{N_k\}k\nabla T_e\cdot\hat{\mathbf{n}}\, d\sigma - \int_{R_e^n} \nabla\{N_k\}\cdot k\nabla T_e\, d\tau \tag{4.20}$$

It is sufficient to consider a two-dimensional specification, and the linear natural coordinate basis

$$T_e(\mathbf{x}) \equiv \{N_1(\mathbf{x})\}^T\{Q\}_e \tag{4.21}$$

In the local rectangular cartesian coordinate system $\mathbf{x}$ [see Sec. 3.4], recall

$$\nabla\{N_1(\bar{x}_i)\} = \nabla\{\zeta\} = \frac{1}{\bar{X}1_2}\begin{Bmatrix}-1\\ 1\\ 0\end{Bmatrix}\hat{\mathbf{i}} + \frac{1}{\bar{X}2_3}\begin{Bmatrix}\dfrac{\bar{X}1_3}{\bar{X}1_2}-1\\ -\dfrac{\bar{X}1_3}{\bar{X}1_2}\\ 1\end{Bmatrix}\hat{\mathbf{j}} \tag{4.22}$$

which is a constant vector on R_e^n. For the linear cardinal basis $\{N_1\}$, and uniform thermal conductivity, the left side of (4.20) vanishes identically. The second right term in (4.20) is the familiar thermal conductivity matrix

$$\int_{R_e^2} \nabla\{N_1\}\cdot k\,\nabla\{N_1\}^T\{Q\}_e\,d\tau = A_e t_e k[B211]_e\{Q\}_e \tag{4.23}$$

The necessary step is to show that (4.20), written on a single finite-element domain $R_e^2 \cup \partial R_e$, vanishes identically. For this to occur, the closed surface integral on ∂R_e must identically cancel (4.23). Referring to Fig. 4.1, the surface integral is evaluated as the sum

$$\oint_{\partial R_e} \{N_1\}k\,\nabla T_e\cdot\hat{\mathbf{n}}\,d\sigma = \sum_{i=1}^{3} k \int_{\partial R_e(\mathrm{i})} \{N_1\}k\,\nabla\{N_1\}^T\cdot\hat{\mathbf{n}}^{(i)}\,d\sigma^{(i)}\{Q\}_e \tag{4.24}$$

where discrete boundary segments are signified by outward pointing unit normal vectors $\hat{\mathbf{n}}^{(i)}$. Using (3.39) and (4.22), (4.24) is evaluated for an element domain of thickness t_e and boundary length Δ_e as

$$\oint_{\partial R_e} \{N_1\}k\,\nabla T_e\cdot\hat{\mathbf{n}}\,d\sigma = k\sum_{i=1}^{3}\left[\Delta_e^{(i)} t_e\{N_1\}\nabla\{N_1\}^T\cdot\hat{\mathbf{n}}^{(i)}\right]\{Q\}_e$$

$$= kt_e\left[\frac{\bar{X}1_2}{2}\begin{Bmatrix}1\\1\\0\end{Bmatrix}\frac{1}{\bar{X}2_3}\left\{\frac{\bar{X}1_3}{\bar{X}1_2}-1,\ -\frac{\bar{X}1_3}{\bar{X}1_2},\ 1\right\}\right.$$

$$+\frac{\bar{X}2_3}{2}\begin{Bmatrix}0\\1\\1\end{Bmatrix}\frac{1}{\bar{X}1_2}\{-1,1,0\}+\frac{\bar{X}1_2-\bar{X}1_3}{2}\begin{Bmatrix}0\\1\\1\end{Bmatrix}\frac{1}{\bar{X}2_3}\left\{\frac{\bar{X}1_3}{\bar{X}1_2}-1,\ -\frac{\bar{X}1_3}{\bar{X}1_2},\ 1\right\}$$

$$-\frac{\bar{X}2_3}{2}\begin{Bmatrix}1\\0\\1\end{Bmatrix}\frac{1}{\bar{X}1_2}\{-1,1,0\}$$

$$\left.+\frac{\bar{X}1_3}{2}\begin{Bmatrix}1\\0\\1\end{Bmatrix}\frac{1}{\bar{X}2_3}\left\{\frac{\bar{X}1_3}{\bar{X}1_2}-1,\ -\frac{\bar{X}1_3}{\bar{X}1_2},\ 1\right\}\right]\{Q\}_e \tag{4.25}$$

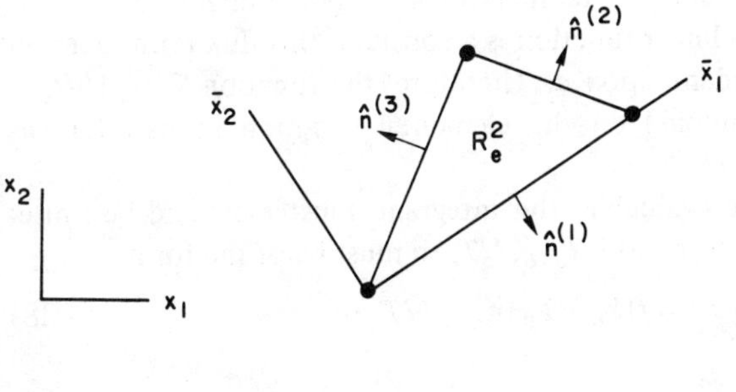

Figure 4.1 Two-dimensional finite-element domain.

Completing the matrix products in (4.25), and extracting the common multiplier $\frac{1}{2}\bar{X}1_2 \cdot \bar{X}2_3 = A_e$, yields for (4.24)

$$\oint_{\partial R_e} \{N_1\} k \nabla T_e \cdot \hat{\mathbf{n}}\, d\sigma = k t_e A_e \left(\frac{1}{(\bar{X}1_2)^2} \begin{bmatrix} 1 & -1 & 0 \\ & 1 & 0 \\ \text{(sym)} & & 0 \end{bmatrix} \right.$$

$$\left. + \frac{1}{(\bar{X}1_2 \cdot \bar{X}2_3)^2} \begin{bmatrix} \left(\frac{\bar{X}1_3}{\bar{X}1_2} - 1\right)^2, & -\frac{\bar{X}1_3}{\bar{X}1_2}\left(\frac{\bar{X}1_3}{\bar{X}1_2} - 1\right), & \frac{\bar{X}1_3}{\bar{X}1_2} - 1 \\ , & \left(\frac{\bar{X}1_3}{\bar{X}1_2}\right)^2, & -\frac{\bar{X}1_3}{\bar{X}1_2} \\ \text{(sym)} & , & 1 \end{bmatrix} \right)$$

$$= A_e t_e k [B211]_e \{Q\}_e \tag{4.26}$$

Comparing (4.23) and (4.26), the right side of (4.20) indeed does vanish identically. Hence, a justification is required for discarding the elemental surface integrals generated by the MWR formulation of the finite-element algorithm. This is of some fundamental importance, since many different algorithm statements can be constructed from the basic MWR formulation (4.1). Specifically, a finite-difference algorithm emerges by specifying $\{W\}$ the set of (arbitrary) constants C in (4.9). Since $\{W\} \equiv C\{ONE\}$ supports no differentiability, the second right term in (4.20) is identically zero, and the surface integral is the total replacement for the left-hand term.

This is perhaps one of the fundamental distinctions between the two methodologies. For the finite-element construction, and since the surface integral does not vanish on an elemental domain, one interprets in (4.11) that the assembly (S_e) of surface integrals must vanish, i.e.,

$$S_e \left[\oint_{\partial R_e : \partial R_e \cap \partial R = 0} \{N_k\} k_e \nabla \{N_k\}^T \{Q\}_e \cdot \hat{\mathbf{n}}\, d\sigma \right] = \{0\} \tag{4.27}$$

With reference to Fig. 4.2, the assembly operation on common closure segments $\partial R_e(i)$ for adjacent finite element domains $R_e(i)$ involves row addition of pairs of corresponding contributions. Using the two-dimensional linear cardinal basis element, we can focus on formation of the line integral connecting nodes a and b. Since $\nabla\{N_1\}^T\{Q\}_e \cdot \hat{\mathbf{n}}_e^{(1)}$ involves nodal values of temperatures at node c of R_p^2 and node d of R_q^2, and since the gradient of a linear function is a constant, this flux term takes on different (constant) values dependent upon e. Therefore, the function $\nabla\{N_1\}^T\{Q\}_e$ appears undefined (i.e., discontinuous) on the elemental common intersection, as shown in Fig. 4.3.

For the integral (4.27) to be evaluable, the integrand must exist and be finite; therefore, on the common closure segment ∂R_{a-b}, $\nabla T_e \cdot \hat{\mathbf{n}}$ must be of the form

$$k \nabla T_e \cdot \hat{\mathbf{n}}|_{\partial R_{a-b}} \equiv f(k_p \nabla T_p \cdot \hat{\mathbf{n}}, k_q \nabla T_q \cdot \hat{\mathbf{n}}) \tag{4.28}$$

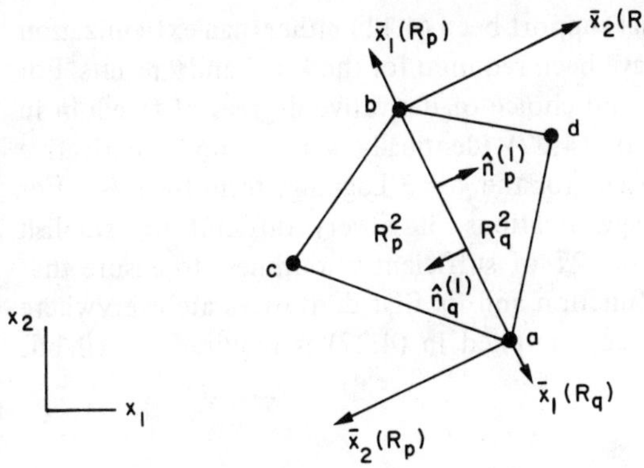

Figure 4.2 Adjacent finite-elements in domain discretization.

The functional form in (4.28) need not be specified further (as an algebraic average, for example) to generate the required result. Equation (4.27) evaluated on closure segment $\partial R_{a\text{-}b}$ using (4.28), yields

$$\underset{e=p}{\overset{q}{S}} \left[\oint_{\partial R_e} \{N_1\} k_e \nabla \{N_1\}^T \{Q\}_e \cdot \hat{\mathbf{n}} \, d\sigma \right]$$

$$= \int_{\partial R_p} \{N_1\} f(k_p \nabla \{N_1\}^T \{Q\}_p, k_q \nabla \{N_1\}^T \{Q\}_q) \cdot \hat{\mathbf{n}}_p^{(1)} \, d\bar{x}$$

$$+ \int_{\partial R_q} \{N_1\} f(k_p \nabla \{N_1\}^T \{Q\}_p, k_q \nabla \{N_1\}^T \{Q\}_q) \cdot \hat{\mathbf{n}}_q^{(1)} \, d\bar{x} \tag{4.29}$$

Since $\hat{\mathbf{n}}_p^{(1)} = -\hat{\mathbf{n}}_q^{(1)}$, the right side of (4.29) vanishes identically. Therefore (4.27) vanishes throughout ∂R_e: $\partial R_e \cap \partial R = 0$ and the desired result is achieved. The result extends directly to R^3.

Some additional comments are appropriate with regard to increasing the degree of the finite-element interpolation function $\{N_k\}$ in (4.24). Recall the thick cylinder example problem in solutions of Chap. 2, and the associated accuracy and convergence

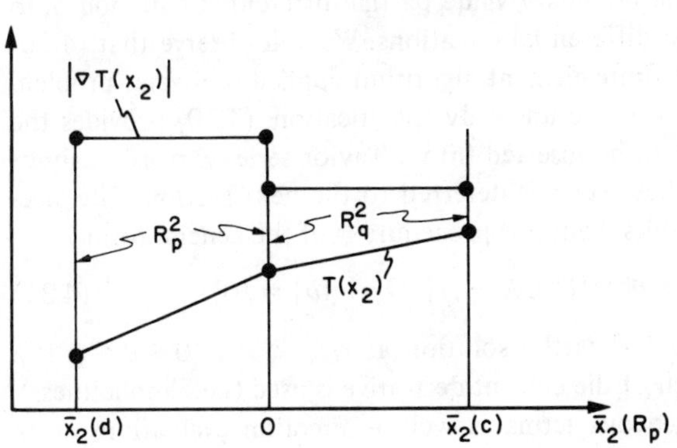

Figure 4.3 Temperature and temperature gradient distributions using $\{N_1\}$ in adjacent finite elements, R_p^2 and R_q^2.

for $\{N_k\}$, $1 \leqslant k \leqslant 3$. Had the theoretical support been (4.11) rather than extremization of a functional, (4.27)-(4.28) would have been required for the $k = 1$ and 2 results. For $k = 3$, constant thermal conductivity and choice of derivative degrees of freedom in $\{N_3'\}$ [see (2.150)] yields vanishing of (4.27) identically via the nodal derivative degrees of freedom. This would not occur for the $k = 3$ Lagrange form for $\{N_3\}$. For two- or three-dimensional problem specifications, it is very difficult to establish finite-element cardinal basis $\{N_k(\mathbf{x})\}$ on R_e^n of sufficient smoothness to ensure that the function lies in C^1, i.e., that the function and its first derivatives are everywhere smoothly continuous. Hence, the concept implied in (4.27) is required for all but strictly linear problems.

4.5 MATRIX ITERATIVE SOLUTION PROCEDURES

Equation (4.18), with the last term deleted, is the finite-element algorithm for the generalized, multidimensional convection-diffusion energy statement. Independent of the dimension of R^n and for general variation of material properties, the finite-element statement (4.18), for the energy conservation specification (4.12)-(4.15) is of the form

$$L(\{Q\}) = [C]\{Q(t)\}' + [U + K + H]\{Q(t)\} + \{b(t)\} = \{0\} \tag{4.30}$$

Equation (4.30) represents the upper partition global form of the finite-element algorithm [see (2.40)-(2.41)], and $\{Q\}$ contains all node point temperatures lying on $R^n \cup \partial R$. The square matrix $[C]$ represents the distribution of thermal capacity, $[U]$ represents convection, $[K]$ is the diffusion equivalent, $[H]$ contains the homogeneous convective boundary condition, while $\{b\}$ contains all nonhomogeneous terms. Contributions from those node points lying on ∂R_2 (hence fixed and not eligible for integration) are also included in the (load) matrix $\{b(t)\}$. The sparse and banded matrices $[C(Q)]$ and $[K(Q)]$ are mildly nonlinear, since each contain the discretized equivalent influence of variable thermal capacity and thermal conductivity. The initial distribution of node point temperatures on $R^n \cup \partial R$ is obtained by mapping (4.15) onto the nodes of the discretization.

In a sense then, the finite-element algorithm may be considered an integral transformation, casting an initial-elliptic boundary value partial differential equation onto a larger order system of ordinary differential equations. We will observe that (4.30) is uniformly representative of the finite-element algorithm applied to diverse problem specifications in fluid mechanics. For the unsteady specification, (4.30) provides the expression for the time derivative to be inserted into a Taylor series expansion about t_j. The detailed examination of these steps is deferred to the next section. The algebraic solution requirement that results from this procedure is of the general form

$$\{F(Q)\} = [C]\{Q\} + \theta\,\Delta t[U + K + H]\{Q\} + \{b\} = \{0\} \tag{4.31}$$

In (4.31), the dependent variable $\{Q\}$ is the solution at t_{j+k}, $k \geqslant 1$, $0 \leqslant \theta \leqslant 1$ is a factor which determines how much of the current derivative is used (i.e., implicitness), and $\{B\}$ contains the nonhomogeneous terms as well as function evaluations at t_j.

Similarly, if only the steady-state solution of (4.30) is sought, the lead term in (4.30) is deleted, yielding the matrix solution requirement

$$\{F(Q)\} = [U + K + H]\{Q\} + \{b\} = \{0\} \tag{4.32}$$

Note that both (4.31) and (4.32) are (potentially) nonlinear algebraic equation systems. The induced requirement is thus to examine matrix iterative solution procedures in order to introduce the essential concepts of convergence (rate) and error. This examination is facilitated by considering a nonlinear algebraic equation written on the single dependent variable y.

$$f(y) \equiv 0 \tag{4.33}$$

Assume (4.33) can be rewritten in a form that extracts a linear term in y from $f(y)$, that is,

$$f(y) \equiv y - g(y) = 0 \qquad \text{or} \qquad y = g(y) \tag{4.34}$$

Any solution to (4.34) is then also a solution to (4.33), and there may be several ways of expressing (4.33) in the form of (4.34).

The direct solution of (4.34) is termed linear iteration. Assuming $y = y^0$ is the initial approximation to the root (solution) $y = \alpha$ of (4.34), that is, $f(\alpha) = 0$, linear iteration generates successive approximations to α by solving (4.34) directly as

$$y^{p+1} = g(y^p) \qquad p = 0, 1, 2, \ldots, n, \tag{4.35}$$

Convergence of (4.35) to the solution $y = \alpha$ is assured, on an interval I of the y axis containing the point $y = \alpha$, provided that $|y - \alpha| < \epsilon$ for some given ϵ. Assume $g(y)$ and $g'(y) \equiv dg/dy$ are continuous on I. Then, if $|g'(y)| \leqslant K < 1$ at all points on I, and if the initial estimate y^0 lies on I, then (4.35) will converge to the root $y = \alpha$. Since α is the root, from (4.35), $\alpha = g(\alpha)$. Subtracting this from (4.35) yields

$$y^{p+1} - \alpha = g(y^p) - g(\alpha) = g'(\bar{y})[y^p - \alpha] \tag{4.36}$$

using the mean value theorem of calculus, and $\bar{y}$ lies on the interval $y^{p+1} \leqslant \bar{y} \leqslant y^p$. For $p = 0$, and using the triangle inequality,

$$|y^1 - \alpha| \leqslant |g'(\bar{y})| \cdot |y^0 - \alpha| < |y^0 - \alpha|$$

since $\bar{y}$ lies in I and $|g'(\bar{y})| < 1$ by assumption. Hence,

$$|y^1 - \alpha| < \epsilon$$

and y^1 is in I. By induction then, every y^p remains in I for the assumption $|g'(\bar{y})| \leqslant K < 1$ for every p, and y^p converges to the root α as p increases.

The rate of convergence of y^p to the solution α is linear, as follows. Define the error e^p at the pth iterate as

$$e^p \equiv y^p - \alpha \tag{4.37}$$

Then, by combining (4.36) and (4.37)

$$e^{p+1} = g'(\bar{y})e^p \tag{4.38}$$

The limit behavior of e^p, as p becomes large, determines convergence rate. From (4.38), and the assumption $|g'(\bar{y})| \leqslant K$,

$$|e^{p+1}| \leqslant K|e^p| \qquad p = 0, 1, 2, \ldots, n,$$

Applying this inequality recursively yields

$$e^{p+1} \leqslant K^2|e^{p-1}| \leqslant \cdots \leqslant K^{p+1}|e^0|$$

where e^0 is the error in the initial approximation. Since $|K| < 1$,

$$\lim_{p\to\infty} |K^{p+1}| = 0$$

hence,

$$\lim_{p\to\infty} |e^{p+1}| = 0 \tag{4.39}$$

regardless of the initial error e^0, provided the iteration converges, that is, y^0 lies in I. For a convergent process, from (4.38),

$$\lim_{p\to\infty} \frac{e^{p+1}}{e^p} = \lim_{p\to\infty} g'(\bar{y}) = g'(\alpha) \tag{4.40}$$

since $y^{p+1} \leqslant \bar{y} \leqslant y^p$ and $g'(\bar{y})$ is assumed continuous. Then, (4.40) states that the error in the $(p + 1)$st iteration is linearly proportional to the error at the pth step, the constant of proportionality approximately equal to $g'(\alpha)$. Hence, (4.40) provides proof that (4.35) defines a linear iteration procedure.

The more favorable quadratic rate of convergence can be achieved for (4.34) rearranged to the specific form

$$g(y) \equiv y - \frac{f(y)}{f'(y)} \tag{4.41}$$

where $f(y)$ is the parent equation (4.33), and $f'(y) \equiv df/dy$ is the jacobian. The resultant solution algorithm, which is called Newton (Newton-Raphson) iteration, is the form

$$y^{p+1} = y^p - \frac{f(y^p)}{f'(y^p)} \tag{4.42}$$

If the sequence of iterates y^p, $p = 1, 2, \ldots$, converges to the root $y = \alpha$, and if $f'(\alpha) \neq 0$, then clearly $f(\alpha)$ must be zero, (4.42), which is the solution to (4.33).

On some interval of the y axis containing α, let I denote the set of all points satisfying $|y - \alpha| < \epsilon$ for some given ϵ. Since $f'(\alpha) \neq 0$, there must be continuity of $f(y)$ on some subset I_1 of I, such that $f'(y) \neq 0$ for all of y on I_1. Then, from (4.41), $g(y)$ is continuous on I_1. Differentiating,

$$g'(y) = 1 - \frac{f'^2 - ff''}{f'^2} = \frac{f(y)f''(y)}{[f'(y)]^2} \tag{4.43}$$

Assuming $f''(y)$ is continuous on I_1, and since $f'(y) \neq 0$, then $g'(y)$ is also continuous on I_1. Furthermore, from (4.43), $g'(\alpha) = 0$. Then, from continuity there must be some subset of I, call it I_2, on which $|g'(y)| < 1$. Then, if I is the set of points on the y axis containing coordinates common to both I_1 and I_2, thereupon $g(y)$ and $g'(y)$ are continuous and $|g'(y)| < 1$. If y^0 is chosen to lie in I, then the iteration (4.42) converges. Explicitly, if the initial guess y^0 is chosen such that

$$|g'(y^0)| = \frac{f(y^0)f''(y^0)}{[f'(y^0)]^2} < 1 \tag{4.44}$$

then the iteration algorithm (4.42) is convergent.

A most desirable feature of Newton iteration is the associated quadratic rate of convergence, which is readily proved. Substituting the root $y = \alpha$ into (4.34), and subtracting it from (4.34) written at the pth iteration, yields

$$y^{p+1} - \alpha = g(y^p) - g(\alpha)$$

Expand $g(y^p)$ about $y = \alpha$ in a Taylor series.

$$g(y^p) = g(\alpha) + g'(\alpha)(y^p - \alpha) + g''(\alpha) \left| \frac{(y^p - \alpha)^2}{2!} \right| + \cdots$$

Noting that $g'(\alpha) = 0$, and substituting (4.37) for the definition of error at the pth iteration, these equations combine to yield

$$e^{p+1} = \tfrac{1}{2} g''(\alpha)(e^p)^2 \tag{4.45}$$

Equation (4.45) states that the error in any Newton iterate is proportional to the square of the error in the previous iterate, hence convergence is quadratic assuming that $g''(\bar{y})$ is continuous in the vicinity of $y = \alpha$.

These examinations for a single dependent variable have provided the desired insight. The true matrix solution requirement is for (4.31)-(4.32), both of which are of the form

$$\{F(Q)\} = \{0\} \tag{4.46}$$

The matrix solution statement remains (4.34), written as

$$\{Q\} = \{G(Q)\} \tag{4.47}$$

where $\{G\}$ is a nonlinear column matrix. Restricting attention to Newton iteration, the equivalent form for (4.41) is

$$\{G(Q)\} \equiv \{Q\} - \frac{\{F(Q)\}}{[J(F)]} \tag{4.48}$$

where $[J(F)]$ is the jacobian, the multivariable matrix equivalent of $f'(y)$ in (4.41). The matrix elements of $[J]$ are thus defined as

$$[J(F)] \equiv \frac{\partial\{F\}}{\partial\{Q\}} \tag{4.49}$$

Define the solution vector at the $(p + 1)$st iteration, in terms of the incremental change $\{\delta Q\}^{p+1}$, as

$$\{Q\}^{p+1} = \{Q\}^p + \{\delta Q\}^{p+1} \tag{4.50}$$

Substituting (4.48) into (4.47) yields the algebraic equation system for solution of $\{\delta Q\}^{p+1}$ as

$$[J(F)]^p\{\delta Q\}^{p+1} = -\{F\}^p \tag{4.51}$$

The proof of convergence for (4.50)-(4.51) is a direct extension of that outlined in (4.43)-(4.45). If the components of $[J(F)]^p$ are continuous in the neighborhood of a hyperpoint $\{\alpha\}$, where $\{F(\alpha)\} = \{0\}$, and for det $[J(F(\alpha))] \neq 0$, and if $\{Q\}^0$ is near $\{\alpha\}$, then

$$\lim_{p\to\infty} \{Q\}^p = \{\alpha\} \tag{4.52}$$

The rate of convergence remains quadratic; its proof is left as an exercise.

Construction of the jacobian (4.49), or a decent approximation, is among the most crucial aspects of computational fluid mechanics, especially in regards to efficiency. This activity will constitute a major focus in the remaining chapters of this text. The finite-element methodology being developed is particularly well suited to the task, since the formalisms are written using a pseudo-FORTRAN appearing functional form. For example, if (4.32) is the problem to be solved, and the thermal conductivity k is dependent upon temperature, the construction of (4.49) is

$$[J(F)] \equiv \frac{\partial\{F\}}{\partial\{Q\}} = S_e\left[\frac{\partial}{\partial\{Q\}_e}\,[[U]_e + [K(Q)]_e + [H]_e]\{Q\}_e + \{b\}_e\right]$$

$$= S_e\left[[U]_e + [K(Q)]_e + [H]_e + \frac{\partial[K(k)]_e}{\partial\{k\}_e}\frac{d\{k\}_e}{d\{Q\}_e}\right] \tag{4.53}$$

Since the thermal conductivity is assumed variable, the specific form for $[K(Q)]_e$ is, using the hypermatrix concept introduced in Chaps. 2 and 3,

$$[K(Q)]_e \equiv \int_{R_e^n} \nabla\{N_k\}\cdot\{N_k\}^T\{k\}_e\,\nabla\{N_k\}^T\{Q\}_e\,d\tau = \Delta_e\{k\}_e^T[M30LL]_e\{Q\}_e \tag{4.54}$$

In (4.54), the discrete indices sum $1 \leqslant L \leqslant n$, M takes on (A, B, C) dependent upon n, Δ_e is the element measure, and the elements of $\{k\}_e$ are the nodal conductivities. Assuming the temperature dependence for k is of the elementary form $k(T) = \beta(T - T_0)$, and interchanging the pre- and postmultiplications in (4.54), the last term in (4.53) becomes

$$\frac{\partial[K(k)]_e}{\partial\{k\}_e}\frac{d\{k\}_e}{d\{Q\}_e} = \beta\,\Delta_e\{Q\}_e^T[M3LL0]_e \tag{4.55}$$

We will make ample use of this methodology, as the fluid dynamic problem classes become more detailed.

The final step is review of the matrix techniques for solution of (4.51). This equation is of standard form

$$[A]\{y\} = \{b\} \tag{4.56}$$

where $[A]$ is a sparse, banded, N-square nonsingular matrix with constant coefficients, $\{y\}$ is the column matrix of unknowns, and $\{b\}$ is a vector of constants. The formal solution to (4.56) is

$$\{y\} = [A]^{-1}\{b\} \tag{4.57}$$

However, formation of $[A]^{-1}$ is to be avoided as expensive and subject to accumulation of round-off error. The alternative approach, which takes explicit advantage of the sparse, usually diagonally dominant matrix structure of $[A]$, utilizes an elimination procedure. The present requirement is served by examining Gauss elimination (Strang and Fix, 1973, Chap. I). The first operation is elimination of the first matrix element of $\{y\}$, that is, $y(1)$, from all $N-1$ equations, $N \neq 1$, by rowwise scalar multiplication followed by subtraction. Similarly, eliminate $y(2)$ from the last $N-2$ equations, $y(3)$ from the last $N-3$ equations, and so on, until $y(N-1)$ has been eliminated from the Nth equation. The resultant matrix $[U]$, that results from this operation, is upper triangular, i.e., all matrix elements below the principal diagonal of $[U]$ are zero. Thus, (4.56) takes the form

$$[U]\{y\} = \begin{bmatrix} u_{11} & u_{12} & u_{13} & \cdots & u_{1N} \\ 0 & u_{22} & u_{23} & \cdots & u_{2N} \\ 0 & 0 & u_{33} & \cdots & u_{3N} \\ \vdots & & & \ddots & \vdots \\ 0 \ldots & & \ldots 0 & & u_{NN} \end{bmatrix} \{y\} = \{b'\} \tag{4.58}$$

In (4.58), the elements of $\{b'\}$ are linear combinations of those of $\{b\}$, as formed by the substitution process. Solution of (4.58) is direct using back substitution, i.e., solve for $y(N)$ from the last equation, use this to determine $y(N-1)$ from equation $(N-1)$, and so on, until the first equation is solved for $y(1)$.

The matrix manipulations used in the elimination process, yielding (4.58), can be further examined to advantage. In particular, reverse the process so that (4.56) is regained from (4.58). In equation N of (4.58), add the multiple $l_{N,N-1}$ subtracted off during the elimination of $y(N-1)$ from equation N. Next, add back the previous two equations, with multiples $l_{N-1,N-2}$ and $l_{N,N-2}$, used to eliminate $y(N-2)$ from the last equation pair in (4.58). Repeat this process until (4.56) is regained, which amounts to multiplication of (4.58) by a matrix $[L]$:

$$[L][U]\{y\} = [L]\{b'\} \tag{4.59}$$

where

$$[L] = \begin{bmatrix} 1 & 0 & 0 & 0 & \cdots & 0 \\ l_{21} & 1 & 0 & 0 & \cdots & 0 \\ l_{31} & l_{32} & 1 & 0 & \cdots & 0 \\ \vdots & & & & & \vdots \\ & & & \ddots & 1 & 0 \\ l_{N1} & l_{N2} & l_{N3} & \cdots & l_{N,N-1} & 1 \end{bmatrix} \tag{4.60}$$

Comparing (4.60) and (4.56), gaussian elimination constitutes factorization of $[A]$ into the product of upper and lower triangular matrices $[L]$ and $[U]$.

$$[A] = [L]\,[U] \tag{4.61}$$

Therefore, (4.57) can be written as,

$$\{y\} = [A]^{-1}\{b\} = [U]^{-1}[L]^{-1}\{b\} \tag{4.62}$$

and the inverse of a triangular matrix is easy to form (see Problem 3 at the end of this section). Establishing and storing the LU decomposition of $[A]$, or more appropriately $[U]^{-1}$ and $[L]^{-1}$, provides the ability to evaluate (4.62) for multiple load vectors $\{b\}$. In particular, as the subject matter develops, we strive to establish (4.56) as the final matrix form, and consider the theoretical development complete at that point.

A few final comments are appropriate on the actual operation of forming the LU decomposition (4.61). Elimination is undoubtedly the favorite procedure, since it usually yields matrices that retain diagonal dominance. However, mechanisms exist that can numerically destabilize the elimination algorithm, such as a small coefficient on a diagonal entry in $[A]$. Pivoting procedures exist to reorder the equations to eliminate this. For multidimensional problems, the bandwidth of (4.58) is crucially dependent on node numbering. Algorithmic procedures are available to minimize the numbering sequences (George, 1971).

If (4.64) is symmetric, a similar form for the decomposition of $[A]$ exists by dividing out the diagonal entries u_{ii} of $[U]$, into a matrix $[D]$ with positive entries as

$$D \equiv \begin{bmatrix} u_{11} & 0 & 0 & 0 & \ldots \\ 0 & u_{22} & 0 & 0 & \\ 0 & 0 & u_{33} & 0 & \\ \vdots & & & \ddots & \\ \vdots & & & & u_{NN} \end{bmatrix} \tag{4.63}$$

Ones are then placed on the diagonal of $[U]$, see (4.58), in the manner similar to $[L]$, (4.60). Therefore, (4.61) becomes

$$[A] = [L]\,[D]\,[D]^{-1}\,[U] \tag{4.64}$$

Since $[A]$ is symmetric,

$$[D]^{-1}\,[U] = [L]^T$$

Therefore, the symmetric decomposition form of (4.61) is

$$[A] = [L]\,[D]\,[L]^T \tag{4.65}$$

An alternative form for (4.65) is called Cholesky factorization and involves specification of a new lower triangular form, $[\tilde{L}] \equiv [L]\,[D^{1/2}]$. Then, using (4.64)–(4.65),

$$[A] = [\tilde{L}]\,[\tilde{L}]^T \tag{4.66}$$

The interested student is referred to the literature on linear algebra and matrix iterative techniques for additional detail on this subject (Varga, 1962).

Problems

1 Compute the solution to (4.33) in the specific form $f(y) = y^2 - 3y - 4 = 0$, using the linear and Newton iteration algorithms (4.35) and (4.42), respectively. Assume $y^0 = 0$ and $y^0 = 2$ as starting solutions. Evaluate the convergence rate for each procedure, and interpret your results in terms of the convergence proofs and the extent of the convergence intervals I.

2 Prove that the convergence rate for the multiple-dependent variable Newton iteration algorithm (4.46)–(4.51) is quadratic.

3 Reestablish the solution to the matrix equation system, $Ay = b$, from Example 2.6, (2.161) using gaussian elimination, and establish the LU decomposition of A. Then prove that L^{-1} and U^{-1} are easy to form

$$A = \begin{bmatrix} 5.3 & -3.0 & 0.10 & 0 \\ -3.3 & 7.2 & 0.10 & 0.15 \\ 0.058333 & 0.10 & 0.20 & -0.0291667 \\ 0 & 0.15 & -0.0291667 & 0.125 \end{bmatrix} \qquad b = \begin{bmatrix} 3450 \\ 1288.78 \\ -1.12942 \\ 46.0279 \end{bmatrix}$$

4.6 INTEGRATION ALGORITHMS FOR ORDINARY DIFFERENTIAL EQUATIONS

Equation (4.30), the finite-element algorithm expression for the energy equation system (4.12)–(4.15), is a (large) order system of ordinary differential equations. As noted in Sec. 4.5, application of an integration algorithm reduces the solution requirement to algebra. This section reviews the essence of numerical algorithm formulation for solution of ordinary differential equations of the type produced in fluid mechanics analysis. The subject area is considerably broader than considered herein [see, for example, Gear (1971) and Ralston (1965)].

As utilized in Sec. 4.5, the essential features of the methodology become transparent upon examination of a scalar equation. The equivalent of (4.33), for the present requirement, is

$$y'(x) \equiv \frac{dy}{dx} = f(y(x), b) \tag{4.67}$$

$$y(x_0) = y_0 \tag{4.68}$$

Assuming the x axis not a characteristic, the solution to (4.67) is obtained parallel to the positive x direction, between the points x_0 and, say, x_1, by constructing a Taylor series expansion.

$$y(x_1) = y(x_0) + \frac{dy}{dx}\bigg|_{\bar{x}} \Delta x + \frac{1}{2!}\frac{d^2y}{dx^2}\bigg|_{\bar{x}} (\Delta x)^2 + \frac{1}{3!}\frac{d^3y}{dx^3}\bigg|_{\bar{x}} (\Delta x)^3 + \cdots \tag{4.69}$$

In (4.69), $\bar{x}$ is a coordinate on the x axis, $x_0 \leqslant \bar{x} \leqslant x_1$, at which the derivative is evaluated, and $\Delta x \equiv x_1 - x_0$. Using (4.67)–(4.68), (4.69) takes the form

$$y(x_1) = y(x_0) + f(\bar{x})\,\Delta x + f'(\bar{x})\,\frac{\Delta x^2}{2!} + f''(\bar{x})\,\frac{\Delta x^3}{3!} + \cdots \tag{4.70}$$

Generalizing, let (4.70) lie between any two coordinates on the x axis $x_n \leqslant \bar{x} \leqslant x_{n+K}$, and denote $\Delta x \equiv x_{n+K} - x_n \equiv \mathrm{h}$, the uniform integration step size. Restricting attention to forms of (4.70) that explicitly retain the first derivative only (since the typical equation in fluid mechanics is first order), the basic consideration becomes evaluation of (4.70) in the form

$$y_{n+K} \equiv y(x_{n+K}) = \sum_{k=1}^{K} a^k y_{n+k-1} + h \sum_{k=0}^{K} b^k f(x_{n+k}) + O(h^2 f'(\bar{x})) + \cdots \tag{4.71}$$

Equation (4.71) represents a multistep integration algorithm for (4.67)-(4.68), wherein the newest value of $y(x_{n+K}) \equiv y_{n+K}$ is determined from the previous K values of $y(x_{n+K-k})$, $k = 1, 2, \ldots, K$ (excluding the present value), and the present and previous K values of the derivative, $f'(x_{n+k})$, $k = 0, 1, \ldots, K$. The last right-side term presents the order (O) of the term at which (4.70) has been truncated in arriving at the form (4.71). The expansion coefficients a^k and b^k in (4.71) are evaluated algebraically to imbed desired accuracy and stability characteristics into the resultant integration algorithm. For example, restricting attention to $K = 1$, (4.71) produces the family of one-step integration algorithms

$$y_{n+1} = a^1 y_n + h\,[b^0 f(x_n) + b^1 f(x_{n+1})] + O(h^2 f'(\bar{x})) + \cdots \tag{4.72}$$

Since (4.72) must be consistent with the Taylor series expansion (4.69), this requires that $a^1 = 1$ and $b^0 + b^1 = 1$. Generalizing [see Henrici (1962)], the fundamental consistency requirements for (4.71) are

$$\sum_{k=1}^{K} a^k = 1 \qquad \sum_{k=0}^{K} b^k = 1 \tag{4.73}$$

Comparing (4.73) and (4.71), the consistency requirement generates two algebraic equations for determination of the $2K + 1$ expansion coefficients in (4.71). Hence, in (4.72) for example, one of the expansion coefficients b^k remains arbitrary and forms a parameter in the generation of specific integration algorithms derivable from (4.72).

Several very familiar algorithms can be derived from (4.72) and (4.73). For example, denoting $f'(x_{n+k}) \equiv f'_{n+k}$, the forward Euler algorithm is obtained from (4.72) by specifying $b^1 \equiv 0$

$$y_{n+1} = y_n + hf_n \tag{4.74}$$

In a similar manner, the trapezoidal rule is obtained by setting $b^0 = \frac{1}{2} = b^1$. This is equivalent to requiring that (4.72) exactly interpolate a second-degree polynomial, and the integration form is

$$y_{n+1} = y_n + \frac{h}{2}\,(f_n + f_{n+1}) \tag{4.75}$$

Algorithm (4.75) is implicit since $f_{n+1} = f(y(x_{n+1}))$ is unknown. The completely implicit, or backward Euler formula, is obtained from (4.72) by setting $b^0 = 0$ and $b^1 = 1$.

$$y_{n+1} = y_n + hf_{n+1} \tag{4.76}$$

For (4.67) a linear, constant-coefficient equation, (4.74)-(4.76) represent linear algebraic equations written on y_{n+1}. For the more general case, where $f(y(x), b)$ is arbitrary, only (4.74) remains linear, while (4.75) and (4.76) become nonlinear algebraic equations. By completing the Taylor series expansions for all terms in (4.74) and (4.76), it is readily determined (Henrici, 1962) that these integration formulas are each first-order accurate, i.e., the truncation error term is $O(h^2 f'(\bar{x}))$. It is left as an exercise to show that (4.75) is second-order accurate.

A second property of fundamental impact regarding usefulness of integration algorithms is stability. A numerical integration algorithm is defined as unconditionally stable if the error generated in the solution (excepting roundoff error, which stems from use of finite word length on a digital computer) is independent of the integration step size h, as the integration process proceeds indefinitely. Alternatively, the algorithm is designated as relatively stable if the error is monotonically decreasing for a monotone decreasing solution, as the integration process proceeds indefinitely. The simple forward Euler algorithm (4.74) has a severe absolute stability limitation, which typically necessitates marching at very small step sizes. Both the trapezoidal and backward Euler formulas (4.75)-(4.76) are unconditionally stable, for (4.67) a homogeneous linear equation. This feature is molified somewhat for the nonlinear equation of interest however, since solution of either (4.75) or (4.76) requires iteration with its associated convergence interval as a function of h.

Alternative algorithm formulations exist within the framework of (4.71) for $K \geqslant 1$, as well as the predictor-corrector variants. For $K = 2$, for example, (4.71) becomes

$$y_{n+2} = a^1 y_n + a^2 y_{n+1} + h(b^0 f_n + b^1 f_{n+1} + b^2 f_{n+2}) \tag{4.77}$$

The five expansion coefficients are determined subject to the consistency constraints (4.73). A second-order accurate explicit algorithm, with good stability characteristics, is the midpoint, or leap-frog rule, established from (4.77) by setting $a^2 = 0 = b^0$, yielding

$$y_{n+2} = y_n + hf_{n+1} \tag{4.78}$$

A starting solution for (4.78) is required to establish y_{n+1}, hence f_{n+1}, and may be chosen from any of the one-step methods. Many alternative algorithms may be established from (4.77) and its many more complex counterparts for $K \geqslant 2$. For example, the entire family of Adams-Bashforth-Moulton algorithms (see Ralston, 1965; Gear, 1971; Henrici, 1962) can be derived from (4.71).

The alternative to selecting $K > 1$, is to develop multistep predictor-corrector techniques for (4.67). For example, Nigro (1971) and Lomax (1968) have derived various-order accurate, explicit, one-step, multistage predictor-corrector algorithms. In these instances (4.71) takes the form (replacing f_n with y'_n for clarity)

$$
\begin{aligned}
p_{n+1} &= y_n + hy'_n \\
q_{n+1}^{(1)} &= y_n + h(b_1^0 y'_n + b_1^1 p'_{n+1}) \\
q_{n+1}^{(2)} &= y_n + h(b_2^0 y'_n + b_2^1 q_{n+1}^{(1)\prime}) \\
&\vdots \\
q_{n+1}^{(K-1)} &= y_n + h(b_{K-1}^0 y'_n + b_{K-1}^1 q_{n+1}^{(K-2)\prime}) \\
y_{n+1} &= y_n + h(b_K^0 y'_n + b_K^1 q_{n+1}^{(K-1)\prime})
\end{aligned}
\tag{4.79}
$$

In (4.79), p_{n+1} is the predicted value of y_{n+1}; $q_{n+1}^{(j)}$ represents the jth correction to the predicted value of y_{n+1}; and the prime (′) components $q_{n+1}^{(j)\prime}$ represent (4.67) evaluated by the jth iterate $q^{(j)}$ of y. The several expansion coefficients in (4.79) are evaluated by imposing desired constraints on accuracy and stability for the desired algorithms.

The Taylor series expansion of any established integration algorithm (4.70) provides an estimate of the order of accuracy for both explicit and implicit formulas; generally speaking, more than one solution of the same problem is required to quantify an error estimate. Of the many available methods, Richardson extrapolation is fundamental to the concept (Ralston, 1965, p. 118). Choosing the trapezoidal rule for example, (4.75), the Taylor series expansion (see Problem 1 at the end of this section) determines the truncation error term e_{n+1} to be

$$
e_{n+1} = -\frac{h^3}{12} f''(\bar{x}) + O(h^4 f'''(\bar{x})) + \cdots \tag{4.80}
$$

where $x_n \leqslant \bar{x} \leqslant x_{n+1}$. Repeating the integration (4.75) over the same interval using half the step size of the previous integration produces a second solution $\tilde{y}_{n+1}$. Note that this involves one additional derivative evaluation $f'_{n+1/2}$. Thus, two distinct approximations to the true solution Y_{n+1} at x_{n+1} are

$$
\begin{aligned}
Y_{n+1} &\approx y_{n+1} - \frac{h^3}{12} f''(\bar{x}) + O(h^4 f'''(\bar{x})) + \cdots \\
Y_{n+1} &\approx \tilde{y}_{n+1} - \frac{(h/2)^3}{12} f''(\bar{x}) + O((h/2)^4 f'''(\bar{x})) + \cdots
\end{aligned}
\tag{4.81}
$$

Equations (4.81) are algebraically combined to produce a third approximation y^h, the corresponding Taylor series expansion for which is free of the $f''(\bar{x})$ term, i.e.,

$$
y_{n+1}^h \equiv \frac{8\tilde{y}_{n+1} - y_{n+1}}{7} = \tilde{y}_{n+1} + \left(\frac{\tilde{y}_{n+1} - y_{n+1}}{7}\right) + O(h^4 f'''(\bar{x})) + \cdots \tag{4.82}
$$

Hence, (4.82) is a higher-order accurate estimate of the true solution at t_{n+1}, since its truncation error term is proportional to h^4.

Equations (4.75) and (4.80)–(4.82) illustrate a special case of Richardson extrapolation, which is generally applicable to all numerical integration algorithms. The error in the numerical computation on the interval h can be expressed for any algorithm in the form

$$e = \sum_{j=K}^{\infty} c_j h^j, \qquad c_K \neq 0, h \to 0 \tag{4.83}$$

where the c_j's are constants independent of h but are in general a function of $y'(\bar{x})$. Integrating (4.67) at two integration intervals h_{I} and h_{II} yields two approximations to the exact solution Y, as

$$Y \approx y_{\mathrm{I}} + \sum_{j=K}^{\infty} c_j h_{\mathrm{I}}^j \qquad Y \approx y_{\mathrm{II}} + \sum_{j=K}^{\infty} c_j h_{\mathrm{II}}^j \tag{4.84}$$

Multiplying the first of (4.84) by h_{II}^K, and the latter by h_{I}^K, and subtracting yields the general form for Richardson extrapolation.

$$Y \approx \frac{1}{h_{\mathrm{I}}^K - h_{\mathrm{II}}^K}(h_{\mathrm{I}}^K y_{\mathrm{II}} - h_{\mathrm{II}}^K y_{\mathrm{I}}) + \sum_{j=K+1}^{\infty} c_j \left(\frac{h_{\mathrm{I}}^K h_{\mathrm{II}}^j - h_{\mathrm{II}}^K h_{\mathrm{I}}^j}{h_{\mathrm{I}}^K - h_{\mathrm{II}}^K} \right) \tag{4.85}$$

Note that the lead truncation error term in (4.85) is always at least of order $K+1$, for (4.84) representing integration using a Kth order-accurate algorithm. In particular, when $h_{\mathrm{I}} = 2h_{\mathrm{II}}$, the general form of (4.82) is

$$Y \approx \frac{1}{2^K - 1}(2^K y_{\mathrm{II}} - y_{\mathrm{I}}) + \sum_{j=K+1}^{\infty} \frac{2^K - 2^j}{2^K - 1} c_j h^j \tag{4.86}$$

Extension of these concepts to a multiple dependent variable system is direct.

Richardson extrapolation can be utilized to estimate an integration step size h, that yields a solution of (4.67) approximating a given accuracy. The computation is based upon estimation of error in the current solution obtained at integration step size h. Using the trapezoidal rule (4.75) as the example, the truncation error is (4.80). Identifying a factor of safety $C \leqslant 1$, (4.80) yields an equation for a new integration size αh, as

$$Ce_{n+1} \approx \tfrac{1}{12}(\alpha h)^3 f''(\bar{x}) + O(\alpha h)^4 f'''(\bar{x}) \tag{4.87}$$

Retaining only the first term, assuming $\bar{x} \approx x_{n+1}$, and evaluating $f''(x_{n+1})$ using a second-order accurate difference formula [e.g., (2.136)], (4.87) becomes an explicit expression for αh.

$$\alpha h \approx \left[\frac{12C|e_{n+1}|}{(2/h^2)(f_n + f_{n+1} - 2f_{n+1/2})} \right]^{1/3} \tag{4.88}$$

where $h \equiv x_{n+1} - x_n$ and the numerator is (4.87). No additional derivative evaluations are required, so the new integration step size αh is achieved "free," following a Richardson extrapolation to estimate solution accuracy e_{n+1}. For the example development, the estimated error in y_{n+1} is obtained from (4.82) as

$$e_{n+1} \approx \tfrac{1}{7}(\tilde{y}_{n+1} - y_{n+1}) \tag{4.89}$$

A higher order accurate formula (4.87) is obtained by retaining additional terms in the Taylor series, or using the more general formulation (4.85).

With this introduction, consider the integration of (4.30). The requirement remains completion of the Taylor series expansion (4.69) written for the column matrix $\{Q(t)\}$, which in turn requires expression of the derivatives $\{Q(t)\}'$. While not performed in actual practice, the matrix solution of (4.30) is the expression

$$\{Q\}' = -[C]^{-1}([U+K+H]\{Q\} + \{b\}) \tag{4.90}$$

The family of one-step integration algorithms (4.74)-(4.76) can be written for the multidependent variable system (4.90), for example, as

$$\{Q\}_{j+1} = \{Q\}_j + h[\theta\{Q\}'_{j+1} + (1-\theta)\{Q\}'_j] \tag{4.91}$$

The factor θ, $0 \leqslant \theta \leqslant 1$, controls implicitness, hence also stability and order of accuracy; subscript j is the integration step index; and h is the step size. Substituting (4.90) into (4.91), combining matrix products on $\{\cdot\}_{j+1}$ and $\{\cdot\}_j$, and employing the identity matrix $[I]$, yields

$$\begin{aligned}[I + h\theta[C]^{-1}_{j+1}[U+K+H]_{j+1}]\{Q\}_{j+1} &= [I - h(1-\theta)[C]^{-1}_j[U+K+H]_j]\{Q\}_j \\ &\quad - h\theta[C]^{-1}_{j+1}\{b\}_{j+1} - h(1-\theta)[C]^{-1}_j\{b\}_j \end{aligned} \tag{4.92}$$

as the matrix solution statement for the energy conservation equation system. As written, (4.92) is nonlinear and not directly solvable. Modifying the matrix multiplying $\{Q\}_{j+1}$, to evaluation at step j, produces a linearization, and (4.92) then corresponds to the solution procedure outlined in (4.34)-(4.35) with linear convergence.

As indicated, it is not desirable to form the inverse of $[C]$. Specification of the trapezoidal integration formula ($\theta \equiv \frac{1}{2}$) in (4.91) provides a preferable algorithm formulation as

$$\{Q\}_{j+1} = \{Q_j\} + h\{Q\}'_{j+1/2} \tag{4.93}$$

Substituting (4.90), and then denoting the midpoint evaluation as the algebraic average yields

$$\begin{aligned}\{Q\}_{j+1} = \{Q_j\} - \frac{h}{2}[C]^{-1}_{j+1/2}([U+K+H]_{j+1}\{Q\}_{j+1} + \{b\}_{j+1} \\ + [U+K+H]_j\{Q\}_j + \{b\}_j)\end{aligned} \tag{4.94}$$

Premultiplying (4.94) by $[C]_{j+1/2}$ and rearranging yields

$$\begin{aligned}\left[C_{j+1/2} + \frac{h}{2}[U+K+H]_{j+1}\right]\{Q\}_{j+1} &= \left[C_{j+1/2} - \frac{h}{2}[U+K+H]_j\right]\{Q\}_j \\ &\quad - \frac{h}{2}(\{b\}_{j+1} + \{b\}_j)\end{aligned} \tag{4.95}$$

as the matrix solution statement for (4.90)-(4.91). Note that (4.95) does not require formation of $[C]^{-1}$; it is directly solvable upon linearization of the matrix modifying $\{Q\}_{j+1}$.

The alternative to these matrix iterative solution statements that exhibit linear rates of convergence is utilization of the Newton iterative form, see (4.50)-(4.51). Here, (4.91) is written as

$$\{F\}_{j+1} = \{Q\}_{j+1} - \{Q\}_j - h(\theta\,\{Q\}'_{j+1} + (1-\theta)\{Q\}'_j) = \{0\} \tag{4.96}$$

and (4.90) provides the expression for the derivative matrices. The Newton solution form for (4.96) is

$$[J(F)]^p_{j+1}\,\{\delta Q\}^{p+1}_{j+1} = -\{F\}^p_{j+1} \tag{4.97}$$

where
$$\{\delta Q\}^{p+1}_{j+1} \equiv \{Q\}^{p+1}_{j+1} - \{Q\}^p_{j+1} \tag{4.98}$$

Completing the substitution of (4.90) in (4.96), it is left as an exercise to show that

$$\begin{aligned}\{F\}^p_{j+1} = [C]^p_{j+1/2}(\{Q\}^p_{j+1} - \{Q\}_j) + h(\theta\,[U+K+H]^p_{j+1}\{Q\}^p_{j+1} + \theta\,\{b\}_{j+1}\\ + (1-\theta)[U+K+H]_j\{Q\}_j + (1-\theta\,\{b\}_j)\end{aligned} \tag{4.99}$$

By definition, the jacobian in (4.97) is the derivative of (4.99) with respect to Q^p_{j+1}. The lead terms in the expression, see (4.43), upon differentiation of (4.99), are

$$\frac{\partial\{F\}}{\partial\{Q\}} \approx [C] + h\theta\,[U+K+H] + \cdots \tag{4.100}$$

assuming $[C]_{j+1/2}$ evaluated at step $j+1$.

The Newton algorithm specification (4.96)-(4.100) should exhibit a quadratic rate of convergence, as proved for the scalar system (4.41)-(4.42), upon completion of the remaining terms in (4.100). If these additional terms are due only to nonlinearities such as thermal conductivity dependence on temperature, then the quadratic convergence should not be measurably degraded by their omission. A great deal of attention will be given to jacobian formation in the remainder of the text.

Problems

1 Complete the Taylor series expansions for the (*a*) Euler, (*b*) trapezoidal, (*c*) backward Euler, (*d*) leap-frog integration algorithms, Eqs. (4.74)-(4.76) and (4.78), and determine their truncation error, hence their order of accuracy.

2 Establish (4.88) for the step-size estimate based on error evaluation using Richardson extrapolation.

3 Establish the form (4.94)-(4.95).

4 Derive (4.99) using (4.96) and (4.90).

4.7 SOLUTIONS FOR ONE-DIMENSIONAL CONVECTION/DIFFUSION

We are now in the position to examine the transient finite-element solution algorithm for the convection-diffusion problem statement (4.12)-(4.15). The procedure of Chap. 2 is repeated wherein an elementary discretization of the basic problem is employed to facilitate explicit hand assembly and analysis of the basic operations. Once the fundamentals become enforced, accuracy, convergence and versatility are then documented in Sec. 4.8.

Two problem classes are considered in these sections. The analysis of heat transmission in the thick axisymmetric cylinder, subject to convective loading, is repeated transient using both explicit and implicit integration. This provides the opportunity to evaluate the initial-value matrix condensation process, often employed with an explicit integration procedure to reduce the C matrix inverse to a trivial operation. The second problem corresponds to pure convection of an energy packet by a uniform velocity field in the total absence of diffusion.

Example 4.1 Establish the finite-element matrix equation system for the transient temperature distribution in a stationary axisymmetric cylinder (see Fig. 2.3) employing the linear basis $\{N_1\}$ and a two finite-element discretization of the solution domain. The cylinder is steel, with a combined ρc of 120 J/m^3 K; the initial temperature is 306.85282 K, and h, k, and T_r are identical with the example problems in Chap. 2. The convection velocity $\mathbf{u}$ is zero. From (3.52)-(3.55), the required matrix forms on R_e^1, with span $1.0 \leqslant r \leqslant 1.5$, are (see also Examples 2.1 and 2.2):

Conductivity matrix:

$$\int_{R_1^1} \nabla\{N_1\} \cdot k_e \nabla T_e \, d\tau = 50\pi \begin{bmatrix} 1 & -1 \\ -1 & 1 \end{bmatrix} \begin{Bmatrix} Q1 \\ Q2 \end{Bmatrix}_1$$

Boundary condition matrix:

$$\int_{\partial R_1} \{N_1\} h_e (T_e - T_r) \, d\sigma = 40\pi \left(\begin{bmatrix} 1 & 0 \\ 0 & 0 \end{bmatrix} \begin{Bmatrix} Q1 \\ Q2 \end{Bmatrix}_1 - \begin{Bmatrix} 1500. \\ 0. \end{Bmatrix} \right)$$

The axisymmetric thermal capacity matrix is established from (3.48)-(3.49), with $\{T\}_e$ replaced by $\{R\}_e$, yielding

Capacity matrix:

$$\int_{R_1^1} \rho c_e \{R\}_e^T \{N_1\}\{N_1\}\{N_1\}^T \{Q\}_e' \, d\tau = \frac{60\pi}{12} \begin{bmatrix} 9 & 5 \\ 5 & 11 \end{bmatrix} \begin{Bmatrix} Q1 \\ Q2 \end{Bmatrix}_1'$$

Repeating these operations for element R_2 [see Example 2.2 and (3.48)-(3.55)]:

Conductivity matrix:

$$\int_{R_2^1} \nabla\{N_1\} \cdot k_e \nabla T_e \, d\tau = 70\pi \begin{bmatrix} 1 & -1 \\ -1 & 1 \end{bmatrix} \begin{Bmatrix} Q1 \\ Q2 \end{Bmatrix}_2$$

Capacity matrix:

$$\int_{R_2^1} \rho c_e \{R\}_e^T \{N_1\}\{N_1\}^T \{Q\}_e' \, d\tau = \frac{60\pi}{12}\begin{bmatrix} 13 & 7 \\ 7 & 15 \end{bmatrix}\begin{Bmatrix} Q1 \\ Q2 \end{Bmatrix}_2'$$

The global finite-element matrix system, using the assembly operator S_e, (2.188)-(2.191), and after division by a common denominator and π, is

$$\frac{1}{2}\left[\begin{array}{cc|c} 9 & 5 & 0 \\ 5 & 24 & 7 \\ \hline 0 & 7 & 15 \end{array}\right]\begin{Bmatrix} Q(1) \\ Q(2) \\ Q(3) \end{Bmatrix}' = -\left[\begin{array}{cc|c} 9 & -5 & 0 \\ -5 & 12 & -7 \\ \hline 0 & -7 & 7 \end{array}\right]\begin{Bmatrix} Q(1) \\ Q(2) \\ Q(3) \end{Bmatrix} + \begin{Bmatrix} 6000 \\ 0 \\ \hline 0 \end{Bmatrix} \tag{4.101}$$

Partitioning (4.101) to account for $Q(3)$ held constant at 306.85282 K, yields

$$\frac{1}{2}\begin{bmatrix} 9 & 5 \\ 5 & 24 \end{bmatrix}\begin{Bmatrix} Q(1) \\ Q(2) \end{Bmatrix}' = -\begin{bmatrix} 9 & -5 \\ -5 & 12 \end{bmatrix}\begin{Bmatrix} Q(1) \\ Q(2) \end{Bmatrix} + \begin{Bmatrix} 6000. \\ 2147.97 \end{Bmatrix} \tag{4.102}$$

Equation (4.102) is the finite-element matrix statement of the transient thick-cylinder problem. Note the right side is identical with the steady-state statement of the problem [see (2.71)-(2.72)]. The transient problem specification is completed by the initial conditions (4.15)

$$\begin{Bmatrix} Q(1) \\ Q(2) \\ Q(3) \end{Bmatrix}_0 = 306.85282\begin{Bmatrix} 1 \\ 1 \\ 1 \end{Bmatrix} \tag{4.103}$$

Numerical solution of (4.102)-(4.103) requires selection of an integration algorithm. Hence,

Example 4.2 Solve (4.102)-(4.103) to steady state, using the explicit Euler integration algorithm (4.74). Written on $\{Q\}$, with elements $Q(1)$ and $Q(2)$, (4.74) yields

$$\{Q\}_{j+1} = \{Q\}_j + \Delta t\,\{f\}_j \tag{4.104}$$

where

$$\{f\}_j \equiv -[C]^{-1}([K]\{Q\}_j + \{b\}) \tag{4.105}$$

Using (4.102) in (4.105) yields

$$\{f\}_j = -2\begin{bmatrix} 9 & 5 \\ 5 & 24 \end{bmatrix}^{-1}\left(\begin{bmatrix} 9 & -5 \\ -5 & 12 \end{bmatrix}\begin{Bmatrix} Q(1) \\ Q(2) \end{Bmatrix}_j + \begin{Bmatrix} 6000. \\ 2147.97 \end{Bmatrix}\right)$$

$$= \frac{-2}{191}\begin{bmatrix} 24 & -5 \\ -5 & 9 \end{bmatrix}\left(\begin{bmatrix} 9 & -5 \\ -5 & 12 \end{bmatrix}\begin{Bmatrix} Q(1) \\ Q(2) \end{Bmatrix}_j + \begin{Bmatrix} 6000. \\ 2147.97 \end{Bmatrix}\right)$$

$$= \frac{-2}{191}\left(\begin{bmatrix} -241 & 180 \\ 90 & -133 \end{bmatrix}\begin{Bmatrix} Q(1) \\ Q(2) \end{Bmatrix}_j + \begin{Bmatrix} 133{,}260.1 \\ -10{,}668.3 \end{Bmatrix}\right) \tag{4.106}$$

Solution of (4.104) with (4.103) and (4.106) produces the transient evolution of $\{Q\}$. An acceptable integration step size Δt must be established to maintain absolute stability during integration. The real absolute stability interval of the Euler integration algorithm is $-2 \leqslant \Delta t\, \lambda_{ext} < 0$ (Ralston, 1965), where Δt is the integration step size and λ_{ext} is the extremum eigenvalue of the jacobian of (4.106), that is, $\partial\{f\}/\partial\{Q\}$. Since the problem is linear, these (constant) eigenvalues can be determined analytically by solution of the determinental equation

$$\det\begin{bmatrix} \left(-241 - \frac{191}{2}\lambda\right) & 180 \\ 90 & \left(-133 - \frac{191}{2}\lambda\right) \end{bmatrix} \equiv 0 \tag{4.107}$$

Expansion of (4.107) yields the quadratic equation for λ:

$$\lambda^2 + 3.9162304\,\lambda + 1.7767671 = 0$$

The solutions for λ are

$$\{\lambda\} = \begin{Bmatrix} -3.40587 \\ -0.51036 \end{Bmatrix} \tag{4.108}$$

Therefore, the maximum allowable integration step size that retains absolute stability during integration of (4.104) is

$$\Delta t_{max} \leqslant \left| \frac{2}{\lambda_{ext}} \right| = 0.5872\ \text{h} \tag{4.109}$$

Maintenance of adequate accuracy for the solution of (4.102) may require use of a Δt smaller than Δt_{max} to control truncation error during the transient evolution. The steady-state solution is unaffected by truncation error, of course, but in no case may the integration step-size exceed Δt_{max}.

Figure 4.4 graphs the computed temperature distribution, for the first 1.25 h into the transient, in comparison to the exact solution, and that solution obtained by numerical solution of Example 4.2 using a 64-element discretization. Observe that the surface temperature prediction, for the truly coarse two-element discretization, follows fairly closely that of the exact solution, with a maximum deviation of about 15 percent. Note also that the accuracy of the interior node temperature is not adequate. In particular, during the first few time steps, the corase grid solution erroneously predicts a depression of this node temperature below its initial value.

This performance is not unexpected; it is strictly a function of the coarse discretization and amenable to elimination through grid refinement. Similar results have been reported for higher-dimensional problem specifications, (Baker and Manhardt, 1972). An ad hoc means for correction of this erroneous negative heat flow is condensation of the element heat capacity matrix $[C]_e$. The $[C]$ matrix for this problem specification is [see (4.102)]

$$[C] = \frac{1}{2} \begin{bmatrix} 9 & 5 \\ 5 & 24 \end{bmatrix} \tag{4.110}$$

which has been termed "consistent" in the literature. The alternative form, called "condensed," is defined to yield a diagonal capacity matrix, as obtained using most finite-difference algorithms. The definition is

$$[C] \equiv \begin{bmatrix} c_{11} & & 0 \\ & c_{22} & \\ 0 & & \ddots \; c_{nn} \end{bmatrix} = \underset{\sim}{c}_{(jj)} [I] \tag{4.111}$$

where $[I]$ is the identity matrix. The matrix coefficients $\underset{\sim}{c}_{(jj)}$ are formed, either at the element or global level, from the consistent matrix elements c_{ij} by several different techniques. One method is rowwise summation,

$$\underset{\sim}{c}_{(jj)} \equiv \sum_{i=1}^{n} c_{ij} \tag{4.112}$$

The second is normalization of the diagonal elements of $[C]$ and outright discarding of the off-diagonal entries. The former is explored in the following example.

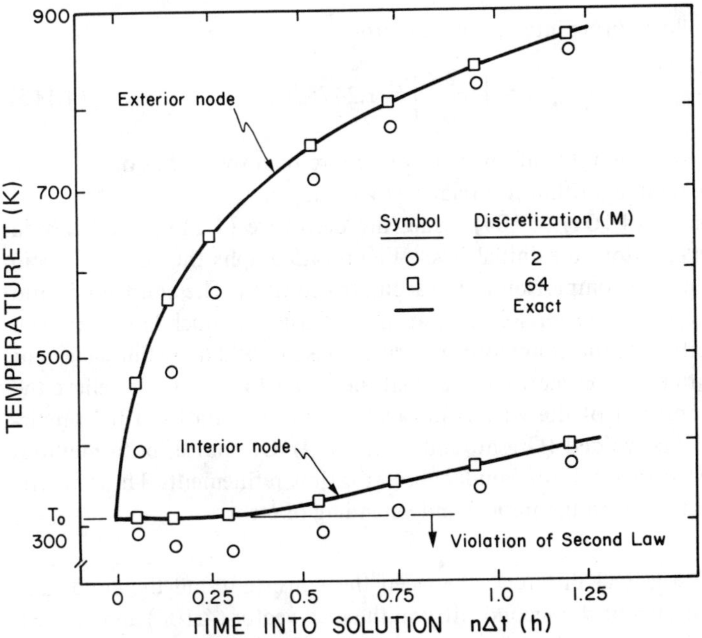

Figure 4.4 Transient temperature distributions, axisymmetric cylinder with convection, $\{N_1\}$.

Example 4.3 Solve (4.102)–(4.103) to steady state, using the explicit euler integration algorithm (4.74) and the condensed capacity matrix (4.111). From (4.102), using (4.112),

$$[C] = \frac{1}{2}\begin{bmatrix} 14 & 0 \\ 0 & 29 \end{bmatrix}$$

Equations (4.104)–(4.105) remain the basic matrix definition. However, the derivative matrix $\{f\}_j$ is replaced, see (4.106), as

$$\{f\}_j = -2\begin{bmatrix} 14 & 0 \\ 0 & 29 \end{bmatrix}^{-1}\left(\begin{bmatrix} 9 & -5 \\ -5 & 12 \end{bmatrix}\begin{Bmatrix} Q(1) \\ Q(2) \end{Bmatrix}_j + \begin{Bmatrix} 6000. \\ 2147.97 \end{Bmatrix}\right)$$

$$= \frac{2}{406}\left(\begin{bmatrix} 261 & -145 \\ -70 & 168 \end{bmatrix}\begin{Bmatrix} Q(1) \\ Q(2) \end{Bmatrix}_j + \begin{Bmatrix} 174{,}000 \\ 30{,}071.6 \end{Bmatrix}\right) \tag{4.113}$$

As before, the maximum integration step size must be determined, based upon the eigenvalues of the jacobian of (4.113). Solution of the matrix equation equivalent to (4.107) yields for (4.113)

$$\{\lambda\} = \begin{Bmatrix} -1.60326 \\ -0.510048 \end{Bmatrix} \tag{4.114}$$

For absolute stability during integration, therefore,

$$\Delta t_{max} \leqslant \left|\frac{2}{\lambda_{ext}}\right| = 1.2475 \text{ h} \tag{4.115}$$

Note that this maximum integration step size is more than twice that of the "consistent" finite-element algorithm formulation (4.109).

The solution of (4.102)–(4.104), using the derivative (4.113), produces no depression of $Q(2)$ below the initial level. Figure 4.5 graphs the consistent and condensed solutions in comparison to the accurate solutions. The condensed form has yielded a smoother interior solution, at the expense of a much larger error on the surface. Specifically, the condensing operation has smoothed the finite-element solution wiggles that in fact alert the user that the grid is too coarse to believe the results. The suppression of the wiggles has really removed data from the prediction, and should be avoided (Gresho and Lee, 1979). Of course, both methods converge to the correct solution under discretization refinement. These results confirm the need for a firm theoretical understanding of error.

As an aside, the sole real difference between the consistent and the condensed formulations lies in the sign of the second entry in the load vector (4.106) and (4.113). It is left as an exercise to prove that, for any uniform initial temperature distribution and for arbitrary reference temperature both greater and lesser than the initial-condition

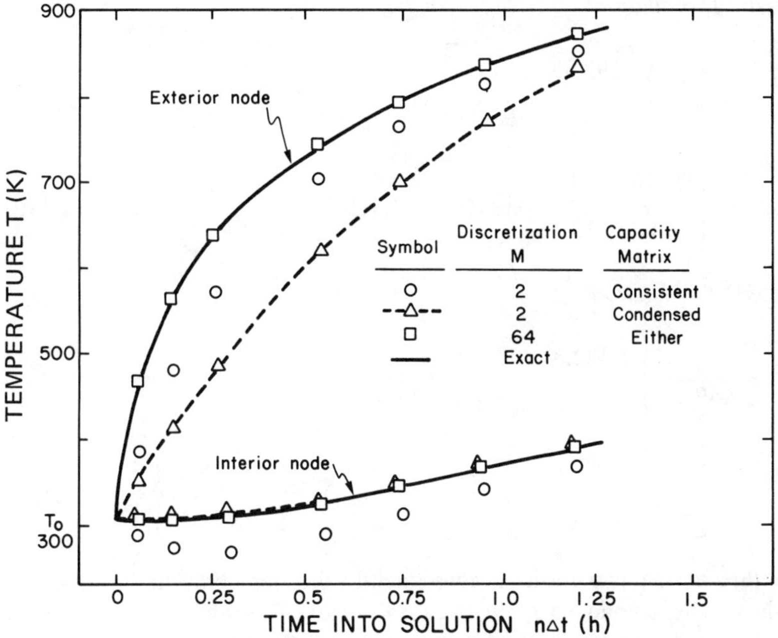

Figure 4.5 Transient temperature distributions, axisymmetric cylinder with convection, $\{N_1\}$.

temperature, the condensed formulation yields a solution that cannot violate the second law of thermodynamics. Conversely, the explicit consistent formulation will produce the spurious temperature excursion. An additional exercise proves that this phenomenon is independent of the degree k of the approximation basis $\{N_k\}$.

Example 4.4 Complete the finite-element algorithm statement (4.102)–(4.103), utilizing the trapezoidal integration algorithm (4.75) and the Newton solution statement for both the consistent and condensed formulations of the capacity matrix. The form of (4.97) for the problem definition is [see (4.100)]

$$\left[[C] + \frac{h}{2}\,[K + H] \right] \{\delta Q\}_{j+1}^{p+1} = -\{F(Q)\}_{j+1}^{p} \tag{4.116}$$

From (4.99), the expression for $\{F\}_{j+1}^{p}$ is

$$\{F(Q)\}_{j+1}^{p} \equiv [C](\{Q\}_{j+1}^{p} - \{Q\}_j) + \frac{h}{2}(\{f\}_{j+1}^{p} + \{f\}_j) \tag{4.117}$$

where

$$\{f\} \equiv [K + H]\{Q\} + \{b\} \tag{4.118}$$

All matrices necessary for evaluating these equations were presented in Examples 4.2 and 4.3. Completing the various products, the matrix equations for determination of $\{\delta Q\}_{j+1}^{p+1}$, for integration step size $h = \Delta t = 0.1$, are

"Consistent" formulation:

$$\{\delta Q\}_{j+1}^{p+1} = \frac{1}{194.7}\left\{\begin{bmatrix} 192.33 & 1.8 \\ 0.9 & 193.41 \end{bmatrix}(\{Q\}_{j+1}^{p} - \{Q\}_j)\right.$$

$$\left. - \begin{bmatrix} 24.183 & 14.5 \\ 7.0 & 13.383 \end{bmatrix}(\{Q\}_{j+1}^{p} + \{Q\}_j) + \begin{Bmatrix} 26{,}829.7 \\ -1{,}840.98 \end{Bmatrix}\right\} \tag{4.119}$$

"Condensed" formulation:

$$\{\delta Q\}_{j+1}^{p+1} = \frac{1}{449.73}\left\{\begin{bmatrix} 422.8 & 14.5 \\ 7.0 & 432.1 \end{bmatrix}(\{Q\}_{j+1}^{p} - \{Q\}_j)\right.$$

$$\left. - \begin{bmatrix} 26.93 & -14.5 \\ -7.0 & 17.63 \end{bmatrix}(\{Q\}_{j+1}^{p} + \{Q\}_j) + \begin{Bmatrix} 36{,}528.0 \\ 6{,}848.43 \end{Bmatrix}\right\} \tag{4.120}$$

The structure of the two forms is consequently different only in the sign and magnitude of the second entry in the load vector. The minus sign in (4.119) indicates that a depression of the interior node point temperature will occur, in agreement with the explicit solution. Similarly, the lack of negative entries in the load vector of (4.120) indicates no depression for the condensed formulation solution. The differences result, therefore, from the MWR theoretical construction and not from the selected integration procedure.

We now turn attention to the second example problem specification, wherein both the conductivity k and generation rate $\dot{q}$ in (4.12) are identically zero. The versatility of the finite-element algorithm statement (4.18) is illustrated by the following example.

Example 4.5 Establish the finite-difference recursion relation form, of the finite-element algorithm solution statement (4.96)–(4.99), for a one-dimensional problem specification of (4.12)–(4.15). Assume ρ a constant, $c_e = 1$, and $k \equiv 0 \equiv \dot{q}$. Employ the trapezoidal rule integration algorithm and use the linear basis $\{N_1\}$.

In this instance, one need only consider a representative finite element domain R_e^1, of measure Δ_e and spanned by $\bar{x}$.

Capacity matrix:

$$\int_{R_e^1} \rho c_e \{N_1\}\{N_1\}^T \{Q\}_e' \, d\bar{x} = \frac{\rho\,\Delta_e}{6}\begin{bmatrix} 2 & 1 \\ 1 & 2 \end{bmatrix}\{Q\}_e' \tag{4.121}$$

Convection matrix:

$$\int_{R_e^1} \rho\{N_1\}\mathbf{U}_e\cdot\nabla\{N_1\}^T\{Q\}_e\,d\bar{x} = \rho\{U\}_e^T \int_{R_e^1} \{N_1\}\{N_1\}\frac{d}{d\bar{x}}\{N_1\}^T\,d\bar{x}\{Q\}_e$$

$$= \frac{\rho}{6}\{U\}_e^T \begin{bmatrix} -\begin{Bmatrix}2\\1\end{Bmatrix} & \begin{Bmatrix}1\\1\end{Bmatrix} \\ -\begin{Bmatrix}1\\1\end{Bmatrix} & \begin{Bmatrix}1\\2\end{Bmatrix} \end{bmatrix} \{Q\}_e \qquad (4.122)$$

In forming (4.122), the $\bar{x}$ component of velocity u_e was interpolated on R_e^1 using $\{N_1\}$ and the nodal values $\{U\}_e$. The resultant scalar expression was rearranged, such that the $\bar{x}$-independent matrix $\{U\}_e$ could be extracted outside the integral, as done in Example 2.1 for the radius. Since $1/\Delta_e$ results from the single $\bar{x}$ derivative, no element measure appears in (4.122).

Since there are no source terms or homogeneous boundary condition contributions in the problem definition, (4.121)-(4.122) completes the element statement. Using the matrix definition nomenclature defined in Chap. 3, the finite-element algorithm statement (4.18) becomes

$$S_e[\rho\,\Delta_e[A200]\{Q\}_e + \rho\,\Delta_e\{U\}_e^T[A3001]\{Q\}_e] \equiv \{0\} \qquad (4.123)$$

where $[A200]$ and $[A3001]$, as constructed using $\{N_1\}$, are given in (4.121)-(4.122). The recursion relation equivalent of (4.123) is established by considering the directly adjacent finite-element domains sharing node coordinate x_j. Assuming for simplicity a uniform discretization of R^1, and noting that ρ can be cancelled from (4.123), it is left as an exercise to verify that

$$\underset{e=1}{\overset{2}{S}}\ [\Delta_e[A200]\{Q\}_e'] \to \frac{\Delta}{6}(Q_{j-1}' + 4Q_j' + Q_{j+1}') \qquad (4.124)$$

By the same token, assuming a constant imposed convection velocity u, such that $\{U\}_e = U\{1\}$,

$$\underset{e=1}{\overset{2}{S}}\ [\Delta_e U\{1\}^T[A3001]\{Q\}_e] \to \frac{U}{2}(-Q_{j-1} + Q_{j+1}) \qquad (4.125)$$

Therefore, the finite-difference recursion relation equivalent of (4.123) for uniform discretization and constant convection velocity is

$$\frac{\Delta}{6}(Q_{j-1}' + 4Q_j' + Q_{j+1}') + \frac{U}{2}(-Q_{j-1} + Q_{j+1}) = 0 \qquad (4.126)$$

Applying the trapezoidal rule integration algorithm to (4.126), and using superscript t and $t+1$ to indicate the time-step index, the recursion relation equivalent of the finite-element algorithm statement (4.99) is

$$\frac{1}{6}(Q_{j-1}^{t+1} + 4Q_j^{t+1} + Q_{j+1}^{t+1}) - \frac{1}{6}(Q_{j-1}^t + 4Q_j^t + Q_{j+1}^t)$$

$$+ \frac{U\Delta t}{2\Delta}[(-Q_{j-1}^{t+1} + Q_{j+1}^{t+1}) + (-Q_{j-1}^t + Q_{j+1}^t)] = 0 \qquad (4.127)$$

The form of (4.127), as derived by the meteorological community using alternative procedures (Pepper et al., 1979), has been termed the *chapeau* finite-difference algorithm. An even more familiar form can be established as follows:

Example 4.6 Establish the finite-difference recursion relationship, analogous to (4.127), but using the condensed capacity matrix procedure to establish (4.124).

The condensed element capacity matrix $[A200]$ is established from (4.121) by inspection as

$$\frac{\rho\,\Delta_e}{6}[A200] = \frac{\rho\,\Delta_e}{2}\begin{bmatrix} 1 & 0 \\ 0 & 1 \end{bmatrix}$$

Hence, (4.124) becomes

$$\underset{e=1}{\overset{2}{S}}\ [\Delta_e[A200]\{Q\}_e'] \Rightarrow \Delta Q_j' \qquad (4.128)$$

Therefore, for a uniform discretization and constant convection velocity, the resultant finite-difference recursion relation comparable to (4.127) is

$$Q_j^{t+1} - Q_j^t + \frac{U\Delta t}{2\Delta}[(-Q_{j-1}^{t+1} + Q_{j+1}^{t+1}) + (-Q_{j-1}^t + Q_{j+1}^t)] = 0 \qquad (4.129)$$

This form is immediately recognized as the familiar Crank-Nicolson finite-difference algorithm statement.

Therefore, the MWR formulation for the finite-element algorithm statement for convection-diffusion has indeed yielded, under appropriate constraints, several familiar algorithm statements derived by completely independent procedures. The requirement is to assess what benefit, if any, accrues to the more formal procedures being developed as finite element. For illustration consider the convection, by a constant imposed velocity U, of an "energy packet" parallel to the x axis. The initial condition (4.15) for packet is the "cosine hill"

$$T(x, 0) = 1 + \cos\left(\frac{2\pi x}{\lambda} - \frac{\pi}{2}\right) \qquad 0 \leqslant x \leqslant \lambda \qquad (4.130)$$

(see Fig. 4.6*a*), with the wavelength λ discretized uniformly into M finite-element domains. The solution domain R^1 is spanned by $4M$ elements, and the solution is

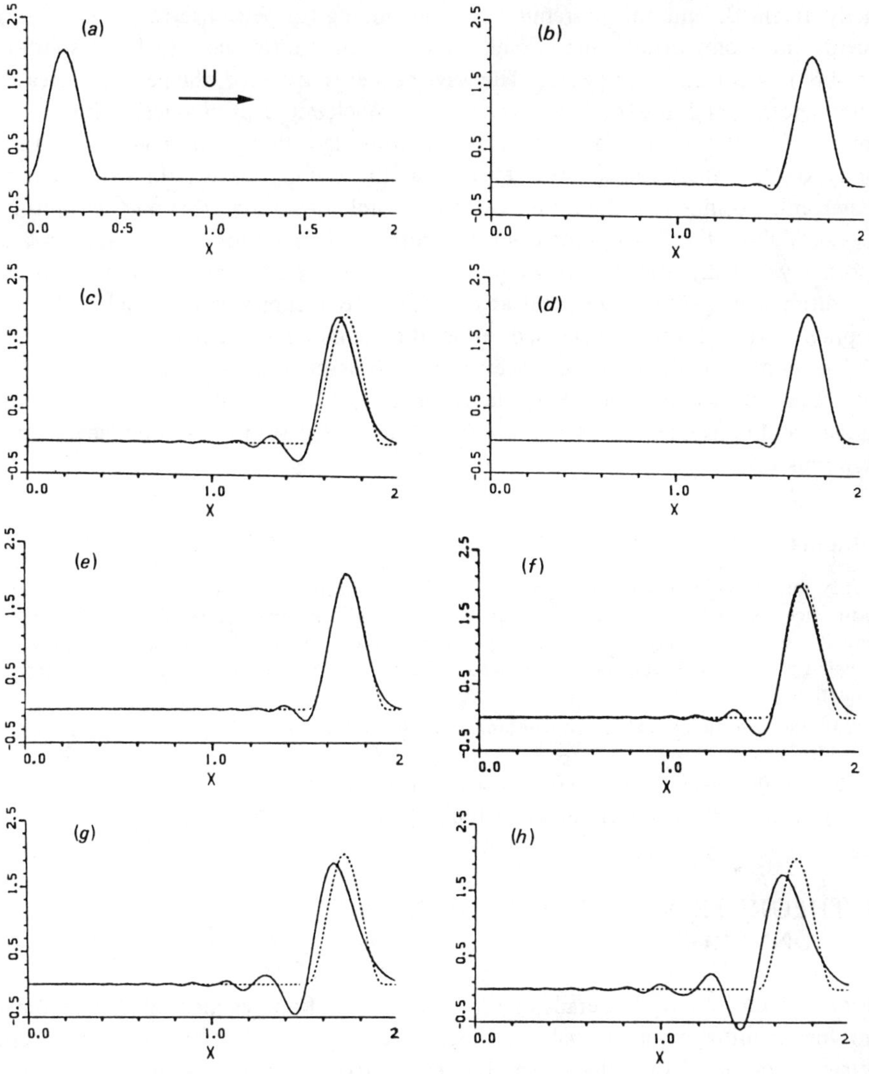

Figure 4.6 One-dimensional pure convection of an energy packet, finite element and Crank-Nicolson solution algorithms. (*a*) Initial condition; (*b*) finite element ($k = 1$), $C = 0.4$; (*c*) Crank-Nicolson, $C = 0.4$; (*d*) finite element ($k = 2$), $C = 0.4$; (*e*) finite element ($k = 1$), $C = 0.8$; (*f*) finite element ($k = 1$), $C = 1.2$; (*g*) finite element ($k = 1$), $C = 1.6$; (*h*) Crank-Nicolson, $C = 1.6$. Exact solution represented by dotted line.

stopped when the wave packet is centered between $3M$ and $4M$. The analytical solution for this problem definition is exact preservation of the initial-condition profile. Figure 4.6*b* shows the final solution obtained by the linear ($\{N_1\}$) finite-element algorithm (4.127) for $M = 20$ and for nondimensional time step (Courant number) $C = U\Delta t/\Delta = 0.4$. The exact final solution is shown by the dashed line, and the $k = 1$ finite-element solution is in excellent agreement. The peak value is almost exactly retained, and the extremum for the trailing (dispersion error) wake is −3 percent. In comparison, the Crank-Nicolson finite-difference (4.129) solution (Fig. 4.6*c*), is considerably poorer. The wave packet is distorted, the peak is decreased to 95 percent, and the trailing wake error is much more pronounced with an extremum of −12 percent. The $k = 2$ finite-element algorithm solution (Fig. 4.6*d*) lies exactly on the analytical solution except for the trailing wake error extremum of −1 percent. To illustrate the influence of temporal truncation error on the solution, Fig. 4.6*e*–*f* show the $k = 1$ finite-element solutions obtained for $C = 0.8$ and $C = 1.2$, respectively. Finally, Fig. 4.6*g*–*h* compare the $k = 1$ finite element and Crank-Nicolson finite-difference solutions obtained at $C = 1.6$. The accuracy is degraded to an unacceptable level, with the Crank-Nicolson solution still marginally poorer.

The numerical results of this section have illustrated solution behavior for the convection-diffusion problem class. The requirement is now to identify the theoretical accuracy and convergence statements and to quantize algorithm performance in suitable norms.

Problems

1 Verify that, for the thick cylinder problem discussed in Examples 4.1–4.3, use of the condensed capacity matrix (4.111), coupled with an arbitrary uniform initial condition (4.103) and a boundary condition fixing $Q(3) \equiv Q_0(3)$, yields a derivative vector $\{f\}$ (4.113) that prevents depression of any nodal temperature below its initial value. Verify the converse for the consistent formulation.

2 Verify the assertion that the conclusions in Problem 1 are independent of degree k of the cardinal basis $\{N_k\}$.

3 Verify that the assembly operations yield (4.124) and (4.125).

4 Verify the finite-difference relationship (4.128).

4.8 THEORETICAL ANALYSIS, ACCURACY AND CONVERGENCE

Section 4.7 illustrated the details of formation of the finite element algorithm statement for an initial-boundary value differential equation and introduced the concept of diagonalization of the capacity matrix. This matrix operation has been commonly practiced in the literature to facilitate direct use of an explicit integration algorithm. The theoretical statement of convergence is required, as a generalization of the development in Chap. 2 to include initial-value behavior. The finite-element energy error norm remains the basic foundation. However, the solution energy, hence finite-element error, is no longer stationary but changes in time according to the evolution of the transient problem statement. An accounting must also be made of the contribution to solution error due to truncation error associated with the integration algorithm.

Oden and Reddy (1976, Chap. 9) develop the theoretical statement of convergence for the linear initial-value problem statement. In their analysis, the error in the finite element solution is constituted of

Semidiscrete approximation error: $\epsilon^h(x, n\,\Delta t) = q(x, n\,\Delta t) - q^h(x, n\,\Delta t)$

Discrete approximation error: $\sigma(x, n\,\Delta t) = q(x, n\,\Delta t) - Q(x, n\,\Delta t)$

Temporal truncation error: $\tau(x, n\,\Delta t) = Q(x, n\,\Delta t) - q^h(x, n\,\Delta t)$ (4.131)

For any choice of norm, the triangle inequality yields

$$\|\epsilon^h\| = \|\sigma + \tau\| \leqslant \|\sigma\| + \|\tau\| \tag{4.132}$$

Oden and Reddy (1976) then establish [see their equation (9.66)]:

Theorem I The error in the numerical solution of the linear parabolic problem (4.12), with $\mathbf{u} \equiv 0$, as obtained using the fully explicit Euler integration algorithm (4.74) satisfies the inequality

$$\|\epsilon^h(n\,\Delta t)\|_{H^m(\Omega)} \leqslant C_1\,\Delta_e^{(k+1-m)}\|q(n\,\Delta t)\|_{H^{k+1}(\Omega)} + C_5\,\Delta t\|Q_0\|_{H^m(\Omega)} \tag{4.133}$$

The C_α are constants independent of Δ_e, the measure of the uniform finite-element discretization of R^1, and $m = 1$ for the parabolic specification. The first term in (4.133) is similar to the right-hand side of the convergence statement for the linear elliptic equation [see (2.174)], and $\|Q_0\|_{H^m}$ is the H^m norm of the interpolation of the initial data. For the finite-element algorithm statement (4.17), the energy norm for the kth degree approximate solution is then of the form [see (3.26)]

$$\|\epsilon^h\|_E \equiv E(\epsilon^h(n\,\Delta t), \epsilon^h(n\,\Delta t)) \leqslant C_1\,\Delta_e^{2(k+1-m)}\|F(n\,\Delta t)\|_{H^0}^2 + C_5\,\Delta t^2\,\|Q_0\|_{H^1}^2 + \cdots \tag{4.134}$$

Recall that $\|\cdot\|_{H^0}$ is the L_2 norm of the data of the problem specification [see (2.117)]. Equation (4.134) states that convergence in energy occurs at degree $2(k + 1 - m)$, under discretization refinement, in agreement with the steady-state theory. The numerical estimate of the finite-element solution energy $\|T^h\|_E \equiv E(T^h(t), T^h(t))$, see Sec. 2.5, is formed from the solution as

$$\|T^h\|_E \equiv \frac{1}{2}\sum_{e=1}^{M} [\{Q\}_e^T(k\,\Delta_e\{R\}_e^T[A3011] + h\bar{r}[A0])\{Q\}_e] \tag{4.135}$$

Since the focus is determination of accuracy and convergence with discretization refinement, a half time-step solution may be generated and Richardson extrapolation employed to determine the significant digit affected by the integration algorithm truncation error in the energy evaluation (4.135). The integration time step is then selected such that convergence measurement is not obscured by truncation error.

Accuracy and convergence in energy (Baker and Soliman, 1979), for the consistent finite-element algorithm solution for the axisymmetric transient heat transfer problem is graphed in Fig. 4.7. The curves shown are of integer slope, and the convergence rates are in essentially exact agreement with theory (4.134), except for the Hermite cubic with derivative degrees of freedom ($k = 3'$). The absolute accuracy and convergence rate for the $k = 3'$ basis are commensurate with the linear ($k = 1$) algorithm results, with the former well below the anticipated value of 4. These data are

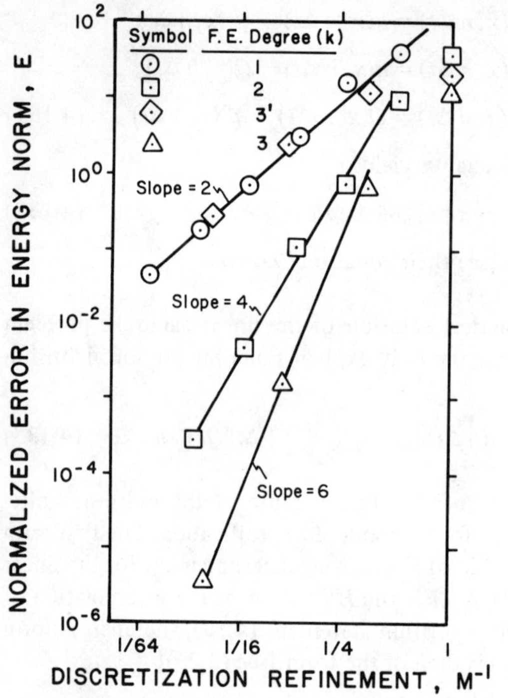

Figure 4.7 Normalized error in consistent finite-element solution energy norm, transient parabolic equation with convection boundary condition, $n\,\Delta t = 0.1$ h.

illustrative of the worst case, however. Since the cylinder is loaded only by the derivative at the boundary, the $k = 3'$ cubic is expected to be most sensitive to this influence, during the first few time steps into the solution. The energy norm reflects this strongly. On the progression to steady state, the convergence rate exponent will of course increase to 4, in agreement with the results at the close of Chap. 2.

Several additional aspects warrant comment. Only for linear elements is convergence in energy monotonic and from below. For the $k = 2$ and $k = 3$ basis solutions for this problem, convergence was oscillatory and started from below. For $k = 3'$, it was oscillatory and started from above. For all basis, the coarse grid solutions are more accurate than strict adherence to the convergence curve would predict, in agreement with the steady-state results discussed in Chap. 2. Finally, the consistent finite-element algorithm can produce results in violation of the second law of thermodynamics, i.e., prediction of energy flow from a lower to higher temperature, for a coarse discretization. However, for all k evaluated, this spurious phenomena diminished with discretization refinement, and was eliminated on the finest ($M = 64$) discretization results plotted.

Figure 4.8 graphs accuracy and convergence for the identical problem statement, for the finite-element algorithm constructed using the condensed capacity matrix form; see (4.111). The solid lines are drawn at a slope of 2, which accurately interpolate the data for all k, $1 \leqslant k \leqslant 3$. The condensed element convergence rate remains 2, with an absolute error about five times larger than the standard results. The convergence rate for all higher degree basis is also equal to 2, a severe degradation from the data of Fig. 4.7. The ad hoc diagonalized capacity matrix is therefore totally inappropriate for use with higher degree basis functions. Finally, in distinction to prior experience, the absolute inaccuracy in coarse grid solution energy generally exceeds that for adherence to the convergence curves.

The second required accuracy and convergence assessment corresponds to (4.12) hyperbolic, as illustrated by the traveling wave packet solutions in the previous section. The problem statement is completed with (4.14)-(4.15), since the convection boundary condition (4.13) is inappropriate for zero thermal conductivity. For constant velocity and explicit Euler integration (4.75), Oden and Reddy (1976) prove:

Theorem II If the components of the error in the finite-element solution are given by (4.131), then the error in the solution of the linear hyperbolic equation using explicit Euler integration satisfies the inequality

$$\|\epsilon^h(n\,\Delta t)\|_{H^1} \leqslant C_1\,\Delta_e^{k+1}\,\|q\|_{H^{k+1}(\Omega)} + C_5\,\Delta t\|Q_0\|_{H^0} + C_6\,\Delta_e \int_0^{n\,\Delta t} \|q\|_{H^{k+1}}\,dt \tag{4.136}$$

The C_α are constants independent of Δ_e, the measure of the uniform finite-element discretization of R^1. The first term is the familiar reduction of error under discretization refinement, and the second term remains the norm of the interpolation of the initial data. The third term is new, corresponding to an additional discretization-sensitive error generated through propagation of the $(k + 1)$st derivative of the analytical solution over $n\,\Delta t$. The distressing feature is the exponent of unity on Δ_e, which is always smaller than the exponent $k + 1$ on the lead term. Hence, enhanced reduction of error in energy or H^1 with use of a higher degree basis is not assured a priori.

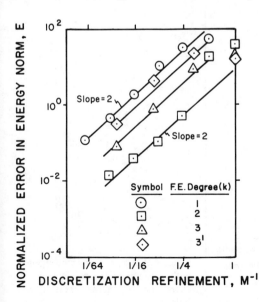

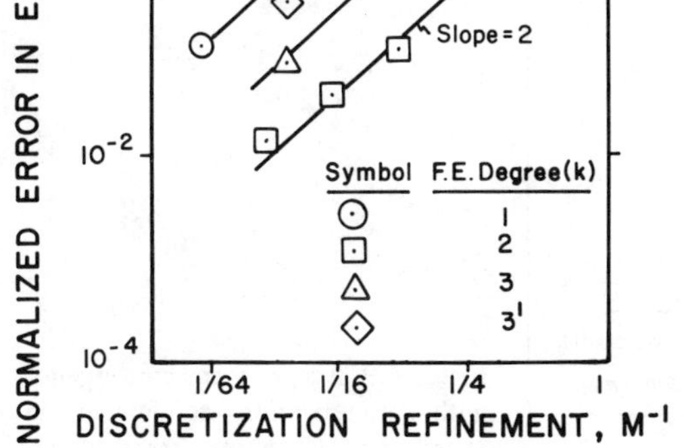

Figure 4.8 Normalized error in condensed finite-element solution energy norm, transient parabolic equation with convection boundary condition, $n\,\Delta t = 0.1$ h.

That this is indeed the case is reported by Baker and Soliman (1979), for the traveling energy packet example case illustrated in Fig. 4.6. Although there are no terms in (4.12) for $k \equiv 0$ that correspond to a quadratic contribution to an energy functional, the energy norm is simply defined as

$$\|q^h\|_E \equiv \frac{1}{2} \sum_{e=1}^{M} \Delta_e \{Q\}_e^T [A211] \{Q\}_e \tag{4.137}$$

From (4.136), convergence in energy is bounded as

$$\|q^h\|_E \leqslant C_6 \Delta_e^2 \int_0^{n\Delta t} \|q\|_{H^{k+1}}^2 \, dt + C_5 \Delta t^2 \|Q_0\|_{H^0}^2 + \cdots \tag{4.138}$$

Figure 4.9 graphs computed convergence in E using the $k = 1$ and $k = 2$ finite-element algorithm formulations. These data are accurately interpolated by a straight line of slope equal to 2, in agreement with theory (4.138). The accuracy level and convergence rate in E for the $k = 1$ condensed algorithm solution data (Fig. 4.9) are essentially identical to the consistent results, in marked distinction to the "visually" poorer solution (compare Fig. 4.6*b*–*c*). A "norm" that responds to solution sign is the simple integral under the solution curve,

$$\|q^h\|_{L_1} \equiv \int_{R^1} q^h \, dx = \sum_{e=1}^{M} \Delta_e \{A10\}^T \{Q\}_e \tag{4.139}$$

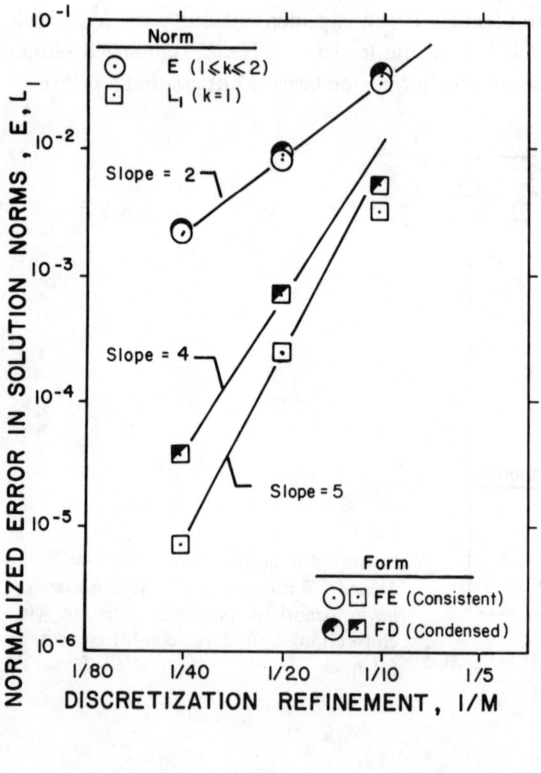

Figure 4.9 Accuracy and convergence with discretization refinement in energy and L_1 norm, linear hyperbolic equation.

In $\|\cdot\|_{L_1}$ the convergence rate for the $k = 1$ consistent algorithm solution appears an integer superior to the condensed formulation (Fig. 4.9) with an improvement in absolute level of accuracy. Baker and Soliman (1979) also verify the quadratic convergence under time-step refinement predicted in (4.138).

These results appear to indicate that the energy norm is a rather insensitive indicator of solution accuracy and acceptability for the hyperbolic problem class. Alternative methods are available to estimate theoretical performance, specifically von Neumann stability analysis (Roache, 1972). The starting point is (4.126), divided through by the uniform element measure $\Delta_e \equiv \Delta x$, yielding

$$\frac{1}{6}\frac{d}{dt}(Q_{j-1} + 4Q_j + Q_{j+1}) + \frac{U}{2\,\Delta x}(Q_{j+1} - Q_{j-1}) = 0 \qquad (4.140)$$

Performing a Taylor series expansion of (4.140) about $x = x_j$ (Problem 1 at the end of this section) produces the difference-differential equation, comparable to (4.12) for $k = 0, u =$ constant, as

$$L(Q) = \frac{\partial Q}{\partial t} + U\frac{\partial Q}{\partial x} + \left(\frac{1}{120} - \frac{1}{72}\right)U\,\Delta x^3\,\frac{\partial^4 Q}{\partial x^4} + \cdots = 0 \qquad (4.141)$$

Equation (4.141) is the partial differential equation satisfied by the semidiscrete approximate solution $Q(j\,\Delta x, t)$. The lead two terms are identical to the form of (4.12) under consideration, and the third term is a false (truncation error) term due to the use of the approximation. The order of this term indicates that (4.140) is a spatially fourth-order accurate approximation to the exact solution. In distinction, the ordinary differential equation associated with the condensed finite-element formulation (4.129), i.e., Crank-Nicolson finite difference, is

$$\frac{dQ_j}{dt} + \frac{U}{2\,\Delta x}(Q_{j+1} - Q_{j-1}) = 0 \qquad (4.142)$$

The associated difference-differential equation is

$$L(Q) = \frac{\partial Q}{\partial t} + U\frac{\partial Q}{\partial x} + \frac{1}{12}U\,\Delta x\,\frac{\partial^2 Q}{\partial x^2} + \cdots = 0 \qquad (4.143)$$

Hence, the Crank-Nicolson algorithm is spatially only second-order accurate. Furthermore, since the lead approximation error term contains $\partial^2 Q/\partial x^2$, this yields an effective "artificial" viscosity term in the semidiscrete approximation, with viscosity coefficient $\mu = U\,\Delta x/12$. The loss in peak value of the traveling wave solution (Fig. 4.6*c*) is partially attributable to this diffusion coefficient, which is totally absent in the consistent finite-element formulation (4.141).

This type analysis can be pursued to characterize the fully discrete approximate solution $Q_j^n = Q(j\,\Delta x, n\,\Delta t)$. Inserting the θ implicit integration algorithm into (4.140) yields

$$L(Q_j^n) = \frac{1}{6}\left[(Q_{j-1}^{n+1} - Q_{j-1}^n) + 4(Q_j^{n+1} - Q_j^n) + (Q_{j+1}^{n+1} - Q_{j+1}^n)\right]$$

$$+ \frac{C}{2}\left[\theta(Q_{j+1}^{n+1} - Q_{j-1}^{n+1}) + (1-\theta)(Q_{j+1}^n - Q_{j-1}^n)\right] = 0 \qquad (4.144)$$

where $C \equiv U\,\Delta t/\Delta x$ is the Courant number (nondimensional time step). The theoretical assessment of how (error-induced) perturbations propagate through the fully discrete approximation is established using Fourier modal analysis (Roache, 1972). The approach is to expand Q_j^n into spatial Fourier components in the form

$$Q_j^n \equiv g^n e^{i(\lambda j \Delta x)} \tag{4.145}$$

where $i \equiv \sqrt{-1}$. The growth or decay of solution perturbations, e.g., the trailing dispersion error wake in Fig. 4.6, is described by determination of the function form for g^n, the amplitude of the Fourier series expansion. It is a suggested exercise to insert (4.145) into (4.144) and verify that, for $\theta = \frac{1}{2}$, the amplification factor is

$$g^n \to g = \frac{1 + (1/2)\cos(\lambda\,\Delta x) - i(3C/4)\sin(\lambda\,\Delta x)}{1 + (1/2)\cos(\lambda\,\Delta x) + i(3C/4)\sin(\lambda\,\Delta x)} \tag{4.146}$$

Since the numerator and denominator are complex conjugates, the magnitude of g is unity for all $\Delta t(C)$ and Δx, and is independent of n. Hence, the finite-element algorithm statement (4.143) is defined as neutrally stable, i.e., perturbations to the solution are neither damped nor amplified as the solution proceeds.

The von Neumann stability analysis can also be completed for the Crank-Nicolson algorithm statement (4.143). Proceeding through the details, Problem 4, the amplification factor is

$$g^n \to g = \frac{1 - i(C/2)\sin(\lambda\,\Delta x)}{1 + i(C/2)\sin(\lambda\,\Delta x)} \tag{4.147}$$

Therefore, as for (4.146), the Crank-Nicolson algorithm is also neutrally stable for all λ, Δt, and Δx, and solution perturbations are neither damped nor amplified. This character of neutral stability is the direct result of selection of $\theta = \frac{1}{2}$. For $\frac{1}{2} < \theta \leqslant 1$, for either the consistent or condensed algorithm formulations, $|g| < 1$ and an additional artificial damping is introduced into the solution. Determination of the form of $g(\theta)$ is a suggested exercise.

General algorithm performance, in particular the poorer accuracy of the Crank-Nicolson algorithm solution for the pure convection problem, can be quantized from the amplification factor. Ideally, each Fourier mode should travel with a nondimensional phase speed of unity to retain the information packet. The trailing dispersion wakes are the result of the short-wavelength modes lagging the group velocity. Pepper and Cooper (1980) compare (4.146)-(4.147) in terms of the phase velocity θ, defined as

$$\theta(C) = \frac{1}{\lambda\,\Delta x}\tan^{-1}\left(\frac{g_{\text{imag}}}{g_{\text{real}}}\right) \tag{4.148}$$

Table 4.1 summarizes the comparison between the linear finite-element and Crank-Nicolson algorithms for $C = 0.5$. The finite-element algorithm phase velocity $\theta > 0.9$ for all $\lambda \geqslant 4$, while the Crank-Nicolson algorithm achieves $\theta > 0.9$ only for $\lambda \geqslant 10$. It is the magnitude of the phase lag for $2 < \lambda \leqslant 10$ that causes the coalescence of the dispersion wakes shown in Fig. 4.6, and increasing Courant number aggravates the phase lag.

Table 4.1 Phase velocity distributions as function of wavelength, linear pure advection problem, Courant number = 0.5†

	Phase velocity θ	
Wavelength $(n\ \Delta x), n$	Finite element (4.141)	Finite difference (4.143)
2.0	0.0	0.0
2.25	0.340	0.122
2.50	0.564	0.232
2.75	0.698	0.326
3.0	0.780	0.407
3.5	0.869	0.532
4.0	0.913	0.623
5.0	0.953	0.743
6.0	0.970	0.814
8.0	0.985	0.891
10.0	0.991	0.928
20.0	0.997	0.981
40.0	0.999	0.995
60.0	0.999	0.998

†From Pepper and Cooper (1980).

Problems

1 Verify the difference-differential partial differential equation (4.141).

2 Verify (4.142).

3 Substitute (4.145) in (4.144) and verify the expression (4.146) for the amplification factor g.

4 Repeat Problem 3 for the condensed Crank-Nicolson algorithm, hence verify (4.147).

5 Determine the θ dependence of the amplitude factor $g(\theta)$ for $\frac{1}{2} < \theta < 1$, for the consistent and condensed $k = 1$ finite-element algorithm statements (4.140) and (4.142).

6 Verify some of the entries in Table 4.1 using (4.148).

4.9 A COMPARISON FINITE-VOLUME ALGORITHM FOR HEAT TRANSFER

The previous two sections have exposed the essential features of the weighted residuals finite-element algorithm applied to the convection-diffusion equation for heat transmission. In one dimension, an ad hoc operation on the algorithm yielded the familiar Crank-Nicolson finite-difference algorithm, with accuracy and convergence compared to theory and to the finite-element algorithm form. This section expands this comparison to a multidimensional construction, which introduces the finite-volume algorithm construction as based upon the weighted residuals concept (4.6).

The problem definition is unsteady heat conduction in the absence of convection, i.e., (4.12)-(4.15) with $\mathbf{u}(\mathrm{x}, t) \equiv 0$. The weighted residuals algorithm statement (4.6), with the time-dependent term added is

$$S_e \left[\int_{R_e^n} \{W\} \left(\rho c_p \frac{\partial \bar{T}_e}{\partial t} - \nabla \cdot k \nabla \bar{T}_e - \rho \dot{q} \right) d\tau \right.$$
$$\left. - \lambda \int_{\partial R_e \cap \partial R} \{W\} [k \nabla \bar{T}_e \cdot \hat{\mathbf{n}} + h(\bar{T}_e - T_r)] \, d\sigma \right] \equiv \{0\} \tag{4.149}$$

In distinction to (4.10), which produced the finite-element algorithm, define

$$\{W(\mathbf{x})\}^T \equiv C\{1, 0, 0, \ldots, 0\} \tag{4.150}$$

where C is any nonzero constant. Hence, the algorithm statement (4.149) is simply the direct integration of the approximation $\bar{T}_e$ to solution $T(\mathbf{x}, t)$ of the heat transfer problem.

Guidance on construction of the solution approximation from $\bar{T}^h \equiv \Sigma_e \bar{T}_e$ comes from the thermal conductivity term in (4.149). Since $\{W\}$ is a constant scalar, the appropriate Green-Gauss theorem is the divergence theorem, yielding

$$S_e \left[\int_{R_e^n} \nabla \cdot k_e \nabla \bar{T}_e \, d\tau \right] = S_e \left[\oint_{\partial R_e} k_e \nabla \bar{T}_e \cdot \hat{\mathbf{n}} \, d\sigma \right] \tag{4.151}$$

Figure 4.10 illustrates a portion of a two-dimensional discretization $\cup R_e^n$ of R^n. The requirement is to evaluate (4.151) in a manner that is consistent and repetitive throughout the mesh. The obvious first choice is to assume that

$$\bar{T}_e \equiv Q_e(\mathbf{x}_c, t) \tag{4.152}$$

where $\mathbf{x}_c$ is the centroidal coordinates of R_e^n, and to replace $\nabla \bar{T}_e$ by a divided difference of centroidal values. Letting $\hat{\mathbf{s}}$ denote the unit vector parallel to the line connecting the centroid nodes of elements R_e^2 and R_α^2 (see Fig. 4.11), then

$$\nabla \bar{T}_e(\bar{x}_c^\alpha, t) \approx \frac{1}{\Delta s_{e\alpha}} [Q_\alpha(\bar{x}_c, t) - Q_e(\bar{x}_c, t)] \, \hat{\mathbf{s}}_{e\alpha} \qquad e \neq \alpha \tag{4.153}$$

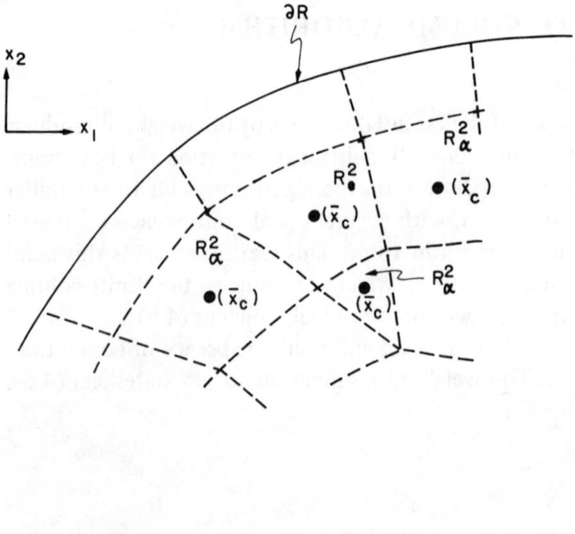

Figure 4.10 Example of discretization of domain R^2 for a finite-volume algorithm.

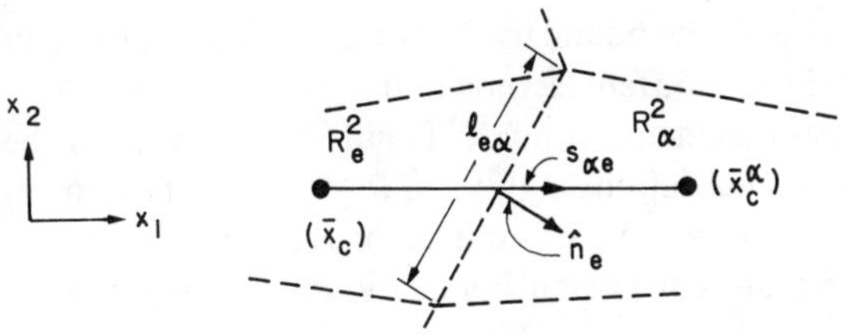

Figure 4.11 Interface between two finite-volume domains.

Therefore, on the finite volume R_e^2, the evaluation of (4.151) becomes, using (4.153)

$$S_e\left[\oint_{\partial R_e} k_e \nabla \bar{T}_e \cdot \hat{\mathbf{n}}\, d\sigma\right] = S_e\left\{\sum_{\alpha=1} \frac{k_e(\mathbf{x}_c) l_{e\alpha}}{\Delta s_{e\alpha}} \times [Q_\alpha(\mathbf{x}_c, t) - Q_e(\mathbf{x}_c, t)]\, \hat{\mathbf{s}}_{e\alpha} \cdot \hat{\mathbf{n}}_e\right\}_{\substack{\partial R_e \cap \partial R_\alpha \neq 0 \\ \partial R_e \cap \partial R = 0}} \tag{4.154}$$

In (4.154), the summation is over all volumes R_α^n sharing at least one boundary segment ($l_{e\alpha}$) with R_e^n (see Fig. 4.11 for the two-dimensional sketch). Furthermore, (4.154) is restricted to volume boundaries not coincident with the solution domain boundary ∂R, since a special treatment will be required. It is left as an exercise to prove that (4.154), for a regular rectangular cartesian discretization of R^n and constant thermal conductivity, yields the second-order accurate central difference approximations to $\nabla^2 T$, for $1 \leqslant n \leqslant 2$. In this instance as well, one also verifies that an exact canceling of the extraneous surface integrals occurs, as the global system is assembled using S_e (recall the discussion in Sec. 4.4).

The remaining two terms in the domain integral in (4.149) are elementary to evaluate using (4.152). The assembly operator S_e becomes identical with conventional summation, yielding

$$S_e\left[\int_{R_e^n} \rho c_p \frac{\partial \bar{T}_e}{\partial t}\, d\tau\right] = \sum_{e=1}^{M} [\Delta_e \rho_e c_p Q_e'(\mathbf{x}_c, t)]$$

$$S_e\left[\int_{R_e^n} \rho \dot{q}_e\, d\tau\right] = \sum_{e=1}^{M} [\Delta_e \rho_e \dot{q}_e(\mathbf{x}_c, t)] \tag{4.155}$$

In (4.155), Δ_e is the n-dimensional measure of R_e^n.

The final requirement is to complete the domain boundary integral term in (4.149), for the definition (4.150). This requires resolution of the basic issue of the finite-volume discrete approximation $\bar{T}^h(\bar{x}, t)$; specifically,

$$\bar{T}^h(\mathbf{x}, t) \equiv \sum_{e=1}^{M} T_e \ , \quad T_e \equiv Q_e(\mathbf{x}_c, t) \tag{4.156}$$

contains no nodal coordinates which lie on the boundary ∂R for the definition of $\bar{T}_e$ in (4.152). The resolution employed in the difference community is to define "half-sized" domains R_e^n with boundaries coincident with ∂R. Figure 4.12 illustrates the concept for R^2; the approach indeed yields definition of $\mathbf{x}_c$ of R_e to lie on the domain boundary ∂R. By taking the sign for λ in (4.149) as positive, the (unformed) terms in $k\nabla\bar{T}_e \cdot \hat{\mathbf{n}}$ on R_e^n and ∂R cancel, and the convection boundary condition statement becomes

$$S_e\left[-\int_{\partial R_e \cap \partial R} h_e(\bar{T}_e - T_r)\,d\sigma\right] = \sum_e \left[-\Delta_e^1 h_e(\mathbf{x}_c)(Q_e(\mathbf{x}_c, t) - T_r(t))\right]_{\partial R_e \cap \partial R \neq 0} \tag{4.157}$$

where Δ_e^1 is the measure of the intersection of the bisector of appropriate R_e^n with ∂R.

The finite volume multidimensional algorithm statement for the heat transfer problem is now complete. For the solution approximate $\bar{T}^h$ given in (4.156), the construction for the algorithm (4.149) is defined by (4.154), (4.155), and (4.157). It is quite apparent that finite difference-like formalisms were required during the construction to compensate for the fact that the distribution of the spatial dependence in $\bar{T}^h$ is not specified exactly, i.e., it did not employ the concept of the cardinal basis $\{N_k(\mathbf{x})\}$. As a consequence, spatial derivatives were required approximated without strict knowledge of the nodal coordinates. Finally, the boundary half-volume was required defined, the accuracy of which certainly needs substantiation. Overall, however, the derived finite volume algorithm can be a second-order accurate, multidimensional equivalent of the one-dimensional Crank-Nicolson finite-difference algorithm derived in the previous section. Problem 2 suggests that this be verified for the one-dimensional problem definition.

Baker and Manhardt (1972) report a detailed comparison of solution accuracy for the linear basis $\{N_1\}$ embodiment of the finite-element algorithm (4.18) and the finite-volume algorithm (4.154), (4.155), (4.157), for a highly transient heat transfer problem specification (4.12)–(4.15). The physical problem is heat transfer to the walls of a small (0.15 m O.D.) thrust vector control rocket motor during an ignition transient. Figure 4.13 illustrates the axisymmetric motor and graphs the parent finite volume (FV) quadrilateral discretization mesh. The triangular cross-section ring finite element (FE) discretization for $\{N_1(\zeta)\}$ was formed by striking a diagonal across each finite volume domain. The centroidal nodes of the 52 cell FV discretization

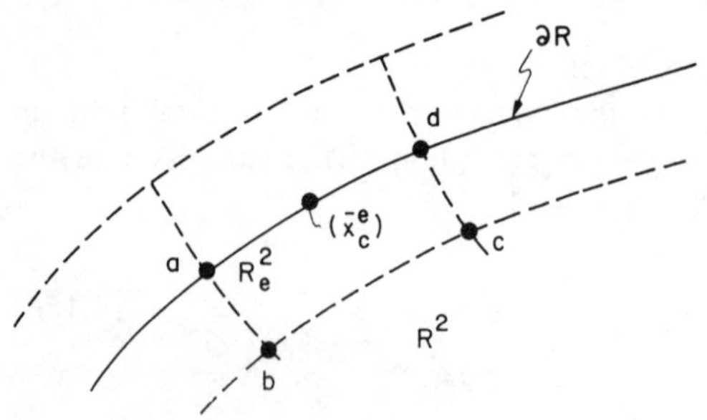

Figure 4.12 Difference elements at the domain boundary.

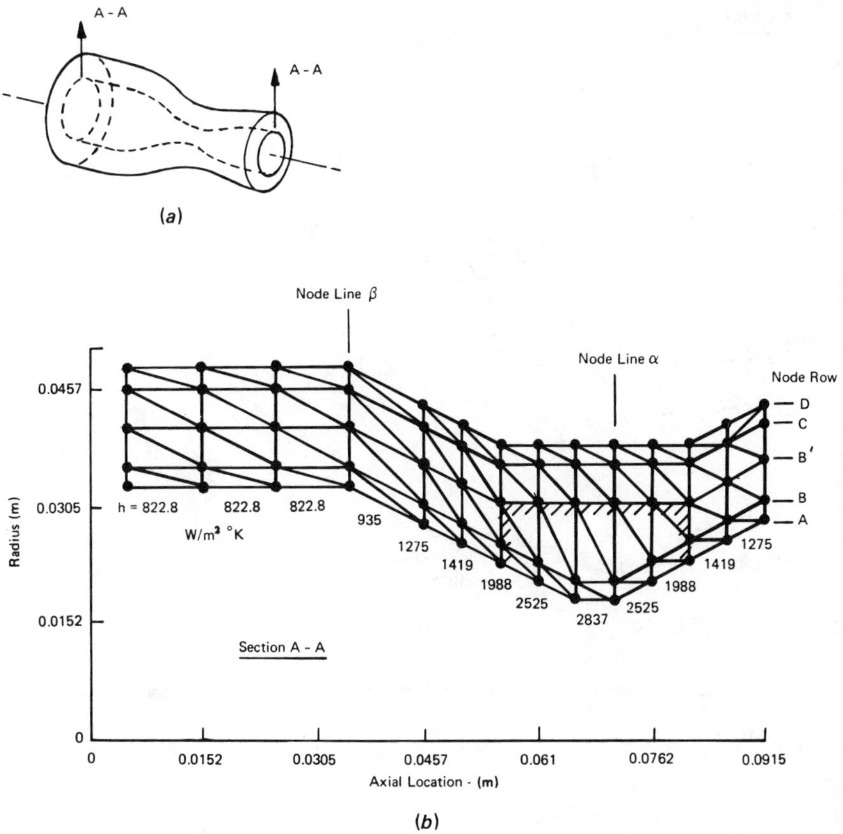

Figure 4.13 Discretization of axisymmetric rocket motor into 52 finite-volume quadrilaterals and 104 triangular cross-sectional ring finite elements. (*a*) Cylindrical configuration; (*b*) finite-element and finite-volume discretizations.

are denoted by x, the nodes of the FE $M = 104$ discretization by a raised dot (•), and none coincide exactly. No heat sources were present in R^2, the initial temperature distribution was uniform, and the exterior shell wall was assumed adiabatic. Vanishing normal derivatives were applied to the end wall sections, and the (true) complicated radiation loading on the nozzle and the motor interior was modeled using the noted distribution of convection coefficient h (W/m² K) (Fig. 4.13) for $T_r = 3610$ K. The resultant maximum energy flux occurring at the nozzle throat was 9.5×10^5 W/m². The material was assumed to be stainless steel, the thermal properties of which vary by a factor of two over the temperature range encountered during the simulation of a 10-s burn.

Figure 4.14 summarizes the accuracy comparison in terms of axial temperature distributions on and near the interior and exterior surfaces of the device after a 10-s firing. The node rows of the FE algorithm results are noted in Fig. 4.13. The FV solution, based on the considerations of the previous section and near equilibrium, must be bounded by the finite-element solution. In addition, the FV-computed temperatures should lie nearer the extremum FE-computed temperatures if the

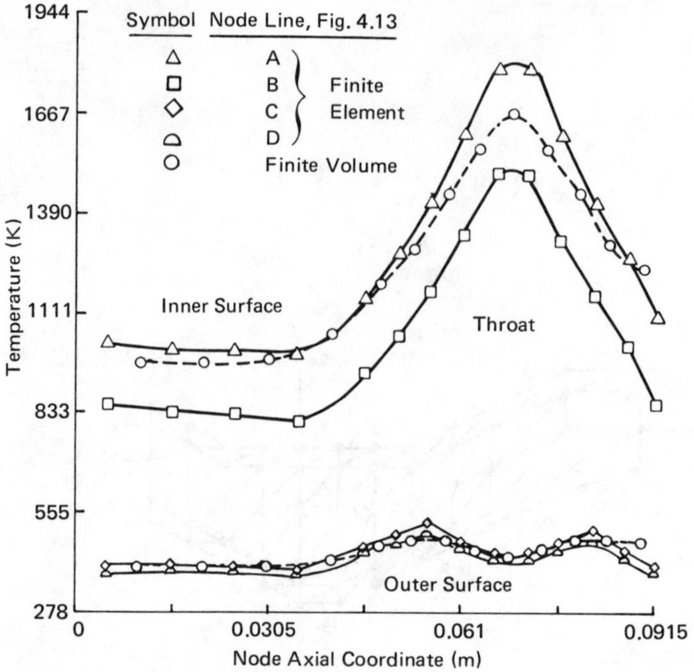

Figure 4.14 Comparison of computed axial temperature distributions after 10-second transient.

concept of the boundary half-element is the correct interpretation. The data of Fig. 4.14 tend to confirm these considerations at both surfaces. The agreement is poorest where the temperature levels and spatial gradients (hence, departure from equilibrium) are largest. At the throat, the FE temperatures are approximately 150 K higher, and the FV solution is effectively the mean of the FE solution. Conversely, along the throat entrance, no significant axial temperature gradient exists and the FV and FE predictions for surface temperature are essentially identical. The FV solution excursion beyond the FE bound at the right end of the nozzle is (probably) associated with incorrect usage of half-domain boundary concept. A vanishing gradient on two surfaces common to a corner actually requires a quarter-domain cell. Along the low temperature outer surface, the FE results uniformly bound the FV predictions, with variations in agreement with the minor spatial gradients. These results confirm the interpretive considerations involved in the FV algorithm construction and its associated weaknesses regarding spatial uncertainty of the $Q(\mathbf{x}_c, t)$.

Figure 4.15 compares the FE and FD computed transient radial temperature distributions at the nozzle throat section, node line α in Fig. 4.13. Along the exterior wall, the FE solution bounds uniformly the FV solution, as expected. At the rapidly heated interior surface, the FV solution badly misses the surface temperature rise by up to 400 K, confirming fully the solution character quantized in the elementary examples of Sec. 4.7. This underprediction yields modest overshoot at $t \approx 3.5$ s whereafter the FV solution returns to the mean of node rows A and B. Thus, the boundary half-volume assumption for the convection boundary condition appears quite inaccurate during transients with large spatial gradients. Refined discretization solutions were performed to confirm that the course grid solution underpredicted the extremum transients. Figure 4.16 compares the radial temperature distributions computed by the FE algorithm for $M = 104$ and $M = 538$. The added definition of the spatial gradients by the finer grid provides the required confirmation. Overall, therefore, the FV algorithm appears to offer accuracy no advantages over the FE embodiment of the weighted residuals algorithm statement for this problem class.

Problems

1 Prove that (4.154) yields the second-order accurate difference star for $\nabla^2 T$, on a uniform rectangular cartesian discretization of R^2.

2 Prove that the finite-volume algorithm (4.154), (4.155), and (4.157) reproduces the Crank-Nicolson finite-difference algorithm for a one-dimensional problem specification.

4.10 CONVECTION–DIFFUSION TIME–SPLIT SOLUTION ALGORITHM

The preceding sections have analyzed essential aspects of the finite-element algorithm applied to the one-dimensional form of the energy convection-diffusion equation

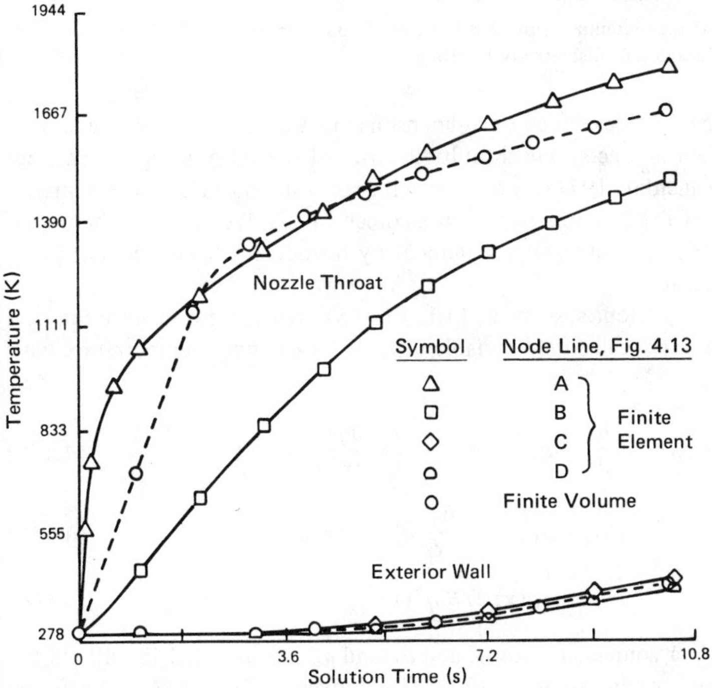

Figure 4.15 Comparison of computed transient temperature distributions at nozzle throat during 10-second transient.

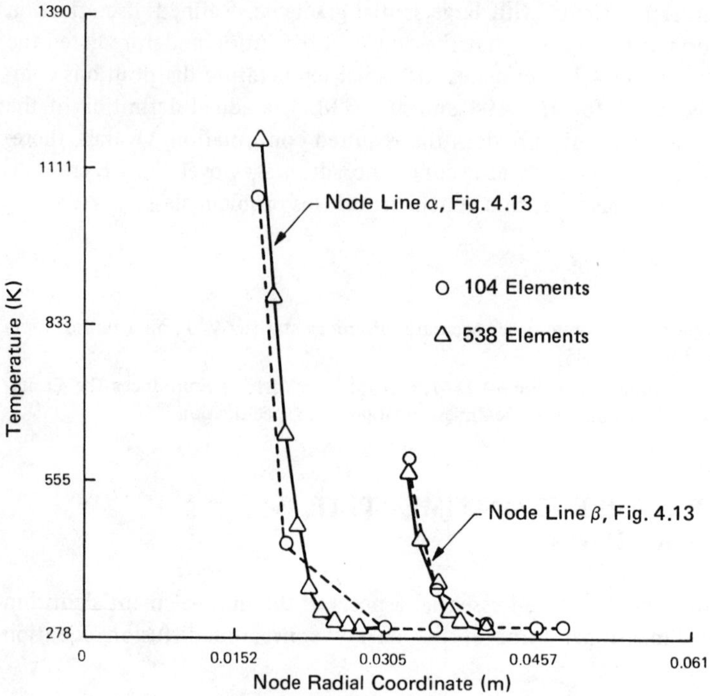

Figure 4.16 Computed radial temperature distributions through rocket nozzle throat and combustion chamber as a function of discretization refinement.

system (4.12)-(4.15). The developed one-dimensional matrix structures can be used to formulate an efficient and economical multidimensional algorithm using the concept of time-splitting (Yanenko, 1971) in concert with construction of the tensor matrix product equivalent of the Newton algorithm jacobian (4.97). We also take the opportunity to augment the basic algorithm statement by introducing the concept of phase (dispersion) error control.

The governing equation system is (4.12)-(4.15), written for convection and diffusion of an arbitrary scalar field variable $q(\mathbf{x}, t)$, for example, temperature, mass fraction, pollutant.

$$L(q) = \frac{\partial q}{\partial t} + u_j \frac{\partial q}{\partial x_j} - \frac{\partial}{\partial x_j}\left(k \frac{\partial q}{\partial x_j}\right) + s = 0 \tag{4.158}$$

$$l(q) = a_1 q + k \frac{\partial q}{\partial x_j} \hat{n}_j + a_3 = 0 \tag{4.159}$$

$$q(\mathbf{x}, 0) \equiv q^0(\mathbf{x}) \tag{4.160}$$

In (4.158), $s(\mathbf{x}, t)$ is a source/sink for q, and a_1 and a_3 are specified to enforce the appropriate boundary conditions in (4.159). The domain of $L(q)$ is Ω, and a finite-element domain is $\Omega_e \equiv R_e^n \times t$, where $\cup R_e^n$ is the finite element discretization of R^n.

The dependent variable $q(\mathbf{x}, t)$ is approximated on Ω as $q^h(\mathbf{x}, t)$, and on Ω_e in the usual manner.

$$q \approx q^h(\mathbf{x}, t) \equiv \sum_e q_e(\mathbf{x}, t) \tag{4.161}$$

$$q_e(\mathbf{x}, t) \equiv \{N_k(\mathbf{x})\}^T \{Q(t)\}_e \tag{4.162}$$

The elements of $\{N_k(\mathbf{x})\}$ are polynomials complete to degree k, and the expansion coefficients $\{Q(t)\}_e$ are the time-dependent unknowns. Using the developed algorithm methodology [see (4.4)-(4.6) and (4.10)], substitute (4.161) into (4.158)-(4.159) and set to zero the assembly of the integrals of each over R_e^n and ∂R_e, respectively, after weighting by $\{N_k\}$. As a generalization for dispersion error control (Raymond and Garder, 1976), in addition, set the weighted integral of the vector gradient of the semidiscrete approximate solution error to zero, for the convection (only) terms in (4.158). Denoting this term as $\nabla L^c(q^h)$ and defining the associated vector and scalar multipliers as $\boldsymbol{\beta}$ and λ, each of which must be determined, these linearly independent constraints are combined into the generalized finite-element algorithm statement for (4.158)-(4.159) as

$$S_e \left[\int_{R_e^n} \{N_k\} L(q_e)\, d\tau - \boldsymbol{\beta} \cdot \int_{R_e^n} \{N_k\} \nabla L^c(q_e)\, d\tau + \lambda \int_{\partial R_e \cap \partial R} \{N_k\} l(q_e)\, d\sigma \right] \equiv \{0\} \tag{4.163}$$

The various terms in (4.163) will be expanded on completion of the basic matrix solution statement. Viewing (4.158)-(4.159), and drawing on the experience to this point, (4.163) represents a system of ordinary differential equations on the temporal evolution of the expansion coefficients $\{Q\}$ of the semidiscrete approximation. Let $[C]_e$, $[U]_e$, $[K]_e$, and $[H]_e$ denote the elemental matrices resulting in (4.163) for the capacity, convection, diffusion, and gradient boundary condition terms in (4.158)-(4.159). Further, let $\{b\}_e$ denote the nonhomogeneous data specifications in (4.159) and s in (4.158). Then, (4.163) is an ordinary differential equation system of the familiar form

$$S_e[[C]_e\{Q\}_e' + [U + K + H]_e\{Q\}_e + \{b\}_e] = \{0\} \tag{4.164}$$

The fully discrete approximation is constructed on definition of a solution algorithm for (4.164). As before [see (4.96)] the θ-implicit integration of (4.164) yields the algebraic equation system

$$\{F\}_{j+1} = \{Q\}_{j+1} - \{Q\}_j - h[\theta\{Q\}_{j+1}' + (1-\theta)\{Q\}_j'] = \{0\} \tag{4.165}$$

where j is the time-step index, h is the integration step size Δt, and $0 \leqslant \theta \leqslant 1$ is the implicitness parameter. The Newton algorithm statement for (4.165) is

$$[J(F)]_{j+1}^p \{\delta Q\}_{j+1}^{p+1} = -\{F\}_{j+1}^p \tag{4.166}$$

and the dependent variable is the iteration vector that defines the solution

$$\{Q\}_{j+1}^{p+1} \equiv \{Q\}_{j+1}^{p} + \{\delta Q\}_{j+1}^{p+1} \tag{4.167}$$

Equations (4.165)-(4.167) represent the algebraic finite-element algorithm statement for the convection-diffusion problem statement (4.158)-(4.159). With definition of the parameters β and λ in (4.163), and selection of k in (4.162) and $\theta > 0$ in (4.165), the statement is reduced to the calculus operations to form $[C]_e$, etc. For an $n = 3$ dimensional domain Ω, however, one rapidly realizes that the computer resources required to solve (4.166) are excessive. However, since (4.158) is of the suitable form, the time-split algorithm of Yanenko (1971) (see also Dendy and Fairweather, 1975, and Denley, 1977) can be applied to (4.165)-(4.167), yielding an accurate and efficient implicit formulation.

The fundamental step is to replace the multidimensional matrix evaluations in (4.163)-(4.164), hence (4.165), with the outer (tensor) product of one-dimensional matrix evaluations. Referring to Sec. 4.7, the first term in the finite-element statement (4.163), for (4.158) a one-dimensional specification, is simply

$$S_e\left[\int_{R_e^1} \{N_k\} L(q_e)\, d\tau\right] = S_e\left[\int_{R_e^1} \{N_k\}\left[\frac{\partial q_e}{\partial t} + u_1\frac{\partial q}{\partial x_1} - \frac{\partial}{\partial x_1}\left(k\,\frac{\partial q}{\partial x_1}\right) + s\right] d\tau\right]$$

$$= S_e[\Delta_e[A200]\{Q\}_e' + \Delta_e(\{U1\}_e^T[A3001]$$

$$+ \{K1\}_e^T[A3011])\{Q\}_e + \Delta_e[A200]\{S\}_e] \tag{4.168}$$

In (4.168), the standard matrices $[A\cdot\cdot]$ denote integrals over R_e^1 of appropriate products of elements of $\{N_k\}$ and their derivatives, for arbitrary k.

The second term in (4.163) is reexpressed using a vector identity as

$$S_e\left[-\beta\cdot\int_{R_e^n}\{N_k\}\nabla L^c(q_e)\, d\tau\right] = S_e\left[-\beta\cdot\int_{R_e^n}\nabla(\{N\}_k L^c(q_e))\, d\tau\right.$$

$$\left. + \beta\cdot\int_{R_e^n}\nabla\{N_k\}L^c(q_e)\, d\tau\right] \tag{4.169}$$

The first right term corresponds to a net efflux over a closed surface integral, the assembly of which vanishes according to the arguments of Sec. 4.4. Define $\beta = \Delta_e \nu$ where ν is an n-dimensional vector of constants parallel to $\mathbf{u}$, to be determined, and Δ_e is the mesh measure. The evaluation of (4.169), for a one-dimensional specification, is then

$$S_e\left[\beta\cdot\int_{R_e^n}\nabla\{N_k\}L^c(q_e)\, d\tau\right] = S_e\left[\nu_1\,\Delta_e\int_{R_e^1}\frac{\partial\{N_k\}}{\partial x_1}\left[\frac{\partial q_e}{\partial t} + u_1\frac{\partial q_e}{\partial x_1}\right] dx_1\right]$$

$$= S_e[\nu_1\,\Delta_e[A210]\{Q\}_e' + \nu_1\,\Delta_e\{\overline{U1}\}_e^T[A3011]\{Q\}_e] \tag{4.170}$$

As for (4.168), the standard matrices $[\mathbf{A}\cdot\cdot]$ in (4.170) denote the appropriate integrals for arbitrary k in (4.162). Further, the elements of $\{\overline{U1}\}_e$ are the magnitudes of the velocity $u\hat{\mathbf{i}}$ at the nodes of R_e^1.

The third term in (4.163) is quite familiar; its evaluation for the one-dimensional specification is, for $\lambda = 1$,

$$S_e \left[\lambda \int_{\partial R_e \cap \partial R} \{N_k\} l(q_e) \, d\tau \right] = S_e [a_1 [A] \{Q\}_e + a_3 \{A\}] \qquad (4.171)$$

In (4.171), $[A]$ and $\{A\}$ denote matrices of rank $k + 1$ with null elements everywhere except a_{11} or a_{nn}, the values of which are unity (recall Sec. 2.4).

For application in the time-split formulation, therefore, the generalized finite-element algorithm statement (4.163)-(4.165) is expressed by combining (4.168), (4.170), and (4.171). Deleting the subscript e notation for clarity, (4.165) is then

$$\begin{aligned} \{F1\}_{j+1}^p = S_e[&\Delta_1 [A200 + \nu_1 A210](\{Q\}_{j+1}^p - \{Q\}_j) \\ &+ h\theta \, \Delta_1((\{U1\}_e^T [A3001] + \{K1 + \nu_1 \overline{U1}\}_e^T [A3011] + a_1 [A])\{Q\}_{j+1}^p \\ &+ [A200] \{S\}_{j+1} + a_3 \{A\}) + h(1-\theta) \Delta_1((\{U1\}_e^T [A3001] \\ &+ \{K1 + \nu_1 \overline{U1}\}_e^T [A3011] + a_1 [A])\{Q\}_j + [A200] \{S\}_j + a_3 \{A\})] \end{aligned} \qquad (4.172)$$

The action of $\nu_1 \{\overline{U1}\}$ as an artificial viscosity type term is clearly visible in (4.172). The action of ν_1 in the first term will emerge as antidiffusive. Noting that each hypermatrix $[A\cdot\cdot]$ is independent of the element, the generalization of (4.172) for orientation parallel to any coordinate axis, say x_i, is

$$\begin{aligned} \{FI\}_{j+1}^p = S_e[&\Delta_i [A200 + \nu_i A210](\{Q\}_{j+1}^p - \{Q\}_j) \\ &+ h\theta \, \Delta_i((\{UI\}_e^T [A3001] + \{KI + \nu_i \overline{UI}\}_e^T [A3011] + a_1^i [A])\{Q\}_{j+1}^p \\ &+ [A200] \{S\}_{j+1} + a_3^i \{A\}) + h(1-\theta) \Delta_i((\{UI\}_e^T [A3001] \\ &+ \{KI + \nu_i \overline{UI}\}_e^T [A3011] + a_1^i [A])\{Q\}_j + [A200] \{S\}_j + a_3^i \{A\})] \end{aligned} \qquad (4.173)$$

In (4 173), the index (i, I) is a free tensor denoting components parallel to x_i. The jacobian for the Newton algorithm (4.166), for the time-split construction is obtained from (4.173) by its definition.

$$\begin{aligned} [JI] \equiv [J(FI)]_{j+1}^p \equiv \frac{\partial \{FI\}}{\partial \{Q\}_{j+1}^p} = S_e[&\Delta_i [A200 + \nu_i A210] + h\theta \, \Delta_i(\{UI\}_e^T [A3001] \\ &+ \{KI + \nu_i \overline{UI}\}_e^T [A3011] + a_1^i [A])] \end{aligned} \qquad (4.174)$$

The time-split solution statement for (4.166)-(4.167) is then the following sequence of operations defined on (4.173)-(4.174). At time step $h = \Delta t_{j+1} = \frac{1}{3}(t_{j+1} - t_j)$, the initial guess is $\{\delta Q\}_{j+1}^1 \equiv \{0\}$, hence $\{Q\}_{j+1}^1 = \{Q\}_j$. Equation (4.173)-(4.174) are both evaluated for a grid sweep parallel to (say) x_1 yielding $\{F1\}_{j+1}^1$ and $[J1]_{j+1}^1$; hence, solving

$$[J1]_{j+1}^1 \{\delta Q\}_{j+1}^2 = -\{F1\}_{j+1}^1 \qquad (4.175)$$

yields

$$\{Q\}_{j+1}^2 \equiv \{Q\}_j + \{\delta Q\}_{j+1}^2 \qquad (4.176)$$

Sweeping the mesh parallel to x_2 (say), (4.176) permits evaluation of $\{F2\}_{j+1}^2$. Since (4.174) is also readily evaluable,

$$[J2]_{j+1}^2 \{\delta Q\}_{j+1}^3 = -\{F2\}_{j+1}^2 \tag{4.177}$$

yields

$$\{Q\}_{j+1}^3 \equiv \{Q\}_{j+1}^2 + \{\delta Q\}_{j+1}^3 \tag{4.178}$$

Finally, sweeping the mesh parallel to x_3 (say), using (4.177) to evaluate $\{F3\}_{j+1}^3$, and with (4.174), yields

$$[J3]_{j+1}^3 \{\delta Q\}_{j+1}^4 = -\{F3\}_{j+1}^3 \tag{4.179}$$

hence

$$\{Q\}_{j+1}^4 \equiv \{Q\}_{j+1}^3 + \{\delta Q\}_{j+1}^4 \tag{4.180}$$

In the case of (4.158)-(4.159), an elementary linear partial differential equation system, $\{Q\}_{j+1}^4$ corresponds to the discrete approximation solution at t_{j+1}. For mild nonlinearity, for example the diffusion coefficient k a function of q, each of the sweep steps (4.175)-(4.180) could be iterated to permit reevaluation of elements of $\{KI\}_e$. Alternatively, it is probably equally accurate to lag evaluation of $\{KI\}_e$ using the previous time-step solution $\{Q\}_j$.

Equations (4.173)-(4.180) define the time-split generalized finite-element algorithm statement for the three-dimensional, unsteady convection-diffusion equation statement (4.158)-(4.159). For this problem class, the basic Newton algorithm statement (4.165)-(4.167), with its associated large computer resource demands, has been replaced by a sequence of very efficient steps using a grid sweeping technique. Specifically, each of the $[JI]$ is only tridiagonal ($k = 1$) or pentadiagonal ($k = 2$). Further, core storage is required only for one $[JI]$ and one $\{FI\}$ at a time, hence the major memory demand is to store the nodal arrays $\{Q\}$, $\{UI\}$, $\{KI\}$, and $\{S\}$. It is important to emphasize that the range of applicability of the time-split algorithm is quite limited, generally to simple scalar field equations of the type (4.158)-(4.159). The concept of decomposition of the large sparse matrix jacobian (4.166), into its (tensor matrix product) factors $[JI]$, however enjoys great generality which will be put to significant use in the remainder of this text. (Specifically, $\{F\}$ in (4.166) will be evaluated using the full, multidimensional cardinal basis, while the $[JI]$ are constructed using the one-dimensional basis.) The time-split algorithm provides the vehicle to develop the concept, as well as the opportunity to construct a very efficient and useful numerical algorithm for an important problem class. Prior to discussion of applications, the following section presents the theoretical analysis for estimation of $\beta = \Delta_e \nu$.

Problems

1 Verify (4.168).

2 Verify (4.170).

3 Establish the generalized statement (4.173) using (4.168)-(4.172).

4 Verify (4.174) using (4.173).

4.11 THEORETICAL ANALYSIS, THE PARAMETER β

Equation (4.163) expresses the generalized finite-element algorithm, while (4.173)–(4.180) define the time-split solution formulation. A von Neumann stability analysis for determination of the coefficient β is facilitated using the one-dimensional matrix structures. This analysis is constructed for the strictly linear, constant velocity, diffusion-free form of (4.158), i.e.,

$$L(q) = \frac{\partial q}{\partial t} + \mathbf{U}_0 \cdot \nabla q = 0 \tag{4.181}$$

Restrict attention to the linear cardinal basis algorithm, $k = 1$ in (4.162). Hence, the standard matrix equivalent of the time-split initial-value term in (4.173) is

$$[CI]_e \equiv \Delta_i[A200 + \nu_i A210] = \frac{\Delta_i}{6}\begin{bmatrix} 2 & 1 \\ 1 & 2 \end{bmatrix} + \frac{\nu_i \Delta_i}{2}\begin{bmatrix} -1 & -1 \\ 1 & 1 \end{bmatrix} \tag{4.182}$$

In (4.182), $i = \{1, 2, 3\}$ is dependent upon the operational sequence being considered, and Δ_i is the corresponding element measure. For the convection term in (4.181) and $k = 1$ in (4.162), (4.173) yields

$$[UI]_e = \frac{1}{6}\{UI\}_e^T \begin{bmatrix} \begin{Bmatrix} 2 \\ 1 \end{Bmatrix} & \begin{Bmatrix} 2 \\ 1 \end{Bmatrix} \\ -\begin{Bmatrix} 1 \\ 2 \end{Bmatrix} & -\begin{Bmatrix} 1 \\ 2 \end{Bmatrix} \end{bmatrix} + \frac{\nu_i}{2}\{\overline{UI}\}_e^T \begin{bmatrix} \begin{Bmatrix} 1 \\ 1 \end{Bmatrix} & -\begin{Bmatrix} 1 \\ 1 \end{Bmatrix} \\ -\begin{Bmatrix} 1 \\ 1 \end{Bmatrix} & \begin{Bmatrix} 1 \\ 1 \end{Bmatrix} \end{bmatrix} \tag{4.183}$$

The matrix elements of $\{UI\}_e$ are the nodal values of the ith scalar component of the velocity vector $\mathbf{U}_0$. The first term in (4.183) is the regular convection term, while the second corresponds to an added dissipation-like term, wherein the "viscosity" is $\nu_i\{\overline{UI}\}_e$. Note that for both terms, the element measure Δ_e for $k = 1$ has canceled out in the algebra.

The basic requirement is to estimate the value for ν_i in (4.182)–(4.183); the procedure employs the von Neumann stability analysis. Since (4.181) is linear and separable, the exact solution for a one-dimensional specification is the Fourier expansion

$$q(x, t) = V \exp\,[i\omega(x - U_0 t)] \tag{4.184}$$

where $i \equiv \sqrt{-1}$, $\omega = 2\pi/\lambda$ is the wave number of wavelength (Fourier mode) λ, and V is the initial distribution. Direct substitution of (4.184) into (4.181) establishes its validity; the solution corresponds to the diffusion- and dispersion-free convection of the initial wave form V parallel to the x axis with velocity $U_0\hat{\mathbf{i}}$. For the von Neumann analysis, the Fourier expansion for the semidiscrete approximate solution is

$$q^h(\Delta x, t) = V \exp\,[i\omega(j\,\Delta x - \lambda t)] \tag{4.185}$$

where $\Delta x = \Delta_1$, the uniform discretization of R^1. In (4.185), $1 \leqslant j \leqslant M+1$ is the node indicator, and $\lambda \equiv \gamma + i\mu$, where γ and μ are real numbers. Comparing (4.184) and (4.185), a difference between γ and U_0 constitutes a disparity in the group velocity of propagation of V, hence phase error in the semidiscrete solution. Correspondingly, $\mu < 0$ introduces a real argument into the exponent yielding a damping (or growth, $\mu > 0$) of the amplitude of V. Substituting (4.185) into (4.164) [see (4.126)], and expanding the resultant expressions for γ and μ in a Taylor series yields (Raymond and Garder, 1976)

$$\gamma = U_0 \left[1 + \left(-\frac{1}{180} + \frac{\nu^2}{12} \right) d^4 + O(d^6) \right] \tag{4.186}$$

$$\mu = U_0 \left[-\frac{\nu d^3}{12} + O(d^5) \right] \tag{4.187}$$

where $d \equiv \omega \Delta x$, and $O(\cdot)$ indicates the order of the truncated term. Since γ is the real part of λ, it can be made identical to U_0 to order $(\Delta x)^6$ by requiring the second term in (4.186) to vanish, yielding $\nu^{-1} \equiv \sqrt{15}$. With $\nu > 0$, $\mu < 0$ in (4.187) and an artificial damping is introduced. For $\nu \equiv (15)^{-1/2}$, the semidiscrete solution Fourier expansion (4.185) is the form

$$q^h(\Delta x, t) = V \exp\,[i\omega(j\,\Delta x - (U_0 + O(\Delta x^6))t)]\, \exp\,[-\omega^4 kt + O(\Delta x^5)] \tag{4.188}$$

In (4.188), $k \equiv U_0(\Delta x)^3/12\sqrt{15}$ is the artificial diffusion coefficient, and highly selective damping occurs for sufficiently large wave numbers ω (small wavelengths) due to the ω^4 factor. It is left as an exercise to verify that, upon adding the physical viscosity term $k\,\partial^2 q/\partial x^2$ to (4.181), and setting $\nu \equiv 0 = \beta$ in (4.163), the discrete Fourier analysis yields (4.185) in the form

$$q^h(\Delta x, t) = V \exp\,[i\omega(j\,\Delta x - (U_0 + O(\Delta x^4))t)]\, \exp\,[-\omega^2 kt + O(\Delta x^3)] \tag{4.189}$$

The fourth-order phase accuracy for (4.189) is identical to that determined by the truncation error analysis in Sec. 4.8. The "artificial" damping $\omega^2 k$ is less selective, due to the diminution of the wave number exponent to 2, as well as to the appearance of the term of order Δx^3.

A complete discrete von Neumann analysis can further quantize key elements. The fully discrete approximation nodal solution is the form

$$q_n^h(\Delta x, \Delta t) = g^n \exp\,(i2\pi\omega j\,\Delta x) \tag{4.190}$$

It is left as an exercise to verify that substitution of (4.190) into the one-dimensional form of (4.164), with replacement of the time derivative by the trapezoidal rule, yields the amplification factor for the generalized finite-element algorithm (4.163) as (Pepper and Cooper, 1980).

$$g = \frac{1 + (1/2)\cos(\omega\,\Delta x) - 3C\nu \sin^2[(1/2)\omega\,\Delta x] - i(3/4)(C + 2\nu)\sin(\omega\,\Delta x)}{1 + (1/2)\cos(\omega\,\Delta x) + 3C\nu \sin^2[(1/2)\omega\,\Delta x] + i(3/4)(C - 2\nu)\sin(\omega\,\Delta x)} \tag{4.191}$$

Recall that $C \equiv U_0 \, \Delta x/\Delta t$ is the Courant number. The algorithm is now neutrally stable, that is, $|g| = 1$, only for $\nu \equiv 0$. Hence, in general, g is constituted of real and imaginary parts,

$$g = \gamma + i\Gamma \tag{4.192}$$

and $\gamma < 0$ yields a dissipative mechanism, while Γ determines the phase accuracy. Recalling Sec. 4.8,

$$\theta \equiv \frac{1}{\lambda \, \Delta x} \tan^{-1}\left(\frac{\Gamma}{\gamma}\right) \tag{4.193}$$

defines the normalized phase velocity of a specific Fourier mode of the fully discrete solution q_n^h. Figure 4.17 graphs (4.193) for the nondissipative algorithm ($\nu \equiv 0$), for select Courant numbers, as a function of wavelengths resolved on the scale of the mesh. The analytical solution is the horizontal line at $\theta = 1$, that is, each phase velocity is identical to the group velocity. The dashed curves correspond to the diagonalized matrix finite-difference form discussed in Sec. 4.8. The poorer performance of this construction is clearly evident. At modest Courant numbers, $0.01 < C < 0.5$, the $k = 1$ finite-element algorithm accurately resolves all wavelengths $\lambda \geqslant 5\,\Delta x$, while for the Crank-Nicolson form, this occurs only for $\lambda > 15\,\Delta x$.

Pepper and Cooper (1980) report the evaluation of (4.193) for $\nu = (15)^{-1/2}$ in (4.191); this optimal value is determined by extremizing order of accuracy in (4.186). These data for $C = 0.5$ are shown in Fig. 4.17 as solid squares. Note that the phase velocity $\theta \geqslant 0.96$ for all wavelengths $n\,\Delta x$, $n > 2$. While this improvement appears to

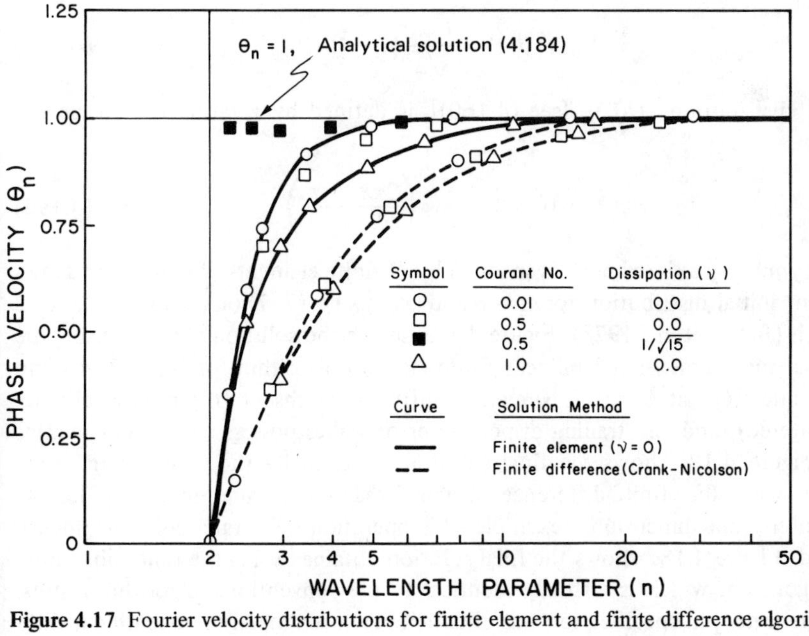

Figure 4.17 Fourier velocity distributions for finite element and finite difference algorithms.

be excellent, it comes only at the price of an excessively large induced artificial viscosity level. Therefore, even though the trailing dispersion wake can be made to vanish, (see Fig. 4.6), the peak concentration also essentially vanishes after a sufficient number of time steps. The remainder of this chapter is devoted to pertinent assessments.

Problems

1 Derive (4.188).
2 Establish the form of (4.189).
3 Derive (4.191) using (4.189).

4.12 MULTIDIMENSIONAL CONVECTION/DIFFUSION

An accuracy and efficiency evaluation is required for the basic (nondissipative, $\beta \equiv 0$) time-split finite-element algorithm, (4.173)-(4.180). The multidimensional equivalent of the one-dimensional, diffusion-free convection problem studied in Sec. 4.8 provides the test. Hence, solution to (4.158) is required for the specified n-dimensional velocity field

$$\mathbf{U}_0(x_i, t) = u\hat{\mathbf{i}} + v\hat{\mathbf{j}} + w\hat{\mathbf{k}} \tag{4.194}$$

The first verification regards an accuracy comparison between the time-split and standard multidimensional algorithm solutions. The test case is the two-dimensional equivalent of the one-dimensional problem of Sec. 4.8, with constant diagonal convection velocity field

$$\mathbf{U}_0(x, y, t) = \frac{U_\infty}{\sqrt{2}}\,[\hat{\mathbf{i}} + \hat{\mathbf{j}}] \tag{4.195}$$

The initial distribution $\{Q(0)\}$ [see (4.160)] is defined by rotating the cosine hill distribution,

$$q_0(x, y, 0) \equiv 1 + \cos\left(\frac{2\pi x}{\lambda} - \frac{\pi}{2}\right) \tag{4.196}$$

about the symmetry axis, where λ is spanned by M finite elements. Figure 4.18*a* shows the resultant initial distribution for $M = 8$ and $(x_0, y_0) = (7, 7)$ on a uniform 32×32 square mesh (Baker et al., 1978). Figure 4.18*b* shows the solution obtained using the conventional multidimensional bilinear finite element algorithm for $U_\infty = 2$ m/s and after 150 time steps at $C = 0.1$. Numerical diffusion is absent (the peak level is retained unaltered), and the trailing dispersion error wakes possess ± 3 percent relative extrema. Figure 4.18*c* shows the final solution obtained by the conventional algorithm, but with the finite-difference diagonalized initial-value matrix $[C]_e$. As occurred in the one-dimensional example, this operation obliterates solution fidelity on this grid. Figure 4.18*d* shows the final solution obtained using the time-split finite-element algorithm, which is virtually identical to the conventional algorithm results. Of note, the time-split specification was obtained in approximately one-tenth expendi-

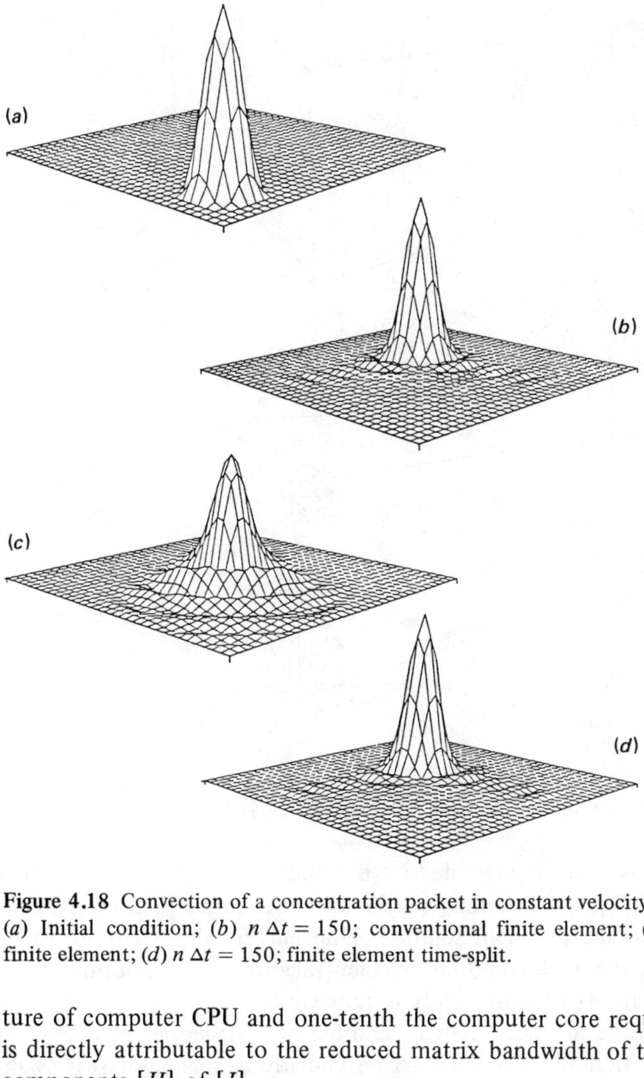

Figure 4.18 Convection of a concentration packet in constant velocity field $\mathbf{U} = u[\hat{\mathbf{i}} + \hat{\mathbf{j}}]$, $C = 0.1$. (*a*) Initial condition; (*b*) $n\,\Delta t = 150$; conventional finite element; (*c*) $n\,\Delta t = 150$; diagonalized finite element; (*d*) $n\,\Delta t = 150$; finite element time-split.

ture of computer CPU and one-tenth the computer core requirement. This difference is directly attributable to the reduced matrix bandwidth of the tensor matrix product components $[JI]$ of $[J]$.

The three-dimensional test case, equivalent to the two-dimensional cosine hill, employs a spherically symmetric initial distribution with planar contours corresponding to appropriate sections through the two-dimensional distribution. The imposed constant diagonal convection velocity in three-dimensions is

$$\mathbf{U}_0(x, y, z, t) = \frac{U_\infty}{\sqrt{3}}\,[\hat{\mathbf{i}} + \hat{\mathbf{j}} + \hat{\mathbf{k}}] \tag{4.197}$$

Figure 4.19 summarizes the three-dimensional solution, in the form of particle density distributions, obtained using the nondissipative ($\nu \equiv 0$) time-split finite-element solution algorithm. The particles located in the wake of the major concentration are shed

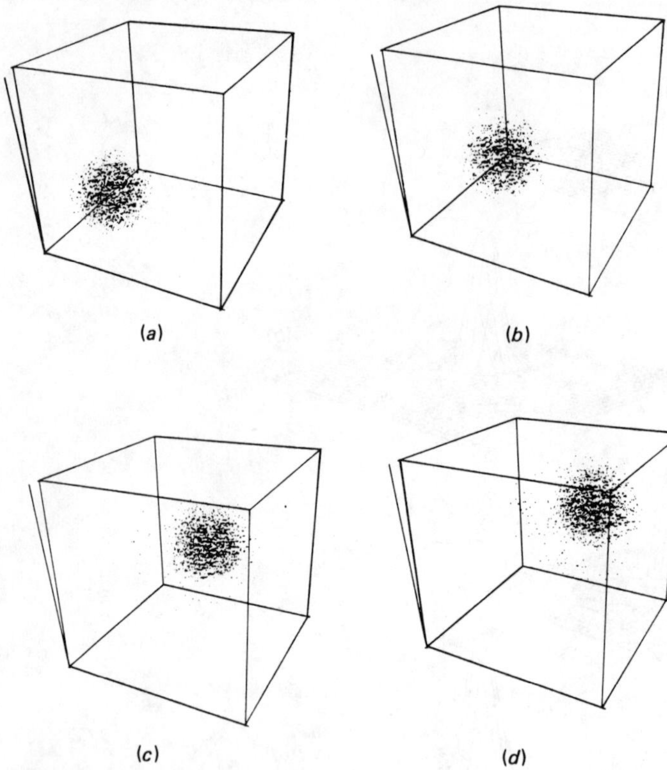

Figure 4.19 Solution of three-dimensional convection equation, time-split linear finite-element algorithm, $k = 1$, $\nu = 0$. (a) $n\,\Delta t = 0$; (b) $n\,\Delta t = 50$; (c) $n\,\Delta t = 100$; (d) $n\,\Delta t = 150$.

by the associated dispersion error; their density is certainly modest for the solution Courant number $C = 0.5$. Table 4.2 summarizes the computer core efficiency comparison between the standard and time-split solution algorithms for these two test cases. The basic superiority of the time-split finite element algorithm, for solution of the convection-diffusion equation (4.158)-(4.160), is quite clear.

The next requirement is to assess accuracy and use of a higher degree basis for a range of imposed convection velocity fields. A particularly demanding test is estab-

Table 4.2 Standard and tensor product time-split algorithm efficiency summary

Efficiency measure	Finite element degree	Two-dimensional solution		Three-dimensional solution	
		Standard	Tensor product	Standard	Tensor product
Equation rank	1, 2	1,030	1,030	4,100	4,100
Storage words					
Jacobian	1	66,000	100	1,200,000	50
Jacobian	2	128,000	200	~5,000,000	80
Program	1, 2	180,000	70,000	~5,000,000	125,000

lished by specifying $\mathbf{U}_0 \equiv r\dot{\omega}\hat{\theta}$, which is solid body rotation with angular velocity $\dot{\omega}$. The initial distribution is again the cosine hill (see Fig. 4.18*a*), but moved to the 9 o'clock position on the grid. The exact solution is diffusion- and dispersion-free convection clockwise around the solution domain. Figure 4.20 shows the typical linear element solution at the quarter, three-quarter, and full-rotation time steps. The ripple structure in the background plane is induced by dispersion error due to short wavelength phase lag. Utilization of the artificial dissipation parameter $\beta > 0$ to modify this type error is discussed in the next section.

The factors controlling solution accuracy are degree k of the approximation, (4.162), and the normalized integration step size $C = u\,\Delta t/\Delta_e$, the Courant number. Figure 4.21*a* illustrates the initial and exact final solutions. Figure 4.21*b* shows the final solution following 320 integration steps at $C = 0.25$ for the quadratic ($k = 2$) form of the algorithm. Comparing the exact solution, accuracy is excellent in maintenance of the peak and symmetries. The maximum amplitude of the traveling wake error is 2 percent, which occurs directly behind the solution and is quantized by the depth of the base of the graph. Decreasing k and/or increasing C increases solution error levels. Figure 4.21*c* shows the final solution obtained for $k = 2$, $C = 0.5$. The group velocity of these solutions is substantially retarded, hence, the peak is flattened

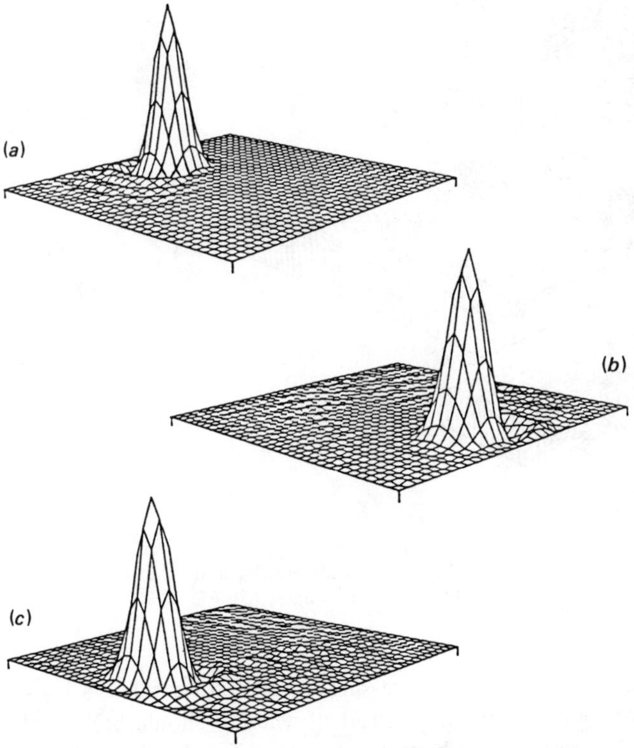

Figure 4.20 Convection of a concentration packet in solid-body rotation velocity field $\mathbf{U}$, $C = 0.1$. (*a*) $n\,\Delta t = 80$, one-quarter turn; (*b*) $n\,\Delta t = 240$, three-quarter turn; (*c*) $n\,\Delta t = 320$, full turn.

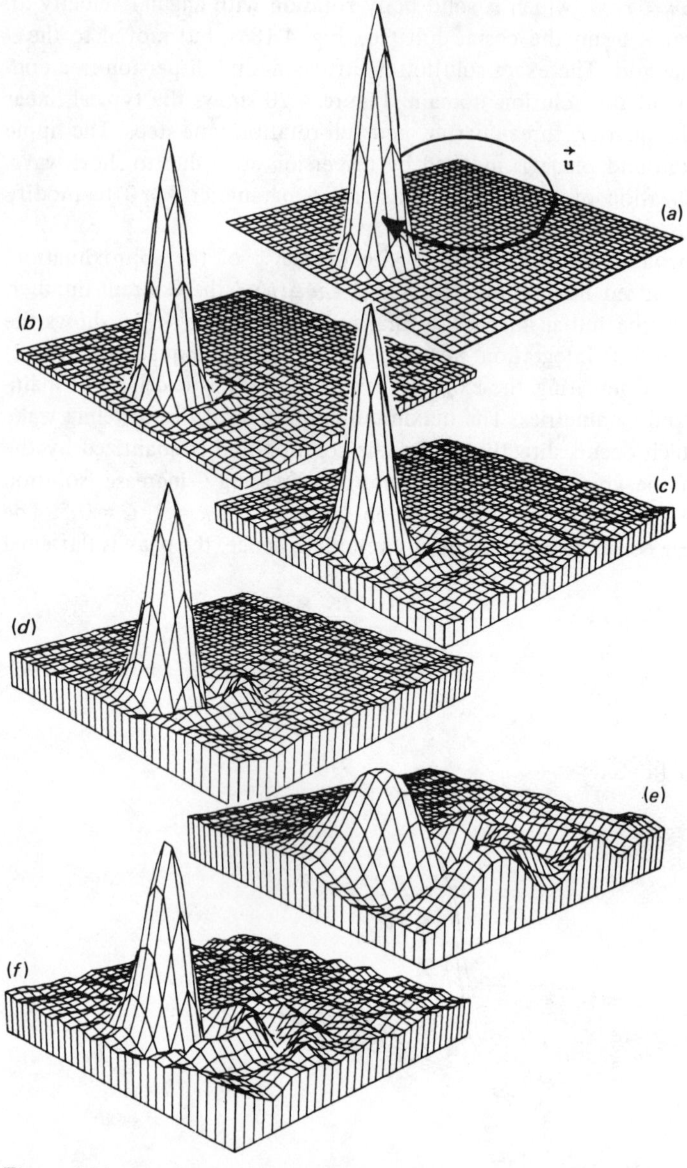

Figure 4.21 Rotational convection of a cosine hill distribution, (*a*) h_0 and exact final solution; (*b*) FE, $k = 2$, $C = 0.25$; (*c*) FE, $k = 2$. $C = 0.5$; $k = 1$, $C = 0.25$; (*d*) FE, $k = 1$; $C = 0.5$; (*e*) FD/CN, $C = 0.25$; (*f*) FE/CN, $k = 2$, $C = 0.5$.

and the extremum wake error is 9 percent. Increasing to $C = 0.5$ for the $k = 1$ algorithm (Fig. 4.21*d*), the peak returns (one node short of where it should be) and the extremum wake error is 17 percent. Note, however, that even for this relatively poor solution, there is no evidence of numerical diffusion. The distribution has not broadened and the peak is within 4 percent of the correct value. For comparison,

Fig. 4.21e shows the Crank-Nicolson finite-difference solution for $C = 0.25$, which is identical in complexity to the $k = 1$ algorithm. Accuracy is poor, the peak has diffused to a broad plateau with peak level loss to 47 percent, and the extremum wake error is 25 percent. Figure 4.21f shows the solution obtained using the Crank-Nicolson equivalent of the $k = 2$ algorithm at $C = 0.5$. While it is an improvement over Fig. 4.21e it is poor in comparison to Fig. 4.21c, as the peak has diffused 15 percent and the wake error extremum is 21 percent. Regarding computer costs, the $k = 2$ algorithm CPU cost is nominally 15 percent larger than the $k = 1$ algorithm, with a negligible increase in computer storage. Written as a recursion relation, the $k = 1$ algorithm CPU is identical to that for the Crank-Nicolson finite-difference algorithm.

An alternative specification for the parameters in (4.158), that yields an exact comparison for accuracy, corresponds to a continuous source in a one-dimensional convection velocity field with directional, multidimensional diffusion. The exact solution is the gaussian plume (Fabrick et al., 1977, p. 19).

$$q(x_i) = \frac{S}{2\pi\sigma_y\sigma_z u} e^{-y^2/2\sigma_y^2}\left(e^{-(H-z)^2/2\sigma_z^2} + e^{-(H+z)^2/2\sigma_z^2}\right) \tag{4.198}$$

where q = pollutant concentration at point x, y, z
S = emission rate of the source
u = average wind speed ($\mathbf{U}_0 = u\,\hat{\mathbf{i}}$)
x = downwind distance from source
y = crosswind distance measured from plume centerline
z = elevation above ground level
H = elevation of the source above ground level
σ_y = horizontal diffusion coefficient
σ_z = vertical diffusion coefficient

Baker et al. (1980) report results using the linear and quadratic, nondissipative time-split algorithm. A symmetric nine-cell continuous emitting source was defined, with maximum emission of 100 g/m^2 s, with uniform convection velocity parallel to the x_1 axis. For the two-dimensional test, the diffusion coefficient is specified nonzero parallel to the x_2 axis only. The steady-state gaussian comparison solution was generated using $U_1 = 1$ m/s and $\sigma_2 = 0.1$ m^2/s. The linear and quadratic solutions were generated using a constant time-step at $C = 0.5$, for which the integration truncation error was assessed to be negligible. The lateral span of the solution domain was specified sufficient to contain the plume spread, and a downstream outflow gradient boundary condition was enforced.

The numerical solutions were terminated following 100 h of continuous emission, which yields the steady-state solution. Both the $k = 1$ and $k = 2$ solutions displayed exact symmetry about the trajectory center line. Figure 4.22 is a summary composite representation of the solutions. The upper half is the $k = 1$ nodal solution, the lower half is the $k = 2$ nodal solution, and the separating array is the symmetry plane gaussian plume solution. In addition, the separated columns of data at the far right are the gaussian-predicted lateral spread. The location of the plume source is also indicated. The $k = 2$ algorithm solution is in essentially exact agreement with the gaussian for both centerline concentration and lateral spread. This level of agreement

Finite element, $k = 1$

																				1
															1	1	2	2	3	3
	Source				−1				1	1	2	3	5	5	6	8	9	9	10	10
						4	6	9	12	14	16	18	20	21	22	24	25	25	26	26
		2	12	21	28	35	38	41	44	45	46	47	48	48	48	49	49	49	49	48
0	8	50	93	100	97	96	93	90	88	86	83	81	79	77	75	74	72	71	69	71
0	16	92	159	156	142	132	123	116	110	105	100	97	94	90	87	85	82	80	78	81
U → 0	25	98	162	166	145	137	129	121	115	109	105	100	97	93	90	88	85	83	81	Gaussian
−2	10	94	169	164	148	138	129	122	116	111	106	101	98	95	91	89	86	83	81	81
−1	4	50	97	103	101	98	95	93	90	88	86	83	81	80	77	76	74	73	71	71
		2	10	19	26	31	35	38	41	43	44	45	46	47	47	48	48	48	48	48
			−2	−2	−1	1	3	6	9	11	14	15	17	19	20	22	23	24	25	26
										1	2	2	4	5	5	7	8	8	9	10
																1	1	2	2	3
																				1

Finite element, $k = 2$

Figure 4.22 Composite comparison of linear and quadratic finite-element solutions with gaussian plume with two-dimensional convection, one-dimensional diffusion.

Finite element, $k = 1$

Source

																1	1	1
								1	1	1	2	2	3	3	3	3	3	2
					3	4	5	7	8	8	8	8	8	8	8	8	8	5
		2	11	19	23	23	23	21	20	19	18	17	16	16	15	14	14	11
	7	42	74	73	55	48	43	35	32	29	27	25	23	22	20	19	18	17
	15	80	122	105	70	59	51	40	36	33	30	28	26	24	22	21	20	20
U→	25	93	137	113	79	62	52	44	39	35	31	28	26	24	22	21	20	Gaussian
	12	81	131	110	72	61	54	43	38	35	32	29	27	25	23	22	21	20
	4	43	78	76	57	50	45	36	33	31	28	26	24	23	21	20	19	17
	−1	2	12	20	25	25	24	22	21	20	19	18	17	16	16	15	14	11
					4	5	6	8	8	8	9	9	9	9	9	9	8	5
								1	1	2	2	3	3	3	3	3	4	2
															1	1	1	1

Finite element, $k = 2$

Figure 4.23 Composite comparison of linear and quadratic finite-element solution, gaussian plume for three-dimensional convection, two-dimensional diffusion.

pervades the entire $k = 2$ solution, except immediately downstream of the source where select differences up to 2 percent were predicted. The $k = 1$ solution is less accurate, in comparison, with centerline concentrations low by nominally 3-5 percent. The agreement with the gaussian on lateral spread is essentially exact. The modest negative solution levels shown are indicative of inadequate grid resolution for the solution gradients. Figure 4.23 summarizes the horizontal symmetry plane accuracy for the corresponding three-dimensional continuous source specification solutions.

As a final example, with nonelementary convection velocity field coupled with directional diffusion, consider the calculation of the three-dimensional steady-flow distribution from a continuous source located at a specified distance beneath the surface of a channel flow (Baker and Soliman, 1982). The hydrodynamic velocity vector $\mathbf{u}_0$, assumed uniform in planes perpendicular to the x_3 axis, corresponds to the pseudoturbulent distribution of u_3, shown as isovels in Fig. 4.24, and a superimposed roll vortex pair. The continuous source is assumed to be situated in the first solution plane, at the location marked X, and three-dimensional diffusion may be present, with distinct principal values for σ_i. The half-channel domain, of unit transverse aspect ratio, is discretized into a $17 \times 17 \times 17$ mesh, yielding 4096 brick finite-element domains for the $k = 1$ time-split algorithm solutions.

Figure 4.25*a* illustrates the concentration distribution one plane downstream of injection, with contour levels of 0.2, 0.4, and 0.6. For orientation, the boundary tic marks correspond to every other boundary node of the $k = 1$ discretization. In the absence of any convection, and with a uniform three-dimensional diffusion coefficient, successive solution planes would show symmetric spreading and a decay in the peak level. For zero diffusion, and a uniform velocity $\mathbf{U}_0 = u_3\hat{\mathbf{k}}$, the concentration peak would be maintained with negligible lateral spreading. Figures 4.25*b*–*d* show the $k = 1$

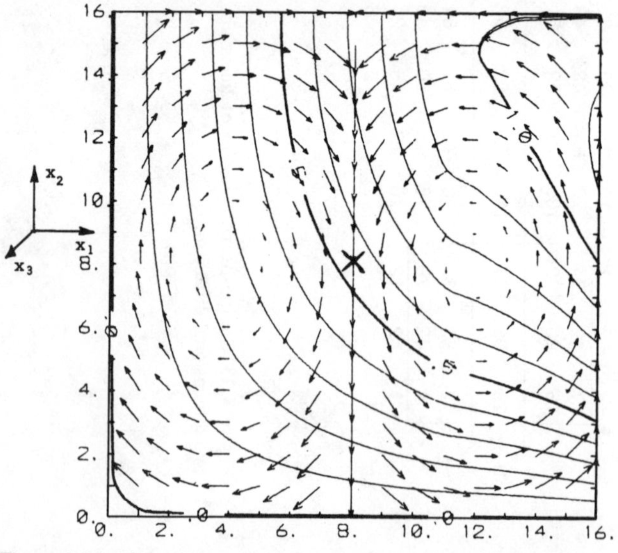

Figure 4.24 Three-dimensional channel flow velocity distribution.

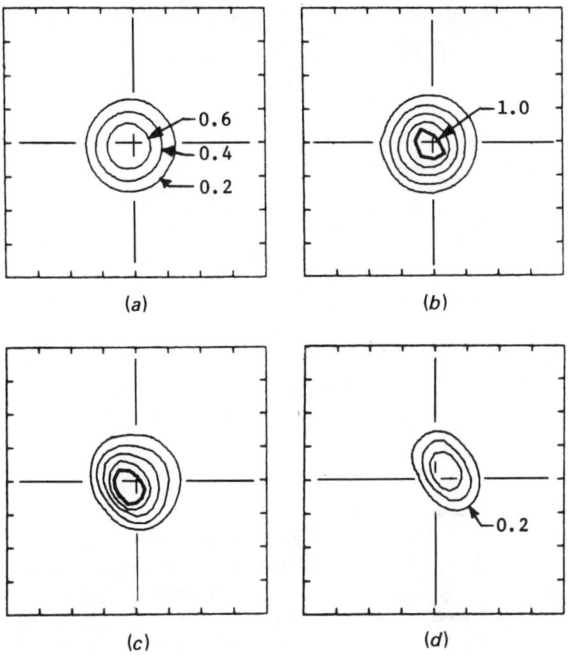

Figure 4.25 Computed three-dimensional isograms, one-dimensional convection, no diffusion. (*a*) Plane 2; (*b*) plane 5; (*c*) plane 8; (*d*) plane 11.

solutions at planes 5, 8, and 11, following penetration of the solution into plane 15, for zero diffusion and $\mathbf{U}_0 = 0i + 0\hat{\mathbf{j}} + u_3\hat{\mathbf{k}}$. Contour levels of 0.8 and 1.0 (double curve) have occurred at stations 5 and 8, while 0.6 is the maximum contour at plane 11. The cross hair denotes the channel geometric centerline; the action of the distribution of u_3 induces the contour distortion into the upper right quadrant, as material is preferentially convected into the higher-velocity region.

Variations on the base case (see Fig. 4.26), were obtained by adding three-dimensional diffusion, with $\sigma_1 = 2\sigma_2 = 5\sigma_3$, to the uniform velocity field. Some spreading of the contour shapes is discernible, but the dominant difference is reduced peak levels throughout. Figure 4.27 illustrates the solution obtained with addition of the roll vortex velocity field with zero diffusion. Consequential differences in contour location and shape result, as the concentration centerline rolls downward to the right. The small, closed double-lined contours surround levels of $\{Q\} < -0.005$, as an indication of solution error due to inadequate resolution. Figure 4.28 shows the comparison solution obtained with three-dimensional convection and three-dimensional diffusion. The latter has almost eliminated the dispersion error, and maximum levels are lower everywhere. Again, diffusion is a minor modification to convection.

These results confirm the basic accuracy and efficiency of the time-split algorithm for parametric studies in three-dimensional transport. The diffusion and convection phenomena, inseparable in the physical simulation, can be individually analyzed using a sufficiently high order-accurate algorithm. The error produced using any consistent numerical algorithm is controllable with discretization refinement, but computer resource constraints place a severe limitation on number of solution nodes for three-

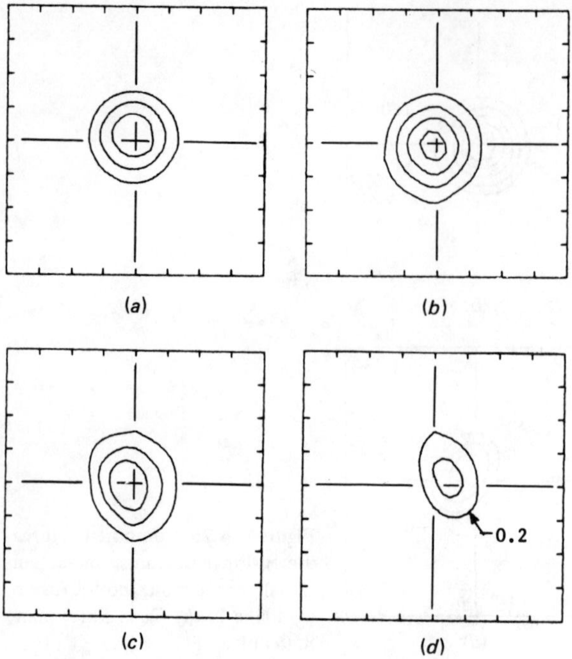

Figure 4.26 Computed three-dimensional isograms, one-dimensional convection, three-dimensional diffusion. (*a*) Plane 2; (*b*) plane 5; (*c*) plane 8; (*d*) plane 11.

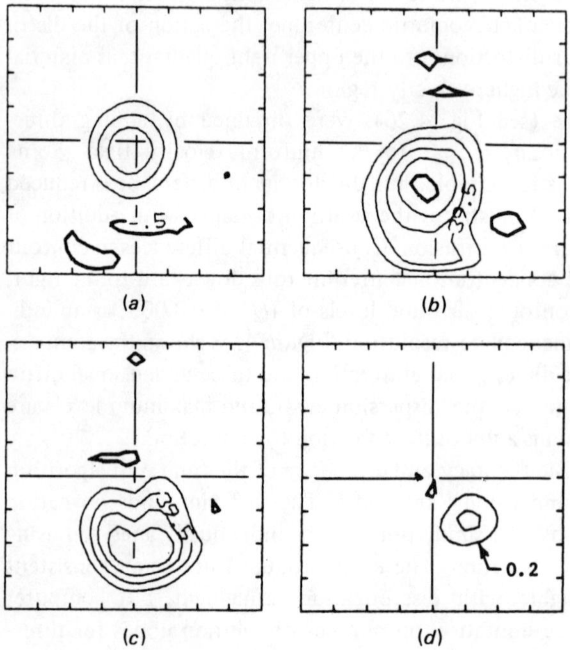

Figure 4.27 Computed three-dimensional isograms, three-dimensional convection, no diffusion. (*a*) Plane 2; (*b*) plane 5; (*c*) plane 8; (*d*) plane 11.

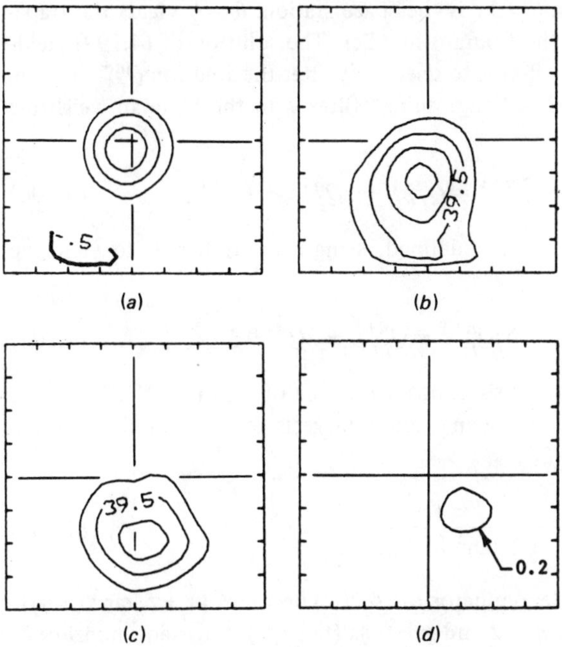

Figure 4.28 Computed three-dimensional isograms, three-dimensional convection and diffusion. (*a*) Plane 2; (*b*) plane 5; (*c*) plane 8; (*d*) plane 11.

dimensional flows. The time-split finite-element algorithm successfully addresses the combined key issues of accuracy and efficiency.

4.13 DISPERSION ERROR CONTROL THROUGH DISSIPATION

The analyses of the preceding section have documented the excellent accuracy for the convection-diffusion problem class intrinsic to the time-split finite-element algorithm. (Comparable accuracy accrues to the non-time-split algorithm as well, although computer cost would then become unacceptable, especially for the quadratic basis algorithm.) There exist problem specifications wherein the phase lag dispersion error can become unacceptably large, due to large-scale distortion of the solution on a coarse grid. In these instances, the dissipation parameter β can be specified nonzero, yielding an artificial diffusion mechanism [see (4.163) and (4.186)–(4.187).

Pepper et al. (1979) document a comparison analysis between the dissipative finite-element algorithm, and a Shuman-type digital filter, for the two-dimensional rotating cone test case. Since the digital filter is a recursive formulation, it is convenient to consider (4.172) [recall (4.126)] written as

$$\frac{1}{6}\left[(Q_{j+1}^{n+1} - Q_{j+1}^{n}) + 4(Q_j^{n+1} - Q_j^n) + (Q_{j-1}^{n+1} - Q_{j-1}^{n})\right]$$

$$+\frac{C}{2}\left[\theta(Q_{j+1}^{n+1} - Q_{j-1}^{n+1}) + (1-\theta)(Q_{j+1}^{n} - Q_{j-1}^{n})\right] = 0 \qquad (4.199)$$

In (4.199), $n\,\Delta t$ is the time station, $j\,\Delta x$ is the space station, $\theta = \frac{1}{2}$ yields the trapezoidal rule, and $C = U_0\,\Delta t/\Delta x$ is the Courant number. The solution of (4.199) yields Q_j^{n+1}. The concept of the digital filter is to selectively alter the solution Q_j^{n+1} to produce the revised solution $\bar{Q}_j^{n+1}$. The "do-nothing" filter with the Shuman weighting is the recursion

$$\bar{Q}_{j+1}^{n+1} + 2\bar{Q}_j^{n+1} + \bar{Q}_{j-1}^{n+1} = Q_{j+1}^{n+1} + 2Q_j^{n+1} + Q_{j-1}^{n+1} \tag{4.200}$$

The coefficients modifying $\bar{Q}$ are then redefined, using a multiplier δ, to yield the filter recursion relation

$$(1-\delta)\bar{Q}_{j+1}^{n+1} + 2(1+\delta)\bar{Q}_j^{n+1} + (1-\delta)\bar{Q}_{j-1}^{n+1} \equiv Q_{j+1}^{n+1} + 2Q_j^{n+1} + Q_{j-1}^{n+1} \tag{4.201}$$

The von Neumann stability analysis exposes the role of δ in (4.201). Using the fully discrete Fourier expansion (4.190), an exercise suggests verification of the amplification factor g for (4.201) as

$$g = \frac{1}{1 + \delta \tan^2 [(1/2)\omega\,\Delta x]} \tag{4.202}$$

For $\lambda = n\,\Delta x$, $\omega = 2\pi/n\,\Delta x$, the denominator of (4.202) becomes $[1 + \delta \tan^2 (\pi/n)]$. For the shortest resolvable wave, $n = 2$ and $g \to 0$ as $(\tan \pi/2)^{-2}$ for any nonzero δ. Hence, the $2\,\Delta x$ waves in the approximate solution produced by dispersion error will become absolutely obliterated. For $n > 2$, the argument in (4.202) is bounded, and $0 < g < 1$. Hence, all Fourier modes in the approximation q_j^h will be diffused. Unfortunately, the true peaks in the solution also become damped by the induced artificial diffusion, hence a reasonable minimum estimate for δ is required.

The test case is the discussed two-dimensional solid-body rotation of the "cosine-hill" distribution, with imposed velocity field

$$\mathbf{U}_0 \equiv r\dot{\omega}\hat{\theta} \tag{4.203}$$

where $\dot{\omega}$ is the (constant) angular velocity, r is radius, and $\hat{\theta}$ is the unit tangent vector. Figure 4.29 summarizes the results reported by Pepper et al. (1979). The upper left plot is the analytical solution, devoid of the ripple structure. The upper right is the nondissipative ($\beta = 0$) linear basis finite-element time-split solution after one revolution. The solutions in the left column were obtained for various δ (§ in Fig. 4.29) in (4.201). The results in the right column are for the time-split finite-element algorithm, for β (ρ in Fig. 4.29) $\equiv \nu\,\Delta x$ for the range $0.01 \leqslant \nu \leqslant 0.15$. Recall the optimal order-of-accuracy analysis produced $\nu_{\text{opt}} = (15)^{-1/2} \approx 0.25$. Comparing, the time-split finite-element solution yields marginally superior results for the same nominal level of overall artificial diffusion, i.e., the same reduction of peak level below the exact value of 100. While $\nu \approx \nu_{\text{opt}}$ does indeed smooth the dispersion error, the induced artificial diffusion is unacceptable for this problem. In fact, $\nu \approx 0.1\nu_{\text{opt}}$ is representative of an acceptable solution, which does induce some smoothing of the background dispersion error. Importantly, the generalized finite-element algorithm (4.163) does appear to contain the basic Shuman filter concept as a special case.

Numerical results on use of the digital filter concept for a more demanding problem class are reported by Baker et al. (1978). The test case corresponds to dual

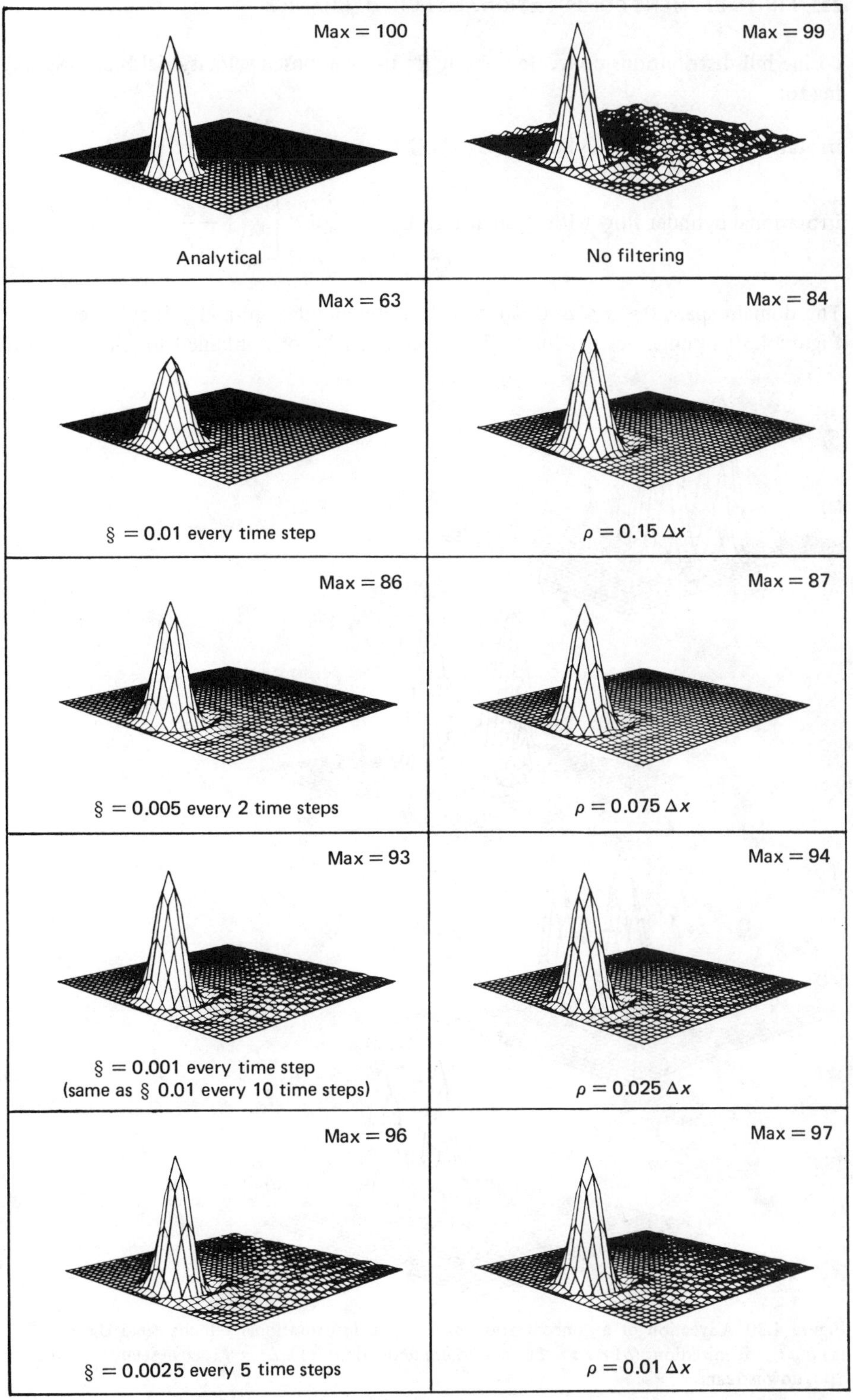

Figure 4.29 Effects of filtering on a cosine hill distribution after 2π revolutions, chapeau finite element, $C = 0.25$. After Pepper et al. (1979), with permission.

cosine hill distributions convected about R^2 using imposed velocity fields corresponding to:

irrotational flow about a cylinder: $$\mathbf{U}_0 = U_\infty \nabla \times y\left(1 - \frac{\alpha^2}{r^2}\right)\hat{\mathbf{k}} \tag{4.204}$$

irrotational cylinder flow with circulation: $$\mathbf{U}_0 = U_\infty \nabla \times \left[y\left(1 - \frac{\alpha^2}{r^2}\right) + \frac{\Gamma}{2\pi}\ln\left(\frac{r}{\alpha}\right)\right]\hat{\mathbf{k}} \tag{4.205}$$

The domain spans $0 \leqslant x \leqslant a$, $0 \leqslant y \leqslant b$; Γ is the circulation, and α is cylinder radius. Figure 4.30 summarizes the linear finite-element solutions obtained for (4.204), with

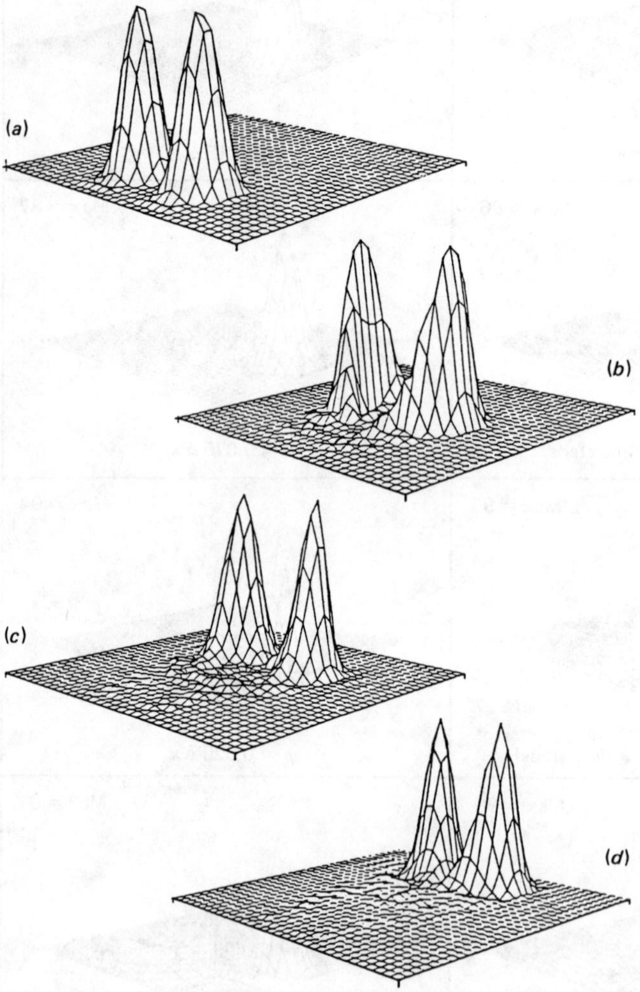

Figure 4.30 Advection of a concentration packet pair in irrotational velocity field $\mathbf{U}_0$, $C = 0.1$. (*a*) $n\,\Delta t = 5$, initiation; (*b*) $n\,\Delta t = 50$, maximum deflection; (*c*) $n\,\Delta t = 75$, coalescence; (*d*) $n\,\Delta t = 100$, downstream.

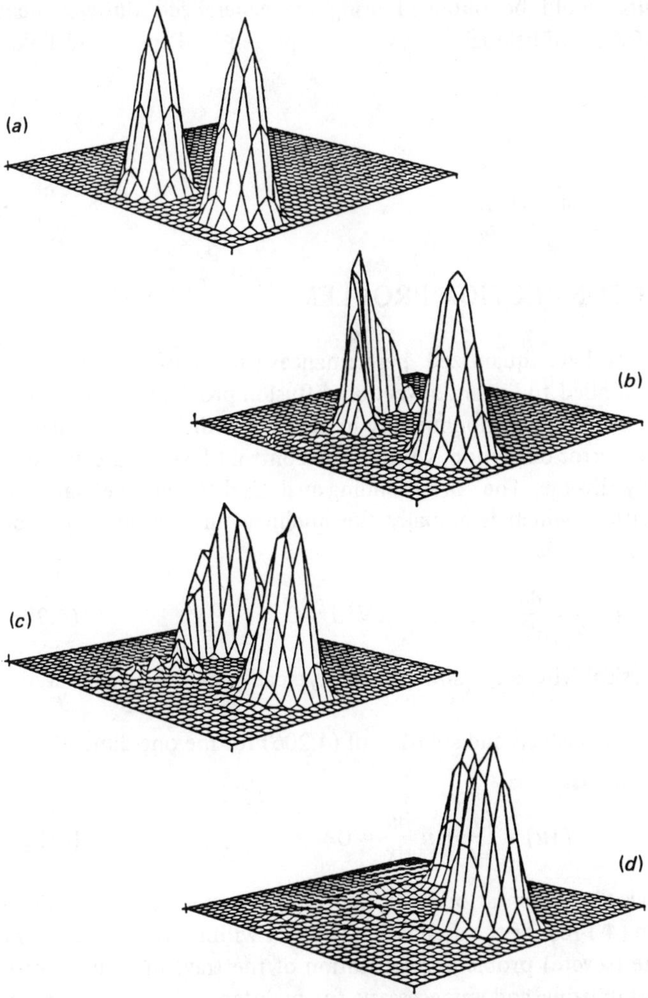

Figure 4.31 Advection of a concentration packet pair in irrotational velocity field $\mathbf{U}_0$ with circulation, $C = 0.1$. (*a*) $n\,\Delta t = 0$, initiation; (*b*) $n\,\Delta t = 40$, near deflection; (*c*) $n\,\Delta t = 75$, far deflection; (*d*) $n\,\Delta t = 100$, downstream.

the digital filter applied every $5\,\Delta t$ and $\delta = 0.001$. Note the extremely steep solution gradients exhibited at $n\,\Delta t = 50$, yet there is a return to acceptable distributions at the final station $n\,\Delta t = 100$ with peak level equal to 100. Furthermore, the solution twin peaks are exactly mirror-symmetric throughout. Figure 4.31 summarizes the solution for the potential flow velocity distribution with circulation (4.205). Note the extreme distortion in the upper distribution, Fig. 4.31*b*, yet the return to the nominal distributions following passage around the cylinder. The nonfiltered finite-element solutions using either (4.204) or (4.205) exhibit larger levels of dispersion-error induced waves in the immediate vicinity of the cylinder stagnation point. These errors were effectively controlled using the digital filter. Based on the rotating cone test case, identical results would be obtained using the generalized finite-element algorithm with $\beta \approx 0.025\,\Delta x$. Additional analyses are reported by Pepper and Baker (1979).

Problem

1 Derive the amplification factor g in (4.202).

4.14 A NONLINEAR CONVECTION PROBLEM

The previous two sections have quantized performance aspects of the time-split finite-element algorithm, applied to linear convection-diffusion problems, with respect to phase error and its control. Explicit nonlinearity in the subject differential equation can induce disastrous phase error distortion, without the control of which the approximate solution will actually diverge. The corresponding analysis differential equation is termed the Burgers equation, which is actually the nonlinear momentum equation without the pressure term, i.e.,

$$L(u) = \frac{\partial u}{\partial t} + \mathbf{U}\cdot\nabla u - \mu\,\nabla^2 u = 0 \tag{4.206}$$

In (4.206), μ is the physical viscosity, and for the typical one-dimensional study, $\mathbf{U}(x, t) \equiv u\hat{\mathbf{i}}$.

Baker (1979) reports the analysis and solution of (4.206) for the one-dimensional, inviscid ($\mu \equiv 0$) form

$$L(u) = \frac{\partial u}{\partial t} + u\,\frac{\partial u}{\partial x} = 0 \tag{4.207}$$

The results of numerical experimentation indicated that the nonsymmetric time-dependent contribution in (4.170), of the dissipation concept within the finite element algorithm (4.163), for the (severe) problem specification of the traveling square wave (see Fig. 4.32*a*), was destabilizing and unnecessary for maintenance of solution accuracy. Hence, the dissipative semidiscrete finite-element algorithm solution statement equivalent to (4.172), for (4.207) is

$$S_e[\Delta_1\,[A200]\,\{Q\}'_e + \{U1\}_e^T[A3001]\,\{Q\}_e + \nu_1\,\{\overline{U1}\}_e^T[A3011]\,\{Q\}_e] \equiv \{0\} \tag{4.208}$$

In (4.208), note that $\{U1\}_e = \{Q\}_e$ and $\{\overline{U1}\}_e = \{\bar{Q}\}_e$. Further, recall that the semi-discrete approximate solution statement is

$$u(x, t) \approx u^h(x, t) = \sum_{e=1}^{M} \{N_k(x)\}^T\{Q(t)\}_e \tag{4.209}$$

An exercise suggests verification of the finite-element recursion relation form of (4.208), for the $k = 1$ basis in (4.209) and a uniform discretization of R^1, as

$$L(Q_j) \to \frac{\Delta_e}{6}\,[Q'_{j-1} + 4Q'_j + Q'_{j+1}] + \frac{1}{6}\,[(-Q_{j-1} - 2Q_j)Q_{j-1} + (Q_{j-1} - Q_{j+1})Q_j$$

$$+ (2Q_j + Q_{j+1})Q_{j+1}] + \frac{\nu}{2}\,[(-\bar{Q}_{j-1} - \bar{Q}_j)Q_{j-1}$$

$$+ (\bar{Q}_{j-1} + 2\bar{Q}_j + \bar{Q}_{j+1})Q_j + (-\bar{Q}_j - \bar{Q}_{j+1})Q_{j+1}] = 0 \qquad (4.210)$$

Note how the nonlinearity in both the convection and the dissipation terms in (4.208) pervades the difference representation (4.210). Factually, the form (4.210) would not be derived in a head-on finite-difference approximation to (4.207), since a consistent interconnection among evaluations at x_j and $x_{j\pm 1}$ is difficult to establish. For example,

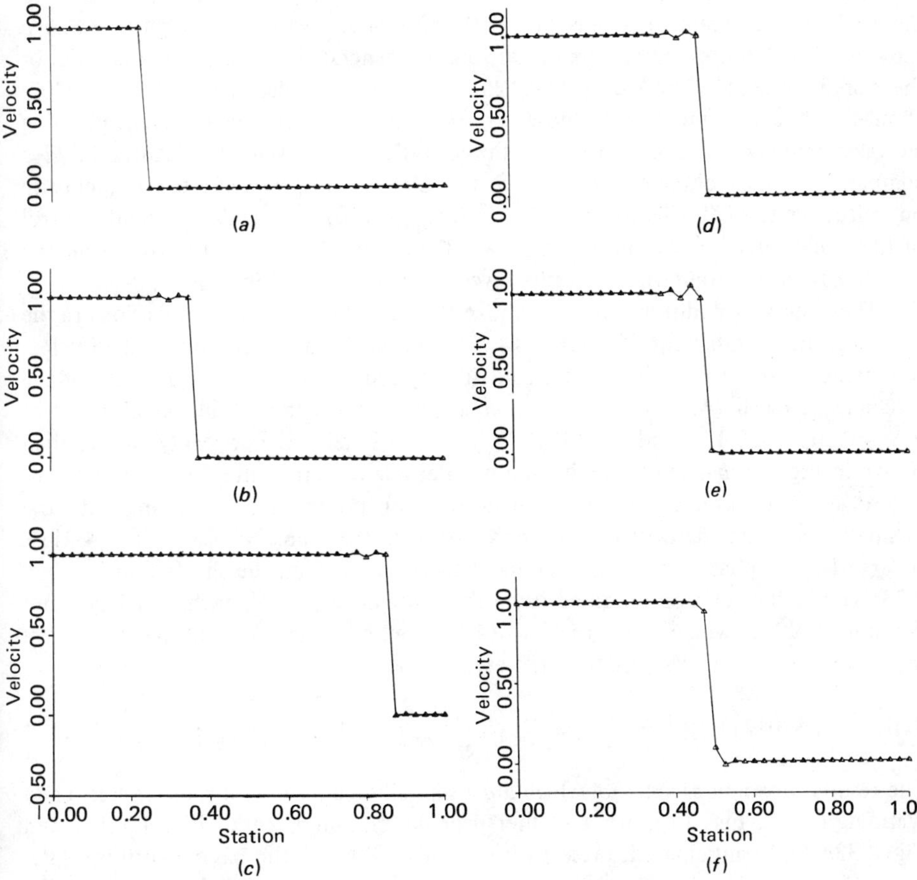

Figure 4.32 Solution of inviscid one-dimensional Burgers equation, dissipative finite-element algorithm. (*a*) $n\,\Delta t = 0$, $\nu = (30)^{-1/2}$, $C = 0.125$; (*b*) $n\,\Delta t = 40$, $\nu = (30)^{-1/2}$, $C = 0.125$; (*c*) $n\,\Delta t = 200$, $\nu = (30)^{-1/2}$, $C = 0.125$; (*d*) $\nu = (30)^{-1/2}$, $C = 0.5$; (*e*) $\nu = (30)^{-1/2}$, $C = 1.0$; (*f*) $\nu = (15)^{-1/2}$, $C = 1.0$.

failing to distinguish location of the multipliers $Q_{j\pm 1}$ in (4.210) produces a familiar Crank-Nicolson algorithm form for (4.207) as

$$L(Q_j) \to Q_j' + \tfrac{1}{2} Q_j(-Q_{j-1} + Q_{j+1}) + \nu \bar{Q}_j[-Q_{j-1} + 2Q_j + Q_{j+1}] = 0 \qquad (4.211)$$

Certainly, many other variations of the form (4.211) could be established from (4.210).

Based upon our expanding experience, one anticipates that ad-hoc modification to (4.208) or (4.210), of the form (4.211), will not enhance solution accuracy. The results documented by Baker (1979) tend to confirm this assertion, for the case of solution of (4.207) for a traveling square wave. Figure 4.32*a* graphs the initial condition, where the symbols correspond to nodal coordinates x_j of (4.209). In analogy with the one-dimensional, linear traveling sine wave (Fig. 4.6) the correct solution is diffusion-free convection of the shock downstream, with group velocity $\phi = u\,\Delta t/2\Delta x$, with retaining of the shock definition across one (only) element and maintenance of the leading and trailing plateaus at $u = 0$ and $u = 1$, respectively. Figures 4.32*b–c* show the $k = 1$ finite-element algorithm solution generated at $n\,\Delta t = 40$ and 200, for the nondimensional time step $C = 0.125$. The solution nodal values at $n\,\Delta t = 200$, about the shock, are identical to those at $n\,\Delta t = 40$, to five significant digits, indicating an exact numerical approximation to the analytical group velocity. Figures 4.32*d–e* compare solutions obtained at $C = 0.5$ and $C = 1.0$, respectively; the numerically optimized level of dissipation $\nu = (2)^{-1/2} \times \nu_{\text{opt}} = (30)^{-1/2}$ yields excellent control of the nonlinearly induced phase error over the range $0.125 \leqslant C \leqslant 1.0$. Increasing the level to ν induces a somewhat excessive level of artificial diffusion (Fig. 4.32*f*).

The results of additional tests quantize the impact of ad hoc modifications to the basic algorithm statement (4.208) or (4.210). In particular, alteration of the dissipation term in (4.210) to that written in (4.211) reduces the phase selectivity of the mechanism; recall (4.189). Figure 4.33*a* graphs the resultant solution obtained at $n\,\Delta t = 120$, $C = 0.125$ and $\nu = (30)^{-1/2}$. Solution quality is noticeably poorer than shown in Fig. 4.32*b–c*, with the shock now interpolated across three element domains. Figure 4.33*b* illustrates the additional degradation produced by replacing both the dissipation and time derivative terms in (4.210) with the Crank-Nicolson form (4.211). A large lagging phase error has become induced just behind the shock. Finally, Fig. 4.33*c* graphs the solution obtained using the finite-difference algorithm of Beam and Warming (1977), which is identical to (4.211) with replacement of the dissipation term with the fourth-order accurate representation

$$S_e[\nu\{\bar{Q}\}_e^T[A3011]\{Q\}_e] \to \frac{\nu}{3}\,\bar{Q}_j(Q_{j-2} - 8Q_{j-1} + 14Q_j - 8Q_{j+1} + Q_{j+2}) \quad (4.212)$$

The results shown in Fig. 4.33*c*, which are essentially identical with those in Beam and Warming (1977, Fig. 1.c), are a further degradation compared to Fig. 4.32*b–c* and Fig. 4.33*a–b*. As anticipated, these ad hoc modifications to the basic algorithm statement (4.208) have not produced superior accuracy; in fact, each has degraded the excellent accuracy intrinsic to the basic dissipative finite-element algorithm statement (4.163).

For a multidimensional test case, Baker (1980) reports solution of (4.206) for $\mathbf{U}_0 = (2)^{-1/2}(u\hat{\mathbf{i}} + u\hat{\mathbf{j}})$ and $\mu \equiv 0$, which corresponds to inviscid convection of an initial

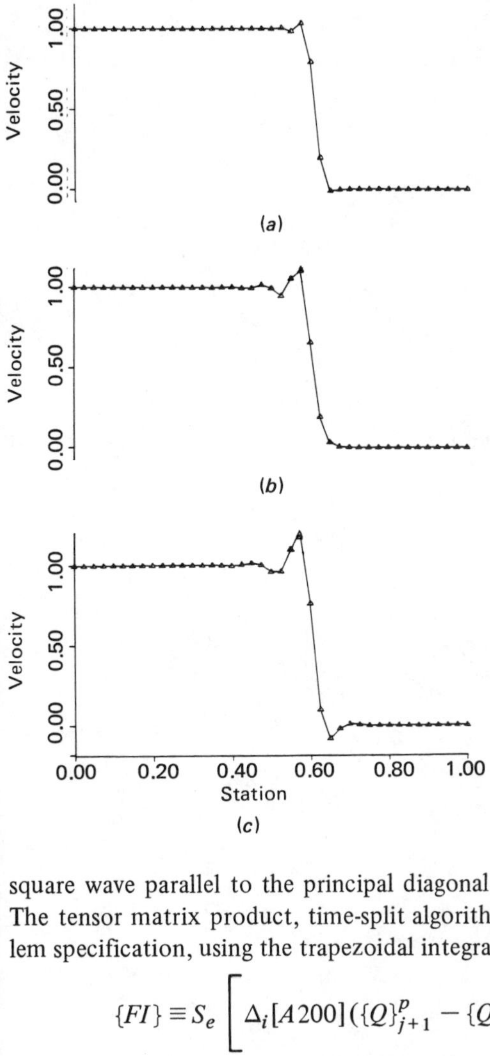

Figure 4.33 Solution of one-dimensional Burgers equation, various finite-difference forms, $\nu = (30)^{-1/2}$, $n\,\Delta t = 120$. (*a*) Equation (4.210) with diffusion term from (4.211), $C = 0.125$; (*b*) Eq. (4.211), $C = 0.5$; (*c*) duplicate of Beam and Warming (1977), $C = 0.5$.

square wave parallel to the principal diagonal of the solution domain (see Fig. 4.34*a*). The tensor matrix product, time-split algorithm statement [see (4.173)] for this problem specification, using the trapezoidal integration rule, yields

$$\{FI\} \equiv S_e \left[\Delta_i [A200](\{Q\}_{j+1}^{p} - \{Q\}_j) + \frac{\Delta t}{2} \left(\{UI\}_e^T [A3001] \{Q\}_e + \nu_i \{\overline{UI}\}^T [A3011] \{Q\}_e \right)_{j+1,j} \right] \tag{4.213}$$

where $(j+1, j)$ indicates averaged evaluation at t_{j+1} and t_j, and $I = \{1, 2\}$ indicates the sweep direction. The jacobian of (4.213) is (see Problem 6 at the end of this section)

$$[JI] \equiv [J(FI)] \equiv \frac{\partial \{FI\}}{\partial \{Q\}_{j+1}} = S_e \left[\Delta_i [A200] + \frac{\Delta t}{2} \left(\{UI\}_e^T [A3001] + (2)^{-1/2} \{Q\}^T [A3100] + \nu_i \{\overline{UI}\}_e^T [A3011] + (2)^{-1/2} \nu_i \{\bar{Q}\}^T [A3110] \right)_{j+1} \right] \tag{4.214}$$

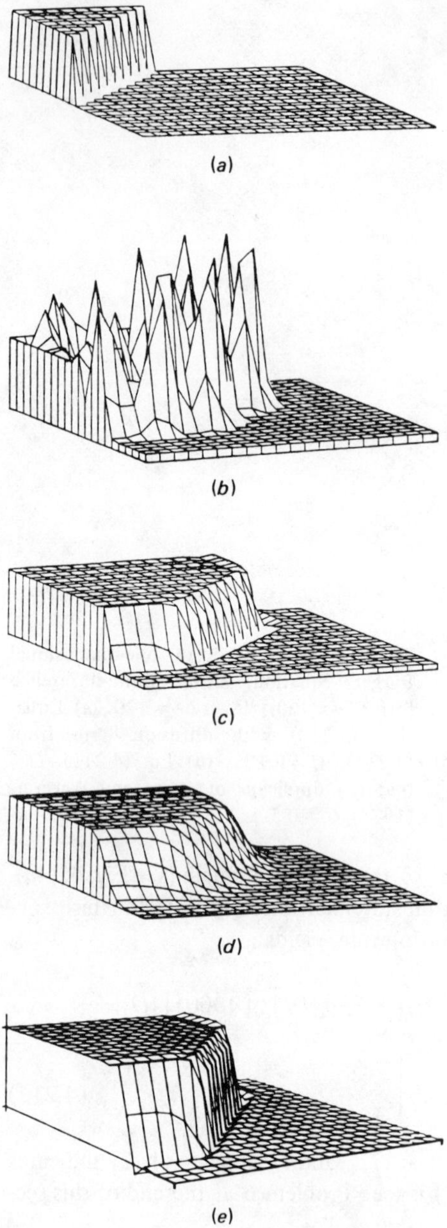

Figure 4.34 Solution of two-dimensional Burgers equation, time-split dissipative finite algorithm, $C = 0.125$. (*a*) Initial condition, $t = 0$; (*b*) downstream, $n\,\Delta t = 120$, $\nu = 0$; (*c*) $n\,\Delta t = 120$, $\nu = (15)^{-1/2}$; (*d*) finite-difference form, $n\,\Delta t = 120$, $\nu = (15)^{-1/2}$; (*e*) quadratic basis, $n\,\Delta t = 120$, $\nu = (15)^{-1/2}$.

using the chain rule and matrix statement transposition as required. Equations (4.175)-(4.178) define the time-split solution sequence, and the intermediate solutions $\{Q\}_{j+1}^{p}$ [see (4.176) and (4.178)] are iterated to convergence on each jacobian sweep.

Figure 4.34 summarizes the solution character for this problem definition. Figure 4.34*b* illustrates the rampant nonlinear instability present for $\nu \equiv 0$. Figure 4.34*c* shows the $k = 1$ solution at $n\,\Delta t = 120$, as obtained for $\nu_i \equiv \nu = (15)^{-1/2} = \nu_{\text{opt}}$ at $C = 0.125$. This is an excellent representation of the correct solution, which is nondiffusive propagation of the square wave parallel to the diagonal, with vanishing normal derivative at the boundaries. The overshoot and undershoot near the wave are less than 4 percent of the plateau level, and the wave is interpolated nominally across two element domains. Figure 4.34*d* shows the overdiffusion of the wave front resulting from use of the finite-difference algorithm statement (4.211) and $\nu_i \equiv \nu = (15)^{-1/2}$. Finally, Fig. 4.34*e* graphs the solution obtained using the $k = 2$ basis in the finite-element algorithm statement (4.213) with $\nu = (15)^{-1/2}$. The wave appears more sharply defined, with negligible undershoot and modestly larger (8 percent) overshoot at the peak.

Problems

1 Establish the matrix form (4.208) for the $k = 1$ and $k = 2$ basis.

2 Verify (4.210) for the $k = 1$ basis.

3 Repeat Problem 2 assuming a nonuniform discretization of R^1.

4 Establish the $k = 2$ basis equivalent of (4.210) for a uniform discretization.

5 Establish the form of (4.211), as a sequence of operations on (4.208) and/or (4.210).

6 Verify the jacobian (4.214).

4.15 CLOSURE

With completion of these introductory chapters, the reader has been exposed to the essential features which in total constitute the finite-element solution algorithm concept for initial-boundary value problems in mechanics. Through the vehicle of the energy equation, the transition from the variationally motivated formulation to Galerkin method of weighted residuals was completed. In the process, the singularly important assembly algorithm was derived, which permits the computational formulation to focus solely on elemental behavior. The essential concepts of accuracy, convergence, stability, and artificial dissipation have been introduced, and algorithm performance has been firmly quantized as a function of complexity (completeness) of the finite-element approximation basis. The significant aspects of equation solving, ordinary differential equation algorithms, matrix iteration, and jacobian construction have been introduced. Finally, numerous examples have illustrated construction of finite-difference algorithm forms, from the finite-element statement, with exact comparisons of theoretical and numerical performance. Therefore, at this point, it is hoped that the reader possesses a certain familiarity with the many disciplines required to comprehend what is termed the finite-element procedure. Many variations on each individually explored facet exist, but they may be well understood and interpreted within the framework developed in these chapters. The remaining four chapters develop the algorithm in completeness for generally nonlinear problem classes in computational fluid mechanics.

REFERENCES

Baker, A. J. (1979). Research on Numerical Algorithms for the Three-dimensional Navier-Stokes Equations, I. Accuracy, Convergence and Efficiency, U.S.A.F. Rept, AFFDL-TR-79-3141.

Baker, A. J. (1980). Research on Numerical Algorithms for the Three-dimensional Navier-Stokes Equations, II. Dissipative Finite Element, U.S.A.F. Rept. AFWAL-TR-80-3157.

Baker, A. J. and Manhardt, P. D. (1972). Finite Element Solution for Energy Conservation Using a Highly Stable Explicit Integration Algorithm, NASA CR-130149.

Baker, A. J. and Soliman, M. O. (1979). Utility of a Finite Element Solution Algorithm for Initial-Value Problems, *J. Comp. Phys.*, vol. 32, no. 3, pp. 289–324.

Baker, A. J. and Soliman, M. O. (1982). Analyais of a Finite Element Algorithm for Numerical Predictions in Water Resources, *J. Adv. Water Res.*, vol. 5, pp. 149–155.

Baker, A. J., Soliman, M. O., and Pepper, D. W. (1978). A Time-Split Finite Element Algorithm for Environmental Release Prediction, *Proceedings Second International Conference on Finite Elements in Water Resources*, Pentech Press, London.

Baker, A. J., Soliman, M. O., and Pepper, D. W. (1980). Environmental Release Prediction with a Non-Classical Split Finite Element Algorithm, *Proceedings Second Joint AMS/APCA Conference. Air Pollution Meteorology*, New Orleans.

Beam, R. M. and Warming, R. F. (1977). An Implicit Finite-Difference Algorithm for Hyperbolic Systems in Conservation-Law Form, *J. Comp. Phys.*, vol. 22, no. 1, pp. 87–110.

Dendy, J. E., Jr. (1977). Alternating-Direction Methods for Nonlinear Time-Dependent Problems, *SIAM J. Numer. Anal.*, vol. 14, no. 2, pp. 313–326.

Dendy, J. E., Jr. and Fairweather, G. (1975). Alternating-Direction Galerkin Methods for Parabolic and Hyperbolic Problems on Rectangular Polygons, *SIAM J. Numer. Anal.*, vol. 12, no. 2, pp. 144–163.

Fabrick, A., Sklarew, R., and Wilson, J. (1977). Point Source Model Evaluation and Development Study, Final Rept. Contract A5-058-87, Science Applications, Inc., California.

Finlayson, B. A. and Scriven, L. E. (1966). The Method of Weighted Residuals–A Review, *Appl. Mech. Rev.*, vol. 19, no. 9, pp. 735–748.

Finlayson, B. A. and Scriven, L. E. (1967). On the Search for Variational Principles, *Int. J. Heat Mass Transfer*, vol. 10, no. 6, pp. 799–821.

Galerkin, B. G. (1915). Series Occurring in Some Problems of Elastic Stability of Rods and Plates, *Eng. Bull.*, vol. 19, pp. 897–908.

Gear, C. W. (1971). *Numerical Initial-Value Problems in Ordinary Differential Equations*, Prentice Hall, Englewood Cliffs, New Jersey.

George, J. A. (1971). Computer Implementation of the Finite Element Method, Stanford University Rept. STAN-CS-71-208.

Gresho, P. M. and Lee, R. L. (1979). Don't Suppress the Wiggles. They're Telling You Something! *Proceedings, ASME Symposium on Finite Element Methods for Convection Dominated Flows*, ASME, New York.

Gurtin, M. E. (1964). Variational Principles for Linear Initial-Value Problems, *Quart. Appl. Math.*, vol. 22, p. 252.

Halmos, P. R. (1958). *Finite Dimensional Vector Spaces*, Van Nostrand, Princeton, New Jersey.

Henrici, P. (1962). *Discrete Variable Methods in Ordinary Differential Equations*, Wiley, New York.

Lomax, H. (1968). On the Construction of Highly Stable, Explicit, Numerical Methods for Integrating Coupled Ordinary Differential Equations with Parasitic Eigenvalues, NASA TND-4547.

Nigro, B. J. (1971). The Derivation of Optimally Stable, Three-Stage, One-Step Explicit Numerical Integration Methods, Bell Aerospace Company Technical Note TCTN-1010.

Oden, J. T. and Reddy, J. N. (1976). *An Introduction to the Mathematical Theory of Finite Elements*, Wiley-Interscience, New York.

Pepper, D. W. and Baker, A. J. (1979). A Simple One-Dimensional Finite Element Algorithm with Multi-Dimensional Capabilities, *Numer. Heat Transfer*, vol. 2, pp. 81–95.

Pepper, D. W., Kern, C. D., and Long, P. E. (1979). Modeling the Dispersion of Atmospheric Pollution Using Cubic Splines and Chapeau Functions, *Atmos. Environ.*, vol. 13, pp. 223–237.
Pepper, D. W. and Cooper, R. E. (1980). Numerical Solution of Recirculating Flow by a Simple Finite Element Recursion Relation, *J. Comp. Fluids*, vol. 8, pp. 213–223.
Ralston, A. (1965). *A First Course in Numerical Analysis*, McGraw-Hill, New York.
Raymond, W. H. and Garder, A. (1976). Selective Damping in a Galerkin Method for Solving Wave Problems with Variable Grids, *Monthly Weather Rev.*, vol. 104, pp. 1583–1590.
Roache, P. J. (1972). *Computational Fluid Dynamics*, Hermosa, Albuquerque, New Mexico.
Strang, G. and Fix, G. J. (1973). *An Analysis of the Finite Element Method*, Prentice Hall, Englewood Cliffs, New Jersey.
Varga, R. S. (1962). *Matrix Iterative Analysis*, Prentice Hall, Englewood Cliffs, New Jersey.
Yanenko, N. N. (1971). *The Method of Fractional Steps*, Springer-Verlag, New York.

CHAPTER

FIVE

VISCOUS INCOMPRESSIBLE TWO-DIMENSIONAL FLOW

5.1 INTRODUCTION

Many of the essential ingredients of finite-element analysis in computational fluid mechanics were covered in Chaps. 1-4. The next step is to assimilate these and additional aspects into construction of solution algorithms for the various systems of partial differential equations governing problem classes in fluid mechanics. Most readers are familiar with the Navier-Stokes equations, at least to the point of realizing that they constitute the statement of the basic conservation laws of mechanics applied to a control volume, i.e., the eulerian description. This equation system is generally considered to be the fundamental description for all laminar flows as well as for turbulent flows, usually following some statistical averaging procedure. The computational dilemma is that this system is generally too complicated to solve, using present (and near future) computer hardware/firmware, on a grid of sufficient refinement. Therefore, it is necessary to impose some simplifying assumptions to render the resultant problem class description tractable in a practical sense. The potential flow description of Chap. 3 is the consequence of enforcing the most comprehensive set of assumptions, i.e., incompressible, inviscid, irrotational, nonturbulent, and steady conditions. The relaxing of any of these yields a generally nonlinear system of partial differential equations to solve. The approach in the remaining four chapters is to address these systems, going from the least complicated to progressively more complex.

The problem class addressed in this chapter is the Navier-Stokes system simplified to govern unsteady and steady, two-dimensional laminar flow of an incompressible fluid. As will be amply verified, the principal issue to be addressed is robust enforcement of the basic requirement to conserve mass, i.e., satisfy the continuity equation.

In this innocent-appearing linear first-order partial differential equation lies the fundamental distinction between the lagrangian and eulerian statements of the basic conservation laws. (Conservation of mass is intrinsic to the lagrangian description of structural mechanics.) The subject of two-dimensional Navier-Stokes equations, for elementary laminar flows, permits substantial analyses, as categorized on the manner selected to enforce conservation of mass. Following statement of the governing system of partial differential equations in the next section, the three major subdivisions of this chapter address this issue and its ramifications in detail.

5.2 TWO-DIMENSIONAL NAVIER-STOKES EQUATIONS

The partial differential equation set governing viscous, laminar two-dimensional flow of an incompressible fluid is a subject class of the familiar and nonlinear Navier-Stokes system. In nondimensional conservation form, and using cartesian tensor notation, with summation implied on repeated latin indices over the range $1 \leqslant i \leqslant 2$, the corresponding basic constraints of conservation of mass, linear momentum, and energy are

$$L(\rho_0) = \frac{\partial u_j}{\partial x_j} = 0 \tag{5.1}$$

$$L(u_i) = \frac{\partial u_i}{\partial t} + \frac{\partial}{\partial x_j}\left(u_i u_j + \frac{p}{\rho_0}\,\delta_{ij} - \sigma_{ij}\right) + \frac{b_i}{\mathrm{Fr}} = 0 \tag{5.2}$$

$$L(e) = \frac{\partial e}{\partial t} + \frac{\partial}{\partial x_j}\left(u_j e + \frac{u_j p}{\rho_0} - \sigma_{ij} u_i + q_j\right) = 0 \tag{5.3}$$

where ρ_0 is the constant density, u_j is the two-dimensional velocity vector, b_i is the (gravity) body force, and p is pressure. Further, e is the specific total energy, σ_{ij} is the Stokes stress tensor, and q_j is the heat flux vector, defined as

$$e = c_v T + \tfrac{1}{2} u_j u_j \tag{5.4}$$

$$\sigma_{ij} = \frac{\nu}{\mathrm{Re}}\left(\frac{\partial u_i}{\partial x_j} + \frac{\partial u_j}{\partial x_i}\right) \tag{5.5}$$

$$q_j = \frac{-\nu}{\mathrm{Re}\,\mathrm{Pr}}\,\frac{\partial T}{\partial x_j} \tag{5.6}$$

In (5.4)-(5.6), the (nondimensional) properties defining the fluid are specific heat (c_v), kinematic viscosity (ν), and thermal conductivity (k), which in general are weak functions of temperature T. The important nondimensional groupings are

Reynolds number: $$\mathrm{Re} = \frac{U_\infty L}{\nu_\infty} \tag{5.7}$$

Prandtl number: $$\mathrm{Pr} = \frac{\rho_0 \nu_\infty c_v}{k_\infty} \tag{5.8}$$

Froude number: $$\mathrm{Fr} = \frac{U_\infty^2}{Lg} \tag{5.9}$$

where subscript ∞ denotes the reference state, L is a suitable length scale, and g is the gravity constant.

Equations (5.1)-(5.6) can be combined and simplified to yield alternative non-conservative forms. For example, (5.2) contains (5.1) in the convection term, and (5.3) contains both (5.1) and (5.2). Furthermore, upon insertion of (5.5) into (5.2), for ν constant, the second term vanishes identically via (5.1). It is a suggested exercise to complete these operations, for constant material properties, yielding the noncon-servative rectangular cartesian vector forms

$$L(\rho_0) = \nabla \cdot \mathbf{u} = 0 \tag{5.10}$$

$$L(\mathbf{u}) = \frac{\partial \mathbf{u}}{\partial t} + (\mathbf{u} \cdot \nabla)\mathbf{u} - \frac{1}{\mathrm{Re}} \nabla^2 \mathbf{u} + \frac{1}{\rho_0} \nabla p + \frac{1}{\mathrm{Fr}} \mathbf{b} = 0 \tag{5.11}$$

$$L(T) = \frac{\partial T}{\partial t} + (\mathbf{u} \cdot \nabla)T - \frac{1}{\mathrm{Re\,Pr}} \nabla^2 T + \sigma_{ij} \frac{\partial u_i}{\partial x_j} = 0 \tag{5.12}$$

Equations (5.11)-(5.12) are easily recognized as containing the example systems examined in detail in the preceding chapter.

The dependent variables in (5.1)-(5.6), and/or (5.10)-(5.12), are the two components of the velocity vector $\mathbf{u} \equiv u(x, y, t)\hat{\mathbf{i}} + v(x, y, t)\hat{\mathbf{j}}$, and the pressure $p(x, y, t)$ and temperature $T(x, y, t)$. Equation (5.11) is an initial-value, elliptic boundary value problem for finite Reynolds number since Re is always positive. Equation (5.10) defines a differential constraint on the admissibility of the computed velocity vector field, i.e., it must be divergence free. Note in (5.11), that as $\mathrm{Re} \to \infty$, the importance of viscosity becomes diminished; in the limit, (5.11) becomes the description for an inviscid rotational flow. Therefore, numerical difficulties are anticipated to emerge as the Reynolds number becomes large, and an artificial dissipation mechanism will be required. However, laminar flow is also Reynolds number limited, and for confined flows we are interested in laminar computations principally for $\mathrm{Re} < 10^4$.

Figure 5.1 is a representative two-dimensional solution domain, suitable for identification of appropriate boundary and initial conditions for solution of (5.10)-(5.12). On segments of the solution domain boundary with inflow, the velocity field is assumed known, as well as the pressure and temperature. Hence,

$$\mathbf{u}_{\mathrm{in}} = u(s, t)\hat{\mathbf{i}} + v(s, t)\hat{\mathbf{j}} \tag{5.13}$$

and

$$p_{\mathrm{in}} = p(s, t) \tag{5.14}$$

where s is the coordinate tangent to ∂R and t is time. At locations on ∂R with outflow, in general no a priori knowledge exists regarding the detailed distribution of the

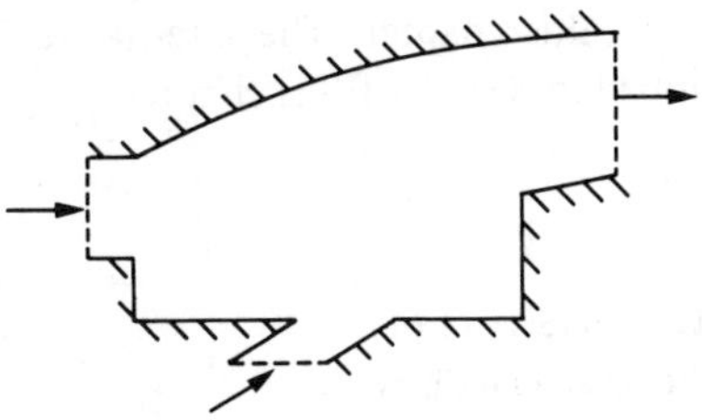

Figure 5.1 Solution domain for two-dimensional Navier-Stokes equations.

efflux velocity vector. Therefore, the least constraining boundary condition for (5.11) would be of the form

$$(\hat{\mathbf{n}}\cdot\nabla)\mathbf{u} = \mathbf{0} \Rightarrow \begin{cases} \nabla u\cdot\hat{\mathbf{n}} = 0 \\ \nabla v\cdot\hat{\mathbf{n}} = 0 \end{cases} \tag{5.15}$$

on segments of ∂R aligned approximately perpendicular to the assumed orientation of the efflux vector $\mathbf{u}$. The pressure and temperature at a particular outflow location are also typically unknown and need to be determined. For symmetry planes forming segments of the domain boundary, the velocity component parallel to the symmetry plane satisfies (5.15), while the transverse component must vanish.

Solid wall segments of ∂R are impervious to mass flux; therefore, the velocity components both normal and tangent to the surface must vanish. Assuming these segments are constant in time, i.e., the walls are not compliant, they can be described by an equation of the form $f(x, y) = \text{constant}$. Then, since ∇f is directed perpendicular to $f = \text{constant}$, the constraint statements for the velocity vector $\mathbf{u}$ at the (no-slip) wall become

$$\mathbf{u}\cdot\nabla f = 0 \tag{5.16}$$

$$\mathbf{u}\cdot\hat{\mathbf{k}} \times \nabla f = 0 \tag{5.17}$$

In (5.17), $\hat{\mathbf{k}}$ is a unit vector perpendicular to the plane of the velocity vector $\mathbf{u}$. The pressure is unspecified on these closure segments as well, and must be obtained from the solution. The temperature may be fixed by a cold wall, or a convective coefficient may be defined for heat transfer.

Finally, the initial condition specification for velocity must satisfy the continuity equation (5.10), and is of the form

$$\mathbf{u}(x, y, 0) \equiv u_0(x, y) \tag{5.18}$$

An appropriate determination for (5.18) could be the solution to the potential flow form of (3.1)–(3.2). Similarly, an initial temperature distribution is required. However, specification of an arbitrary initial pressure distribution is inappropriate. For example, the consistent pressure distribution for an inviscid velocity starting condition is obtained using Bernoulli's equation.

This initial-boundary value differential equation description for the vector velocity field is well-posed and is consistent with the known physical constraints. Since the pressure distribution must be known for solution of (5.11), the differential constraint (5.10) must be employed in a manner yielding a pressure distribution consistent with the computed velocity field. This leads to development of the Navier-Stokes algorithm in primitive variables, given in Sec. B of this chapter. The alternative is redefinition of dependent variables, which is developed in Sec. A of this chapter.

Problems

1 Establish the differential equation system (5.10)–(5.11) from (5.1)–(5.6).

2 Verify that (5.16)–(5.17) yield the constraint of $\mathbf{u}$ vanishing at a no-slip wall.

A. VECTOR POTENTIAL FUNCTION FORMULATION

5.3 STREAMFUNCTION AND VORTICITY

Although the flow fields of present interest are rotational, the constant density restriction has yielded the differential constraint equation (5.10). As discussed in Chap. 3, (5.1) ensures existence of the $\hat{\mathbf{k}}$ scalar component ψ of a vector potential function of the form

$$\mathbf{u} \equiv \nabla \times \psi\hat{\mathbf{k}} \tag{5.19}$$

Recall that by direct substitution (5.19) identically satisfies (5.10). Provided the velocity vector $\mathbf{u}$ is specified at one location at least on ∂R, and since $\nabla \cdot \mathbf{u}$ vanishes, from vector field theory (Jaunzemis, 1967, App. I) $\mathbf{u}$ becomes uniquely specified by determination of its curl. The appropriate differential equation is formed from (5.11). Define the $\hat{\mathbf{k}}$ component ω of the vorticity vector Ω as

$$\omega \equiv \nabla \times \mathbf{u} \cdot \hat{\mathbf{k}} \tag{5.20}$$

An exercise will show that the curl of (5.11), using (5.19)–(5.20), yields the vorticity transport equation in the form

$$L(\omega) = \frac{\partial \omega}{\partial t} + (\nabla \times \psi\hat{\mathbf{k}} \cdot \nabla)\omega - \frac{1}{\mathrm{Re}} \nabla^2 \omega = 0 \tag{5.21}$$

Note that determination of vorticity in (5.21) is obtained completely independent of the pressure. Specifically, the thermodynamics and kinetics for an incompressible flow are separated not only in fact but in the (ω, ψ) dependent variable system. Hence, analogous to irrotational flow, pressure again assumes the role of an engineering parameter to be derived a posteriori from the solution.

Since the fundamental dependent variable is streamfunction ψ, (5.19), compatibility must be established with vorticity (5.20). Noting that (5.19)–(5.20) are uniformly valid everywhere on $R^2 \cup \partial R$, upon direct combination and use of a vector identity, noting that $\psi\hat{\mathbf{k}}$ is divergence-free, yields the compatibility equation

$$L(\psi) = \nabla^2 \psi + \omega = 0 \tag{5.22}$$

Thus, compatibility yields a linear Poisson equation for determination of streamfunction from a distribution of vorticity. More properly, (5.22) serves as the definition equation for vorticity in terms of streamfunction, and is valid throughout $R^2 \cup \partial R$. This interpretation will be instrumental in formation of boundary conditions for vorticity.

The practical value of (5.21)–(5.22), as a viable differential equation system for solution of two-dimensional viscous flows, rests upon transformation of the boundary conditions to the derived dependent variable system. Along an impervious segment of the closure ∂R,

$$f = \text{constant} \qquad \text{corresponds to} \qquad \psi = \text{constant} \tag{5.23}$$

At locations of specified inflow on ∂R, (5.19) yields

$$\Delta\psi(s) = \mathbf{u}\cdot\hat{\mathbf{n}} \equiv U^{\perp}(s) \tag{5.24}$$

For locations on the boundary with outflow, from (5.19),

$$\nabla\psi\cdot\hat{\mathbf{n}} = -U'' \tag{5.25}$$

If the less rigid outflow constraint embodied in (5.15) is required, using (5.19), equivalently

$$(\hat{\mathbf{n}}\cdot\nabla)\,\nabla\times\psi\hat{\mathbf{k}} = (\hat{\mathbf{n}}\cdot\nabla)\left(\frac{\partial\psi}{\partial n}\,\hat{\mathbf{s}} - \frac{\partial\psi}{\partial s}\,\hat{\mathbf{n}}\right) = \frac{\partial^2\psi}{\partial n^2}\,\hat{\mathbf{s}} - \frac{\partial^2\psi}{\partial n\,\partial s}\,\hat{\mathbf{n}} = 0 \tag{5.26}$$

In (5.26), $s(x_i)$ is the coordinate tangent to the boundary segment, and $n(x_i)$ is the normal coordinate. Correspondingly, $\hat{\mathbf{s}}$ and $\hat{\mathbf{n}}$ are the associated unit vectors. Note that since (5.26) is a vector equation, by scalar components

$$\frac{\partial^2\psi}{\partial n^2} = 0 \tag{5.27}$$

$$\frac{\partial^2\psi}{\partial n\,\partial s} = 0 \tag{5.28}$$

Expanding (5.22) in the (n, s) coordinate system, the constraints (5.27)–(5.28) yield the equivalent requirement

$$L(\psi) = \frac{d^2\psi}{ds^2} + \omega = 0 \tag{5.29}$$

Hence, the vanishing derivative outflow boundary condition produces a second-order ordinary differential constraint on the streamfunction $\psi(s)$. Equation (5.29) is eligible for solution using the developed finite-element techniques, subject to endpoint boundary conditions of ψ = constant.

With this successful transformation of boundary conditions, the streamfunction specification (5.19) is well posed for viscous rotational flowfield prediction described by the parent Navier-Stokes equations (5.10)–(5.11). However, it remains to redefine the no-slip boundary condition (5.17), which becomes enforced on vorticity through the compatibility equation (5.22). Substituting (5.19) into (5.17) yields that $\nabla\psi\cdot\hat{\mathbf{s}}$ vanishes on an impervious boundary. Furthermore, along any no-slip surface, ψ is a constant, (5.23).

Therefore, since (5.22) is the kinematic definition of vorticity valid throughout $R^2 \cup \partial R$, correspondingly, the no-slip boundary condition (5.17) becomes

$$\omega = -\left.\frac{d^2\psi}{dn^2}\right|_s \tag{5.30}$$

Equation (5.30) is the Achilles' heel of the streamfunction-vorticity formulation. The vorticity transport equation (5.21) is an initial-value, elliptic boundary value partial differential equation for finite Re. Therefore, a linear combination of ω and its normal derivative is required to be specified throughout ∂R. Yet, on segments of ∂R

corresponding to a no-slip wall, the value of ω is a priori unknown. Specifically, the wall value of ω depends upon the solution of the problem through (5.22). The alternative is to eliminate ω in (5.21) using the kinematic definition (5.22). This yields (5.21) in the form

$$L(\psi) = \frac{\partial \nabla^2 \psi}{\partial t} + (\nabla \times \psi \hat{\mathbf{k}} \cdot \nabla) \nabla^2 \psi - \frac{1}{\text{Re}} \nabla^4 \psi = 0 \tag{5.31}$$

which is an initial-value, biharmonic partial differential equation. The finite-element solution of (5.31), using the bicubic Hermite basis $\{N_3'(\mathbf{x})\}$, is reported by Tuann and Olsen (1978) for a restricted problem class at modest Re. Note that occurrence of ∇^4 in (5.31) requires at least this degree of completeness of the basis.

Returning to the parent form (5.21), evaluation of (5.30) requires formation of the second normal derivative of streamfunction. To approximate the local normal to a curved wall (see Fig. 5.2), select the bisector of the chords connecting the node point of interest to each adjacent wall node of the discretization. (Hence, for example, the defined normal for a 90° inlet corner is the 45° bisector.) Then, (5.30) can be approximated using finite-difference formulas or by quadrature, using the finite-element basis for ω_e^h and ψ_e^h on R_e^2. Using (5.24)–(5.25), the first-order accurate difference formula for (5.31) is (Roache, 1972, III.C.)

$$\omega_w = \frac{2(\psi_{w+1} - \psi_w)}{(\Delta n)^2} + O(\Delta n) \tag{5.32}$$

where subscript w refers to the nodal value at the no-slip wall, $w + 1$ refers to the adjacent interior node, and Δn is the distance separating this node pair. The second order accurate difference formula for (5.30) is identical to that obtained by direct integration of (5.30), assuming ω_e^h and ψ_e^h are interpolated by the linear cardinal basis $\{N_1^+(\mathbf{x})\}$ (Baker, 1974). The second order accurate approximation to (5.30) is

$$\omega_w = \frac{3(\psi_{w+1} - \psi_w)}{(\Delta n)^2} - \frac{\omega_{w+1}}{2} + O(\Delta n^2) \tag{5.33}$$

Many alternative difference forms of (5.30) have been derived (Roache, 1972). The derivation of (5.33) is left as a problem at the end of this section.

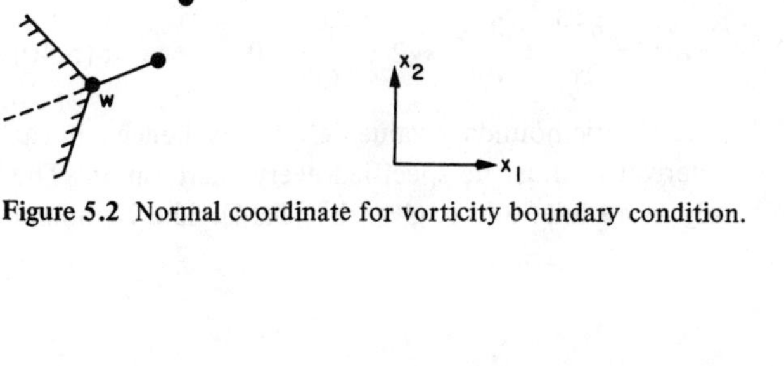

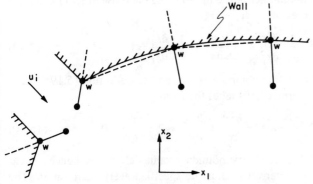

Figure 5.2 Normal coordinate for vorticity boundary condition.

The completion requirement for vorticity is boundary definition on segments of ∂R not coincident with a no-slip wall. At inflow, using the vorticity definition (5.20), the transformation is direct as

$$\mathbf{u}_{\text{in}}(s) \Rightarrow \omega(s) \tag{5.34}$$

At outflow, the specification (5.15) is contained within

$$\nabla\omega \cdot \hat{\mathbf{n}} = 0 \tag{5.35}$$

Along a symmetry plane, the vorticity must vanish via (5.20). Finally, since (5.21) is an initial-value problem specification, from (5.18),

$$\mathbf{u}_0(x,y) \Rightarrow \omega_0(x,y) \equiv \omega(x,y,0) \tag{5.36}$$

Note that the irrotational initial condition is the solution of the homogeneous form of (5.22), i.e.,

$$\omega_0(x,y) \equiv 0 \tag{5.37}$$

For the general case, the initial determination of ψ is the solution

$$L(\psi_0) = \nabla^2 \psi_0(x,y,0) + \omega_0(x,y) = 0 \tag{5.38}$$

These developments confirm that two-dimensional, unsteady laminar flow of a viscous incompressible fluid is a well-posed problem in terms of the dependent variables vorticity and streamfunction. One anticipates that the weakness of the problem definition is evaluation of vorticity at a no-slip wall, (5.30). Numerical experiments indeed confirm that unimaginative handling of this constraint can destabilize a numerical solution. Conversely, the distinctly attractive feature of the formulation is the computational decoupling of the kinematics and kinetics of the flow from the thermodynamics. Hence, the temperature and pressure determinations are reduced to a post-processing operation involving numerical solution of linear equations.

No additional comments are required regarding the energy equation (5.12). However, a principal requirement in a Navier-Stokes solution is determination of pressure distributions, particularly on a solid surface. There are two methods available for this determination within the streamfunction-vorticity formulation. In one method, formation of the divergence of the momentum equation (5.2) and use of (5.1) and (5.5) yields a Poisson equation for pressure:

$$L(p) = \frac{1}{\rho_0}\frac{\partial^2 p}{\partial x_i^2} + \frac{\partial^2 u_i u_j}{\partial x_i\,\partial x_j} + \frac{1}{\text{Fr}}\frac{\partial b_i}{\partial x_i} = 0 \tag{5.39}$$

Alternatively, in rectangular cartesian components, using the definition (5.19)-(5.20) and neglecting the body force term, (5.39) takes the form

$$L(p) = \frac{1}{\rho_0}\nabla^2 p - \omega^2 + \frac{\partial^2\psi}{\partial x^2} + \frac{\partial^2\psi}{\partial y^2} + 2\,\frac{\partial^2\psi}{\partial x\,\partial y} = 0 \tag{5.40}$$

Equations (5.39) and (5.40) are elliptic boundary value definitions, hence a linear combination of p and its normal derivative must be specified everywhere on ∂R. The Dirichlet condition is available only at an inlet and is given by (5.14). The Neumann constraint, which must be specified at outlets and on no-slip walls, is formed by the inner (dot) product of (5.2) with the outward pointing unit normal vector $\hat{\mathbf{n}}_i$. Using (5.1) and (5.5), the general form is

$$l(p) = \frac{1}{\rho_0}\frac{\partial p}{\partial x_i}\hat{\mathbf{n}}_i + u_j\frac{\partial u_i}{\partial x_j}\hat{\mathbf{n}}_i - \frac{1}{\mathrm{Re}}\frac{\partial^2 u_i}{\partial x_j^2}\hat{\mathbf{n}}_i + \frac{b_i\hat{\mathbf{n}}_i}{\mathrm{Fr}} = 0 \tag{5.41}$$

The second term in (5.41) vanishes identically at a no-slip wall, as well as at an outflow segment on ∂R where the flow is parallel ($u_j = 0$). In rectangular cartesian coordinates and by neglecting the body force term, (5.41) on a no-slip wall becomes, using (5.19)–(5.20),

$$l(p) = \frac{1}{\rho_0}\nabla p\cdot\hat{\mathbf{n}} - \frac{1}{\mathrm{Re}}\frac{\partial\omega}{\partial s} = 0 \tag{5.42}$$

Here s is the coordinate tangent to the surface; further, the pressure gradient normal to the wall depends upon the local strain rate of vorticity.

The approach alternative to solution of (5.39)–(5.42) for determination of pressure, which is useful for quantizing pressure distributions along select paths in the flow, is to construct an integro-differential equation from (5.2) or (5.11). Forming the inner product with an arbitrary displacement differential $d\mathbf{r}$, and integrating yields

$$\frac{1}{\rho_0}\Delta p = \frac{1}{\mathrm{Re}}\int(\nabla^2)\mathbf{u}\cdot d\mathbf{r} - \int(\mathbf{u}\cdot\nabla)\mathbf{u}\cdot d\mathbf{r} - \int\frac{\partial\mathbf{u}}{\partial t}\cdot d\mathbf{r} - \frac{1}{\mathrm{Fr}}\int\mathbf{b}\cdot d\mathbf{r} \tag{5.43}$$

where Δ signifies the integral of a perfect differential. Therefore, the pressure difference between points in the flow field is determined by numerical evaluation of (5.43). Transformation of terms in this equation to streamfunction-vorticity is a somewhat complicated task requiring tensor algebra and several vector identities (Baker, 1974). The final form (neglecting the body force), is

$$\frac{1}{\rho_0}\Delta p = \frac{1}{\mathrm{Re}}\int\nabla\omega\times d\mathbf{r} - \int\omega\nabla\psi\cdot d\mathbf{r} - \Delta(\nabla\psi\cdot\nabla\psi) + \int\nabla\psi\cdot\nabla(\nabla\psi\cdot d\mathbf{r})$$
$$+\frac{\partial}{\partial t}\int\nabla\psi\times d\mathbf{r} \tag{5.44}$$

The third right term in (5.44) results from the integral of a perfect differential, hence the Δ notation. While the form of (5.44) appears complex, its evaluation can be elementary on select paths.

Problems

1 Derive (5.21) using the definitions of vorticity and streamfunction (5.19)–(5.20).

2 Establish the streamfunction-vorticity compatibility equation (5.22).

3 Derive (5.33) using
(*a*) finite differences
(*b*) ω_e^h and ψ_e^h interpolated on R_e^2 using $\{N_1^+(\mathbf{x})\}$.

4 Establish (5.39) and simplify it to (5.40).

5 Derive (5.41) and (5.42).
6 Determine the form (5.43).
7 Establish (5.44).

5.4 FINITE-ELEMENT SOLUTION ALGORITHM

The differential equation description for the two-dimensional incompressible Navier-Stokes problem class has been recast onto the streamfunction-vorticity dependent variable set. For clarity, in the rectangular cartesian coordinate description, and in terms of ψ and ω only, the governing partial differential equation system on $\Omega \equiv R^2 \times t$ and $\partial\Omega \equiv \partial R \times t$ is:

Vorticity:

$$\Omega: \quad L(\omega) = \frac{\partial \omega}{\partial t} + (\nabla \times \psi \hat{\mathbf{k}} \cdot \nabla)\omega - \frac{1}{\text{Re}} \nabla^2 \omega = 0 \tag{5.21}$$

$$\partial\Omega_1: \quad l(\omega) = \nabla\omega \cdot \hat{\mathbf{n}} = 0 \tag{5.35}$$

$$\partial\Omega_{21}: \quad \omega = -\left.\frac{d^2\psi}{dn^2}\right|_s \tag{5.30}$$

$$\partial\Omega_{22}: \quad \omega(s) \Leftrightarrow u_{\text{in}}(s) \tag{5.34}$$

Streamfunction:

$$\Omega: \quad L(\psi) = \nabla^2\psi + \omega = 0 \tag{5.22}$$

$$\partial\Omega_1: \quad l(\psi) = \nabla\psi \cdot \hat{\mathbf{n}} + U'' = 0 \tag{5.25}$$

$$\partial\Omega_{21}: \quad \psi(s) = \text{constant}$$

$$\partial\Omega_{22}: \quad \Delta\psi(s) = U^{\perp} \tag{5.24}$$

$$\partial\Omega_{31}: \quad L(\psi) = \frac{d^2\psi}{ds^2} + \omega = 0 \tag{5.29}$$

$$\partial\Omega_{32}: \quad \psi = \text{constant}$$

In addition, as a post-processing operation, the pressure distribution is determined by the differential equation system:

Pressure:

$$\Omega: \quad L(p) = \frac{1}{\rho_0}\nabla^2 p - \omega^2 + \frac{\partial^2\psi}{\partial x^2} + \frac{\partial^2\psi}{\partial y^2} + 2\frac{\partial^2\psi}{\partial x\,\partial y} = 0 \tag{5.40}$$

$$\partial\Omega_1: \quad l(p) = \frac{1}{\rho_0}\nabla p \cdot \hat{\mathbf{n}} - \frac{1}{\text{Re}}\frac{\partial\omega}{\partial s} = 0 \tag{5.42}$$

$$\partial\Omega_2: \quad p(s) = \text{constant} \tag{5.14}$$

Alternately, pressure distributions along select paths on Ω can be determined using (5.44). Finally, an initial condition on vorticity is required, (5.36), which yields the initial streamfunction distribution ψ_0 using (5.22)-(5.25); see (5.38).

The dependent variable set for this problem specification is vector valued, that is, $q_\alpha(\mathbf{x}, t) \equiv \{q_\alpha(\mathbf{x}, t)\} = \{\omega, \psi\}^T$, with pressure as an additional parameter. Aside from this, the construction of the finite-element solution algorithm was essentially completed in Sec. 4.10. Briefly, therefore, on the finite-element discretization $\Omega_e \equiv R_e^2 \times t$ of the solution domain Ω, where $\Omega = \cup \Omega_e$, and its boundary $\partial\Omega$, the semidiscrete approximation $q_\alpha^h(\mathbf{x}, t)$ to the solution $q_\alpha(\mathbf{x}, t)$ is defined as

$$q_\alpha(\mathbf{x}, t) \approx q_\alpha^h(\mathbf{x}, t) \equiv \sum_{e=1}^{M} q_\alpha^e(\mathbf{x}, t) \tag{5.45}$$

As before, the finite-element approximation q_α^e is defined on Ω_e in terms of a cardinal basis as

$$q_\alpha^e(\mathbf{x}, t) \equiv \{N_k(\mathbf{x})\}^T \{QJ(t)\}_e \tag{5.46}$$

In (5.46), the tensor index α (hence J) denotes members of the vector and $1 \leqslant (\alpha, J) \leqslant 2$. The elements of $\{N_k(\mathbf{x})\}$ are polynomials on $\mathbf{x}$, complete to degree k, and the expansion coefficients $\{QJ\}_e \equiv \{OMEG, PSI\}_e^T$ are the time-dependent unknowns at the node coordinates of Ω_e.

The finite-element algorithm concept, as defined within the method of weighted residuals, requires the approximation error in $L(q_\alpha^h)$ and $l(q_\alpha^h)$ to be orthogonal to the basis $\{N_k\}$. In addition [see (4.163)] since nonlinearity induced instabilities can become induced as $\mathrm{Re} \Rightarrow \infty$, the gradient of the error $L(\omega^h)$, for (5.21) written for infinite Reynolds number, is also required to be orthogonal to $\{N_k\}$. Combining these linearly independent constraints, using a multiplier set β_i, the finite-element solution algorithm for (5.21), (5.35), (5.22), (5.25), and (5.29) is

$$\int_{R^2} \{N_k\} L(q_\alpha^h)\, d\tau - \beta_1 \cdot \int_{R^2} \{N_k\} \nabla L^c(q_\alpha^h) \delta_{\alpha 1}\, d\tau + \beta_2 \int_{\partial R} \{N_k\} l(q_\alpha^h)\, d\sigma \equiv \{0\} \tag{5.47}$$

Recall that, in actual practice, (5.47) is evaluated on the discretization $\cup R_e^2$, with the resultant element contributions assembled into the form (5.47) using the operator S_e. Furthermore, the Green-Gauss theorem is employed to transform second derivatives in $L(q_\alpha^h)$, and β_2 is selected to cancel contributions on appropriate segments of ∂R. Finally, $\beta_1 \equiv \nu_\omega^\kappa \Delta_e \{\hat{\mathbf{i}}, \hat{\mathbf{j}}\}$, where Δ_e is the measure of R_e^2, and ν_ω^κ are the scalar magnitudes with common multiplier $(\sqrt{15})^{-1}$ (see Sec. 4.11).

Independent of the degree k of the basis $\{N_k\}$, (5.47) represents a system of ordinary differential (and algebraic) equations written on the unknown $q_\alpha^h(\mathbf{x}, t)$ of the form

$$[C]\{QJ\}' + [U + K]\{QJ\} + \{b\} = \{0\} \tag{5.48}$$

In (5.48), C denotes the capacity matrix, U and K are the convection and diffusion matrices, while $\{b\}$ contains all other nonhomogeneities. Defining a (finite-difference) integration algorithm yields the algebraic equation system

$$\{FJ\} = \{QJ\}_{j+1} - \{QJ\}_j - h[\theta\{QJ\}'_{j+1} + (1-\theta)\{QJ\}'_j] = \{0\} \qquad (5.49)$$

where the appropriate time derivatives are given in (5.48). In (5.49), j is the time-step index, $h = \Delta t \equiv t_{j+1} - t$ is the integration time step, and J denotes the elements of $q_\alpha^h(\mathbf{x}, t)$ at the nodal coordinates of $\cup R_e^2$. Dependent upon the implicitness parameter $0 \leqslant \theta \leqslant 1$, (5.49) is a system of nonlinear (or quasilinearized) algebraic equations. The Newton (iterative) algorithm for solution of (5.49) is

$$[J(FJ)_{j+1}^p]\{\delta QJ\}_{j+1}^{p+1} = -\{FJ\}_{j+1}^p \qquad (5.50)$$

The dependent variable in (5.50) is the iteration vector, which defines the solution step

$$\{QJ\}_{j+1}^{p+1} \equiv \{QJ\}_{j+1}^p + \{\delta QJ\}_{j+1}^{p+1} \qquad (5.51)$$

The jacobian is defined as

$$[J(FJ)] \equiv \frac{\partial\{FJ\}}{\partial\{QI\}} \qquad (5.52)$$

with $\{FJ(\theta, \nu, k)\}$ given by (5.49).

5.5 THEORETICAL ANALYSIS, ACCURACY AND CONVERGENCE

Equations (5.45)-(5.52) constitute an extremely general statement of a numerical solution algorithm for the streamfunction-vorticity form of the two-dimensional Navier-Stokes equations. Including the concept of "condensing" the capacity matrix C, (5.48), practically every solution algorithm ever devised for this problem definition is contained within the statements (5.47)-(5.49). The requirement is to identify the essential ingredients of error, as a function of the choices remaining in the algorithm statement, which constitute selection of k in (5.46), β_1 in (5.47) and θ in (5.49).

The issue of accuracy and convergence, with respect to the degree k of the cardinal basis, was presented in Sec. 4.8, for a linear parabolic equation, and in Sec. 3.3 for a linear elliptic, multidimensional equation. In terms of the semidiscrete approximation error ϵ_1^h [see (4.131)], and generalizing to a multidimensional description [see (3.32)], the semidiscrete error in H^1 can be anticipated to satisfy, in some sense, an inequality of the form

$$\|\epsilon_1^h(n\,\Delta t)\|_{H^1} \leqslant C_1\,\Delta_e^\gamma \|q_1(n\,\Delta t)\|_{H^r} + C_2\,\Delta t^\alpha \|Q_0\|_{H^1} \qquad (5.53)$$

In (5.53), $\alpha \leqslant 1$ depends upon the choice of θ, and $\gamma = \min(k, r-1)$ for $r \leqslant k+1$. Further, subscript 1 on q and ϵ denote the first element of q_α^h, that is, ω^h, and Q_0 is the interpolation of the initial condition $\omega_0(\mathbf{x}, 0)$ onto the nodes of $\cup R_e^2$. Recall that r is a measure of the worst aspect ratio of the discretization [see (3.31)-(3.32)]. Then, in terms of the energy norm $E(\cdot, \cdot)$, which we have observed to be rather comparable with error estimates based upon local truncation error analyses, the semidiscrete error in the finite-element solution to (5.21), with (5.30), (5.34), and (5.35), can be anticipated to satisfy an inequality of the form

$$E(\epsilon_1^h(n\,\Delta t), \epsilon_1^h(n\,\Delta t)) \leqslant C_1'\,\Delta_e^{2\gamma}\|g_1(n\,\Delta t)\|_{H^p(\partial R)}^2 + C_2'\,\Delta t^{2\alpha}\|Q_0\|_{H^1}^2 \qquad (5.54)$$

In (5.54), the first right-side term is the H^p, $p \geqslant \frac{1}{2}$, norm of the data specified on the boundary ∂R, see (5.34). In the worst case of discretization aspect ratio, γ can become independent of k, which destroys the (theoretical) utility of use of a more complete cardinal basis $\{N_k\}$, $k > 1$.

The streamfunction (compatibility) equation (5.22) is a linear elliptic partial differential equation. Therefore, (3.33) is the expected form of the convergence statement in energy, i.e.,

$$E(\epsilon_2^h(n\,\Delta t), \epsilon_2^h(n\,\Delta t)) \leqslant C_3\,\Delta_e^{2\gamma}\|g_2(n\,\Delta t)\|_{H^p(\partial R)}^2 \qquad (5.55)$$

assuming that the distribution of ω^h on R^2 is not considered "data." To within a scalar multiplier (1/Re), the energy in elements of q_α^h is evaluated as

$$E(q_\alpha^h, q_\alpha^h) \equiv \sum_{e=1}^{M} \int_{R_e^2} \nabla q_\alpha^h \cdot \nabla q_\alpha^h \, d\tau \qquad (5.56)$$

with no summation implied on the subscript α.

The role of β and θ are interrelated regarding temporal truncation error evolution. Recall [see (4.131)] that this error is the difference between the approximate and semidiscrete approximate solutions. Based upon the introductory analyses given in Sec. 4.6, $\theta = \frac{1}{2}$ yields a second order accurate integration procedure, while $\theta = 0$ or $\theta = 1$ produces a first order procedure [see (4.74)-(4.76)]. Furthermore, selecting $0.5 < \theta \leqslant 1$ induces the equivalent of an artificial diffusion term into (5.47), according to the von Neumann stability analysis, Sec. 4.8. Correspondingly, selecting $\beta_1 > 0$ also introduces an artificial dissipation mechanism into the algorithm [see (4.191)]. Hence, one anticipates that selection of specific θ and β_1 will exert significant impact on the accuracy of the fully discrete approximation, with the underlying convergence character, as established by use of the finite-element algorithm concept, to behave in the general way described by (5.54)-(5.55).

5.6 IMPLEMENTATION USING THE LINEAR NATURAL BASIS

Many of the finite-element matrices defined in (5.47) are already familiar, when using the linear natural coordinate basis, $k = 1$ in (5.46), with the discretization of R^2 formed by the union of triangles. Specifically, by terms in (5.21), the first integral defined in (5.47), on an element becomes

$$\int_{R_e^2} \{N_1\} L(\omega^h)\, d\tau = \int_{R_e^2} \{N_1\}\{N_1\}^T \{OMEG\}'_e\, d\tau$$

$$+ \int_{R_e^2} \{N_1\} \nabla \times \{N_1\}^T \{PSI\}_e \hat{\mathbf{k}} \cdot \nabla \{N_1\}^T \{OMEG\}_e\, d\tau$$

$$+ \frac{1}{\text{Re}} \int_{R_e^2} \nabla\{N_1\} \cdot \nabla\{N_1\}^T \{OMEG\}_e\, d\tau \qquad (5.57)$$

The first term in (5.57) is

$$\int_{R_e^2} \{N_1\}\{N_1\}^T \{OMEG\}'_e\, d\tau = \frac{\Delta_e}{6} \begin{bmatrix} 2 & 1 & 1 \\ & 2 & 1 \\ \text{sym} & & 2 \end{bmatrix} \{OMEG\}'_e \equiv \Delta_e [B200] \{OMEG\}'_e \qquad (5.58)$$

Similarly, the third term is

$$\frac{1}{\text{Re}} \int_{R_e^2} \nabla\{N_1\} \cdot \nabla\{N_1\}^T \{OMEG\}_e\, d\tau \equiv \frac{\Delta_e}{\text{Re}} [B211]_e \{OMEG\}_e \qquad (5.59)$$

In (5.58) and (5.59), $\Delta_e \equiv A_e$, the plane area of the two-dimensional triangular element. Furthermore, $[B211]_e$ is the standard diffusion matrix given in (3.61), and $[B200]$ was presented in (3.62).

The second term in (5.57) is new, and constitutes the significantly important action of convection. It is left as an exercise to show that

$$\int_{R_e^2} \{N_1\} \nabla \times \{N_1\}^T \{PSI\}_e \hat{\mathbf{k}} \cdot \nabla\{N_1\}^T \{OMEG\}_e\, d\tau$$

$$= \frac{1}{6} \begin{Bmatrix} 1 \\ 1 \\ 1 \end{Bmatrix} \{PSI\}_e^T \begin{bmatrix} 0 & -1 & 1 \\ 1 & 0 & -1 \\ -1 & 1 & 0 \end{bmatrix} \{OMEG\}_e \qquad (5.60)$$

Note that (5.60) is independent of the measure (area) of R_e^2, and that the matrix equivalent of vorticity convection involves a pure antisymmetric matrix. The form of (5.60) prompts the definition of a new standard matrix. In the process of developing (5.60), rearrangement of (5.57) using a vector theorem yields the term $\nabla\{N_1\} \times \nabla\{N_1\}^T \cdot \hat{\mathbf{k}}$, which is readily evaluated in the ζ_i coordinate system as

$$\nabla\{N_1\} \times \nabla\{N_1\}^T \cdot \hat{\mathbf{k}} = \frac{1}{2\Delta_e} \begin{bmatrix} 0 & -1 & 1 \\ 1 & 0 & -1 \\ -1 & 1 & 1 \end{bmatrix} \equiv [B211A] \qquad (5.61)$$

The A suffix signifies that the defined matrix is antisymmetric.

Using the standard matrix notation, the linear cardinal basis form for the first term in the finite element algorithm statement (5.47) for vorticity transport becomes

$$S_e\left[\Delta_e[B200]\{OMEG\}'_e + \left(\frac{\Delta_e}{\text{Re}}[B211]_e + \Delta_e\{B10\}\{PSI\}_e^T[B211A]\right)\{OMEG\}_e\right]$$
$$\equiv \{0\} \tag{5.62}$$

For the second term in (5.47), the inviscid form of the vorticity transport equation is utilized. On the element domain, this becomes

$$\beta_1 \cdot \int_{R_e^2} \{N_k\}\nabla L^c(q_1^h)\, d\tau = \beta_1 \cdot \int_{R_e^2} \nabla\{N_1\}(\{N_1\}^T\{OMEG\}'_e$$
$$+ \nabla \times \{N_1\}^T\{PSI\}_e\hat{\mathbf{k}}\cdot\nabla\{N_1\}^T\{OMEG\}_e)\, d\tau \tag{5.63}$$

Equation (5.63) introduces for the first time the requirement to express the directional derivative of a cardinal basis. To accomplish this within the standard matrix concept, the boolean index is generalized from (0, 1) to (0, K), where zero indicates no differentiation and K indicates differentiation in the (global coordinate) direction x_k. Hence, the standard diffusion matrix $[B211]_e$ could equally well be written as $[B2KK]_e$, with summation implied over repeated indices. Term by term, the elements of $[B2KK]_e$ and $[B211]$ are identical, as given in (3.61).

The parameter β_1 defined in (5.63) is a vector with scalar components parallel to x_k; hence $\beta_1 \equiv \Delta_e[\nu_{11}^{\kappa}\,\hat{\mathbf{i}} + \nu_{12}^{\kappa}\,\hat{\mathbf{j}}]$, where superscript $\kappa = 1, 2$ pertains to the term in (5.63), the first subscript identifies the element of q_α^h, and the second subscript denotes the scalar component on x_k. Therefore, in indicial notation, $\beta_{1k} \equiv \Delta_e \nu_{1k}^{\kappa}$. Hence, the first term in (5.63) becomes

$$\beta_1 \cdot \int_{R_e^2} \nabla\{N_1\}\{N_1\}^T\{OMEG\}'_e\, d\tau = \nu_{1k}^1\,\Delta_e[B2K0]_e\{OMEG\}'_e \tag{5.64}$$

The expression (5.64) is valid for all $\{N_k\}$; for the current specification of $\{N_1\}$, (5.64) is further simplified to

$$\nu_{1k}^1\,\Delta_e[B2K0]_e\{OMEG\}'_e = \nu_{1k}^1\,\Delta_e\{B1K\}_e\{B10\}^T\{OMEG\}'_e \tag{5.65}$$

Summation is implied over the index pair (k, K), the elements of $\{B10\}^T$ are {1/3, 1/3, 1/3} [see (3.62)], and

$$\{B1K\}_e = \frac{\partial}{\partial x_1}\{N_1\}\hat{\mathbf{i}} + \frac{\partial}{\partial x_2}\{N_1\}\hat{\mathbf{j}} \tag{5.66}$$

The evaluation of (5.66) is performed on an element basis. Figure 5.3 illustrates the coordinate transformations yielding $\zeta_i = \zeta_i(x_k)$, where ζ_i is the natural system spanning R_e^2. Recalling $\{N_1\} = \{\zeta\}$, and in terms of the local cartesian system η_l,

$$\{\zeta\} = \begin{Bmatrix} 1 - \dfrac{\eta_1}{\eta_1^2} - \left(1 - \dfrac{\eta_1^3}{\eta_1^2}\right)\dfrac{\eta_2}{\eta_2^3} \\ \dfrac{\eta_1}{\eta_1^2} - \dfrac{\eta_1^3}{\eta_1^2}\dfrac{\eta_2}{\eta_2^3} \\ \dfrac{\eta_2}{\eta_2^3} \end{Bmatrix} \tag{5.67}$$

Here, η_l^α denotes the η_l coordinate for node point α, for the orientation shown in Fig. 5.3. The affine transformation $\eta_i = \eta_i(x_k)$ is a translation and a rotation about node 1, with direction cosines a_{ik}, that is,

$$\eta_i = a_{ik}x_k \tag{5.68}$$

Then, using the chain rule,

$$\frac{\partial}{\partial x_k}\{N_1\} = \frac{\partial}{\partial \zeta_i}\{\zeta\}\frac{\partial \zeta_i}{\partial \eta_j}\frac{\partial \eta_j}{\partial x_k} \tag{5.69}$$

which is easily constructed using (5.67)-(5.68). It is left as an exercise to verify the matrix equivalent of the second term in (5.63) as

$$\beta_1 \cdot \int_{R_e^2} \nabla\{N_1\}\nabla\times\{N_1\}^T\{PSI\}_e\hat{\mathbf{k}}\cdot\nabla\{N_1\}^T\{OMEG\}_e\,d\tau$$

$$= \nu_{1K}^2\{B1K\}\{PSI\}_e^T[B211A]\{OMEG\}_e \tag{5.70}$$

Equations (5.62), (5.65), and (5.70) complete the finite-element algorithm statement for vorticity in the form of the ordinary differential equation system

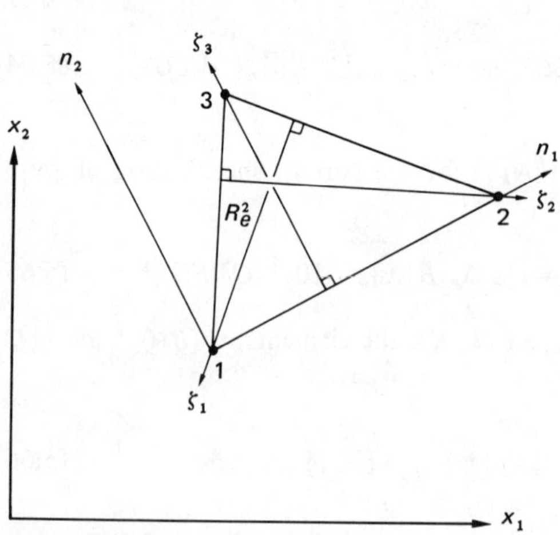

Figure 5.3 Coordinate systems for R_e^2.

(5.48). Assuming specification of the θ-implicit integration algorithm, the $\{N_1\}$ embodiment of the final algebraic algorithm statement (5.49) is

$$\{F1\} = S_e \Bigg[(\Delta_e [B200] + \nu_{1K}^1 \Delta_e [B2K0]_e)(\{OMEG\}_{j+1}^p - \{OMEG\}_j) + h\theta \left(\Delta_e \{B10\}\{PSI\}_{j+1}^T [B211A] + \frac{\Delta_e}{\text{Re}} [B211]_e + \nu_{1K}^2 \{B1K\}\{PSI\}_{j+1}^T [B211A] \right) \{OMEG\}_{j+1}^p + h(1-\theta) \left(\Delta_e \{B10\}\{PSI\}_j^T [B211A] + \frac{\Delta_e}{\text{Re}} [B211]_e + \nu_{1K}^2 \{B1K\}\{PSI\}_j^T [B211A] \right) \{OMEG\}_j \Bigg] \equiv \{0\} \tag{5.71}$$

The form of (5.71) emphasizes that the solution parameters θ and $\beta_1(\nu_{1K}^K)$ remain as variables for refinement of the solution character. The sole final commitment was definition of the linear cardinal basis $\{N_1\}$. Selection of an alternative basis, e.g., $\{N_1^+\}$ or $\{N_2\}$, would not alter the appearance of (5.71), except for the convection terms involving $[B211A]$. Specifically $[B200]$, $[B2K0]$, and $[B211]$ are valid synonyms for the defined integrals of the basis functions. Of course, their rank depends on K, as do the elements, but the variable name does not. The constancy of the derivatives of $\{N_1\}$ was explicitly used in forming the convection term (5.60). For other than $\{N_1\}$, the generalized statement (5.60) is of the form

$$\int_{R_e^2} \{N_1\} \nabla \times \{N_1\}^T \{PSI\}_e \hat{\mathbf{k}} \cdot \nabla \{N_1\}^T \{OMEG\}_e \, d\tau = -\hat{\mathbf{k}} \{PSI\}_e^T \int_{R_e^2} \times \nabla \{N_1\}\{N_1\} \cdot \nabla \{N_1\}^T \{OMEG\}_e \, d\tau \equiv \Delta_e \{PSI\}_e^T [B3K0KA]_e \{OMEG\}_e \tag{5.72}$$

For the linear basis $\{N_1\}$, and using (5.60),

$$[B3KOKA] = \frac{1}{2\Delta_e} \begin{bmatrix} \begin{Bmatrix} 0 \\ 1 \\ -1 \end{Bmatrix} & \begin{Bmatrix} -1 \\ 0 \\ 1 \end{Bmatrix} & \begin{Bmatrix} 1 \\ -1 \\ 0 \end{Bmatrix} \\ \begin{Bmatrix} 0 \\ 1 \\ -1 \end{Bmatrix} & \begin{Bmatrix} -1 \\ 0 \\ 1 \end{Bmatrix} & \begin{Bmatrix} 1 \\ -1 \\ 0 \end{Bmatrix} \\ \begin{Bmatrix} 0 \\ 1 \\ -1 \end{Bmatrix} & \begin{Bmatrix} -1 \\ 0 \\ 1 \end{Bmatrix} & \begin{Bmatrix} 1 \\ -1 \\ 0 \end{Bmatrix} \end{bmatrix} \tag{5.73}$$

The A suffix in (5.73) denotes that the matrix is constructed using the vector cross-product. A suggested exercise is evaluation of $[B3K0KA]$ for a basis other than $\{N_1\}$.

The other formulational step is evaluation of (5.47) for ψ^h, see (5.22)-(5.25). For streamfunction, $\beta_1 \equiv \mathbf{0}$ and $\beta_2 = 1$; it is an elementary operation to establish $\{F2\}$ as

$$\{F2\} = S_e[\Delta_e[B211]\{PSI\}_e - \Delta_e[B200]\{OMEG\}_e + \Delta_e^1[A200]\{UP\}_e] \equiv \{0\} \tag{5.74}$$

In (5.74), Δ_e^1 is the measure of the span of Δ_e on the boundary segment ∂R, whereupon a parallel velocity component u'' (with nodal values $\{UP\}_e$) is specified. Should the less restrictive outflow boundary condition (5.29) be specified for ψ^h, the corresponding algorithm matrix statement is

$$\{F3\} = S_e[\Delta_e[A211]\{PSI\}_e - \Delta_e[A200]\{OMEG\}_e] \equiv \{0\} \tag{5.75}$$

The solution of (5.75) cannot have a Neumann constraint, and the elements Δ_e are one-dimensional.

Equations (5.71) and (5.74), along with the vorticity boundary condition (5.30), e.g., (5.33), constitute the complete finite-element solution algorithm statement, for a general streamfunction-vorticity Navier-Stokes problem statement. While constructed using $\{N_1\}$, for simplicity, with the generalization (5.73) these two statements are really valid for arbitrary $\{N_k\}$! The formulational choice that remains is the implicitness factor θ. If the decision is explicit, that is, $\theta \equiv 0$, then (5.71) becomes a linear equation, since the second term modified by $h\theta$ vanishes. For efficiency, it is necessary to "diagonalize" the matrices $[B200]$ and $[B2K0]_e$. This operation renders $S_e[B2K0] \Rightarrow [0]$, and utterly destroys the good phase accuracy intrinsic to the formulation, as discussed in detail in Chap. 4. These points are not so critical for simulation of a small Reynolds number problem, which can be executed for $\beta_1 \equiv \mathbf{0}$. The degradation of accuracy as Re increases, for example, $\mathrm{Re} \approx O(10^3)$, would certainly be unacceptable.

In the general case, the preferred choice is implicit, $\theta > \frac{1}{2}$. Therefore, the jacobian for the Newton iteration algorithm must be constructed. This is an elementary operation, since (5.71) and (5.74) are written in a functional form that permits partial differentiation. Therefore, for the definition,

$$[J(KL)] = \frac{\partial\{FK\}}{\partial\{QL\}} \tag{5.76}$$

the various system jacobians are

$$[J(11)] \equiv \frac{\partial\{F1\}}{\partial\{Q1\}} = S_e\left[\Delta_e[B200] + \nu_{1K}^1[B2K0] + h\theta\left(\Delta_e\{PSI\}_e^T[B3K0KA] + \frac{\Delta_e}{\mathrm{Re}}[B211]_e + \nu_{1K}^2\{PSI\}_e^T[B3LKLA]_e\right)\right]_{j+1}^{p} \tag{5.77}$$

$$[J(12)] \equiv \frac{\partial\{F1\}}{\partial\{Q2\}} = S_e[h\theta\, \Delta_e\{OMEG\}_e^T[B3K0KA]^T$$

$$+ h\theta v_{1K}^2\{OMEG\}_e^T[B3LKLA]_e^T]_{j+1}^p \tag{5.78}$$

$$[J(22)] \equiv \frac{\partial\{F2\}}{\partial\{Q2\}} = S_e[\Delta_e[B211]_e] \tag{5.79}$$

$$[J(21)] \equiv \frac{\partial\{F2\}}{\partial\{Q1\}} = S_e[-\Delta_e[B200]] \tag{5.80}$$

In (5.77), the final matrix $[B3LKLA]$ is the generalization of $\{B1K\}[B211A]$, see (5.71), where (K, L) are both tensor summation indices. The suffix A emphasizes the matrix results from the vector cross-product. In (5.78), various matrix transpositions were employed to obtain the form shown. In particular, for the $\{N_1\}$ basis, Problem 7 suggests the proof that $[B3K0KA]^T = -[B3K0KA]$.

One last point remains to be defined, regarding implementing the no-slip vorticity boundary condition (5.30) into the jacobian. The finite-difference formula (5.32) and/or (5.33) relates the wall value of vorticity to nearfield streamfunction (and vorticity) distributions. Hence, on those R_e^2 with a common intersection with ∂R with no-slip, the expansion coefficients in the appropriate finite-element approximation become modified. For example, assume the boundary connecting nodes 1 and 2 of Fig. 5.3, conicides with a no-slip boundary condition segment. Then, assuming the node line 2-3 intersects ∂R nominally perpendicular, which it should for a "decent" discretization, then ω_e^h therein takes the form, using (5.33)

$$\omega_e^h(\mathbf{x}, t) \equiv \{N_k(\mathbf{x})\}^T\{OMEG\}_e = \{N_k(\mathbf{x})\}^T \begin{Bmatrix} -\frac{1}{2}\Omega_3 + \dfrac{3(\psi_3 - \psi_1)}{\Delta^2} \\ -\frac{1}{2}\Omega_3 + \dfrac{3(\psi_3 - \psi_1)}{\Delta^2} \\ \Omega_3 \end{Bmatrix}_e \tag{5.81}$$

In (5.81), Δ is the perpendicular distance between node 3 and the line connecting nodes 1 and 2. Then, the order of $[J(11)]$, (5.77), is reduced to extract rows corresponding to wall node locations, and the near-wall node contributions are augmented with the first entries in $\{OMEG\}_e^w$. The second entries in (5.81) constitute additional coupling in $[J(12)]$, $[J(22)]$, and $[J(21)]$, (5.78)-(5.80). Literature citations indicate that an accurate handling of this boundary condition cross-coupling is crucial to stability using an implicit integration procedure. With (5.81), there is never the need to calculate wall values of vorticity, which is itself of some economy.

Problems

1 Verify (5.60).

2 The streamfunction definition (5.19) ensures the velocity field is divergence free. Prove, using (3.21) integrated over an arbitrary subdomain, and the assembly algorithm, that the vorticity efflux from a finite element due to convection is exactly equal to the convected influx into the neighboring finite element possessing the common boundary segment. Hence, (5.60) exhibits the exact vector character for convection of any scalar property of the field.

3 Verify (5.70).
4 Evaluate (5.72) for the basis (*a*) $\{N_1^+\}$; (*b*) $\{N_2\}$.
5 Derive the solution form (5.74).
6 Derive (5.77).
7 Derive (5.78), hence prove that $[B3K0KA]^T = -[B3K0KA]$.
8 Establish the matrix $[B3LKLA]$ for $\{N_1\}$.

5.7 TWO-DIMENSIONAL DUCTED FLOWS

The basic requirement of the finite-element solution algorithm is prediction of separated (and nonseparated) flows in two-dimensional confined (ducted) geometries. Baker (1974) documents results for the $k = 1$ algorithm formulation applied to prediction of the entrance region flow in a duct of uniform rectangular cross section. The nonuniform discretization utilizing $M = (11 \times 12) \times 2 = 264$ triangular finite elements was employed on the symmetric half-domain, $0 \leqslant x/h \leqslant 25$ and $0 \leqslant y/h \leqslant 1.0$, where h is the duct half width. For Re = 200, based on h, the slug inlet flow velocity profile becomes fully developed within the duct length (Schlichting, 1979).

Figure 5.4 graphs the computed steady-state velocity profiles for various stations

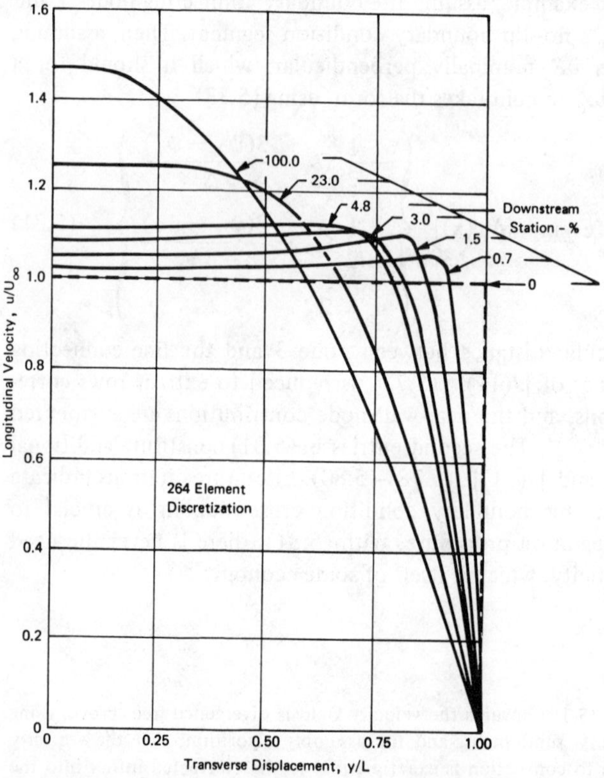

Figure 5.4 Longitudinal velocity distributions for incompressible duct flow, Re = 200, $M = 264$.

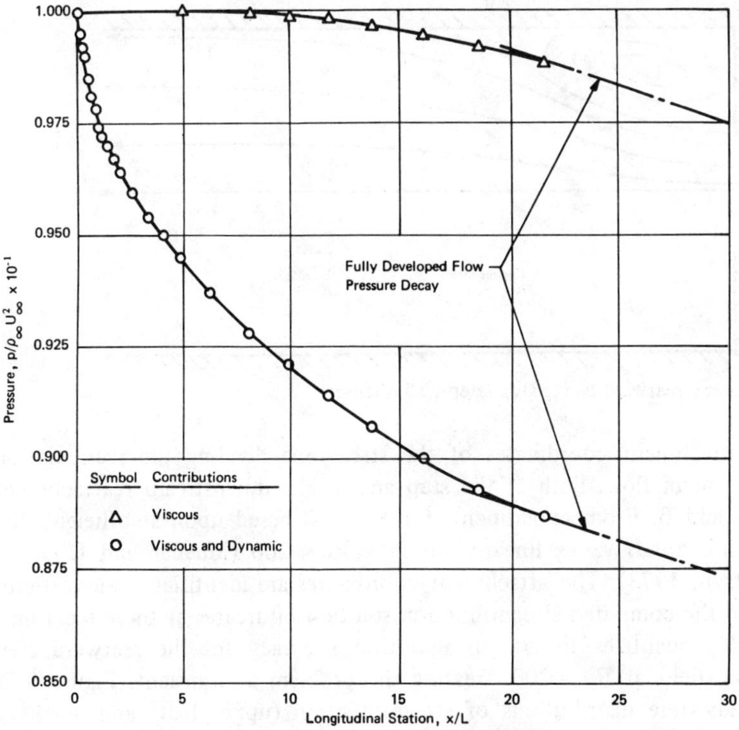

Figure 5.5 Centerplane pressure decay in steady-state duct flow, Re = 200, $M = 264$.

x/h, expressed as percent of total duct length. The terminal profile is in good agreement with the exact (parabolic) solution, and local overshoot directly adjacent to the (no-slip) wall is predicted up to 4.8 percent downstream of the inlet. The magnitudes and distribution of this local wall-displacement effect is in qualitative agreement with comparison finite difference (Gosman et al., 1969) and finite element (Zienkiewicz et al., 1975) solutions. Figure 5.5 graphs the associated solution for centerline pressure distribution, computed using (5.44), which reduces to the form

$$\frac{1}{\rho_0}\,\Delta p(x, y=0) = -\Delta\left(\frac{\partial \psi}{\partial y}\right)^2 + \int_x \left(\frac{\partial^2 \psi}{\partial x\,\partial y}\,\frac{\partial \psi}{\partial y} - \frac{1}{\text{Re}}\,\frac{\partial \omega}{\partial y}\right) dx \tag{5.82}$$

The first two terms represent pressure changes due to streamline convergence, while the third is the viscous loss. On the centerline, the kinetic effects dominate over the first 30 percent of duct length. Thereafter, the viscous effects gradually increase in importance, becoming the sole influence by the end of the duct, where the pressure gradient is in good agreement with that for fully developed flow.

A critical requirement for full Navier-Stokes solutions is prediction of regions of recirculating flow, as illustrated in Fig. 5.6 for a stepwall diffuser. For sufficient Reynolds number, the flow cannot turn the corner, but instead self-generates a smooth area transition by a recirculation region. A key measure of computation accuracy is

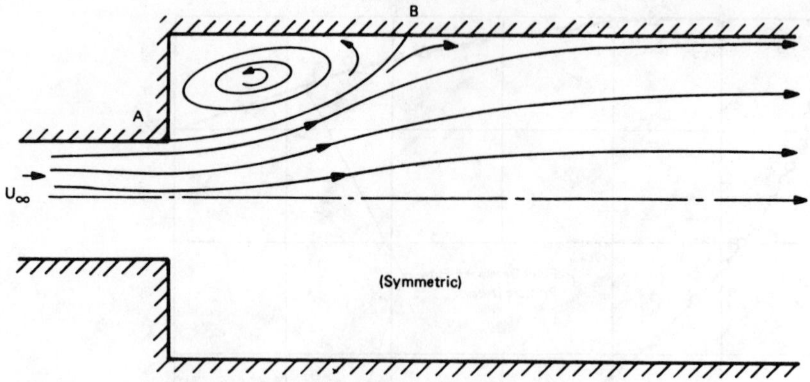

Figure 5.6 Flow over a rearward facing step (step-wall diffuser).

prediction of attachment coordinates of the streamline dividing the recirculation region from the main flow, both at the step and at the downstream reattachment point, points A and B. From experiment, for $\mathrm{Re} > 20$ based upon step height, the attachment coordinate B varies linearly on $20 < \mathrm{Re} < 200$ (Mueller and O'Leary, 1970; Dorodnitsyn, 1973). The attachment coordinates are identified by a vorticity sign change, and the computed streamfunction solution bifurcates at these locations.

Baker (1974) quantizes the $k = 1$ algorithm accuracy for the rearward step steady-state flow field at $\mathrm{Re} = 200$, treating the problem as transient. Figure 5.7*a* graphs the steady-state distributions of streamfunction (upper half) and vorticity

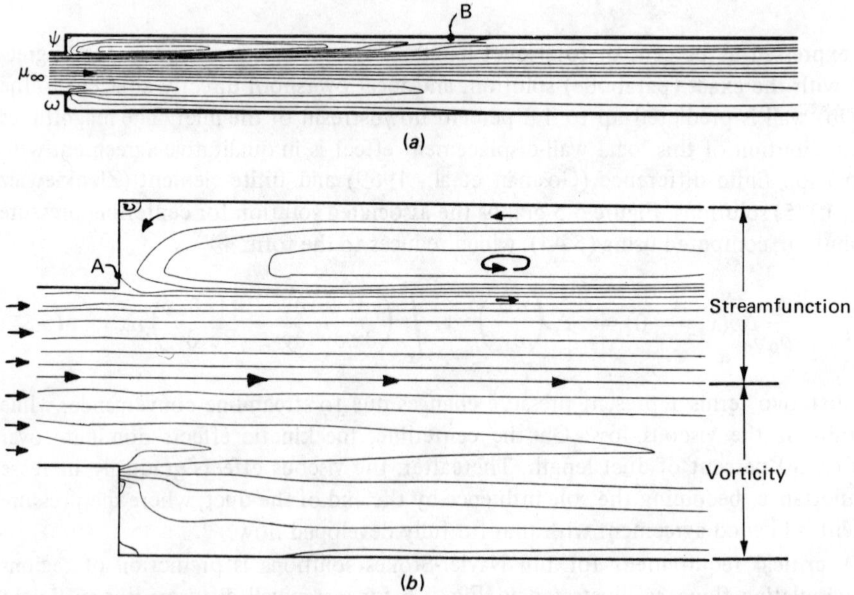

Figure 5.7 Steady-state streamfunction and vorticity distributions for flow over rearward facing step, $\mathrm{Re} = 200$. (*a*) Full flow-field streamfunction and vorticity distribution; (*b*) close-up detail in vicinity of step-wall.

(lower half), as established using an $M = 211$ nonuniform discretization. Figure 5.7*b* provides details of the recirculation region solution in the immediate vicinity of the step. The principal flow detachment occurs just below the step corner, and a smaller zone is predicted at the base. The base region geometry corresponds to a forward facing step, and the fluid again responds to abrupt geometry changes by self-generation of a smooth transition. The computed point of reattachment (B) is 21 step-heights downstream, which agrees within 10 percent of an extrapolation of data (Dorodnitsyn, 1973), and with the computations of Macagno and Hung (1967) for an axisymmetric flow. The predicted steady-state recirculation zone is in qualitative agreement with the flow visualization data of Mueller and O'Leary (1970) at Re = 130.

Modest changes in geometry and/or boundary conditions can induce large changes in the steady-state streamfunction solution. Figure 5.8 illustrates the impact on distributions (Baker, 1974), for which Fig. 5.8*a* was the initial condition. Insertion of a blunt obstacle (Fig. 5.8*b*) drastically shrinks the main recirculation region; the dividing streamline reattachment (B) has moved upstream to within four step-heights. The attachment (A) at the step face is unaltered, and the second base recirculation zone is preserved. Figure 5.8*c* graphs the steady-state streamfunction solution for 10 percent mass removal near the base of the step. The reattachment B for the dividing streamline has moved to the step face, directly adjacent to the attachment point A, the location of which was not altered. Hence, the mass removed at the step base is low momentum reverse flow from far downstream. The comparison for 10 percent mass addition at the base location is shown in Fig. 5.8*d*. The dividing streamline attachment point A has moved from the step face and reattached immediately downstream of injection. The downstream location for reattachment is unaltered from the base case. Hence, the injected mass is predicted to pass directly into the main flow by forcing detachment of the recirculation bubble at the step face.

5.8 TIME-SPLIT FINITE-ELEMENT ALGORITHM

The vorticity transport equation (5.21) is identical in form to the convection-diffusion equation studied in Chap. 4. The finite-element algorithm solution statement (5.47) is therefore amenable to being recast into a time-split formulation [see (4.173)–(4.178)] using the tensor product basis $\{N_k^+(\eta)\}$. Furthermore, if application is restricted to rectangular shaped solution domains R^2, it is possible to recast the finite-element time-split algorithm statement into an efficient recursion relation form (Pepper and Cooper, 1980).

Replacing the convection velocity $\nabla \times \psi\hat{\mathbf{k}}$ with the corresponding velocity $\mathbf{u} = u\hat{\mathbf{i}} + v\hat{\mathbf{j}}$, the time-split form of the semidiscrete algorithm statement (5.62), including (5.64) and (5.70), is

$$S_e\left[\Delta_e([A200] + \nu_{1K}^1[A210])\{OMEG\}_e' + \Delta_e\left(\{UK\}_e^T[A3010] + \frac{1}{\text{Re}}[A211]\right.\right.$$

$$\left.\left.+\,\nu_{1K}^2\{UK\}^T[A3011]\right)\{OMEG\}_e\right] \equiv \{0\} \tag{5.83}$$

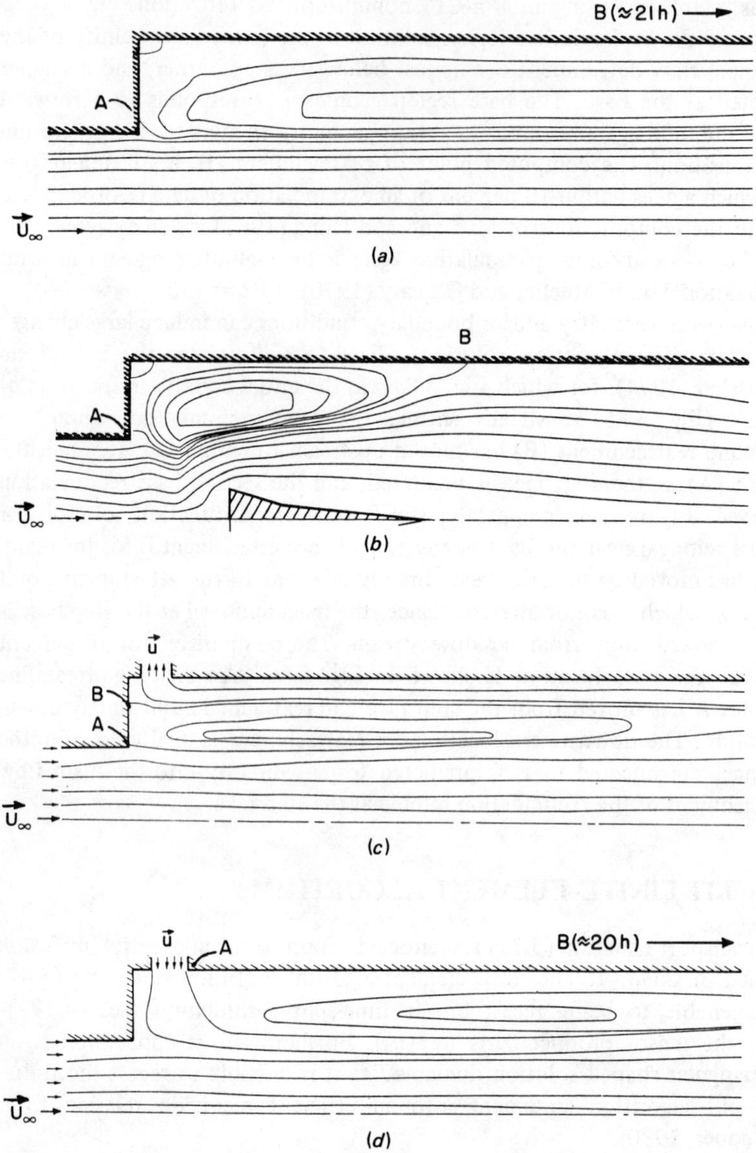

Figure 5.8 Steady-state streamfunction distributions for flow in a step-wall diffuser with variations. (*a*) Base flow; (*b*) internal obstacle; (*c*) mass deletion; (*d*) mass addition.

In (5.83), the index $K = 1, 2$ denotes the parameter defined for the appropriate sweep direction on the discretization $\cup R_e^2$. Using the linear tensor product basis $\{N_1^+(\zeta)\}$, and for a uniform discretization of R^2 of measure Δ, it is left as an exercise to verify that assembly of (5.83) at the node coordinate x_i yields the finite-difference recursion relation.

$$\frac{\Delta}{6}\,[(1+3v_1^1)\Omega'_{i-1}+4\Omega'_i+(1-3v_1^1)\Omega'_{i+1}]$$

$$+\,2\left\{\left[-u_{i-1}-2u_i-\frac{v_1^2}{2}(u_i+u_{i-1})\right]\Omega_{i-1}\right.$$

$$+\left[u_{i-1}-u_{i+1}+\frac{v_1^2}{2}(u_{i+1}+2u_i+u_{i-1})\right]\Omega_i$$

$$\left.+\left[2u_i+u_{i+1}-\frac{v_1^2}{2}(u_i+u_{i+1})\right]\Omega_{i+1}\right\}$$

$$+\frac{1}{\Delta\,\mathrm{Re}}(-\Omega_{i-1}+2\Omega_i-\Omega_{i+1})=0 \qquad (5.84)$$

In (5.84), the subscript K has been omitted for clarity. For the algorithm sweep parallel to the x axis, the convection velocity u at node i, j is evaluated as

$$u_i\,(=u_{i,j})=\tfrac{1}{2}(\psi_{i,j-1}-\psi_{i,j+1}) \qquad (5.85)$$

For the grid sweep parallel to the y axis, correspondingly,

$$u_i\,(=v_{i,j})=\tfrac{1}{2}(\psi_{i+1,j}-\psi_{i-1,j}) \qquad (5.86)$$

Defining the trapezoidal rule for integration of (5.84), the fully discrete algorithm statement for (5.84) can be written in the form

$$A\Omega_{i-1}^{n+1}+B\Omega_i^{n+1}+C\Omega_{i+1}^{n+1}-D=0 \qquad (5.87)$$

where the coefficients A, B, C, and D are (Pepper and Cooper, 1980)

$$A=1+3v_1^1+\frac{\Delta t}{2\Delta}[-2u_i-u_{i-1}-3v_1^2(u_i+u_{i-1})]-\frac{3\,\Delta t}{\Delta^2\,\mathrm{Re}}$$

$$B=4+\frac{\Delta t}{2\Delta}[u_{i-1}-u_{i+1}+3v_1^2(u_{i+1}+2u_i+u_{i-1})]+\frac{6\,\Delta t}{\Delta^2\,\mathrm{Re}}$$

$$C=1-v_1^1+\frac{\Delta t}{2\Delta}[2u_i+u_{i+1}-3v_1^2(u_i+u_{i+1})]-\frac{3\,\Delta t}{\Delta^2\,\mathrm{Re}}$$

$$D=\left\{-4+\frac{\Delta t}{2\Delta}[u_{i-1}-u_{i+1}+3v_1^2(u_{i+1}+2u_i+u_{i-1})]+\frac{6\,\Delta t}{\Delta^2\,\mathrm{Re}}\right\}\Omega_i^n$$

$$+\left\{-1-3v_1^1+\frac{\Delta t}{2\Delta}[-2u_i-u_{i-1}-3v_1^2(u_i+u_{i+1})]-\frac{3\,\Delta t}{\Delta^2\,\mathrm{Re}}\right\}\Omega_{i-1}^n$$

$$+\left\{-1+3v_1^1+\frac{\Delta t}{2\Delta}[2u_i+u_{i+1}-3v_1^2(u_i+u_{i+1})]-\frac{3\,\Delta t}{\Delta^2\,\mathrm{Re}}\right\}\Omega_{i+1}^n \qquad (5.88)$$

In (5.88), the convection velocity $u_{i\pm 1,0}$ in coefficients A, B, C is evaluated at time $n+1$, while those terms in D are evaluated at time n. Hence, (5.87) is a nonlinear algebraic equation system requiring iteration. It can be linearized by evaluating the convection velocity at time step n. Then, (5.87) is directly amenable to solution using the Thomas algorithm (Roache, 1972). The velocity distribution remains determined from solution of the compatibility equation (5.22).

Pepper and Cooper (1980) document application of the time-split finite-element algorithm to the "driven-cavity" problem (Fig. 5.9). The solution domain is the unit square, with the lid defined to slide across the domain at a uniform velocity $u = 1$. Figure 5.10 summarizes steady-state streamfunction and velocity contours, as obtained for an $M = 20 \times 20$ discretization, and for $\nu_1^1 = 0.025 = \nu_1^2$ over a range of Reynolds number. At Re = 100, two small recirculation zones are generated in the lower left- and right-hand corners with a large primary cell generated in the center. Steady-state solutions were obtained in 154 time steps (approximately 18 s CPU for IBM 360/195) with a Δt of 0.15. When the Re is increased to 400, the right lower corner cell begins to enlarge, displacing the lower streamlines of the large primary cell upward (and causing the vortex center to move). Steady-state conditions were obtained after 205 time steps (~23 s CPU) with a Δt of 0.20. At Re = 1000, the lower right corner cell has enlarged, along with a noticeable increase in the size of the lower left corner cell. The solution converged in 849 time steps (~86 s) with a Δt of 0.10. Streamfunction and vorticity values at the primary vortex center for $100 \leqslant \text{Re} \leqslant 1000$ are in good agreement with published results (see Table 5.1).

Pepper and Cooper (1980) also present results obtained using the time-split finite-element algorithm for the case of buoyancy-driven natural convection. In this instance, the body-force term **b** in (5.11) is retained in the Bousinesq form, yielding the vorticity transport equation (5.21) as

$$L(\omega) = \frac{\partial \omega}{\partial t} + (\nabla \times \psi \hat{\mathbf{k}} \cdot \nabla)\omega - \frac{1}{\text{Re}} \nabla^2 \omega - \frac{1}{\text{Ra}} \frac{\partial T}{\partial x} = 0 \tag{5.89}$$

where Ra is the Rayleigh number and T is temperature. In this instance, the energy equation (5.12) is also solved, using the time-split finite-element solution algorithm. The solution domain is illustrated in Fig. 5.11, and the boundary conditions are $u(0, y) = 0 = u(1, y)$, $v(x, 0) = 0 = v(x, 1)$, $T(0, y) = 1$, $T(1, y) = 0$, and $\partial T(x, 0)/\partial y = 0 = \partial T(x, 1)/\partial y$.

Figure 5.12 summarizes the solutions obtained for an $M = 20 \times 20$ discretization for the range $10^3 \leqslant \text{Ra} \leqslant 10^5$. One large circulation cell is predicted for $\text{Ra} \leqslant 10^3$, with the cell strength increasing with Rayleigh number. At $\text{Ra} = 10^5$, two cells are created and persist to steady state. Figure 5.13 compares the results of Pepper and Cooper (1980) to available data, for computed average Nusselt number,

$$\text{Nu} \equiv \int_0^1 \left. \frac{\partial T}{\partial x} \right|_{x=0} dy \tag{5.90}$$

and agreement is excellent over the range of Rayleigh numbers.

Problems

1 Verify (5.83).

2 Derive (5.84).

3 Verify (5.88).

4 Derive (5.89).

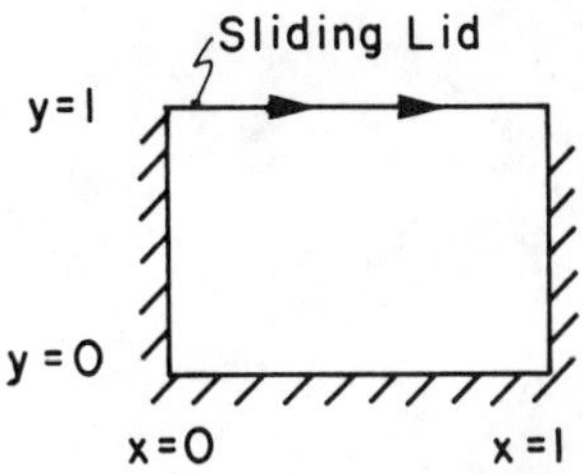

Figure 5.9 Definition of driven cavity problem.

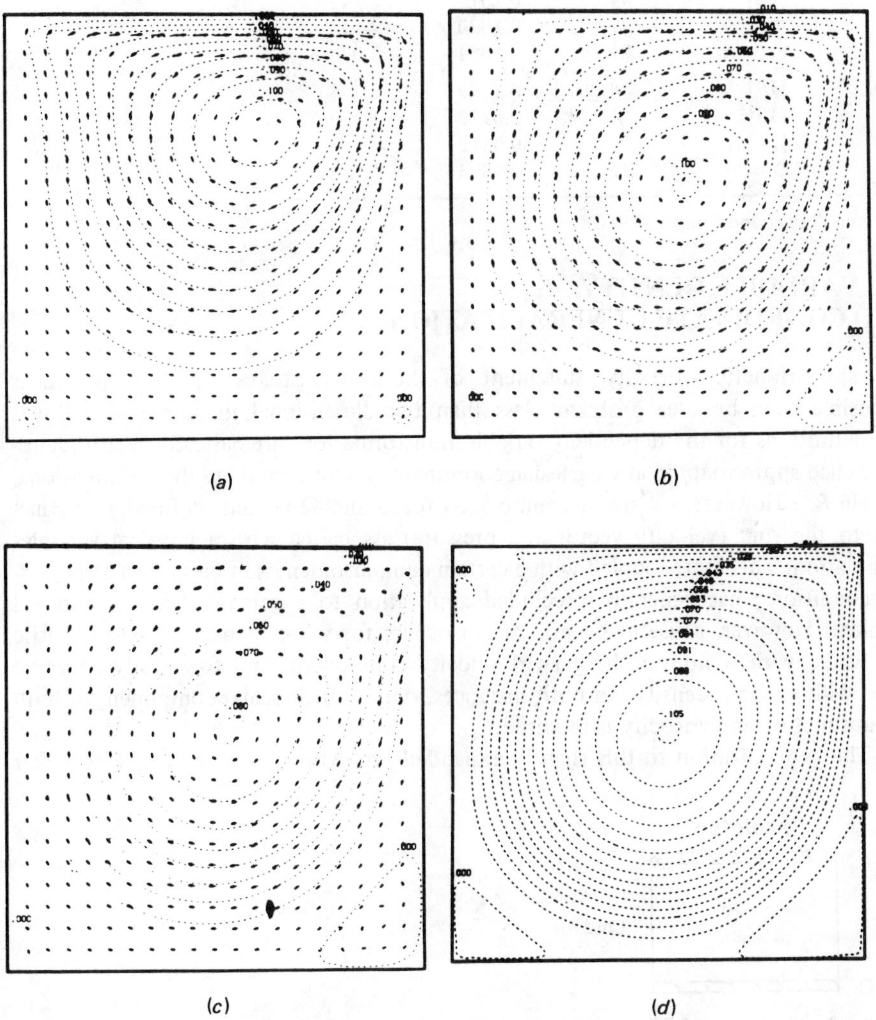

Figure 5.10 Driven cavity flow, streamfunction and velocity contours. (*a*) Re = 100; (*b*) Re = 400; (*c*) Re = 1000; (*d*) Re = 2000. From Pepper and Cooper (1980), reprinted with permission of Pergamon Press, Ltd.

Table 5.1 Square cavity flow comparisons†

Re	Reference	Grid	Primary vortex ψ_{max}	Ω_{max}
100	[19]	8	0.1035	3.098
	[21]	51	0.1032	–
	[20]	41	0.1015	3.143
	[18]	51	0.1026	3.155
	Present	21	0.1086	2.957
400	[19]	8	0.1168	2.415
	[18]	51	0.1014	2.114
	[20]	41	0.1017	2.142
	[24]	21	0.1030	2.170
	Present	21	0.1064	2.070
1000	[19]	8	0.1299	2.653
	[18]	51	0.0977	1.830
	[21]	51	0.0812	–
	Present	21	0.0803	1.550

†From Pepper and Cooper (1980).

5.9 VARIABLE DENSITY AND COORDINATE GENERALIZATION

The streamfunction-vorticity statement of the Navier-Stokes equation system is extensible to a broader problem class than two-dimensional incompressible flows. The definitions for the dependent variable transformations are basically vector identities, hence appropriate in any cartesian coordinate system spanning a three-dimensional domain R^3. However, six scalar components for ψ and Ω become defined, in distinction to the four (velocity vector and pressure) associated with a physical variables formulation. This fact, coupled with a certain cumbersomeness in definition of boundary conditions, has generally precluded application to a general three-dimensional problem. However, a useful generalization occurs for two-dimensional axisymmetric flowfields, with a nonvanishing swirl velocity component, and for steady subsonic flows with variable density. In both instances, only a single scalar component of both streamfunction and vorticity is required.

The generalization to this slightly expanded problem class is presented by Baker

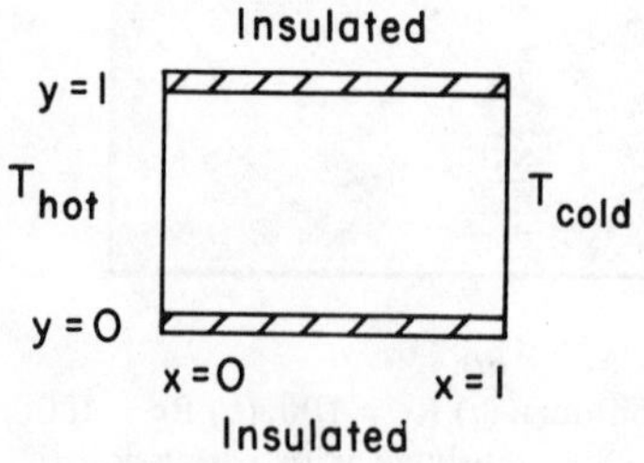

Figure 5.11 Definition of natural convection problem.

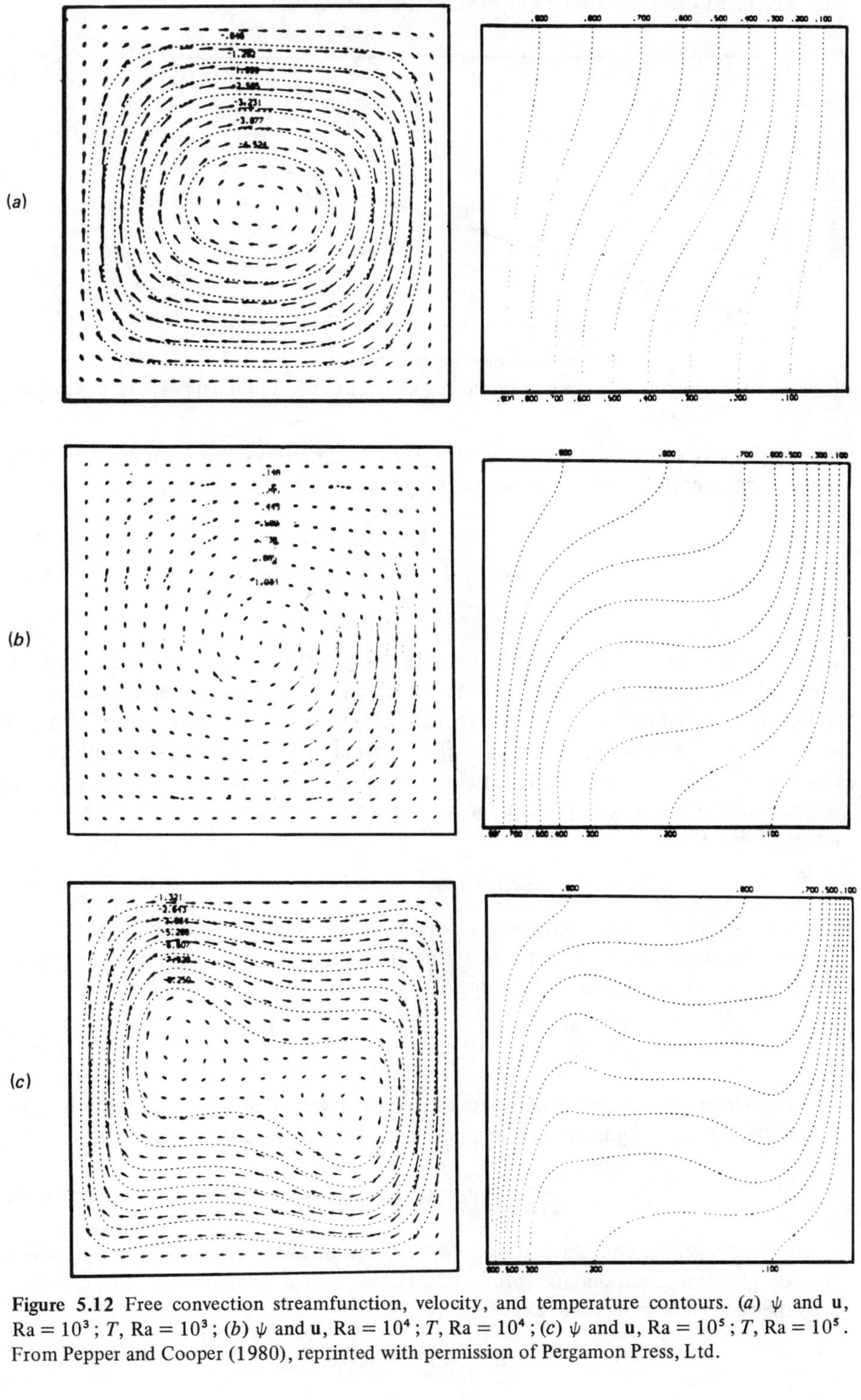

Figure 5.12 Free convection streamfunction, velocity, and temperature contours. (*a*) ψ and $\mathbf{u}$, $\mathrm{Ra} = 10^3$; T, $\mathrm{Ra} = 10^3$; (*b*) ψ and $\mathbf{u}$, $\mathrm{Ra} = 10^4$; T, $\mathrm{Ra} = 10^4$; (*c*) ψ and $\mathbf{u}$, $\mathrm{Ra} = 10^5$; T, $\mathrm{Ra} = 10^5$. From Pepper and Cooper (1980), reprinted with permission of Pergamon Press, Ltd.

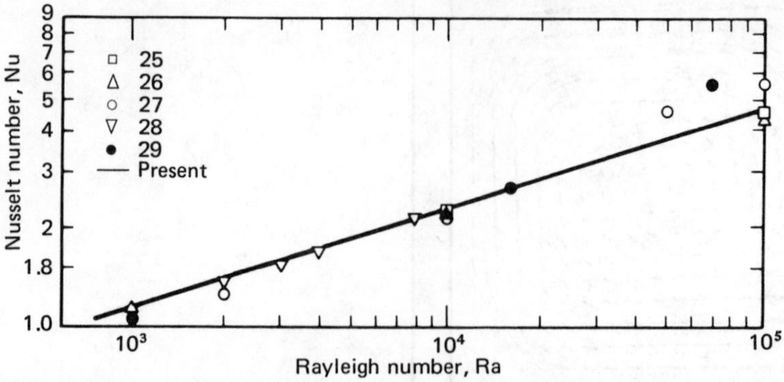

Figure 5.13 Average Nusselt number. From Pepper and Cooper (1980), reprinted with permission of Pergamon Press, Ltd.

(1974), for cylindrical and spherical cartesian coordinate systems spanning R^3. Using tensor index notation, define the scalar components of x_i, $1 \leqslant i \leqslant 3$ as

$$x_i \rightarrow \eta_j \equiv \begin{Bmatrix} x, & y, & 0 \\ r, & z, & \theta \\ r, & \phi, & \theta \end{Bmatrix} \tag{5.91}$$

where $0 \leqslant \theta \leqslant 2\pi$ is the aximuthal coordinate, and $0 \leqslant \phi \leqslant \pi$ is the polar angle in spherical coordinates. It is necessary to generalize the vector calculus operations defining streamfunction and vorticity, (5.19)-(5.20), to include metric coefficients of the coordinate transformation (5.91). The jacobian of (5.91) is diagonal with coefficients $h_{\underline{i}} = \{1, 1, r\}$ and $h_{\underline{i}} = \{1, r, r \sin \phi\}$, for cylindrical and spherical coordinates, respectively. Denoting components of the unit vector set spanning R^3 as $\hat{\epsilon}_i$, the vector invariant notation is

$$\mathbf{v}(x_i) \equiv v_i \hat{\epsilon}_i, \qquad 1 \leqslant i \leqslant 3 \tag{5.92}$$

where v_i signifies scalar components parallel to η_j, with summation over repeated indices. The derivative of a vector in a general cartesian (orthogonal) reference system is then expressed as (Baker, 1974, App. A)

$$\frac{\partial \mathbf{v}}{\partial x_j} = \frac{\partial}{\partial x_j}(v_i \hat{\epsilon}_i) = \frac{\partial v_i}{\partial x_j}\hat{\epsilon}_i + v_i \frac{\partial \hat{\epsilon}_i}{\partial x_j} \tag{5.93}$$

The return to conventional cartesian tensor index summation convention is accomplished by defining the cartesian equivalent of covariant differentiation as

$$\frac{\partial \mathbf{v}}{\partial x_j} \equiv v_{i;j}\hat{\epsilon}_i = (v_{i,j} + \omega_{ijk} v_k)\hat{\epsilon}_i \tag{5.94}$$

where the "wryness coefficients" $\omega_{ijk}(h_{\underline{i}})$ are the cartesian equivalent of Christoffel symbol physical components. From (5.94), by scalar components, the cartesian derivative of a vector becomes expressed as

$$v_{i;j} = v_{i,j} + \omega_{ijk} v_k \tag{5.95}$$

where the subscript common signifies the conventional partial derivative operation.

$$v_{i,j} \equiv \frac{1}{h_{\underline{i}}} \frac{\partial v_i}{\partial x_j} \tag{5.96}$$

The subscript bar signifies the index *not* eligible for the cartesian summation index convention. Finally, the nonvanishing members of the wryness coefficient set are (Baker, 1974)

cylindrical coordinates: $$\omega_{233} = \frac{1}{r}$$

spherical coordinates: $$\omega_{122} = \frac{1}{r} = \omega_{133}$$

$$\omega_{233} = \frac{\cot \phi}{r} \tag{5.97}$$

The calculus operation intrinsic to the streamfunction-vorticity formulation is the vector curl. Hence, in invariant notation,

$$\operatorname{curl} \mathbf{v} \cdot \hat{\mathbf{e}}_i \equiv \frac{1}{J} e_{ijk} v_{k;j} \hat{\mathbf{e}}_i \tag{5.98}$$

where e_{ijk} is the cartesian alternating tensor, with scalar components of (±) unity, and J is the determinant of the metric definition in (5.91), that is, $J \equiv h_1 h_2 h_3$. Hence, the $x_3(\eta_3)$ scalar component of (5.98) is written in conventional cartesian summation notation as

$$\operatorname{curl}_3 \mathbf{v} = \frac{1}{J} e_{3jk} v_{k;j} \tag{5.99}$$

Generalizing to variable density, the two-dimensional Navier-Stokes problem definition (5.1)-(5.6) becomes

$$L(\rho) = \frac{\partial \rho}{\partial t} + (m_k)_{;k} = 0 \tag{5.100}$$

$$L(m_i) = \frac{\partial m_i}{\partial t} + (u_k m_i + p\delta_{ki} - \sigma_{ki})_{;k} + \frac{\rho b_i}{\mathrm{Fr}} = 0 \tag{5.101}$$

$$L(g) = \frac{\partial g}{\partial t} + (u_k(g + p) - \sigma_{ki} u_i + q_k)_{;k} = 0 \tag{5.102}$$

$$\sigma_{ki} = \frac{\rho \nu}{\mathrm{Re}} (u_{k;i} + u_{i;k}) - \frac{\rho \nu}{3\,\mathrm{Re}} u_{j;j} \delta_{ki} \tag{5.103}$$

where $m_i \equiv \rho u_i$ and $g \equiv \rho e$; see (5.4). For either unsteady incompressible flow, or steady flow with variable density, (5.100) can be identically satisfied by defining m_i in terms of Ψ_3, the x_3 scalar component of the vector potential Ψ, and u_3, that is, u_θ, as

$$m_i \equiv \rho u_i \equiv \frac{1}{J} e_{ijk} \Psi_{;j} + \rho u_3 \delta_{i3} \tag{5.104}$$

Equation (5.104) is the generalization of (5.19). In cylindrical and/or spherical coordinates, substituting for J and using (5.99), (5.104) can be rewritten in terms of the scalar streamfunction ψ, i.e., Ψ_3, as

$$m_i = \frac{1}{r \sin^\alpha \phi} e_{3ij}\psi_{,j} + \rho u_3 \delta_{i3} \tag{5.105}$$

where $\alpha \equiv 0$ (1) for cylindrical (spherical) coordinates. Substituting (5.105) into (5.100), and replacing the repeated index, yields

$$\begin{aligned}(m_k)_{;k} &= \left(\frac{1}{r \sin \phi} \epsilon_{3kj}\psi_{,j} + \rho u_3 \delta_{k3}\right)_{,k} \\ &= \frac{1}{r^2 \sin \phi}\left[\left(\frac{1}{r \sin \phi}\psi_{,2}\right)_{;1} - \left(\frac{1}{r \sin \phi}\psi_{,1}\right)_{;2} + (\rho u_3)_{;3}\right]\end{aligned} \tag{5.106}$$

In spherical coordinates, for example, expanding the covariant derivatives in (5.106) yields

$$\begin{aligned}(m_k)_{;k} &= \frac{1}{r^2 \sin \phi}\left[\left(\frac{1}{r \sin \phi} r^2 \sin \phi \frac{1}{r}\frac{\partial \psi}{\partial \phi}\right)_{,r} - \left(\frac{1}{r \sin \phi} r \sin \phi \frac{\partial \psi}{\partial r}\right)_{,\phi} + (\rho u_3)_{,\theta}\right] \\ &= \frac{1}{r^2 \sin \phi}\left(\frac{\partial^2 \psi}{\partial \phi\, \partial r} - \frac{\partial^2 \psi}{\partial r\, \partial \phi} + 0\right) = 0\end{aligned} \tag{5.107}$$

The verification of (5.106) for cylindrical coordinates is similarly direct.

With (5.105) verified, the requirement is to recast the Navier-Stokes equation system (5.100)-(5.103) into the computational variable set $q_\alpha = \{\psi, \omega, u_3, g\}$. The generalization of the vorticity definition (5.20) is

$$\Omega_3 \equiv \omega = \frac{1}{r^\alpha} e_{3jk}u_{k;j} \tag{5.108}$$

Using the definitions (5.95)-(5.96), (5.105), and the skew-symmetric properties of the alternating tensor contraction, the generalization of the streamfunction-vorticity compatibility equation (5.22) is

$$L(\psi) = \left(\frac{1}{\rho r \sin^\alpha \phi}\psi_{,k}\right)_{;k} + r^\alpha \omega = 0 \tag{5.109}$$

Only in rectangular coordinates does (5.109) contain the laplacian operator ∇^2. In cylindrical coordinates, for example, the expanded form for (5.109) is

$$L(\psi) = \frac{\partial}{\partial r}\left(\frac{1}{\rho r}\frac{\partial \psi}{\partial r}\right) + \frac{\partial}{\partial z}\left(\frac{1}{\rho r}\frac{\partial \psi}{\partial z}\right) + \omega = 0 \tag{5.110}$$

The curl of (5.101) parallel to x_3 yields the generalization of the vorticity transport equation (5.21). From Baker (1974), using (5.103) and now permitting the viscosity $\mu = \rho\nu/\rho_\infty\nu_\infty$ to be variable, the final form is

$$L(\omega) = \frac{\partial(\rho r^\alpha \omega)}{\partial t} + \epsilon_{3ki}\left[\left(\frac{r^\alpha \omega \psi_{,i}}{r \sin^\alpha \phi}\right)_{;k} - \frac{1}{2}\left(\frac{\psi_{,l}}{r \sin^\alpha \phi}\right)^2_{;i}\left(\frac{1}{\rho}\right)_{,k}\right.$$
$$\left. + \left(\rho u_3 \epsilon_{3il}\left(\frac{\psi_{,l}}{\rho r \sin^\alpha \phi}\right)_{;3}\right)_{;k}\right] - \frac{1}{\mathrm{Re}}\left[\mu(r^\alpha \omega)_{,j} - \mu_{,j} r^\alpha \omega\right.$$
$$\left. - \mu_{,k}\left(\frac{2\psi_{,k}}{\rho r \sin^\alpha \phi}\right)_{;j} + \mu_{,k}\epsilon_{3ki}\delta_{j3}u_{3;i}\right]_{;j} = 0 \tag{5.111}$$

For example, expanding the third term in the first bracket in (5.111) defines the impact of the swirl velocity component as:

$$\text{cylindrical coordinates, } \epsilon_{3ki}(\,\cdot\,)_{;k} = -\frac{1}{2\rho r}\frac{\partial(\rho u_3)^2}{\partial z}$$
$$\text{spherical coordinates, } \epsilon_{3ki}(\,\cdot\,)_{;k} = \frac{1}{r^2}\frac{\partial \rho u_3^2}{\partial \phi} - \cot\phi\,\frac{\partial(\rho u_3^2/r)}{\partial r} \tag{5.112}$$

The x_3 component of (5.101) is the defining partial differential equation for $m_3 = \rho u_3$. Substitution of (5.105) yields

$$L(m_3) = \frac{\partial m_3}{\partial t} + e_{3ij}\left(\frac{\psi_{,j} u_3}{r \sin^\alpha \phi}\right)_{;i} + m_3 u_{3;3} + p_{,3}$$
$$- \frac{1}{\mathrm{Re}}\left[(\mu u_{3;k})_{;k} + \frac{1}{3}\mu u_{j;j3} + \mu_{,k}u_{k;3}\right] = 0 \tag{5.113}$$

Note in particular that in cylindrical coordinates, $u_{3;3} = u_2/r$ and $u_{3;33} = -u_3/r^2$.

The generalized cartesian tensor formulation yields the appropriate differential equation to be inserted into the finite-element solution algorithm statement (5.47), where $d\tau \equiv J\,d\eta$ is the differential element. For example, in cylindrical coordinates the streamfunction-vorticity compatibility equation (5.110) algorithm statement becomes

$$\int_{R^3} \{N_k\} L(\psi^h)\, d\tau \equiv \{0\}$$
$$= \int_{R^3} \{N_k\}\left[\frac{\partial}{\partial r}\left(\frac{1}{\rho^h r}\frac{\partial \psi^h}{\partial r}\right) + \frac{\partial}{\partial z}\left(\frac{1}{\rho^h r}\frac{\partial \psi^h}{\partial z}\right) + \omega^h\right] r\,dr\,d\theta\,dz$$
$$= 2\pi \int_{R^2}\left[\left(-\frac{\partial\{N\}}{\partial r} - \frac{2}{r}\{N\}\right)\frac{1}{\rho^h}\frac{\partial \psi^h}{\partial r} - \frac{\partial\{N\}}{\partial z}\frac{1}{\rho^h}\frac{\partial \psi^h}{\partial z} + r\omega^h\right] dr\,dz \tag{5.114}$$

The last form in (5.114) results from use of the Green-Gauss theorem and integration over $d\theta$. Using the approximation definition (5.45)-(5.46), the finite-element matrix statement equivalent of (5.114) using $\{N_1(\zeta)\}$ is

$$S_e \left[\Delta_e \{RHOM1\}_e^T \{B10\}(\{B11\}_e \{B11\}_e^T + \{B12\}_e \{B12\}_e^T)\{PSI\}_e \right.$$

$$\left. + \Delta_e \frac{\{RHOM1\}_e^T \{B10\}}{\{R\}_e^T \{B10\}} \{B10\}\{B11\}_e^T \{PSI\}_e - \Delta_e \{R\}_e^T [B3000]\{OMEG\}_e \right] \equiv \{0\} \tag{5.115}$$

The elements of $\{RHOM1\}_e$ are nodal values of $1/\rho$, that is, ρ^{-1}, and those in $\{R\}_e$ are nodal radii of R_e^2. The matrices $\{B11\}$ and $\{B12\}$ are the directional derivatives, where $\{B11\}\{B11\}^T + \{B12\}\{B12\}^T = [B211]$ [see (3.61)]. The element measure Δ_e is the plane area of the triangular cross-section ring element, and in the second term $1/\rho^h$ and $1/r$ are averaged on R_e^2 using $\{B10\}$. The finite-element algorithm statements for the remaining equations of the generalized statement are constructed in the same manner.

Problems

1 Verify (5.105) using (5.104), (5.95)-(5.98), and the definition for $h_{\underline{i}}$.
2 Expand (5.105) for cylindrical coordinates.
3 Verify (5.108).
4 Derive (5.109).
5 Derive the form of (5.110) for spherical coordinates.
6 Prove (5.112).
7 Verify (5.114).
8 Verify (5.115).

B. PHYSICAL VARIABLES FORMULATION

5.10 PENALTY FUNCTION CONCEPTS, THE STOKES PROBLEM

Part A of this chapter has documented the use of vector potential functions in establishing a numerically tractible solution statement for the two-dimensional, incompressible Navier-Stokes problem class. Recall the requirement is to solve (5.1)-(5.6), or equivalently (5.10)-(5.12). The fundamental difficulty is that solutions u_i to (5.11), must also satisfy (5.10), and that from this combination a statement must emerge for solution of the pressure field. The streamfunction-vorticity formulation accomplished this using the mathematical properties of vector fields.

An alternative approach, presented in this section, is to borrow concepts from variational calculus, specifically extremization subject to (differential) constraints. The theory is rigorous only for linear elliptic boundary value problems, so that considerable extension will be required to approach solutions of (5.1)-(5.2) for interesting Reynolds numbers. The formulational stage is the Stokes flow approximation for the steady-state form of (5.2), wherein the influence of convection is neglected as small.

Nondimensionalizing the pressure term by the viscous terms removes the Reynolds number in (5.5), yielding the two-dimensional Stokes equations.

$$L(\rho_0) = \frac{\partial u_j}{\partial x_j} = 0 \tag{5.116}$$

$$L(u_i) = \frac{\partial}{\partial x_j}(p\delta_{ij} - \sigma_{ij}) = 0 \tag{5.117}$$

The requirement is to determine the form of a functional $I(u_1, u_2, p)$, the extremization of which with respect to the available parameters yields (5.116)-(5.117). Recall that these concepts were briefly explored in Sec. 2.3, in the context of including the convection boundary condition within the energy functional for steady heat conduction. In the present case, the functional for (5.117) must be constrained such that (5.116) is satisfied on the domain R^2 (rather than on ∂R, see Sec. 2.3).

Denoting the rectangular cartesian components of $\mathbf{u}$ as u and v, the expanded form for (5.116)-(5.117) is

$$L(\rho_0) = \nabla \cdot \mathbf{u} = \frac{\partial u}{\partial x} + \frac{\partial v}{\partial y} = 0 \tag{5.118}$$

$$L(u) = \nu \nabla^2 u - \frac{\partial p}{\partial x} = 0 \tag{5.119}$$

$$L(v) = \nu \nabla^2 v - \frac{\partial p}{\partial y} = 0 \tag{5.120}$$

The appearance of the laplacians in (5.119)-(5.120) is a giveaway to companion terms in the symmetric quadratic form $I(u, v)$. How the pressure gradient fits is not as obvious. However, if we constrain extremization of $I(u, v)$ with (5.118), times a Lagrange multiplier λ, and proceed through the formalities, the answer will emerge.

Therefore, consider extremization of $I(u, v, \lambda)$ where

$$I(u, v, \lambda) \equiv \frac{\nu}{2} \int_{R^2} (\nabla u \cdot \nabla u + \nabla v \cdot \nabla v)\, d\tau + \int_{R^2} \lambda \nabla \cdot \mathbf{u}\, d\tau \tag{5.121}$$

The formal procedure is to define a set of functions which can be made arbitrarily close to u, v, and λ, for example,

$$U(\mathbf{x}) \equiv u(\mathbf{x}) + \alpha_1 \epsilon(\mathbf{x})$$
$$V(\mathbf{x}) \equiv v(\mathbf{x}) + \alpha_2 \epsilon(\mathbf{x})$$
$$\Gamma(\mathbf{x}) \equiv \lambda(\mathbf{x}) + \alpha_3 \epsilon(\mathbf{x}) \tag{5.122}$$

In (5.122), the α_i are arbitrary constants, and $\epsilon(\mathbf{x})$ is an arbitrary function that vanishes at coordinates on ∂R where $\mathbf{u}$ and λ are specified by boundary conditions. In terms of the new variables (5.122), the functional eligible for extremization becomes

$$I(U, V, \Gamma) \equiv \frac{\nu}{2} \int_{R^2} (\nabla U \cdot \nabla U + \nabla V \cdot \nabla V)\, d\tau + \int_{R^2} \Gamma \nabla \cdot \mathbf{U}\, d\tau \tag{5.123}$$

Obviously, for $\alpha_i \equiv 0$, (5.123) is identical with (5.121). Since these coefficients are arbitrary (recall Chap. 1), the extremum of the functional I occurs when the following criteria are met:

$$\left.\frac{\partial I}{\partial \alpha_i}\right|_{\alpha_i=0} \equiv 0 \qquad \text{for } i = 1, 2, 3 \tag{5.124}$$

It is a suggested exercise to prove that

$$\left.\frac{\partial I}{\partial \alpha_1}\right|_{\alpha_i=0} = \nu \nabla^2 u + \frac{\partial \lambda}{\partial x} = 0 \tag{5.125}$$

$$\left.\frac{\partial I}{\partial \alpha_2}\right|_{\alpha_i=0} = \nu \nabla^2 v + \frac{\partial \lambda}{\partial y} = 0 \tag{5.126}$$

$$\left.\frac{\partial I}{\partial \alpha_3}\right|_{\alpha_i=0} = \nabla \cdot \mathbf{u} = 0 \tag{5.127}$$

Comparing (5.125)-(5.126) to (5.119)-(5.120), the Lagrange multiplier λ must be equal to the negative of the pressure, that is, $\lambda = -p$. Therefore, the extremization of (5.121) yields the Stokes equations (5.119)-(5.120), and the continuity equation (5.118), on definition of the Lagrange multiplier of the constraint as $-p$.

Of course, the form (5.121) with $\lambda \equiv -p$ is limited strictly to the linear Stokes problem. However, (5.121) yields guidance on a functional form for the continuity constraint that should be of use for the more general problem class. The formulation is commonly termed "penalty function," and was first documented for fluid mechanics analysis by Zienkiewicz (1974). The penalty formulation replaces the functional (5.121) with the alternative form (Reddy, 1978)

$$I_n(u_n, v_n, \lambda_n) = \frac{\nu}{2} \int_{R^2} (\nabla u_n \cdot \nabla u_n + \nabla v_n \cdot \nabla v_n)\, d\tau + \frac{\lambda_n}{2} \int_{R^2} (\nabla \cdot \mathbf{u}_n)^2\, d\tau \tag{5.128}$$

In (5.128), the subscript n is a parameter that takes a specific value, hence I_n is indeed dependent upon n. If one proceeds through the extremization of (5.128) (Problem 2), using the procedures outlined in (5.122)-(5.124), the Stokes equations (5.119)-(5.120) are recovered by the definition of the nth approximation penalty function as

$$\lambda_n(\nabla \cdot \mathbf{u}_n) \equiv -p_n \tag{5.129}$$

Equation (5.129) states that the nth solution approximation to the pressure, i.e., p_n, is equal to λ_n times the error in exact satisfaction of continuity by the nth solution velocity field $\mathbf{u}_n$.

The following algebraic example (Reddy, 1982b) serves to amplify the distinctions of the theory.

Example 5.1 Determine the coordinates (x_0, y_0) such that

$$f(x, y) \equiv 3x^2 - 2xy + y^2 + 15x + 6y = 0$$

is stationary, subject to the constraint that

$$g(x,y) \equiv x - 2y = 0$$

The direct solution is simply obtained by substitution of $g(x,y)$ into $f(x,y)$, yielding

$$\hat{f}(y) \equiv f(x(y),y) = 9y^2 + 36y = 0$$

The modified functional $\hat{f}$ is stationary when

$$\frac{\partial \hat{f}}{\partial y} = 0$$

which yields the root $y_0 = -2$, hence $x_0 = -4$.

The Lagrange multiplier solution is obtained by defining the modified functional

$$f_l(x,y,\lambda) \equiv f(x,y) + \lambda g(x,y)$$

The Lagrange functional f_l is stationary when

$$\frac{\partial f_l}{\partial x} \equiv 0 \qquad \frac{\partial f_l}{\partial y} \equiv 0 \qquad \frac{\partial f_l}{\partial \lambda} \equiv 0$$

Substituting f and g, the solution set (x_0, y_0, λ) is determined directly as $x_0 = -4$, $y_0 = -2$, $\lambda = 5$.

The penalty function solution defines the modified functional.

$$f_p(x_\alpha, y_\alpha, \alpha) \equiv f(x,y) + \tfrac{1}{2}\alpha[g(x,y)]^2$$

The penalty functional is stationary when

$$\frac{\partial f_p}{\partial x} = 0 \Rightarrow \frac{\partial f}{\partial x} + \alpha(x - 2y) = 0$$

$$\frac{\partial f_p}{\partial x} = 0 \Rightarrow \frac{\partial f}{\partial y} - 2\alpha(x - 2y) = 0$$

Solving these two equations yields

$$x_\alpha = \frac{-3(7 + 12\alpha)}{4 + 9\alpha} \qquad y_\alpha = \frac{-(33 + 18\alpha)}{4 + 9\alpha}$$

The solutions (x_α, y_α) for various α are

α	x_α	y_α
10	−4.0532	−2.2659
100	−4.0055	−2.0276
1000	−4.0005	−2.0028

Note that in the limit $\alpha \Rightarrow \infty$, $x_\alpha \Rightarrow x_0$, $y_\alpha \Rightarrow y_0$; hence, the extremum of the penalty formulation converges to the stationary value of $f(x,y)$ for α sufficiently large.

Returning to the Stokes problem, then, in the limit $\lambda_n \Rightarrow \infty$, I_n approaches I and (u_n, v_n, p_n) approach (u, v, p). The convergence proof of the penalty function solution for the Stokes problem is given by Temam (1979). Briefly, the Stokes equations for $(\mathbf{u}, p)$ and $(\mathbf{u}_n, p_n)$ are subtracted, yielding

$$\nu[\nabla^2 \mathbf{u}_n - \nabla^2 \mathbf{u}] + \nabla[p_n - p] = 0 \tag{5.130}$$

Multiplying (5.130) by $(\mathbf{u}_n - \mathbf{u})$, integrating over R^2, employing integration by parts and the divergence theorem, and using the triangle inequality [see (4.132)], leads to

$$\nu\|\mathbf{u}_n - \mathbf{u}\|_{H^1}^2 + \frac{1}{2\lambda_n}\|p_n\|_{H^0}^2 < \frac{1}{2\lambda_n}\|p\|_{H^0}^2 \tag{5.131}$$

It follows from (5.131) that as $\lambda_n \to \infty$, $\mathbf{u}_n \to u$ in H^1. Consequently, (5.130) is used to argue that $p_n \to p$ in H^0.

In a practical sense, if λ_n is sufficiently large, then $\mathbf{u}_n$ and p_n will differ negligibly from $\mathbf{u}$ and p. How large is sufficient to enforce a reasonable level of continuity, without inducing numerical ill-conditioning, can be estimated using dimensional analysis. As reported by Hughes et al. (1979),

$$\lambda \approx c \max\{\nu, \nu \mathrm{Re}\} \tag{5.132}$$

where c is a constant which depends on computer word length and is independent of the mesh measure Δ_e, and Re is the Reynolds number. Their numerical studies reveal that $c \approx 10^7$, for a 64 bit floating-point word length, and can vary one or two orders of magnitude with negligible effect on the solutions reported.

This completes the necessary description of the penalty function concept. In the limit $\mathrm{Re} \to 0$, the extremization of (5.128) converges to (5.118)-(5.120) as $\lambda_n \to \infty$. The return of nonvanishing convection to the problem class definition, i.e., the Navier-Stokes equations, will eliminate existence of a functional form for extremization. As we have observed, in Chap. 4, the theoretical foundation is then shifted to the method of weighted residuals applied directly to the parent differential equations. Equation (5.128) provides the necessary insight into construction of the differential constraint of continuity within the MWR statement.

Problems

1 Prove that the extremization of (5.121), see (5.122)-(5.127), yields the Stokes equations for $\lambda \equiv -p$.

2 Prove that the extremization of (5.128) yields the penalty function definition (5.129).

5.11 PENALTY FINITE-ELEMENT SOLUTION ALGORITHM

The problem class is the two-dimensional Navier-Stokes equations (5.1)-(5.6), restricted to constant viscosity and without buoyancy effects. Therefore, the governing equation set is

$$L(\rho_0) = \frac{\partial u_j}{\partial x_j} = 0 \tag{5.133}$$

$$L(u_i) = \frac{\partial u_i}{\partial t} + \frac{\partial}{\partial x_j}\left(u_i u_j + \frac{1}{\rho_0} p\delta_{ij} - \frac{1}{\text{Re}}\frac{\partial u_i}{\partial x_j}\right) = 0 \tag{5.134}$$

$$l(u_i) = a^i u_i + a^i \frac{\partial u_i}{\partial x_j}\hat{\mathbf{n}}_j + a^i_3 = 0 \tag{5.135}$$

where $1 \leqslant (i, j) \leqslant 2$. The solution domain is $\Omega \equiv R^2 \times t$, the typical finite element domain is $\Omega_e \equiv R_e^2 \times t$, and $\cup R_e^2 = R^2$ is the discretization of R^2. Dropping the subscripts n for convenience, the finite-element approximations u_i^h and p^h on Ω are defined as

$$u_i^h(x_j, t) \equiv \sum_e u_i^e(x_j, t) = \sum_e \{N_k(x_j)\}^T\{UI(t)\}_e \tag{5.136}$$

$$p^h(x_j, t) \equiv \sum_e p^e(x_j, t) = \sum_e \{N_p(x_j)\}^T\{P(t)\}_e \tag{5.137}$$

In (5.136)-(5.137), the elements of the cardinal bases $\{N_k(x_j)\}$ and $\{N_p(x_j)\}$ are polynomials on x_j complete to degree k and p, respectively, where $p < k$.

The construction of the penalty finite-element solution algorithm for (5.133)-(5.135) follows the procedures developed in Sec. 4.10 for the convection-diffusion equation. The basic requirement is to extremize the semidiscrete approximation error, hence $L(u_i^h)$ and $l(u_i^h)$ are required to be orthogonal to the space of functions used to construct u_i^h. For large Reynolds number, to control nonlinearly induced instability and dispersion error, the vector gradient of the convection part of $L(u_i^h)$ is similarly extremized, subject to the multiplier set $\beta_\alpha \equiv \beta_{\alpha j}$. Finally, the extremization statement is completed by the incompressibility penalty constraint of the form (5.129). Combining these three expressions yields the finite-element algorithm statement.

$$\int_{R^2} \{N_k\}L(u_i^h)\,d\tau - \beta_{\alpha j}\int_{R^2}\{N_k\}\frac{\partial}{\partial x_j}L(u_i^h)\,d\tau + \beta\int_{\partial R}\{N_k\}l(u_i^h)\,d\sigma$$

$$+\,\alpha\int_{R^2}\frac{\partial}{\partial x_i}\{N_k\}\left(p^h + \lambda_n^*\frac{\partial u_j^h}{\partial x_j}\right)d\tau \equiv \{0\} \tag{5.138}$$

Recall in actual practice that (5.138) is evaluated on the discretization $\cup R_e$, with the resultant element contributions assembled into the global form using the matrix operator S_e. Equation (5.138) can be rearranged to a more suitable form. Using a vector identity and substituting (5.134), the first term in (5.138) becomes

$$\int_{R^2} \{N_k\} L(u_i^h)\, d\tau = \int_{R^2} \{N_k\} \frac{\partial u_i^h}{\partial t}\, d\tau$$

$$+ \oint_{\partial R} \{N_k\} \left(u_i^h u_j^h + \frac{1}{\rho_0} p^h \delta_{ij} - \frac{1}{\text{Re}} \frac{\partial u_i^h}{\partial x_j} \right) \cdot \hat{\mathbf{n}}_j\, d\sigma$$

$$- \int_{R^2} \frac{\partial}{\partial x_j} \{N_k\} \left(u_i^h u_j^h + \frac{1}{\rho_0} p^h \delta_{ij} - \frac{1}{\text{Re}} \frac{\partial u_i^h}{\partial x_j} \right) d\tau \quad (5.139)$$

Similarly, using (5.134), the second term in (5.138) can be reexpressed as

$$\beta_{\alpha l} \int_{R^2} \{N_k\} \frac{\partial}{\partial x_l} L(u_i^h)\, d\tau = \beta_{\alpha l} \oint_{\partial R} \{N_k\} \left(\frac{\partial u_i^h}{\partial t} + u_j^h \frac{\partial u_i^h}{\partial x_j} \right) \cdot \hat{\mathbf{n}}_l\, d\sigma$$

$$- \beta_{\alpha l} \int_{R^2} \frac{\partial}{\partial x_l} \{N_k\} \left(\frac{\partial u_i^h}{\partial t} + u_j^h \frac{\partial u_i^h}{\partial x_j} \right) d\tau \quad (5.140)$$

Defining $\alpha \equiv 1/\rho_0$ yields a cancellation of pressure terms in (5.138), see (5.139), hence, $\alpha\lambda_n^* \equiv \lambda_n$. The no-slip viscous boundary condition removes the generated surface integrals in (5.139)-(5.140), except for the last term in (5.139) involving Re^{-1}, which is removed by identifying $a_2^i \beta \equiv 1/\text{Re}$ in (5.135) and (5.138).

Hence, the final form for the penalty finite-element algorithm statement (5.138) is

$$\int_{R^2} \{N_k\} \frac{\partial u_i^h}{\partial t} - \int_{R^2} \frac{\partial \{N_k\}}{\partial x_j} \left(u_i^h u_j^h - \frac{1}{\text{Re}} \frac{\partial u_i^h}{\partial x_j} \right) d\tau + \int_{\partial R} \{N_k\}(a_1^i u_i^h + a_3^i)\, d\sigma$$

$$+ \beta_{\alpha l} \int_{R^2} \frac{\partial \{N_k\}}{\partial x_l} \left(\frac{\partial u_i^h}{\partial t} + u_j^h \frac{\partial u_i^h}{\partial x_j} \right) d\tau + \lambda_n \int_{R^2} \frac{\partial \{N_k\}}{\partial x_i} \frac{\partial u_j^h}{\partial x_j}\, d\tau \equiv \{0\} \quad (5.141)$$

The first three terms in (5.141) are conventional, as established by the basic semi-discrete approximation error extremization. The fourth term is the artificial dissipation mechanism, where $\beta_{\alpha l} \equiv \Delta_e \nu_{\alpha l}^{\kappa}$, Δ_e is the element measure, and $\nu_{\alpha l}^{\kappa}$ is a parameter of order $(15)^{-1/2}$ (recall Sec. 4.11). The fifth term is the penalty term that enforces the incompressibility differential constraint (5.133) to order $(\lambda_n)^{-1}$.

Since i is a free index, and for all (any) degree k in (5.136), (5.141) is a coupled nonlinear system of ordinary differential equations describing evolution of the two components of u_i^h. The pressure field is recovered from its definition (5.129). Recalling (5.48), the matrix statement (5.141) is equivalently

$$[C]\{UI\}' + \{K(UJ, \beta_l, \lambda_n)\} + \{b\} = \{0\} \quad (5.142)$$

where $[C]$ is the "capacity" matrix, $\{K(\cdot)\}$ is a complicated nonlinear function of its argument, $\{b\}$ contains all nonhomogeneous data, and superscript prime denotes the ordinary time derivative. The θ-implicit finite-difference integration algorithm defines the algebraic equation system,

$$\{FI\} \equiv \{UI\}_{j+1} - \{UI\}_j - h[\theta\{UI\}'_{j+1} + (1-\theta)\{UI\}'_j] = \{0\} \qquad (5.143)$$

upon substituting (5.142) for the expressed derivatives. As before, $h \equiv \Delta t \equiv t_{j+1} - t_j$ defines the integration time step, and $\theta = \frac{1}{2}$ yields the trapezoidal rule. Since (5.143) is strongly nonlinear, the Newton procedure is an appropriate iteration algorithm; hence,

$$[J(FI)^p_{j+1}]\{\delta UI\}^{p+1}_{j+1} = -\{FI\}^p_{j+1} \qquad (5.144)$$

The dependent variable in (5.144) is the iteration vector, which defines the solution step

$$\{UI\}^{p+1}_{j+1} \equiv \{UI\}^p_{j+1} + \{\delta UI\}^{p+1}_{j+1} \qquad (5.145)$$

As before, the jacobian in (5.144) is defined as

$$[J(\cdot)] \equiv \frac{\partial\{FI\}}{\partial\{UJ\}} \qquad (5.146)$$

and is evaluated directly from (5.142)-(5.143).

Problem

1 Verify (5.141).

5.12 THEORETICAL ANALYSIS, ACCURACY AND CONVERGENCE

The basic theoretical considerations on semidiscrete approximation error and temporal truncation error, as predicted in Sec. 5.5, remain appropriate for the basic portion of the finite-element algorithm (5.141). However, there are several additional essential controlling factors, on convergence and stability, introduced by the addition of the penalty term. The mathematical expertise required to develop these concepts is beyond the scope of this text, hence the essential results can only be summarized. The interested reader is referred to Ladyshenskaya (1969), Finn (1965), Temam (1979), and Girault and Raviart (1979) for treatises on the complete mathematical aspects.

The central aspect concerns admissibility of the finite-element function subspaces, i.e., the cardinal bases (5.136)-(5.137), for the velocity and pressure approximations. Only a few combinations of k and p satisfy the theoretical requirements on stability and convergence. In all cases, the basic requirement is $p < k$, that is, the approximation for pressure must be of lower degree than that for velocity. Table 5.2 summarizes the basic admissible combinations for $k \leqslant 2$, and graphically illustrates the nodal arrangement on the master element domain.

It is of some interest to note that number 3 in Table 5.2, i.e., $\{N_1^+\}$ and $\{N_0^+\}$, is

Table 5.2 Admissible basis for penalty algorithm

	Basis		Element nodal arrangement	
Number	Velocity	Pressure	Velocity	Pressure
1	$\{N_1\}$	$\{N_0\}$		
2	$\{N_2\}$	$\{N_1\}$		
3	$\{N_1^+\}$	$\{N_0^+\}$		
4	$\{N_2^+\}$	$\{N_1^+\}$		

graphically similar to the usual finite-difference construction involving cell-corner velocities and cell-centered pressure, as exemplified by the SIMPLE algorithm (Patankar, 1980). This is solely a tenuous visual similarly however, since all other aspects of algorithm construction are totally dissimilar. In particular, the finite-element penalty algorithm does not explicitly compute the pressure to determine u_i^h. Instead, determination of the pressure field p^h is the post-solution operation (5.129), which can be performed on an element basis. Conversely, the SIMPLE algorithm "adjusts" the computed pressure approximation to "correct" for velocity divergence in some sense.

The second key aspect of the finite-element algorithm is the requirement for use of "reduced integration" for evaluating the penalty (last) term in (5.141). This procedure was rather ingeniously devised by Zienkiewicz et al. (1971), for a problem class in elasticity, and extended to fluid mechanics analysis by Zienkiewicz and Godbole (1975), Taylor and Hood (1973), and Gartling (1974), among others. Recalling the discussion in Sec. 3.6 on Gauss quadrature, one may evaluate any defined finite-element matrix to a given exactness by choosing the numerical integration of sufficiently high order. Conversely, one may purposely select an order of integration lower than required by the degree k of the basis $\{N_k\}$. This is reduced integration, which is an essential penalty algorithm factor. The next section provides the detailed algorithm construction for the bilinear tensor product basis, including this aspect.

The final key point is of fundamental importance in relation to convergence under discretization refinement. Equation (5.131) documents the convergence proof for the penalty algorithm construction, prior to discretization and use of the discrete approximation, for the steady Stokes problem definition. Reddy (1980) proves the extension to the steady Navier-Stokes definition, whereupon the exponent on λ_n is reduced to one-half on the right side of (5.131). In proceeding to the discrete approximation, the form of the convergence statement is

$$\begin{aligned} \|u_i - u_i^h\|_{H^1} &\leq C_1\,\Delta_e^{m_1}\,\|\cdot\|_{H^r} \\ \|p - p^h\|_{H^0} &\leq C_2\,\Delta_e^{m_2}\,\|\cdot\|_{H^r} \end{aligned} \tag{5.147}$$

where $\|\cdot\|$ is a suitable norm of the "data" of the problem specification, recall (5.54), and m_1 and m_2 are constants. However, in marked distinction to (5.54), the coefficients C_1 and C_2 are not constants, but can vary as the mesh measure Δ_e to an inverse power. Hence, under discretization refinement, the right side of (5.147) can grow in an unbounded manner, actually yielding divergence of the approximate solution as the grid is refined. Solution existence can be guaranteed, provided the approximation function subspace satisfies the discrete Babuska-Brezzi condition (Babuska and Aziz, 1972; Brezzi, 1974):

$$C_3 \|Q^h\|_{H^0} \leqslant \max_{v^h \in V^h} \frac{\int_{R^n} Q^h \,\nabla \cdot v^h \, d\tau}{\|v^h\|_{H^1}} \tag{5.148}$$

In (5.148), $C_3 > 0$ is a constant, v^h are members of the finite dimensional approximation subspace V^h, of functions possessing square-integrable first derivatives, and $Q^h = \nabla \cdot V^h$ (Reddy, 1982a; Oden et al., 1979; and Oden, 1982a).

Elements for which (5.148) is satisfied have been established. In particular (see Carey and Krishnan, 1982, and refer to Table 5.2), the first combination, $\{N_1\}$ and $\{N_0\}$, does not satisfy (5.148), since it is "over-constraining" on mesh refinement which leads to "locking" (Zienkiewicz et al., 1971). The second entry combination of $\{N_2\}$ and $\{N_1\}$ does satisfy (5.148), provided at least one node for p_e lies interior to ∂R_e. The third entry combination in Table 5.2 also satisfies the Babuska-Brezzi condition (5.148) (Bercouvier and Pironneau, 1979; Glowinski and Pironneau, 1979), as does the last entry. A summary of admissible and optimal basis is given by Oden (1982b), and Oden and Jacquotte (1982) represent a comprehensive analysis for Stokesian flows.

5.13 BILINEAR TENSOR PRODUCT ALGORITHM CONSTRUCTION

In this section, the penalty finite-element algorithm statement (5.141) is developed in completeness using $\{N_1^+\}$ for u_i^h and $\{N_0^+\}$ for p^h, (5.136)-(5.137); see number 3 in Table 5.2. Insertion of (5.141) into (5.143), for $\theta > 0$ yields a nonlinear algebraic equation system for solution by (5.144). The global matrix statement (5.143) is obtained using S_e on the sequence of elemental definitions, i.e.,

$$\{FI\} \equiv S_e[\{FI\}_e] \tag{5.149}$$

The elemental expression $\{FI\}_e$ is constructed using the master element hypermatrix definitions $[B\cdots]$ (recall Sec. 3.6). In the following expressions, the subscripts e are deleted for clarity, since every matrix expression pertains to $(\cdot)_e$.

Denote the members of the discrete dependent variable set as $\{QI\} = \{U1, U2\}$. Define the members of the dissipation vector set β_α as $\beta_{\alpha j} \equiv \Delta_e \nu_{\alpha j}^\kappa$, where $\alpha = 1, 2$ for u_1^h and u_2^h, and $\kappa = 1, 2$ for the time and space derivative terms, respectively [see (5.141)]. Following the developed procedures and standardized nomenclature, an exercise suggests verification of the general form for (5.143) as

$$
\begin{aligned}
\{FU1\}_e = {} & [\Delta_e[B200] + \nu^1_{11}\Delta_e[B210] + \nu^1_{12}[B220]]\{U1\}'_{j+1} \\
& + \frac{\Delta t}{2}\Big[-\Delta_e(\{U1\}^T[B3010] + \{U2\}^T[B3020])\{U1\} \\
& + \frac{\Delta_e}{\mathrm{Re}}([B211] + [B222])\{U1\} + L_e(a^1_1[A200]\{U1\} + a^1_3\{A10\}) \\
& + \Delta_e\nu^2_{11}(\{U1\}^T[B3011] + \{U2\}^T[B3012])\{U1\} \\
& + \Delta_e\nu^2_{12}(\{U1\}^T[B3021] + \{U2\}^T[B3022])\{U1\} \\
& + \Delta_e\lambda_n([P211]\{U1\} + [P212]\{U2\})\Big]_{j+1,j}
\end{aligned} \tag{5.150}
$$

$$
\begin{aligned}
\{FU2\}_e = {} & [\Delta_e[B200] + \nu^1_{21}\Delta_e[B210] + \nu^1_{22}\Delta_e[B220]]\{U2\}'_{j+1} \\
& + \frac{\Delta t}{2}\Big[-\Delta_e(\{U1\}^T[B3010] + \{U2\}^T[B3020])\{U2\} \\
& + \frac{\Delta_e}{\mathrm{Re}}([B211] + [B222])\{U2\} + L_e(a^2_1[A200]\{U2\} + a^2_3\{A10\}) \\
& + \Delta_e\nu^2_{21}(\{U1\}^T[B3011] + \{U2\}^T[B3012])\{U2\} \\
& + \Delta_e\nu^2_{22}(\{U1\}^T[B3021] + \{U2\}^T[B3022])\{U2\} \\
& + \Delta_e\lambda_n([P221]\{U1\} + [P222]\{U2\})\Big]_{j+1,j}
\end{aligned} \tag{5.151}
$$

Equations (5.150)–(5.151) as written are generally valid for all degree k in (5.136). In both equations, $\{\cdot\}'_{j+1}$ denotes $\{\cdot\}^p_{j+1} - \{\cdot\}_j$ [see (5.145)] and $[\cdot]_{j+1,j}$ defines evaluation of the argument $[\cdot]$ at t_{j+1}, and at t_j, followed by addition after multiplication by θ and $(1-\theta)$ [see (5.143)]. Δ_e is the measure of the two-dimensional rectangular element domain R^2_e, with spans of length $2a$ and $2b$ (see Fig. 3.13). Conversely, L_e is the measure ($2a$ or $2b$) of the intersection of R^2_e with ∂R. The elemental hypermatrices $[BN\cdots]$ are of rank $0 \leqslant N \leqslant 1$, defined for R^2_e, $[A200]$ and $\{A10\}$ are evaluations on $\partial R \to R^1_e$, and $[P2\cdot\cdot]$ are the penalty term matrices evaluated on R^2_e using reduced integration. Finally, evaluation of each of the dissipation terms premultiplied by $\nu^2_{\alpha J}$ is accomplished using the magnitude of the velocity in the elemental left contraction matrix $\{UI\}^T_e$, $1 \leqslant I \leqslant 2$.

Restricting attention to $\{N^+_1\}$, each of the element matrices in (5.150)–(5.151) is easy to evaluate. For the boundary condition terms, $L_e = 2a$ or $2b$ and [see (3.51)]

$$
[A200] = \frac{1}{6}\begin{bmatrix} 2 & 1 \\ 1 & 2 \end{bmatrix} \qquad \{A10\} = \frac{1}{2}\begin{Bmatrix} 1 \\ 1 \end{Bmatrix} \tag{5.152}
$$

On R_e^2, $\Delta_e = 4ab$, and the newly defined rank zero hypermatrices are

$$[B200] \equiv \frac{1}{\Delta_e} \int_{R_e^2} \{N_1^+\}\{N_1^+\}^T \, d\tau = \frac{1}{36} \begin{bmatrix} 4 & 2 & 1 & 2 \\ & 4 & 2 & 1 \\ & & 4 & 2 \\ (\text{sym}) & & & 4 \end{bmatrix} \tag{5.153}$$

$$[B210] \equiv \frac{1}{\Delta_e} \int_{R_e^2} \frac{\partial}{\partial x_1} \{N_1^+\}\{N_1^+\}^T \, d\tau = \frac{1}{12a} \begin{bmatrix} -2 & -2 & -1 & -1 \\ 2 & 2 & 1 & 1 \\ 1 & 1 & 2 & 2 \\ -1 & -1 & -2 & -2 \end{bmatrix} \tag{5.154}$$

$$[B220] \equiv \frac{1}{\Delta_e} \int_{R_e^2} \frac{\partial}{\partial x_2} \{N_1^+\}\{N_1^+\}^T \, d\tau = \frac{1}{12b} \begin{bmatrix} -2 & -1 & -1 & -2 \\ -1 & -2 & -2 & -1 \\ 1 & 2 & 2 & 1 \\ 2 & 1 & 1 & 2 \end{bmatrix} \tag{5.155}$$

The diffusion matrix $[B211] + [B222]$ has already been derived; see (3.75)-(3.76). In the case of a discretization using square elements $R_e^2(a = b)$, this matrix combination becomes [see (3.77)]

$$[B211] + [B222] = \frac{1}{6a^2} \begin{bmatrix} 4 & -1 & -2 & -1 \\ & 4 & -1 & -2 \\ & & 4 & -1 \\ (\text{sym}) & & & 4 \end{bmatrix} \tag{5.156}$$

Recall that on assembly over all elements sharing node (i, j), (5.156) yields a near likeness of the second-order accurate four-point finite-difference star [see (3.78)].

The penalty term matrices $[P2IJ]$ are the evaluation of (3.75) using a reduced order of integration. Recalling the discussion on gaussian quadrature (Sec. 3.6), Table 3.3 lists the coordinates and weights for integration of order $k \leqslant 2$. Reduced integration for $\{N_1^+\}$ corresponds to use of order $k = 1$, which is simply evaluation at the element centroid. Hence, the penalty matrix evaluations yield

$$[P211] \equiv \frac{1}{\Delta_e} \int_{R_e^2} \frac{\partial}{\partial x_1} \{N_1^+\} \frac{\partial}{\partial x_1} \{N_1^+\}^T \, d\tau = \frac{\partial}{\partial x_1} \{N_1^+\} \frac{\partial}{\partial x_1} \{N_1^+\}^T \bigg|_{\eta_i \equiv 0} \tag{5.157}$$

$$[P211] = \frac{1}{4a^2}\begin{bmatrix} 1 & -1 & -1 & 1 \\ & 1 & 1 & -1 \\ & & 1 & -1 \\ \text{(sym)} & & & 1 \end{bmatrix} \tag{5.157 (Cont.)}$$

$$[P212] = \frac{1}{4ab}\begin{bmatrix} 1 & 1 & -1 & -1 \\ -1 & -1 & 1 & 1 \\ -1 & -1 & 1 & 1 \\ 1 & 1 & -1 & -1 \end{bmatrix} \tag{5.158}$$

$$[P221] = [P212]^T \tag{5.159}$$

$$[P222] = \frac{1}{4b^2}\begin{bmatrix} 1 & 1 & -1 & -1 \\ & 1 & -1 & -1 \\ & & 1 & 1 \\ \text{(sym)} & & & 1 \end{bmatrix} \tag{5.160}$$

Construction of the first order hypermatrices $[B3\cdots]$ is tedious but follows the identical procedures. For example,

$$[B3010] \equiv \frac{1}{\Delta_e}\int_{R_e^2} \{N_1^+\}\frac{\partial}{\partial x_1}\{N_1^+\}\{N_1^+\}^T\,d\tau = \frac{1}{144a}\begin{bmatrix} \left\{\begin{matrix}-6\\-3\\-1\\-2\end{matrix}\right\} & \left\{\begin{matrix}-3\\-6\\-2\\-1\end{matrix}\right\} & \left\{\begin{matrix}-1\\-2\\-2\\-1\end{matrix}\right\} & \left\{\begin{matrix}-2\\-1\\-1\\-2\end{matrix}\right\} \\ \left\{\begin{matrix}6\\3\\1\\2\end{matrix}\right\} & \left\{\begin{matrix}3\\6\\2\\1\end{matrix}\right\} & \left\{\begin{matrix}1\\2\\2\\1\end{matrix}\right\} & \left\{\begin{matrix}2\\1\\1\\2\end{matrix}\right\} \\ \left\{\begin{matrix}2\\1\\1\\2\end{matrix}\right\} & \left\{\begin{matrix}1\\2\\2\\1\end{matrix}\right\} & \left\{\begin{matrix}1\\2\\6\\3\end{matrix}\right\} & \left\{\begin{matrix}2\\1\\3\\6\end{matrix}\right\} \\ \left\{\begin{matrix}-2\\-1\\-1\\-2\end{matrix}\right\} & \left\{\begin{matrix}-1\\-2\\-2\\-1\end{matrix}\right\} & \left\{\begin{matrix}-1\\-2\\-6\\-3\end{matrix}\right\} & \left\{\begin{matrix}-2\\-1\\-3\\-6\end{matrix}\right\} \end{bmatrix} \tag{5.161}$$

$$
[B3020] = \frac{1}{144b}\begin{bmatrix}
\begin{Bmatrix}-6\\-2\\-1\\-3\end{Bmatrix} & \begin{Bmatrix}-2\\-2\\-1\\-1\end{Bmatrix} & \begin{Bmatrix}-1\\-1\\-2\\-2\end{Bmatrix} & \begin{Bmatrix}-3\\-1\\-2\\-6\end{Bmatrix} \\
\begin{Bmatrix}-2\\-2\\-1\\-1\end{Bmatrix} & \begin{Bmatrix}-2\\-6\\-3\\-1\end{Bmatrix} & \begin{Bmatrix}-1\\-3\\-6\\-2\end{Bmatrix} & \begin{Bmatrix}-1\\-1\\-2\\-2\end{Bmatrix} \\
\begin{Bmatrix}2\\2\\1\\1\end{Bmatrix} & \begin{Bmatrix}2\\6\\3\\1\end{Bmatrix} & \begin{Bmatrix}1\\3\\6\\2\end{Bmatrix} & \begin{Bmatrix}1\\1\\2\\2\end{Bmatrix} \\
\begin{Bmatrix}6\\2\\1\\3\end{Bmatrix} & \begin{Bmatrix}2\\2\\1\\1\end{Bmatrix} & \begin{Bmatrix}1\\1\\2\\2\end{Bmatrix} & \begin{Bmatrix}3\\1\\2\\6\end{Bmatrix}
\end{bmatrix} \tag{5.162}
$$

$$
[B3011] \equiv \frac{1}{\Delta_e}\int_{R_e^2} \{N_1^+\}\,\frac{\partial}{\partial x_1}\,\{N_1^+\}\,\frac{\partial}{\partial x_1}\,\{N_1^+\}^T\,d\tau
$$

$$
= \frac{1}{96a^2}\begin{bmatrix}
\begin{Bmatrix}3\\3\\1\\1\end{Bmatrix} & \begin{Bmatrix}-3\\-3\\-1\\-1\end{Bmatrix} & \begin{Bmatrix}-1\\-1\\-1\\-1\end{Bmatrix} & \begin{Bmatrix}1\\1\\1\\1\end{Bmatrix} \\
 & \begin{Bmatrix}3\\3\\1\\1\end{Bmatrix} & \begin{Bmatrix}1\\1\\1\\1\end{Bmatrix} & \begin{Bmatrix}-1\\-1\\-1\\-1\end{Bmatrix} \\
 & & \begin{Bmatrix}1\\1\\3\\3\end{Bmatrix} & \begin{Bmatrix}-1\\-1\\-3\\-3\end{Bmatrix} \\
\text{(sym)} & & & \begin{Bmatrix}1\\1\\3\\3\end{Bmatrix}
\end{bmatrix} \tag{5.163}
$$

$$[B3022] = \frac{1}{96b^2}\begin{bmatrix} \begin{Bmatrix}3\\1\\1\\3\end{Bmatrix} & \begin{Bmatrix}1\\1\\1\\1\end{Bmatrix} & \begin{Bmatrix}-1\\-1\\-1\\-1\end{Bmatrix} & \begin{Bmatrix}-3\\-1\\-1\\-3\end{Bmatrix} \\ & \begin{Bmatrix}1\\3\\3\\1\end{Bmatrix} & \begin{Bmatrix}-1\\-3\\-3\\-1\end{Bmatrix} & \begin{Bmatrix}-1\\-1\\-1\\-1\end{Bmatrix} \\ & & \begin{Bmatrix}1\\3\\3\\1\end{Bmatrix} & \begin{Bmatrix}1\\1\\1\\1\end{Bmatrix} \\ \text{(sym)} & & & \begin{Bmatrix}3\\1\\1\\3\end{Bmatrix} \end{bmatrix} \tag{5.164}$$

The second step in algorithm formulation is to construct the jacobian (5.146) of the Newton algorithm (5.144). As before, this is a direct calculus operation since (5.150)–(5.151) are analytical in $\{UI\}$. Recalling that $[J] \equiv S_e[J]_e$ and deleting the e subscript for clarity, the elemental jacobians, as established from the definition (5.146), are

$$\begin{aligned}[J11]_e \equiv \frac{\partial \{FU1\}_e}{\partial \{U1\}_e} &= \Delta_e([B200] + \nu_{11}^1 [B210] + \nu_{12}^1 [B220]) \\ &+ \frac{\Delta_e \Delta t}{2}\Bigg[-2\{U1\}^T[B3010] - \{U2\}^T[B3020] + \frac{1}{\text{Re}}([B211] + [B222]) \\ &+ \frac{L_e a_1^1}{\Delta_e}[A200] + \nu_{11}^2(\{U1\}^T([B3011] + [B3110]) + \{U2\}^T[B3012]) \\ &+ \nu_{12}^2(\{U1\}^T([B3021] + [B3120]) + \{U2\}^T[B3022]) + \lambda_n[P211]\Bigg]\end{aligned} \tag{5.165}$$

$$\begin{aligned}[J12]_e \equiv \frac{\partial \{FU1\}_e}{\partial \{U2\}_e} &= \frac{\Delta_e \Delta t}{2}[-\{U1\}^T[B3020] + \nu_{11}^2\{U1\}^T[B3210] \\ &+ \nu_{12}^2\{U1\}^T[B3220] + \lambda_n[P212]]\end{aligned} \tag{5.166}$$

$$[J21]_e \equiv \frac{\partial \{FU2\}_e}{\partial \{U1\}_e} = \frac{\Delta_e \Delta t}{2}\left[-\{U2\}^T[B3020] + \nu_{21}^2\{U2\}^T[B3210] + \nu_{22}^2\{U2\}^T[B3220] + \lambda_n[P221]\right] \tag{5.167}$$

$$\begin{aligned}[J22]_e \equiv \frac{\partial \{FU2\}_e}{\partial \{U2\}_e} &= \Delta_e([B200] + \nu_{21}^1[B210] + \nu_{22}^1[B220]) \\ &+ \frac{\Delta_e \Delta t}{2}\Bigg[-\{U1\}^T[B3010] - 2\{U2\}^T[B3020] + \frac{1}{\mathrm{Re}}([B211] + [B222]) \\ &+ \frac{L_e a_1^2}{\Delta_e}[A200] + \nu_{21}^2(\{U1\}^T[B3011] + \{U2\}^T([B3012] + [B3210])) \\ &+ \nu_{22}^2(\{U1\}^T[B3021] + \{U2\}^T([B3022] + [B3220])) + \lambda_n[P222]\Bigg]\end{aligned} \tag{5.168}$$

Note in forming (5.165)-(5.168) that indices in various hypermatrix definitions $[B3\cdots]$ have been permuted to permit the required differentiation by the right contraction matrix [see (1.58)-(1.59)]. These newly defined hypermatrices are constructed by appropriate permutations of the rows and columns in (5.161)-(5.164). The final form for the Newton algorithm jacobian is, using (5.165)-(5.168),

$$S_e\left[\begin{bmatrix}[J11]_e & [J12]_e \\ [J21]_e & [J22]_e\end{bmatrix}\begin{Bmatrix}\{\delta U1\}_e \\ \{\delta U2\}_e\end{Bmatrix}_{j+1}^{p+1} + \begin{Bmatrix}\{FU1\}_e \\ \{FU2\}_e\end{Bmatrix}_{j+1}^{p}\right] = \{0\} \tag{5.169}$$

Problems

1 Verify (5.150)-(5.151).

2 Verify (5.153)-(5.155).

3 Verify the definition of the reduced integration penalty term matrices $[P2IJ]$, (5.157)-(5.160).

4 Derive (5.165)-(5.168).

5.14 NUMERICAL SOLUTION RESULTS

Hughes et al. (1979), in their extensive survey paper, document application of the penalty finite-element solution algorithm to a variety of two-dimensional, incompressible flow problem specifications. A very popular problem is the so-called driven cavity, (recall Fig. 5.9). Figure 5.14*a* graphs the domain and boundary condition specification and Fig. 5.14*b* shows the uniform $M = 20 \times 20$ grid employed by Hughes et al. for the $\{N_1^+\}$ and $\{N_0^+\}$ basis algorithm construction. Figures 5.15*a*–*c* summarize the computed steady-state distribution of u_i^h, ψ (streamfunction), p^h and ω (vorticity) distributions, for Re = 0, 100, and 400, respectively, for zero level of artificial dissipation, $\beta_{\alpha l} \equiv 0$ in (5.141).

While the nonphysical "wiggles," (Gresho and Lee, 1981), produced by inadequate

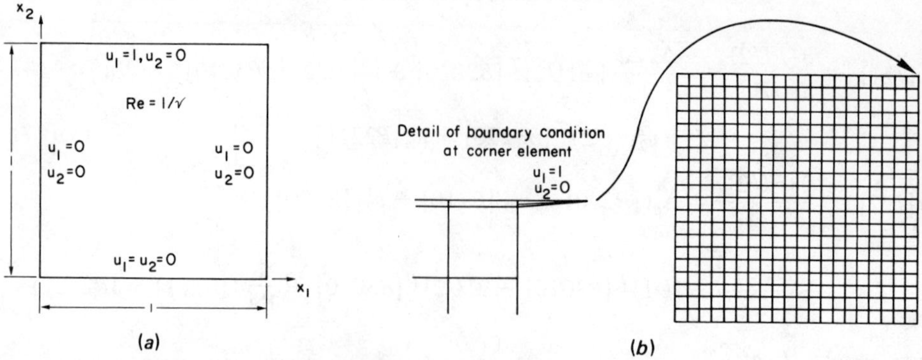

Figure 5.14 Driven cavity flow problem description. (*a*) Boundary conditions; (*b*) uniform discretization for $\{N_1^+\}$. After Hughes et al. (1979).

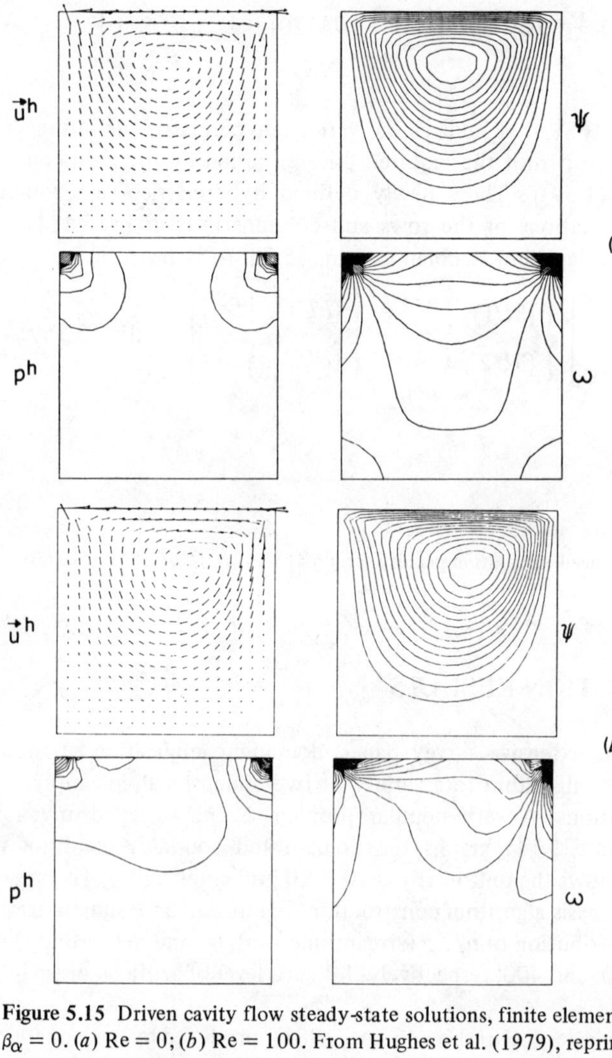

Figure 5.15 Driven cavity flow steady-state solutions, finite element penalty algorithm using $\{N_1^+\}$, $\beta_\alpha = 0$. (*a*) Re = 0; (*b*) Re = 100. From Hughes et al. (1979), reprinted with permission.

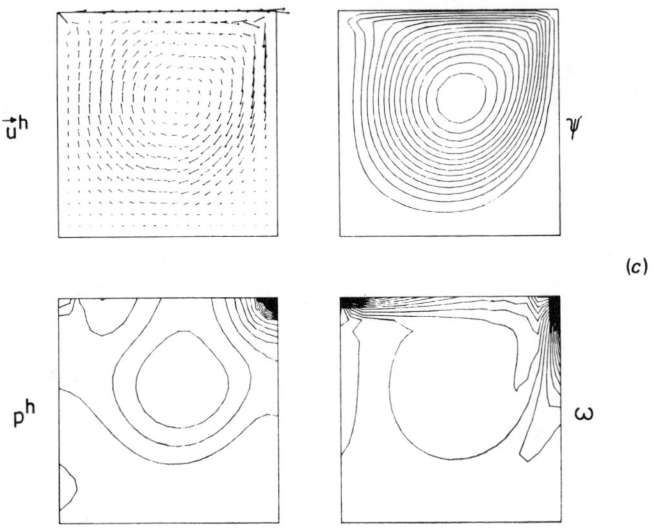

Figure 5.15 Driven cavity flow steady-state solutions, finite element penalty algorithm using $\{N_1^+\}$, $\beta_\alpha = 0$ (*Continued*). (*c*) Re = 400. From Hughes et al. (1979), reprinted with permission.

grid resolution at larger Reynolds numbers are absent in these results, Hughes et al. (1979) observe that some level of artificial dissipation is typically required for other problem definitions. The various forms of "upwinding" reported in the literature to cure the wiggles, are generally obtainable within the developed algorithm construction (5.141), by use of $\beta_{\alpha l} > 0$. Considerable literature is available on this subject, as documented in the referenced survey paper (see also Gresho and Lee, 1981; and Sani et al., 1981).

Using a modified "upwinding" treatment for the convection terms, corresponding to $\beta_{\alpha l} > 0$ in (5.141), Hughes et al. (1979) document application of the unsteady penalty algorithm solution to flow over a two-dimensional step, and flow in an axisymmetric step-wall diffuser. Figure 5.16 graphs the first problem specification, and Fig. 5.17*a* and *b* summarizes the computed temporal evaluation of u_i^h for Re = 200 and Re = 10^7, as obtained using the upwinding convection scheme. The velocity vector

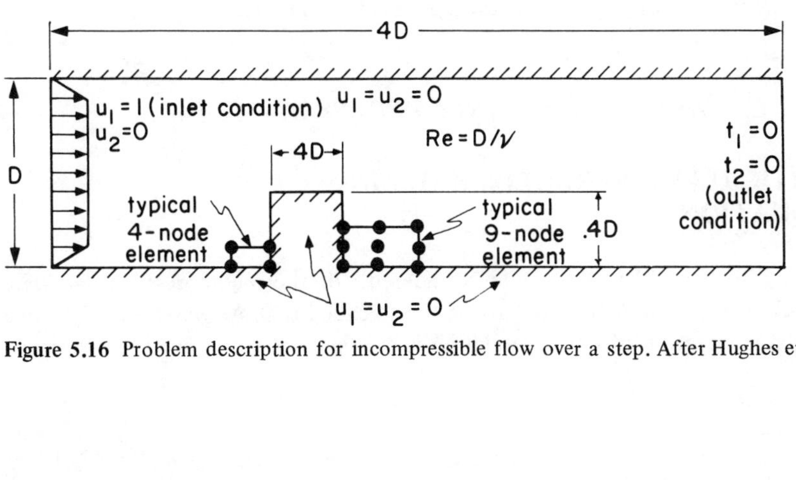

Figure 5.16 Problem description for incompressible flow over a step. After Hughes et al. (1979).

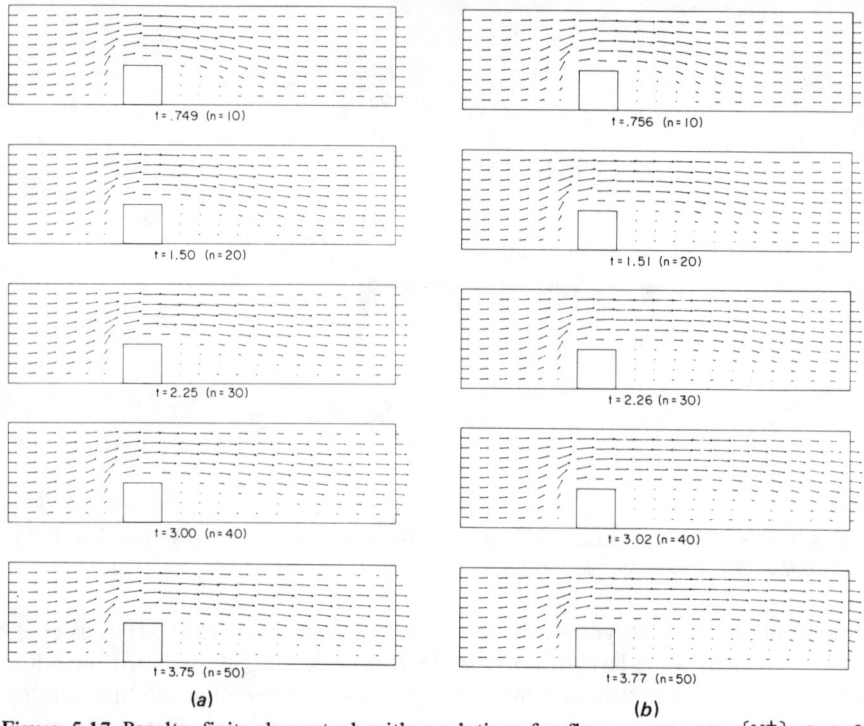

Figure 5.17 Penalty finite-element algorithm solutions for flow over a step, $\{N_1^+\}$, $\beta_\alpha > 0$. (*a*) Re = 200; (*b*) Re = 10^7. From Hughes et al. (1979), reprinted with permission.

distributions are free from spurious oscillations. Figure 5.18 graphs the step-wall diffuser problem specification and illustrates the corresponding discretization for $\{N_1^+\}$ and $\{N_0^+\}$. Figure 5.19 summarizes the computed distributions of p^h, ω, u_i^h, and ψ for Re = 200. Good qualitative agreement with the (ω^h, ψ^h) algorithm results (see Sec. 5.7, Fig. 5.7) is indicated, as well as with the experimental data of Macagno and Hung (1967).

The penalty finite-element numerical solution algorithm (5.141) has been and is being applied to a wide range of incompressible Navier-Stokes problem specifications. The current literature documents these applications at a regular pace.

C. FREE-SURFACE INCOMPRESSIBLE FLOW

5.15 VERTICALLY AVERAGED SHALLOW FLOW EQUATIONS

The third and final problem definition considered, for the incompressible, laminar flow Navier-Stokes equations (5.1)-(5.6), is the so-called shallow water (flow) form. The basic characterization of this formulation is existence of a free surface, whereby

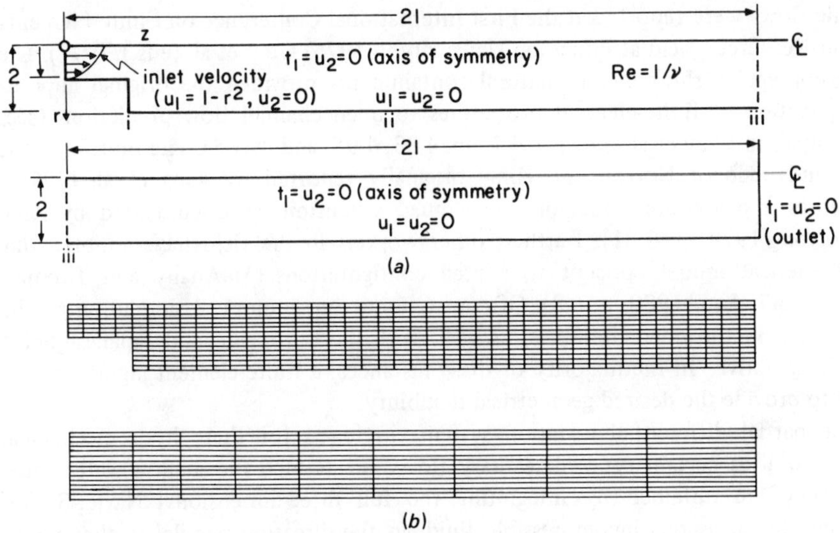

Figure 5.18 Problem description for incompressible flow in a step-wall diffuser. (*a*) Problem statement; (*b*) finite element mesh. After Hughes et al. (1979).

the local depth distribution of the flow adjusts to enforce the continuity equation (5.1). A great variety of naturally occurring hydromechanical flows belong to this categorization, e.g., river, channel, and estuarine flowfields, and flows in partially filled conduits.

Pioneering developments related to finite-element numerical modeling of hydro-

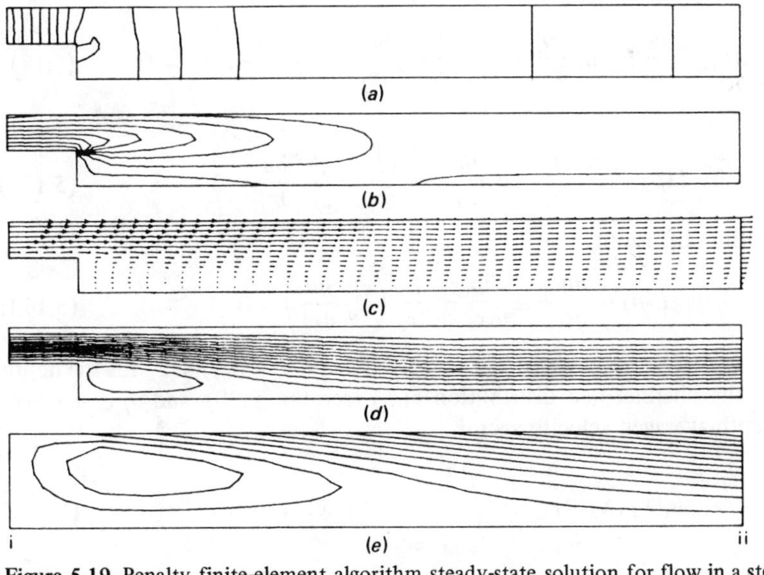

Figure 5.19 Penalty finite-element algorithm steady-state solution for flow in a step-wall diffuser, $\{N_1^+\}$, $\beta_\alpha > 0$, Re = 200. (*a*) Pressure p^h; (*b*) vorticity ω; (*c*) velocity $\mathbf{u}^h$; (*d*) streamlines ψ; (*e*) detailed ψ in recirculation zone. From Hughes et al. (1979), reprinted with permission.

dynamic flows were reported at the First International Conference on Finite Elements in Water Resources, held at Princeton University in 1976) Gray et al. (eds.), 1977). The highly nonregular shorelines of natural containments provided the original impetus for application of finite-element procedures to open channel flow predictions (see, for example, in Gray et al. (eds.), 1977, pp. 4.33, 4.95, and 4.165). The finite-element model and code of Norton and King, originally reported by King et al. (1975), exemplifies a procedure undergoing continued extension, as documented by King and Norton (1978, p. 2.81). Further, other workers in the field have adopted this type numerical model concept to related configurations (McAnally and Thomas, 1980, p. 6.47; Lee, 1980, p. 6.3). Of course, numerous numerical simulation results are reported in the open literature, as well, with the Europeans and Japanese being particularly active. In the majority of these instances, a finite-element algorithm was chosen to provide the desired geometrical flexibility.

The partial differential equation system employed for these hydromechanical flows, as well as certain types of estuary flows, are termed the shallow-water equations. They are obtained by integrating the full three-dimensional Navier-Stokes equations, for a viscous incompressible fluid, in the direction parallel to the gravity vector. Permitting density variations, as might occur in saline-stratified flows, for example, the governing equation system (Shames, 1982, Chap. 12; White, 1979, Chap. 10), is

Continuity:

$$L(h) = \frac{\partial h}{\partial t} + h\,\frac{\partial u_i}{\partial x_i} + u_i\,\frac{\partial h}{\partial x_i} = 0 \tag{5.170}$$

Momentum:

$$L(u_i) = \frac{\partial u_i}{\partial t} + u_j\,\frac{\partial u_i}{\partial x_j} + \frac{1}{\rho}\,\frac{\partial p}{\partial x_i} - \frac{\partial \sigma_{ij}}{\partial x_j} + \Omega_{ij}u_j - \tau_i \Big|_b^h = 0 \tag{5.171}$$

Pressure:

$$L(p) = \frac{1}{\rho}\,\frac{\partial p}{\partial x_i} - g\,\frac{\partial h}{\partial x_i} - g\,\frac{\partial b}{\partial x_i} - \frac{gh}{2\rho}\,\frac{\partial \rho}{\partial x_i} = 0 \tag{5.172}$$

Density convection-diffusion:

$$L(\rho) = \frac{\partial \rho}{\partial t} + u_i\,\frac{\partial \rho}{\partial x_i} - \frac{\partial}{\partial x_i}\left(k_{ij}\,\frac{\partial \rho}{\partial x_j}\right) = 0 \tag{5.173}$$

In (5.170)-(5.173), the range of the tensor indices is $1 \leqslant (i,j) \leqslant 2$, h is the depth of fluid above the channel bed distribution $b(x_i)$ (see Fig. 5.20), and u_i is the two-dimensional depth-averaged velocity vector.

$$u_i(x_1, x_2, t) \equiv \frac{1}{h}\int_b^h \bar{u}_i(x_1, x_2, x_3, t)\,dx_3 \tag{5.174}$$

In (5.171), σ_{ij} is the kinematic Stokes stress tensor (5.4) and $\Omega_{ij} = -2\omega e_{ij} \sin\phi$ is the Coriolis coefficient, where ω is angular velocity, ϕ is the latitude, and e_{ij} is the

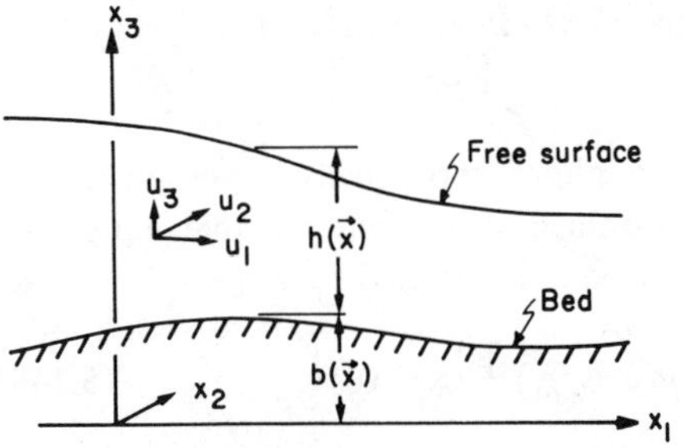

Figure 5.20 Geometry and coordinate system, shallow floe equation.

alternator. Further, $\tau_i \equiv \sigma_{ij}\hat{n}_3\delta_{j3}$ is the x_3 normal component of shear stress, evaluated for wind shear at the free surface h, and drag at the channel bed. Representative forms for these stresses (Brebbia and Partridge, 1976) are

$$\tau_i(h) = \frac{\gamma}{\rho}\frac{w_i}{h}(w_j w_j)^{1/2} \tag{5.175}$$

$$\tau_i(b) = -\frac{g u_i}{C^2 h}(u_j u_j)^{1/2} \tag{5.176}$$

where w_i is the wind velocity vector and C is the Chezy coefficient. Equation (5.173) is a species continuity equation for density, where k_{ij} is the diffusion tensor. The finite-element solution algorithm for (5.173) was examined in detail in Chap. 4, and will not be considered further in this section.

For the finite-element algorithm form to be derived, it is desirable to recast (5.170)–(5.171) into the conservative or divergence form. Multiplying (5.171) by h, and substituting (5.170), (5.172), (5.175)–(5.176), and defining the new dependent variable $m_i \equiv hu_i$, the conservative form for the shallow flow equation system is

$$L(h) = \frac{\partial h}{\partial t} + \frac{\partial}{\partial x_j}[m_j] = 0 \tag{5.177}$$

$$L(m_i) = \frac{\partial m_i}{\partial t} + \frac{\partial}{\partial x_j}\left[u_j m_i + \tfrac{1}{2}gh^2\delta_{ij} - h\sigma_{ij}\right] + hg\epsilon_i - \sigma_{ij}\frac{\partial h}{\partial x_j} + \Omega_{ij}m_j$$
$$- \frac{\gamma w_i}{\rho}(w_j w_j)^{1/2} + \frac{g u_i}{C^2}(u_j u_j)^{1/2} = 0 \tag{5.178}$$

In (5.178), $\epsilon_i(\mathbf{x}, t) \equiv \partial b/\partial x_i$ is the slope distribution of the channel bed. The density derivative term in (5.172) has been discarded, consistent with neglect of (5.173) in the current development.

Problems

1 Derive (5.170) using (5.174).

2 Derive (5.177)–(5.178) using (5.170)–(5.176).

5.16 GENERALIZED COORDINATES FINITE-ELEMENT SOLUTION ALGORITHM

Equations (5.177)-(5.178) are three coupled, nonlinear, principally hyperbolic partial differential equations written on the vector-valued dependent variable $q_\alpha(\mathbf{x}, t) \equiv \{h, m_i, \sigma_{ij}\} = \{h, hu_1, hu_2, \sigma_{11}, \sigma_{22}, \sigma_{12}\}$. Each equation is of the form

$$L(q_\alpha) = \frac{\partial q_\alpha}{\partial t} + \frac{\partial}{\partial x_j}(u_j q_\alpha + f_{j\alpha}) + s_\alpha = 0 \tag{5.179}$$

where $f_{j\alpha} = \frac{1}{2} qh\delta_{ij} - h\sigma_{ij}$, and s_α contains the remaining terms in (5.178). The domain of definition of (5.179) is $\Omega \equiv R^2 \times t = \{(\mathbf{x}, t)\colon \mathbf{x} \in R^2 \text{ and } t \in [t_0, t)\}$. On the boundary $\partial\Omega = \partial R \times t$, the boundary condition statement for (5.179) is

$$l(q_\alpha) = a_1^\alpha q_\alpha + a_2^\alpha \frac{\partial q_\alpha}{\partial x_j} \hat{\mathbf{n}}_j + a_3^\alpha = 0 \tag{5.180}$$

For example, on an inflow boundary, either h or m_i is specified by setting $a_2^\alpha = 0$ in (5.180). At a downstream outflow boundary, the typical boundary condition is vanishing derivative, which is generated by setting $a_1^\alpha \equiv 0 \equiv a_3^\alpha$. The differential equation statement is completed by an initial condition specification

$$q_\alpha(\mathbf{x}, 0) = q_\alpha^0(\mathbf{x}) \tag{5.181}$$

For the finite-element solution algorithm for (5.179)-(5.181), the semidiscrete approximation $q_\alpha^h(\mathbf{x}, t)$ to the dependent variable set q_α is constructed in the usual manner:

$$q_\alpha(\mathbf{x}, t) \approx q_\alpha^h(\mathbf{x}, t) \equiv \sum_{e=1}^{M} q_\alpha^e(\mathbf{x}, t) \tag{5.182}$$

The semidiscrete finite-element approximation, expressed in the cardinal basis form, is

$$q_\alpha^e(\mathbf{x}, t) \equiv \{N_k(\eta)\}^T \{QI(t)\}_e \tag{5.183}$$

In (5.183), the semidiscrete free index "I" denotes q_α^h evaluated at the nodal coordinates $\bar{\mathbf{x}}_i$ of the discretization $\cup R_e^2 = R^2$ at anytime t. The sub- and superscript e denotes that it pertains to the finite-element domain $\Omega_e \equiv R_e^2 \times t$.

To render the error in q_α^h extremum, the finite-element algorithm again requires the semidiscrete approximation error, $L(q_\alpha^h)$ and $l(q_\alpha^h)$, to be orthogonal to the cardinal basis employed to construct q_α^h. Further, the developed multi-term expansion is invoked to constrain the derivative of the error, i.e., $\nabla L(q_\alpha^h)$, since high frequency dispersion is a dominant error mechanism and $L(q_\alpha^h)$ is therefore locally nonsmooth. These constraints are combined, on the assembly (S_e) of the finite-element algorithm statement over $\cup R_e^2 = R^2$, by identification of multiplier set β_α, yielding

$$S_e \left[\int_{R_e^2} \{N_k\} L(q_\alpha^h)\, d\mathbf{x} + \beta_\alpha \cdot \int_{R_e^2} \{N_k\} \nabla L(q_\alpha^h)\, d\mathbf{x} + \beta_1 \int_{\partial R_e \cap \partial R} \{N_k\} l(q_\alpha^h)\, d\mathbf{x} \right] \equiv \{0\} \tag{5.184}$$

Upon definition of k in (5.183), (5.184) is a coupled nonlinear system of ordinary differential equations of the form

$$[C]\{QI\}' + [U]\{QI\} + [FIJ]\{QJ\} + \{SI\} = \{0\} \tag{5.185}$$

The θ-implicit finite-difference algorithm for (5.185), where $\theta = \frac{1}{2}$ yields the trapezoidal rule, is

$$\{FI\} = \{QI\}_{j+1} - \{QI\}_j - \Delta t[\theta\{QI\}'_{j+1} + (1-\theta)\{QI\}'_j] = 0 \tag{5.186}$$

Upon substitution of (5.185), (5.186) becomes a nonlinear algebraic equation system written on $\{QI\}_{j+1}$. The Newton matrix iteration algorithm is

$$[J(FI)]^p_{j+1}\{\delta QI\}^{p+1}_{j+1} = -\{FI\}^p_{j+1} \tag{5.187}$$

The dependent variable $\{\delta QI\}^{p+1}_{j+1}$ yields the solution

$$\{QI\}^{p+1}_{j+1} = \{QI\}^p_{j+1} + \{\delta QI\}^{p+1}_{j+1} \tag{5.188}$$

and the jacobian for (5.188) is defined as

$$[J(FI)] \equiv \frac{\partial\{FI\}}{\partial\{QJ\}} \tag{5.189}$$

A principal requirement for free surface flow prediction is to accurately interpolate global domain boundaries $\partial\Omega$ that are nonregular. The versatility of the triangular finite-element for forming such discretizations on R^2 was an early impetus to generation of finite-element algorithms. A principal departure from the previous developments, that yields significant solution economies when employing an implicit solution algorithm, is definition and use of "boundary fitted" coordinate transformations in a "generalized coordinates" framework. The use of such procedures is commonplace in computational aerodynamics (cf. NASA, 1981 and Chap. 8).

The basic concept is to generate a coordinate transformation

$$x_i = x_i(\eta_j) \tag{5.190}$$

wherein coordinate surfaces of η_j are defined coincident with appropriate segments of ∂R. For example, Fig. 5.21, from Johnson and Thompson (1978) is a graph in physical space of the coordinate system η_j that interpolates the boundary ∂R of a waterway. If this discretization were plotted in the transform space spanned by η_j, it would appear as the assembly of regular rectangular domains illustrated in Fig. 5.22. In this domain, the η_i coordinate system is (ideally) rectangular cartesian, and the discretization uniform. In comparison, the η_1 coordinate runs nominally parallel to the river flow direction, η_2 spans across the channels and the river mouth, and the island is a "hole" in the mesh, in physical space.

The concept of the body-fitted coordinate system fits in a natural way into the finite-element algorithm statement. Each quadrilateral domain R^2_e and R^2 (Fig. 5.21) can be mapped to the unit square using the isoparametric interpolation (see Sec. 3.6). Specifically, the local form of (5.190) on R^2_e is

$$x_i = \{N_k(\eta)\}^T\{XI\}_e \qquad x_i \in R^2_e \tag{5.191}$$

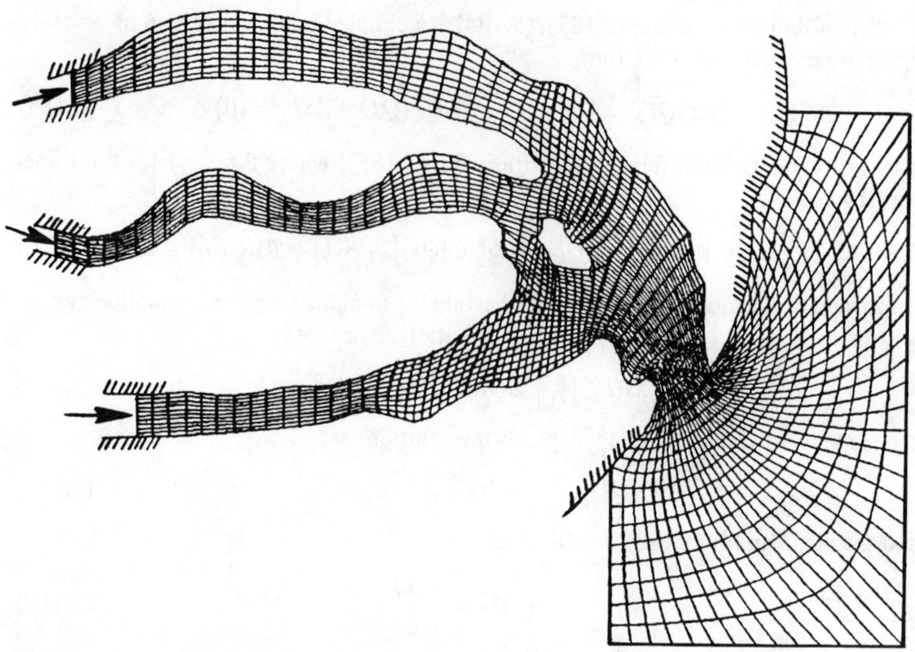

Figure 5.21 Boundary-fitted coordinate system for Charleston Harbor. From Johnson et al. (1978).

The elements of the column matrix $\{XI\}_e$ are the coordinates $\bar{x}_i$ of the nodes of R_e^2. For example, recall the bilinear cardinal basis (3.72),

$$\{N_1^+(\eta)\} = \frac{1}{4}\begin{Bmatrix}(1-\eta_1)(1-\eta_2)\\(1+\eta_1)(1-\eta_2)\\(1+\eta_1)(1+\eta_2)\\(1-\eta_1)(1+\eta_2)\end{Bmatrix} \tag{5.192}$$

The finite-element algorithm statement (5.184) is the assembly of integrals over R_e^2, each of which requires formation of the divergence of a vector field; see (5.177)-(5.178). The computational requirement therefore is to transform the local divergence operator as

$$\frac{\partial(\cdot)}{\partial x_j} = \frac{\partial(\cdot)}{\partial \eta_k}\left[\frac{\partial \eta_k}{\partial x_j}\right]_e \tag{5.193}$$

The transformation matrix $[\cdot]_e$ is explicitly determined, (3.85)-(3.89), as

$$\left[\frac{\partial \eta_k}{\partial x_j}\right]_e = \frac{1}{\det J_e}\,[\text{cofactor } J]_e^T \tag{5.194}$$

where

$$[J]_e = \left[\frac{\partial x_i}{\partial \eta_j}\right]_e \tag{5.195}$$

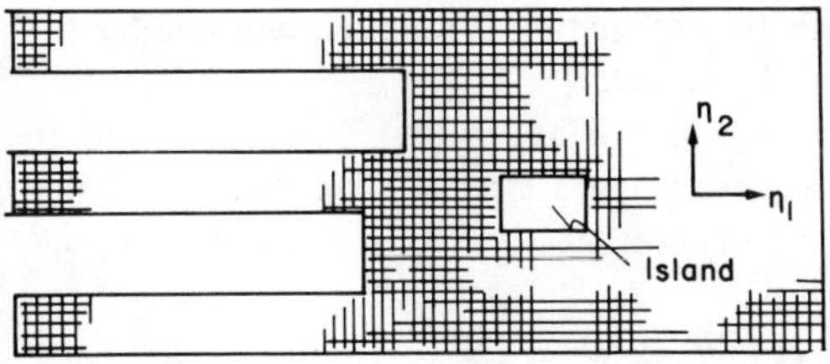

Figure 5.22 Sketch of discretization of Charleston Harbor in transform space.

Recall, (3.91), that the differential element for (5.184) is

$$d\mathbf{x} = \det\,[J]_e\, d\eta \tag{5.196}$$

For the bilinear cardinal basis, for example, assuming the elements of $[\partial\eta_k/\partial x_j]_e$ are interpolated on R_e^2 using (5.183), yields

$$\left[\frac{\partial\eta_k}{\partial x_j}\right]_e \equiv \frac{1}{\det\,[J]_e}\{N_1^+(\eta)\}^T\{ETAKJ\}_e \tag{5.197}$$

It is easy to show, using (5.192)-(5.195), and (5.197), that

$$\{ETAKJ\}_e = \frac{1}{2}\left\{\begin{matrix} \{Y4-Y1, Y3-Y2, Y3-Y2, Y4-Y1\}_e^T, (1,1) \\ \{X1-X4, X2-X3, X2-X3, X1-X4\}_e^T, (1,2) \\ \{Y1-Y2, Y1-Y2, Y4-Y3, Y4-Y3\}_e^T, (2,1) \\ \{X2-X1, X2-X1, X3-X4, X3-X4\}_e^T, (2,2) \end{matrix}\right\} \tag{5.198}$$

In (5.198), the indices in parentheses indicate (K, J), and the entries XI, YI are the nodal coordinates $\bar{x}_i$ of R_e^2 for the conventional numbering sequence (Fig. 5.23). By the same token, for the definition

$$\det\,[J]_e \equiv \{N_1^+(\eta)\}^T\{DET\}_e \tag{5.199}$$

the elements of $\{DET\}_e$ are

$$\{DET\}_e = \frac{1}{4}\left\{\begin{matrix} (X2-X1)(Y4-Y1)-(X4-X1)(Y2-Y1) \\ (X2-X1)(Y3-Y2)-(X3-X2)(Y2-Y1) \\ (X3-X4)(Y3-Y2)-(X3-X2)(Y3-Y4) \\ (X3-X4)(Y4-Y1)-(X4-X1)(Y3-Y4) \end{matrix}\right\}_e \tag{5.200}$$

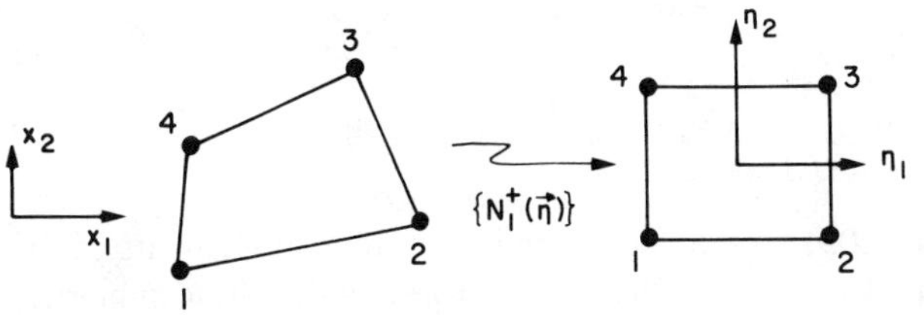

Figure 5.23 Illustration of bilinear isoparametric coordinate transformation.

Therefore, the local elemental coordinate transformation is uniquely defined by the node coordinate pairs of the finite-element domains R_e^2.

The next step is to transform the derivative $\partial/\partial x_j$ in (5.177)-(5.179) and to perform the integrals defined in (5.184) after using a Green-Gauss theorem. Using (5.177) as the example, the first term in (5.184) becomes

$$\int_{R_e^2} \{N_k^+\} L(q_1^h)\, d\mathbf{x} = \int_{R_e^2} \{N_k^+\} \left(\frac{\partial h^h}{\partial t} + \frac{\partial}{\partial x_j} m_j^h \right) d\mathbf{x}$$

$$= \int_{R_e^2} \{N_k^+\} \frac{\partial h^h}{\partial t}\, dx - \int_{R_e^2} \frac{\partial \{N_k^+\}}{\partial x_j} m_j^h\, d\mathbf{x}$$

$$+ \oint_{\partial R_e} \{N_k^+\} m_j^h \hat{\mathbf{n}}_j\, d\sigma \tag{5.201}$$

The last term vanishes identically, upon assembly over all interior boundaries ∂R_e of the discretization. Hence,

$$\int_{R_e^2} \{N_k^+\} L(q_1^h)\, d\mathbf{x} = \int_{R_e^2} \{N_k^+\}\{N_k^+\}^T \{H\}_e' \{DET\}_e^T \{N_k^+\}\, d\eta$$

$$- \int_{R_e^2} \frac{\partial}{\partial \eta_k} \{N_k^+\}\{MJ\}_e^T \{N_k^+\}\{N_k^+\}^T \{ETAKJ\}_e\, d\eta$$

$$+ \int_{\partial R_e \cap \partial R} \{N_k^+\}\{N_k^+\}^T \{MJ\}_e \hat{\mathbf{n}}_j\, d\sigma \tag{5.202}$$

Rearranging the order of scalar terms, and extracting the element dependent matrices $\{\cdot\}_e$ from the integrals, since they possess no η dependence, yields

$$\int_{R_e^2} \{N_k^+\} L(q_1^h)\, d\mathbf{x} = \{DET\}_e^T \int_{R_e^2} \{N_k^+\}\{N_k^+\}\{N_k^+\}^T\, d\eta \{H\}_e'$$

$$- \{ETAKJ\}_e^T \int_{R_e^2} \{N_k^+\} \frac{\partial}{\partial \eta_k} \{N_k^+\}\{N_k^+\}^T\, d\eta \{MJ\}_e$$

$$+ \int_{\partial R_e \cap \partial R} \{N_k^+\}\{N_k^+\}^T\, d\sigma \{MJ\}_e \cdot \hat{\mathbf{n}}_j \tag{5.203}$$

Each of the integrals in (5.203) now involves products (only) of elements of the cardinal basis $\{N_k^+\}$ and the first derivative. These are easily evaluated using numerical quadrature, and are universally valid for each element R_e^2 of the discretization. Noting that $d\sigma = \Delta_e\, d\eta$ on the boundary intersection $\partial R_e \cap \partial R$, and using the developed hypermatrix notation, the final form for (5.203) is

$$\int_{R_e^2} \{N_k^+\} L(q_1^h)\, d\mathbf{x} = \{DET\}_e^T [B3000] \{H\}_e' - \{ETAKJ\}_e^T [B30K0] \{MJ\}_e$$

$$+ \hat{\mathbf{n}}_J \Delta_e [A200] \{MJ\}_e \tag{5.204}$$

In (5.204), $[B3000]$ is the two-dimensional matrix equivalent of interpolation of two variables on R_e^2, $[B30K0]$ is the equivalent of the directional derivative (gradient) parallel to η_k, and $[A200]$ is a one-dimensional interpolation on the boundary ∂R with unit normal vector $\hat{\mathbf{n}}_J$. The range of the embedded tensor indices in (5.204) is $1 \leqslant (K, J) \leqslant 2$.

Inserting (5.193) into the momentum flux term in (5.178) leads to the definition of the contravariant velocity components $\bar{u}_K$, parallel to the η_k coordinate system, of the convection velocity field u_j, as

$$\bar{u}_K \equiv \det\, [J]_e \left[\frac{\partial \eta_k}{\partial x_j}\right]_e u_j \tag{5.205}$$

Using (5.194)–(5.197), the finite-element nodal approximation for (5.205) on R_e^2 becomes

$$\{UBARK\}_e = u_j \{ETAKJ\}_e \tag{5.206}$$

Here, $u_j = m_j/h$ is the convection velocity, in components parallel to the principal coordinates x_j, at the nodes of R_e^2.

With (5.206) and using an integration by parts, the first term of the finite-element algorithm statement for (5.178) becomes

$$\int_{R_e^2} \{N_1\} L(m_i^h)\, d\mathbf{x} = \int_{R_e^2} \{N_1\} \left(\frac{\partial m_i^h}{\partial t} + \frac{\partial}{\partial x_j} (u_j^h m_j^h + \tfrac{1}{2} g h^2 \delta_{ij} - h\sigma_{ij}^h) + s_i^h \right) d\mathbf{x}$$

$$= \{DET\}_e^T [B3000] \{MI\}_e' - \{UBARK\}_e^T [B30K0] \{MI\}_e$$

$$- \frac{g}{2} \{ETAKI\}_e^T ([B40K00] \{H\}_e) \{H\}_e$$

$$+ \{ETAKJ\}_e^T ([B40K00] \{H\}_e) \{SIGIJ\}_e$$

$$+ \{DET\}_e^T [B3000] \{SI\}_e$$

$$+ \int_{\partial R_e \cap \partial R} \{N_1^+\} (u_j^h m_i + \tfrac{1}{2} g h^2 \delta_{ij} - h\sigma_{ij}^h) \hat{\mathbf{n}}_j\, d\sigma \tag{5.207}$$

In (5.207), $[B40K00]$ is a hypermatrix of degree two, which accounts for the added interpolation of $\{H\}_e$ within the directional derivative equivalent $\partial/\partial\eta_k$. As occurred in (5.204), the closed surface integral on ∂R_e vanishes identically upon assembly over $\cup R_e^2$, except for the occurrence $\partial R_e \cap \partial R \neq 0$, whereupon the last term in (5.207) may contain nonzero entries dependent upon the boundary conditions.

As a consequence of the generalized coordinates framework, the form of the dissipation parameter set β_α in (5.184) is modestly altered. Recall that in Sec. 4.11, for the scalar one-dimensional analysis problem, the form for β was

$$\beta = \Delta_e \nu \tag{5.208}$$

and the optimized order-of-magnitude analysis yielded $\nu = (15)^{-1/2}$. Further, for the nonlinear problem (Sec. 4.14), the form of (5.208) was generalized to

$$\beta = \Delta_e(\nu^1 \delta_t + \nu^2 \delta_x) \tag{5.209}$$

In (5.209), δ_t and δ_x are Kronecker delta-type switches that restrict ν^1 to the time-derivative, and ν^2 to the spatial derivative terms, respectively, in the algorithm statement. In the present formulation, $\det J_e$ is now the mesh measure, analogous to Δ_e. Generalizing to multiple dimensions and dependent variables, (5.209) takes the form

$$\beta_{\alpha e} = \det J_e(\nu_\alpha^1 \delta_t + \nu_\alpha^2 \delta_x) \tag{5.210}$$

where subscript α denotes the pertinent dependent variable in q_α^h, (5.182). The parameter vectors ν_α^1, of magnitude order $(15)^{-1/2}$, are expressed in scalar components $\nu_{\alpha J}^\kappa$ in the principal (x_j) coordinate system.

Problems

1 For the definition (5.197), derive (5.198).

2 Verify (5.200).

3 Verify (5.203), starting with (5.201).

4 Derive (5.206) for (5.205) using (5.183).

5 Derive (5.207).

5.17 ALGORITHM CONSTRUCTION FOR ONE-DIMENSIONAL FLOW

The majority of the formulational aspects of the generalized coordinates, free surface flow finite-element algorithm (5.184)-(5.189), can be exposed by examination of the one-dimensional form of (5.177)-(5.178). For simplicity, assume σ_{ij} is negligibly small, which is usual for reasonable Reynolds number, and neglect the Coriolis and wind shear terms in (5.178). By defining the convection velocity $u = m/h$, the governing differential equation system (5.177)-(5.178) simplifies to

$$L(h) = \frac{\partial h}{\partial t} + \frac{\partial}{\partial x}[\mathrm{m}] = 0 \tag{5.211}$$

$$L(m) = \frac{\partial m}{\partial t} + \frac{\partial}{\partial x}[um + \tfrac{1}{2}gh^2] + hg\frac{\partial b}{\partial x} + \frac{gu^2}{C^2} = 0 \tag{5.212}$$

The algorithm statement requires the metric data $\{DET\}_e$ and $\{ETAKJ\}_e$. The one-dimensional, linear tensor product cardinal basis $\{N_1^+(\eta)\}$, with origin at the centroid of Δ_e, is

$$\{N_1^+(\eta)\} = \frac{1}{2}\begin{Bmatrix} 1-\eta \\ 1+\eta \end{Bmatrix} \tag{5.213}$$

Hence, (5.191) becomes

$$x = \{N_1^+(\eta)\}^T\{XI\}_e \tag{5.214}$$

and

$$[J]_e = \left(\frac{\partial x}{\partial \eta}\right) = \tfrac{1}{2}(-XL + XR) = \tfrac{1}{2}\,\Delta_e = \det J_e \tag{5.215}$$

where XL and XR denote the left and right node coordinates of R_e^1. Furthermore, from (5.197) and using (5.215),

$$\left(\frac{\partial \eta}{\partial x}\right) \equiv \frac{1}{\det J_e}\left(\frac{\partial x}{\partial \eta}\right) = 1 \tag{5.216}$$

Therefore, for this simple example,

$$\{DET\}_e = \tfrac{1}{2}\,\Delta_e \begin{Bmatrix} 1 \\ 1 \end{Bmatrix}$$

$$\{ETAKJ\}_e = \delta_{KJ}\begin{Bmatrix} 1 \\ 1 \end{Bmatrix} \tag{5.217}$$

where δ_{KJ} is the Kronecker delta (which is superfluous except to keep the tensor index structure consistent).

With the identifications (5.217) and (5.210), the finite-element algorithm statement (5.184) is readily expressed for (5.211)–(5.212). Recalling that

$$\{FI\} \equiv S_e[\{FI\}_e] \tag{5.218}$$

and suppressing subscript e for clarity, verify as an exercise that (5.186), with $\theta = \frac{1}{2}$, takes the form

$$\begin{aligned}\{FH\}_e &= [\Delta_e[A200] + \nu_H^1[A210]]\,\{H\}'_{j+1} \\ &\quad + \frac{\Delta t}{2}\,[[A210]\,\{M\} + \nu_H^2\{U\}^T[A3011]\,\{H\}]_{j+1,j}\end{aligned} \tag{5.219}$$

$$\begin{aligned}\{FM\}_e &= [\Delta_e[A200] + \nu_M^1[A210]]\,\{M\}'_{j+1} \\ &\quad + \frac{\Delta t}{2}\,[\{U\}^T[A3010]\,\{M\} + \tfrac{1}{2}g\{H\}^T[A3010]\,\{H\} + g\{H\}^T[A3001]\,\{B\} \\ &\quad + \nu_M^2\{U\}^T[A3011]\,\{M\} + g\,\Delta_e C^{-2}\{U\}^T[A3000]\,\{U\}]_{j+1,j}\end{aligned} \tag{5.220}$$

The defined element hypermatrices $[A\cdots]$ in (5.219)–(5.220) are the standard familiar arrays of integers. As in the previous sections, $\{\cdot\}'_{j+1}$ denotes $\{\cdot\}^p_{j+1} - \{\cdot\}_j$, where $\Delta t \equiv t_{j+1} - t_j$, and $[\cdot]_{j+1,j}$ denotes evaluation of the argument at t_{j+1} and t_j and summing.

The second step of algorithm construction is formation of the Newton algorithm jacobian (5.189). Recalling $[J] \equiv S_e[J]_e$, and using the chain rule as required, since $u = m/h$, (5.219) and (5.220) are directly differentiated to yield

$$\frac{\partial\{FH\}_e}{\partial\{H\}_e} \equiv [JHH]_e = \Delta_e[A200] + \nu_H^1[A210] + \frac{\Delta t \nu_H^2}{2}\left[\{U\}^T[A3011] - \left(\frac{m}{h^2}\right)\{H\}^T[A3110]\right]_{j+1} \tag{5.221}$$

$$\frac{\partial\{FH\}_e}{\partial\{M\}_e} \equiv [JHM]_e = \frac{\Delta t}{2}\left[[A210] + \left(\frac{1}{h}\right)\nu_H^2\{H\}^T[A3110]\right]_{j+1} \tag{5.222}$$

$$\frac{\partial\{FM\}_e}{\partial\{H\}_e} \equiv [JMH]_e = \frac{\Delta t}{2}\left[-\left(\frac{m}{h^2}\right)\{M\}^T[A3010] + g\{H\}^T[A3010] + g\{B\}^T[A3100] - \left(\frac{m}{h^2}\right)\{M\}^T[A3110] - \left(\frac{m}{h^2}\right)2g\,\Delta_e C^{-2}\{U\}^T[A3000]\right]_{j+1} \tag{5.223}$$

$$\frac{\partial\{FM\}_e}{\partial\{M\}_e} \equiv [JMM]_e = \Delta_e[A200] + \nu_m^1[A210] + \frac{\Delta t}{2}\left[\{U\}^T[A3101] + \left(\frac{1}{h}\right)\{M\}^T[A3010] + \nu_M^2\{U\}^T[A3011] + \left(\frac{1}{h}\right)\nu_M^2\{M\}^T[A3110] + \left(\frac{1}{h}\right)2g\,\Delta_e C^{-2}\{U\}^T[A3000]\right]_{j+1} \tag{5.224}$$

In (5.221)–(5.224), the boolean indices in various hypermatrices have been permuted to permit differentiation by the right contraction matrix. Furthermore, (m/h^2) and $(1/h)$ denote the average value of $(\cdot)$ on the element domain R_e, and $[\cdot]_{j+1}$ denotes evaluation using $\{QJ\}_{j+1}^p$.

Identification of (5.221)–(5.224) completes the finite-element formulation. Hence, the form of the Newton algorithm (5.187) is

$$S_e\begin{bmatrix}[JHH]_e & [JHM]_e \\ [JMH]_e & [JMM]_e\end{bmatrix}_{j+1}^p \begin{Bmatrix}\delta H \\ \delta M\end{Bmatrix}_{j+1}^{p+1} = -\begin{Bmatrix}FH \\ FM\end{Bmatrix}_{j+1}^p \tag{5.225}$$

Problems

1 Verify (5.217).
2 Derive (5.219)–(5.220) from (5.184)–(5.186).
3 Derive (5.221)–(5.222).
4 Derive (5.223)–(5.224).

5.18 THEORETICAL ANALYSIS, ACCURACY DOCUMENTATION

The partial differential equation system governing the depth-averaged shallow flow problem description, is constituted of a linear hyperbolic equation (5.177), and an explicitly nonlinear elliptic partial differential equation (5.178) for finite Reynolds number. The essential theoretical aspects regarding accuracy and convergence have already been developed in completeness (Secs. 4.8 and 5.5). Decomposing the solution error, the semidiscrete (finite-element) error is bounded by a constant that multiplies the mesh measure to the power of unity and k, respectively [see (4.136) and (5.53)]. Furthermore, the optimized order of accuracy analysis presented in Sec. 4.11 determined the form and order of the dissipation parameter β_α for (5.184).

No detailed numerical results documenting accuracy and convergence of the developed free surface flow finite-element algorithm are published. Such data have been reported for the mathematically similar compressible flow Navier-Stokes algorithm (see Sec. 8.7). However, Baker and Soliman (1982) do document accuracy and stability for the one-dimensional, inviscid flow algorithm applied to a range of appropriate channel bed geometries. A basic test is steady-state flow in a uniform cross-sectional channel with an abrupt change in bed slope. For a step of positive slope, and dependent on whether the upstream velocity is super- or subcritical, where $h_{cr} = \sqrt[3]{m^2/g}$, the velocity and free surface height will accordingly change abruptly. Figure 5.24 summarizes the $\{N_1\}$ algorithm steady-state prediction for h and $u = m/h$, for both the subcritical and supercritical upstream flow specification. The bed profile is

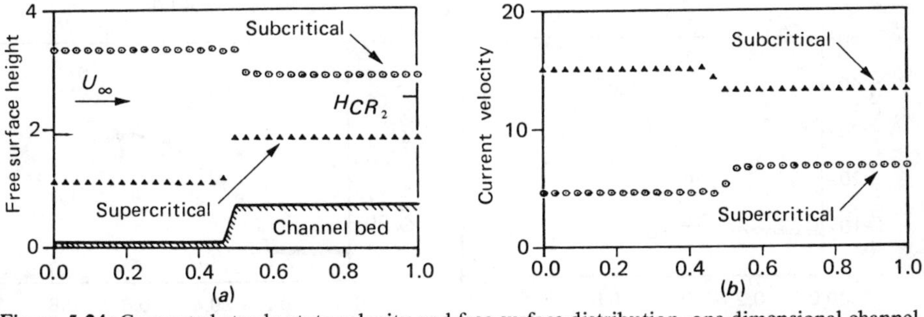

Figure 5.24 Computed steady-state velocity and free surface distribution, one-dimensional channel flow with step. (*a*) Free surface height h^h; (*b*) current velocity u^h. From Baker and Soliman (1982).

also graphed for comparison. Both solution sets are crisp and devoid of excess artificial diffusion using the specification $\nu_\alpha^1 = 0, \nu_\alpha^2 = (15)^{-1/2}$. A very modest $2\,\Delta x$ wave is evidenced in the upstream free surface height for the subcritical specification. Both solutions specified m at inlet, and employed vanishing normal derivatives for h at inlet and both h and m at the outlet.

The second test is subcritical flow from a reservoir onto a broad-crested weir and down a spillway of sufficient slope to induce supercritical flow. The foot of the spillway is given a smooth transition to horizontal, whereupon a geometry change is imposed to induce a hydraulic jump return to subcritical flow. The flow from the reservoir is assumed to occur through a given height opening; therefore, h is specified and m is unknown, hence given a vanishing derivative boundary condition. The downstream boundary condition is vanishing normal derivative for both h and m. Figure 5.25*a* graphs the computed steady-state free surface height distribution without hydraulic jump. Figure 5.25*b* shows the companion case with hydraulic jump, which is computed to occur over about 3-4 mesh intervals. A modest $2\,\Delta x$ wave occurs on the downstream side of the jump, as obtained using the theoretical value for ν_α^2. Figure 5.25*c*-*d* shows the corresponding computed velocity distributions, which clearly illustrate the sharp decrease in speed occurring over about 3-4 mesh intervals for the supercritical case. A rather pronounced velocity overshoot is predicted on the upstream side, but overall the solution appears crisp and of acceptable accuracy. The various occurrences of h_{cr} and u_{cr} are also denoted on the graphs.

The hydraulic jump is the incompressible flow counterpart of a compressible

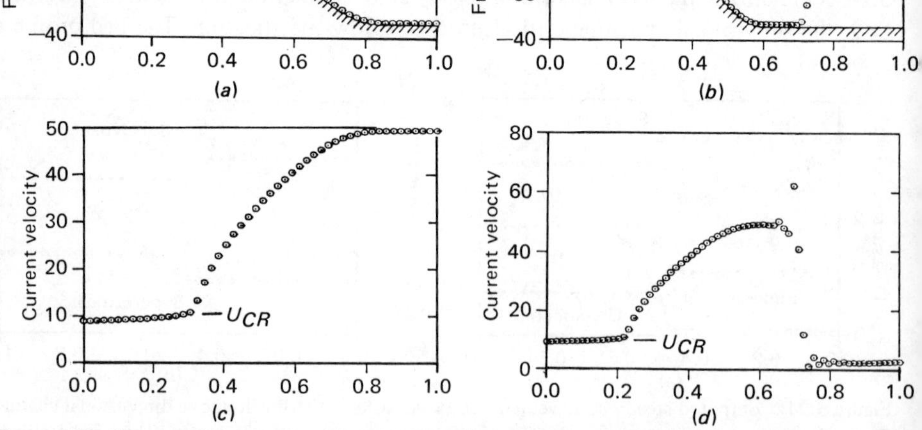

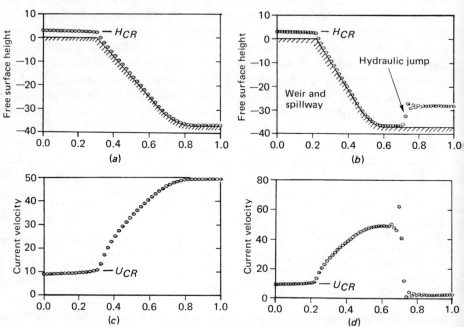

Figure 5.25 Computed steady-state free surface and velocity distribution, broad crested weir with spillway. (*a*) Free surface, without hydraulic jump. (*b*) Free surface with hydraulic jump. (*c*) Velocity distribution, no hydraulic jump. (*d*) Velocity distribution with hydraulic jump.

supersonic flow shocked to subsonic Mach number. The derived dissipative finite-element algorithm, applied to solution of the compressible flow Navier-Stokes equations, is documented in Chap. 8.

5.19 TENSOR PRODUCT ALGORITHM FOR TWO-DIMENSIONAL FLOW

Section 5.17 documents the construction of the shallow flow finite-element numerical solution algorithm for simple one-dimensional flow. This section develops the complete inviscid flow algorithm statement as well as its embodiment using the bilinear tensor product basis $\{N_1^+\}$. The dependent variable set is $q_\alpha^h(\mathbf{x}, t) \equiv \{\overline{QI}\} \equiv \{H, M1, M2\}$, with $\{FI\} \equiv S_e[\{FI\}_e]$ correspondingly denoted, $1 \leqslant I \leqslant 3$. It is a suggested exercise to verify that, for $\theta \equiv \frac{1}{2}$ in (5.186), the generalized coordinates finite-element algorithm statement (5.184) takes the form:

$$\begin{aligned}\{FH\}_e = (\{DET\}_e^T[B3000] + \nu_{HJ}^1\{ETAKJ\}_e^T[B40K00]\{DET\}_e)\{H\}_{j+1}' \\ + \frac{\Delta t}{2}[-\{ETAKJ\}_e^T[B30K0]\{MI\}_e \\ + \nu_{HJ}^2\{ETAKJ\}_e^T[B40KL0]\{UBARL\}_e\{H\}_e]_{j+1,j}\end{aligned} \tag{5.226}$$

$$\begin{aligned}\{FMI\}_e = (\{DET\}_e^T[B3000] + \nu_{IJ}^1\{ETAKJ\}_e^T[B40K00]\{DET\}_e)\{MI\}_{j+1}' \\ + \frac{\Delta t}{2}[-\{UBARK\}_e^T[B30K0]\{MI\}_e - \tfrac{1}{2}g\{ETAKI\}_e^T([B40K00]\{H\}_e)\{H\}_e \\ + g\{ETAKI\}_e^T[B400K0]\{H\}_e)\{B\}_e + \{DET\}_e^T[B3000]\{SI\}_e \\ + \nu_{IJ}^2\{ETAKJ\}_e^T([B30KL0]\{UBARL\}_e)\{MI\}_e]_{j+1,j}\end{aligned} \tag{5.227}$$

The second and last terms in (5.226)-(5.227) are the dissipation terms and the tensor indices J and (I, J) appearing throughout range $1 \leqslant (I, J) \leqslant 2$. In (5.227), the fifth term is explicitly the channel bed gradient $\epsilon_i = \partial b/\partial x_i$, and the sixth contains the remainder of the source terms in (5.178). As before, the notation $\{\cdot\}_{j+1}'$ denotes $\{QI\}_{j+1}^p - \{QI\}_j$, and $[\cdot]_{j+1,j}$ again defines the evaluation $[\cdot]_{j+1}^p + [\cdot]_j$.

As usual, the second algorithm construction step is for the jacobian (5.189) of the Newton iteration algorithm (5.187). Equations (5.226)-(5.227) can easily be analytically differentiated with respect to $\{QI\}$, since all functional dependence is explicit. As a departure, we now construct the tensor (outer) matrix product approximation to $[J]$. The formulational procedures build directly upon those developed in Chap. 4 and Sec. 5.17. Quite simply, the jacobian (5.189) is approximated as

$$[J(FI)] \Rightarrow [J_1] \otimes [J_2] \tag{5.228}$$

where $\otimes$ denotes the tensor matrix product (Halmos, 1958). As will be developed, each component $[J_\eta]$ in (5.228) is constructed from its definition, assuming interpolation and differentiation are basically one-dimensional. With (5.228), the matrix solution statement (5.187) becomes

$$[J_1] \otimes [J_2]\{\delta QI\}_{j+1}^{p+1} = -\{FI\}_{j+1}^p \tag{5.229}$$

Defining, $$[J_2]\{\delta QI\}_{j+1}^{p+1} \equiv \{P1\}_{j+1}^{p+1} \tag{5.230}$$

the matrix operation defined by (5.187) becomes the two-step sequence

$$\begin{aligned}
[J_1]\{P1\}_{j+1}^{p+1} &= -\{FI\}_{j+1}^{p} \\
[J_2]\{\delta QI\}_{j+1}^{p+1} &= \{P1\}_{j+1}^{p+1}
\end{aligned} \tag{5.231}$$

Obviously, other permutations of the index structure for $[J_\eta]$ could be utilized. The key aspect is replacement of the very large (albeit sparse) jacobian matrix $[J]$, with α block-structured matrices $[J_\eta]$. The principal attributes are several orders of magnitude reduction in central memory requirements for the jacobian, and significantly reduced CPU for the LU decomposition and back substitution solution steps. The principal detraction is potential degradation of the quadratic convergence rate for the Newton iteration. In distinction to the time-splitting methods developed in Chaps. 4 and 5, this procedure in no way affects the formation and evaluation of $\{FI\}$, wherein lies the accuracy features intrinsic to the finite-element algorithm statement. Compromises in the evaluation of $\{FI\}$ will invariable produce inferior results for Navier-Stokes equation sets.

The construction of the $[J_\eta] \equiv S_e[[J_\eta]_e]$ is straightforward. For example, for the first initial-value term in (5.226)-(5.227), the resulting expression of self-coupling in the jacobian is

$$\frac{\partial\{FI\}}{\partial\{QJ\}}\delta_{IJ} \equiv [JQQ] = S_e[\{DET\}_e^T[B3000]] \tag{5.232}$$

where δ_{IJ} is the discrete index Kronecker delta. According to definition, the standard elemental operation for forming (5.232) is

$$[JQQ]_e \equiv \{DET\}_e^T[B3000] \equiv \int_{R_e^2} \{DET\}_e^T\{N_k(\eta)\}\{N_k(\eta)\}\{N_k(\eta)\}^T\,d\eta \tag{5.233}$$

Assuming for simplicity the elementary case $\{N_1^+\}$ and $\mathbf{x} \equiv \eta$, that is, the identity transformation, (5.233) becomes

$$\{DET\}_e^T[B3000] = \Delta_e[B200] \equiv \int_{R_e^2} \{N_1(\mathbf{x})\}\{N_1(\mathbf{x})\}^T\,d\mathbf{x} \tag{5.234}$$

Assuming the rectangular element domain R_e^2 characterized by measures $2a$ and $2b$, the evaluation of (5.234) yields the familiar form

$$[JQQ]_e = \Delta_e[B200] = 4ab[B200] = \frac{4ab}{36}\begin{bmatrix} 4 & 2 & 1 & 2 \\ & 4 & 2 & 1 \\ & & 4 & 2 \\ & (\text{sym}) & & 4 \end{bmatrix} \tag{5.235}$$

The tensor product construction for this matrix involves evaluation of (5.234) constrained to one dimension. Hence,

$$[JQQ_\eta]_e \equiv \Delta_\eta [A200] = \int_{R_e^1} \{N_1(x_1)\}\{N_1(x_1)\}^T \, dx_1 \tag{5.236}$$

and
$$[JQQ_1]_e = \frac{2a}{6}\begin{bmatrix} 2 & 1 \\ 1 & 2 \end{bmatrix} \qquad [JQQ_2]_e = \frac{2b}{6}\begin{bmatrix} 2 & 1 \\ 1 & 2 \end{bmatrix} \tag{5.237}$$

assuming $\Delta_1 = 2a$ and $\Delta_2 = 2b$. Accounting for entry locations in $[JQQ]$ using the assembly operator S_e [see (3.78)], it is readily verified that

$$[JQQ] = S_e[[JQQ]_e] = S_e[[JQQ_1]_e \otimes [JQQ_2]_e] \tag{5.238}$$

Assuming direct extension, the tensor matrix product form for (5.232) is

$$S_e[\{DET\}_e^T[B3000]] \Rightarrow S_e[\{DET1\}_e[A3000] \otimes \{DET2\}_e^T[A3000]] \tag{5.239}$$

where the index $1 \leqslant K \leqslant 2$ on $\{DETK\}_e$ denotes the scalar component of the multi-dimensional measure parallel to η_k.

The second term in the typical jacobian for (5.226)-(5.227) is

$$S_e[\nu_{\alpha J}^1\{ETAKJ\}_e^T[B40K00]\{DET\}_e]$$

The discrete tensor summation indices range $1 \leqslant (K, J) \leqslant 2$, and $[B40K00]$ is a hyper-matrix of degree two, and represents the integration over R_e^2 of four cardinal basis $\{N_k^+(\eta)\}$, one of which is differentiated into scalar components parallel to η_k. The tensor matrix product equivalent is

$$S_e[\nu_{\alpha J}^1\{ETAKJ\}_e^T[B40K00]\{DET\}_e] \Rightarrow S_e[\nu_{\alpha J}^1\{ETA1J\}_e^T[A40100]\{DET1\}_e \otimes \{ETA2J\}_e^T[A40100]\{DET2\}_e] \tag{5.240}$$

and J remains a discrete summation index with range $1 \leqslant J \leqslant 2$.

With these developments, the construction of the tensor matrix product approximation to the Newton algorithm jacobian basically involves the one-dimensional formulations given in Sec. 5.17. For notational precision, the boolean index 1 in a one-dimensional hypermatrix is replaced by K, to denote the component parallel to the grid sweep direction η_K, and K becomes a free (nonsummation) index. With this modification, and again recalling $[J_\eta] \equiv S_e[[J_\eta]_e]$, the elemental contributions to the algorithm jacobians are readily verified to be the forms

$$\frac{\partial\{F1\}_e}{\partial\{Q1\}_e} = \frac{\partial\{FH\}_e}{\partial\{H\}_e} \equiv [JHH]_e = \{DETK\}_e^T[A3000] + \nu_{HJ}^1\{ETAKJ\}_e^T[A40K00]\{DETK\}_e + \frac{\Delta t}{2}\nu_{HJ}^2\left[\{ETAKJ\}_e^T[A40KL0]\{UBARL\}_e - \frac{m_L}{h^2}\{ETAKJ\}_e^T[A40K0L]\{H\}_e\right] \tag{5.241}$$

$$\frac{\partial\{FH\}_e}{\partial\{MI\}_e} \equiv [JHMI]_e = \frac{\Delta t}{2}[-\{ETAKI\}_e^T[A30K0]] \tag{5.242}$$

$$\frac{\partial\{FMI\}_e}{\partial\{H\}_e} \equiv [JMIH]_e = -\frac{\Delta t}{2}\left[\left(\frac{m_K}{h^2}\right)\{MI\}_e^T[A30K0] + g\{ETAKI\}_e^T([A40K00]\{H\}_e) - g\{ETAKI\}_e^T([A4000K]\{B\}_e) - \nu_{IJ}^2\left(\frac{m_L}{h^2}\right)\{ETAKJ\}_e^T[A40K0L]\{MI\}_e\right] \tag{5.243}$$

$$\frac{\partial\{FMI\}_e}{\partial\{MI\}_e} \equiv [JMIMI]_e = \{DETK\}_e^T[A3000] + \nu_{IJ}^1\{ETAKJ\}_e^T[A40K00]\{DETK\}_e + \frac{\Delta t}{2}[-\{UBARK\}_e^T[A30K0] + \nu_{IJ}^2\{ETAKJ\}_e^T([A40KL0]\{UBARL\}_e)] \tag{5.244}$$

$$\frac{\partial\{FMI\}}{\partial\{MJ\}} \equiv [JMIMJ]_e = \frac{\Delta t}{2}\frac{1}{h}[-\{MJ\}_e^T[A30K0]\bar{D}_{KI} + \nu_{IJ}^2\{MJ\}_e^T[A40KK0]\{ETAKL\}\bar{D}_{LJ}] \tag{5.245}$$

In (5.245), $\bar{D}_{KI}$ is the element average value of $\det J_e(\partial\eta_k/\partial x_i)_e$ (see Sec. 8.5). Further, the tensor indices K and L are not eligible for summation, but instead denote the matrix component parallel to the grid sweep direction η_k. The components of $\{ETAKJ\}_e$ are equivalent to the direction cosines of the affine transformation $\eta_k = a_{kj}x_j$ at the node coordinates of R_e^1.

The operation of the tensor matrix form of the Newton algorithm is as follows. For the orientation in the transform space (see Fig. 5.22), the grid lines η_k form a cartesian network. The tensor product Newton algorithm sweeps the mesh parallel to lines $\eta_k =$ constant. Hence, two grid sweeps are required to generate $\{\delta QI\}_{j+1}^{p+1}$ using (5.231). For definition and use of $\{N_1^+\}$ in (5.226)-(5.227), the three-block tridiagonal jacobian for (5.231) is

$$S_e\begin{bmatrix}[JHH]_e & [JHM1]_e & 0\\ [JM1H]_e & [JM1M1]_e & 0\\ [JM2H]_e & [JM2M1]_e & [JM2M2]_e\end{bmatrix}\{P1\} = -\{FI\} \tag{5.246}$$

The second algorithm step employs

$$S_e\begin{bmatrix}[JHH]_e & 0 & [JHM2]_e\\ [JM1H]_e & [JM1M1]_e & [JM1M2]_e\\ [JM2H]_e & 0 & [JM2M2]_e\end{bmatrix}\{\delta QI\} = \{P1\} \tag{5.247}$$

The literature citations of the first section, in particular the proceedings of the International Conferences on Finite Elements in Water Resources, amply document the application of a finite element algorithm to solution of the free-surface shallow flow equations. However, no archival documentation exists for the tensor matrix product algorithm construction. The similar construction, for the complete compressible flow Navier-Stokes equations, is well documented (see Chap. 8).

Problems

1 Derive (5.226)–(5.227).

2 Verify (5.238) using (5.235)–(5.237).

3 Verify (5.241)–(5.242).

4 Verify (5.243)–(5.245).

5.20 CLOSURE

This chapter has developed finite-element numerical solution algorithms for the complete two-dimensional Navier-Stokes equations governing laminar flow of an incompressible fluid. The central role played by the continuity equation, in constructing a well-posed differential equation statement, is most noteworthy. The penalty concepts developed in Sec. B will prove most useful in constructing a well-posed finite-element algorithm statement for the more complicated turbulent flow problem classes studied in the next two chapters.

REFERENCES

Babuska, I. and Aziz, A. K. (1972). Survey Lectures on the Mathematical Foundations of the Finite Element Method, in A. K. Aziz (ed.), *Mathematical Foundations of the Finite Element Method*, Academic Press, New York.

Baker, A. J. (1974). A Finite Element Solution Algorithm for the Navier-Stokes Equations, Tech. Rept. NASA CR-2391.

Baker, A. J. (1975). Finite Element Solution Algorithm for Incompressible Fluid Dynamics, Chap. 4, in R. H. Gallagher et al. (eds.), *Finite Elements in Fluids*, vol. 2, Wiley-Interscience, London.

Baker, A. J. (1977). The Finite Element Method Applied to Flow Field Predictions in Environmental Hydrodynamics, in W. G. Gray et al. (eds.), *Proceedings, 1st International Conference on Finite Elements in Water Resources*, Pentech Press, London.

Baker, A. J. and Soliman, M. O. (1982). On the Accuracy and Efficiency of a Finite Element Algorithm for Hydrodynamic Flows, in H. P. Holz et al. (eds.), *Proceedings, 4th International Conference on Finite Elements in Water Resources*, CML Press, Southampton.

Bercovier, M. and Pironneau, O. (1979). Error Estimates for the Finite Element Method Solution of the Stokes Problem in the Primitive Variables, *Numer. Math.*, vol. 33, pp. 211–224.

Brebbia, C. A. and Partridge, P. W. (1976). Finite Element Simulation of Water Circulation in the North Sea, *J. Appl. Math Modeling*, vol. 1, p. 101.

Brezzi, F. (1974). On the Existence, Uniqueness, and Approximation of Saddle-Point Problems Arising from Lagrange Multipliers, *R.A.I.R.O. Numer. Anal.*, vol. 8, pp. 129–151.

Carey, G. F. and Krishnan, R. (1982). Penalty Approximation of Stokes Flow, *Comp. Methods Appl. Mech. Eng.*, vol. 35, pp. 169–206.

Dorodnitsyn, A. A. (1973). Review of Methods for Solving the Navier-Stokes Equation, *Proc. 3rd Int. Conf. Numer. Methods Fluid Mechanics*, Springer-Verlag Lecture Notes in Physics, vol. 35, pp. 1–11.

Finn, R. (1965). Stationary Solutions of the Navier-Stokes Equations, in R. Finn (ed.), *Applied Nonlinear Partial Differential Equations in Mathematics and Physics*, AMS (American Math Society), pp. 121–153.

Gartling, D. K. (1974). Finite Element Analysis of Viscous Incompressible Fluid Flow, Tech. Rept. TICOM 74-8, University of Texas, Austin.

Girault, V. and Raviart, P.-A. (1979). *Finite Element Approximation of the Navier-Stokes Equations*, Lecture Notes in Mathematics Series, vol. 749, Springer-Verlag, Berlin.

Glowinski, R. and Pironneau, O. (1979). On a Mixed Finite Element Approximation of the Stokes Problem (I): Convergence of the Approximate Solution, *Numer. Math.*, vol. 33, pp. 397–424.

Gosman, A. D., Pun, W. M., Runchal, A. K., Spalding, D. B., and Wolfshtein, M. (1969). *Heat and Mass Transfer in Recirculating Flows*, Academic Press, London.

Gray, W. G. (1977). An Efficient Finite Element Scheme for Two-dimensional Surface Water Computation, in W. G. Gray et al. (eds.), *Proceedings, 1st International Conference on Finite Elements in Water Resources*, Pentech Press, London.

Gresho, P. M. and Lee, R. L. (1981). Don't Suppress the Wiggles–They're Telling You Something!, *J. Comp. Fluids*, vol. 9, pp. 223–255.

Halmos, P. R. (1958). *Finite Dimensional Vector Spaces*, Van Nostrand, Princeton, New Jersey.

Hughes, T. R. J., Liu, W. K., and Brooks, A. (1979). Review of Finite Element Analysis of Incompressible Viscous Flows by the Penalty Function Formulation, *J. Comp. Phys.*, vol. 30, no. 1, pp. 1–60.

Jaunzemis, W. (1967). *Continuum Mechanics*, MacMillan, New York.

Johnson, B. H. and Thompson, J. F. (1978). A Discussion of Boundary-Fitted Coordinate Systems and Their Applicability to the Numerical Modeling of Hydraulic Problems, Misc. Paper H-78-9, U.S. Army Engineer Waterways Experiment Station, Vicksburg, Mississippi.

King, I. P. (1977). Finite Element Models for Unsteady Flow Routing Through Irregular Channels, in W. G. Gray et al. (eds.), *Proceedings, 1st International Conference on Finite Elements in Water Resources*, Pentech Press, London.

King, I. P. and Norton, W. R. (1978). Recent Applications to RMA's Finite Element Models for Two-dimensional Hydrodynamics and Water Quality, in C. A. Brebbia et al. (eds.), *Proceedings, 2nd International Conference on Finite Elements in Water Resources*, Pentech Press, London.

King, I. P., Norton, W. R., and Iceman, K. R. (1975). A Finite Element Solution for Two-dimensional Stratified Flow Problems, Chap. 7, in R. H. Gallagher et al. (eds.), *Finite Elements in Fluids*, vol. 1, Wiley-Interscience, London.

Ladyshenskaya, O. A. (1969). *The Mathematical Theory of Viscous Incompressible Flow*, Gordon and Breach, New York.

Lee, J. K. (1980). Two-dimensional Finite Element Analysis of the Hydraulic Effect of Highway Bridge Fills in a Complex Flood Plane, in S. Y. Yang et al. (eds.), *Proceedings, 3rd International Conference on Finite Elements in Water Resources*, Rose Printing, Tallahassee, Florida.

Macagno, E. O. and Hung, T. K. (1967). Computational and Experimental Study of a Captive Annular Eddy, *J. Fluid Mech.*, vol. 28, pt. 1, pp. 43–64.

McAnally, W. H. and Thomas, W. A. (1980). Finite Element Models in a Hybrid Model Study of Estuarine Sedimentation, in S. Y. Wang et al. (eds.), *Proceedings, 3rd International Conference on Finite Element in Water Resources*, Rose Printing, Tallahassee, Florida.

Mueller, T. J. and O'Leary, R. A. (1970). Physical and Numerical Experiments in Laminar Incompressible Separating and Reattaching Flows, AIAA Paper 70-763.

NASA (1981). *Proceedings, Numerical Grid Generation Techniques*, NASA Conference Publication 2166.

Oden, J. T. (1982a). Reduced Integration Penalty Methods for Stokesian Flows, in R. H. Gallagher et al. (eds.), *Finite Elements in Fluids*, vol. 4, Wiley-Interscience, London.

Oden, J. T. (1982b). Reduced Integration for the Analysis of Fluids, *Penalty Finite Element Methods in Mechanics, ASME Appl. Mech. Div. Rept. AMD*, vol. 51, pp. 21–32.

Oden, J. T. and Jacquotte, O. (1982). Stability of Some RIP Finite Element Methods for Stokesian Flow, TICOM Rept., July, University of Texas, Austin.

Oden, J. T., Kikuchi, N., and Song, Y. J. (1979). An Analysis of Exterior Penalty Methods and Reduced Integration for Finite Element Approximations of Contact Problems in Incompressible Elasticity, Tech. Rept. TICOM 79-10, The University of Texas, Austin.

Patankar, S. V. (1980). *Numerical Heat Transfer and Fluid Flow*, Hemisphere, Washington, D.C.

Pepper, D. W. and Cooper, R. E. (1980). Numerical Solution of Recirculating Flow by a Simple Finite Element Recursion Relation, *J. Comp. Fluids*, vol. 8, pp. 213–223.

Reddy, J. N. (1978). On the Accuracy and Existence of Solutions to Primitive Variable Models of Viscous Incompressible Fluids, *Int. J. Eng. Sci.*, vol. 16, pp. 921–929.

Reddy, J. N. (1982a). On Penalty Function Methods in the Finite Element Analysis of Flow Problems, *Int. J. Numer. Meth. Fluids*, vol. 2, pp. 151–171.

Reddy, J. N. (1982b). The Penalty Function Method in Mechanics: A Review of Recent Advances, *ASME Appl. Mech. Div. Rept. AMD*, vol. 51, pp. 1–20.

Roache, P. J. (1972). *Computational Fluid Dynamics*, Hermosa, Albuquerque, New Mexico.

Sani, R. L., Gresho, P. M., Lee, R. L., and Griffiths, D. F. (1981). The Cause and Cure(?) of the Spurious Pressures Generated by Certain FEM Solutions of the Incompressible Navier-Stokes Equations, *Int. J. Numer. Meth. Fluids*, vol. 1, pp. 17–43.

Schlichting, H. (1979). *Boundary Layer Theory*, McGraw-Hill, New York.

Shames, I. H. (1982). *Mechanics of Fluids*, McGraw-Hill, New York.

Taylor, C. and Hood, P. (1973). A Numerical Solution of the Navier-Stokes Equations using the Finite Element Technique, *Comp. Fluids*, vol. 1, pp. 73–100.

Temam, R. (1979). *Navier-Stokes Equations, Theory and Numerical Analysis*, North-Holland Press, Amsterdam.

Tuann, S. and Olsen, M. D. (1978). Review of Computing Methods for Recirculating Flows, *J. Comp. Phys.*, vol. 29, no. 1, pp. 1–19.

White, F. M. (1979). *Fluid Mechanics*, McGraw-Hill, New York.

Zienkiewicz, O. C. (1974). Constrained Variational Principles and Penalty Function Methods in Finite Element Analysis, in G. A. Watson (ed.), *Lecture Notes in Mathematics: Conference on the Numerical Solution of Differential Equations*, Springer-Verlag, Berlin, pp. 207–214.

Zienkiewicz, O. C. (1979). *The Finite Element Method in Engineering Science*, McGraw-Hill, London.

Zienkiewicz, O. C. and Godbole, P. N. (1975). Viscous, Incompressible Flow with Special Reference to Non-Newtonian (Plastic) Fluids, in R. H. Gallagher et al. (eds.), *Finite Elements in Fluids*, vol. 1, Wiley-Interscience, London, pp. 25–55.

Zienkiewicz, O. C., Taylor, R. L., and Too, J. M. (1971). Reduced Integration Technique in General Analysis of Plates and Shells, *Int. J. Numer. Meth. Eng.*, vol. 3, pp. 575–586.

CHAPTER

SIX

TWO-DIMENSIONAL PARABOLIC FLOW

6.1 INTRODUCTION

A large and very important problem class within fluid mechanics is characterized by a steady and unidirectional flow. Specifically, within and about the engineering device of interest, the fluid generally moves in a smooth fashion nominally parallel to the confining surfaces. For example, a wide range of flows in aerodynamics fits this description, from the largest scale of wing boundary layers all the way down to the scale of turbine scrolls. Furthermore, a typical design requirement is to make these flows as smooth as possible for device efficiency, since gross separation of the flow from the confining surfaces usually leads to large losses. Finally, these unidirectional flows are usually characterized by large Reynolds numbers, so the typical situation corresponds to a turbulent flow.

When applied to the steady-flow Navier-Stokes equations, the assumption of unidirectionality coupled with statements regarding pressure (distributions) leads to what has become termed the parabolic simplification. Construction of finite-element numerical solution procedures for the two-dimensional parabolic Navier-Stokes equations are presented in this chapter. The following chapter documents the extension to three-dimensional flows. The elementary, two-dimensional laminar and/or turbulent boundary layer equation system is perhaps the most familiar parabolic form of the steady-flow Navier-Stokes equations (Schlichting, 1979). Blottner and Flugge-Lotz (1963) published one of the earliest accounts of numerical solution of the incompressible laminar boundary layer equation system using a finite-difference algorithm. Among others, Patankar and Spalding (1967) pioneered in finite-difference procedures for turbulent boundary layer differential equations for characterizing turbulence evolution. The late 1960s exhibited a tremendous growth of interest in turbulence closure for boundary layer flows, culminating in the 1968 AFOSR-Stanford Conference, wherein numerical predictions using over 30 different closure models and solution algorithms were critically compared with experimental data (Coles and Hirst, 1968; Kline et al., 1968).

As a consequence of these pioneering activities, finite-difference procedures are now widely utilized for solution of the boundary layer equations. Among the most popular formulations is the second-order accurate Crank-Nicolson algorithm. Blottner (1970, 1975) has prepared detailed surveys of the status of boundary layer numerical solution algorithms. Cebeci and Smith (1974) collate much of the literature for turbulent boundary layer methods, and document the "C-S" finite-difference algorithm based upon the Keller box scheme. Attention has recently turned to algorithms that operate more efficiently than the standard block tridiagonal algorithms on a vector processing computer (Wornom, 1978). Popinski and Baker (1976) first reported results of direct comparison between the Crank-Nicolson and linear finite-element algorithms for an elementary laminar boundary layer. Soliman and Baker (1981a, 1981b) refined the procedures, and, in addition to making direct comparisons, they documented accuracy and convergence in energy for the linear and quadratic basis finite-element formulations for both laminar and turbulent flow. Of greatest significance, perhaps, the results of their closely controlled numerical experiments give firm indication of the plausible extension of the convergence statement (4.133), developed for a simple linear parabolic equation, to a strongly nonlinear parabolic equation system of real engineering importance in fluid mechanics.

As occurred for the material development in Chap. 5, the well-posedness of the two-dimensional parabolic Navier-Stokes equation description must be assured. And, in a repeat performance, the manner in which the conservation of mass (continuity) equation is enforced becomes strongly distinguished, now as a function of solution domain boundedness. This in turn prompts the organization of this chapter into two general categories. A semibounded domain is exemplified by the conventional boundary layer, and forms the content of Part A. Here, the flow is exerted to flow nominally parallel to a single surface, which may be curved (see Fig. 6.1). In this instance, the continuity equation can be solved directly, as a pure initial-value problem on transverse velocity, knowing the distribution of suction (blowing) velocity $v_w(x, 0)$ along the surface. The alternative class (Part B) corresponds to

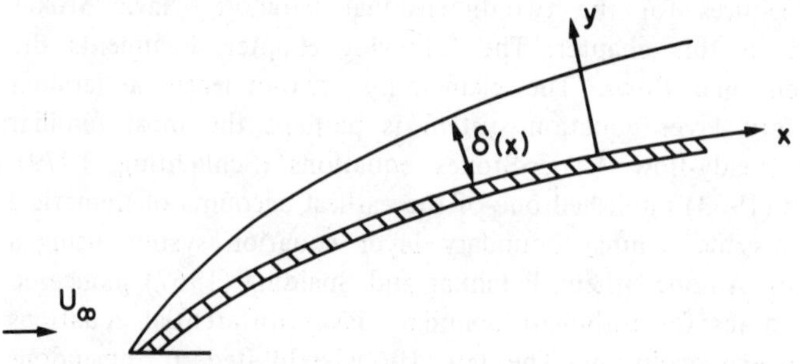

Figure 6.1 The boundary layer flow solution domain.

two-dimensional flows that are either completely unbounded, e.g., jet and/or wake mixing, or are completely confined by duct walls. In either case, a careful examination of the parabolic differential equations shows they are ill-posed for direct solution, generally due to an excess of known data on the boundaries (or free streams). The finite-element algorithm concept developed for these cases is a direct extension of the penalty function procedure developed in Chap. 5 to enforce continuity on a Navier-Stokes solution. The parabolic flows considered in this chapter include incompressible and variable-density fluids, with direct extension to turbulent flows and turbulence closure models, following thorough examination of the expository laminar flow case.

A. SEMIBOUNDED FLOWS

6.2 LAMINAR BOUNDARY LAYER EQUATION SYSTEM

Prandtl (see Schlichting, 1979), originally established the concept of boundary layer flow and the corresponding boundary layer simplification of the parent Navier-Stokes equations. The character of the flow field is illustrated in Fig. 6.1. It is required to establish the two-dimensional velocity and pressure distributions $\mathbf{u}(\mathbf{x})$ and $p(\mathbf{x})$, where

$$\mathbf{u}(\mathbf{x}) = u(\mathbf{x})\hat{\mathbf{i}} + v(\mathbf{x})\hat{\mathbf{j}} \tag{6.1}$$

With use of the familiar laminar boundary layer order of magnitude analysis (Schlichting, 1979), the nondimensional, incompressible Navier-Stokes equations, which express conservation of mass and linear momentum, become simplified to

$$L(\rho_0) = \nabla \cdot \mathbf{u} = 0 \tag{6.2}$$

$$L(u) = (\mathbf{u} \cdot \nabla)u + \frac{1}{\rho_0}\frac{\partial p}{\partial x_1} - \frac{1}{\mathrm{Re}}\frac{\partial}{\partial x_2}\left(\nu \frac{\partial u}{\partial x_2}\right) = 0 \tag{6.3}$$

$$L(v) = \frac{1}{\rho_0}\frac{\partial p}{\partial x_2} = 0 \tag{6.4}$$

For an isoenergetic flow, the energy equation is identically satisfied by a constant total energy

$$e \equiv c_v T + \tfrac{1}{2}\mathbf{u} \cdot \mathbf{u} = \text{const} \tag{6.5}$$

The fluid parameters in (6.2)–(6.5) are ρ_0, the constant density; ν, the kinematic viscosity; and c_v, specific heat. The x_1 axis is assumed to be aligned with the direction of predominant flow, x_2 is the coordinate traversing the thickness of the boundary layer (see Fig. 6.1), and ∇ is the two-dimensional gradient operator. Equations (6.2)–(6.5) are appropriate provided

$$\mathrm{Re} \equiv \frac{U_\infty L}{\nu_\infty} \tag{6.6}$$

and the inverse square root of δ, the local boundary layer thickness (Fig. 6.1) are of the same order of magnitude. In (6.6), U_∞ is a reference (freestream) velocity, ν_∞ is the corresponding kinematic viscosity, and L is a nondimensionalizing length scale.

Under the boundary layer assumption, the transverse momentum equation (6.4) is identically satisfied by a pressure distribution impressed uniformly across the boundary layer thickness, that is, $p(\mathbf{x}) = p_I(x_1)$. The subscript I denotes that this pressure distribution is induced by the freestream inviscid flow about the object (refer to Chap. 3), which is imposed unaltered through the boundary layer thickness. Thus, an equivalent expression for the pressure gradient in (6.3) is

$$\frac{\partial p}{\partial x_1} \Rightarrow \frac{dp_I}{dx_1} = \rho u_I \frac{du_I}{dx_1} \tag{6.7}$$

where $u_I(x_1)$ is the (inviscid flow) streamwise velocity just exterior to the boundary layer edge δ.

Closure of (6.2)–(6.7) requires identification of the constitutive relationship for viscosity ν and establishment of boundary and initial conditions for a well-posed problem. The kinematic viscosity is a property of the fluid constituting the boundary layer. From kinetic theory (Lee et al., 1963), viscosity depends solely on the local static temperature, that is, $\nu = \nu(T)$. Sutherland's law is a familiar functional expression of this relationship. Importantly, $\nu(T)$ is uniformly positive, therefore (6.3) is parabolic for $\mathrm{Re} < \infty$.

The boundary conditions for solution of (6.2)–(6.4) are determined by inspection. At the no-slip surface, $x_2 = 0$, and

$$u(x_1, 0) = 0 \tag{6.8}$$

$$v(x_1, 0) = v_w(x_1) \tag{6.9}$$

which includes fluid injection from the surface (blowing or suction). At the freestream $y > \delta(x_1)$, from (6.3)–(6.7),

$$u(x_1, y) = u_I(x_1) \tag{6.10}$$

$$\frac{\partial u}{\partial x_2}(x_1, y) = 0 \tag{6.11}$$

6.3 FINITE-ELEMENT SOLUTION ALGORITHM

Construction of the finite-element solution algorithm for (6.2)–(6.3) is guided by the boundary conditions. The u momentum equation (6.2) is an elliptic two-point boundary value (parabolic) problem via (6.8), (6.10), or (6.11). Furthermore, the lead term in (6.3) is $u\,\partial u/\partial x_1$, which means that it is an initial-value specification as well; that is, given $p(x_1)$, $\nu(\mathbf{x})$ and an initial condition

$$u(x_1^0, x_2) \equiv u^0(x_1) \tag{6.12}$$

(6.3) can be marched in the direction parallel to x_1. Extending the separation of variables concept developed in Sec. 4.3 [see (4.16)] the finite-element approximation $u^h(\mathbf{x})$ is therefore defined as

$$u(\mathbf{x}) \approx u^h(\mathbf{x}) = \sum_{e=1}^{M} q_1^e(x) \equiv \sum_{e=1}^{M} \{N_k(x_2)\}^T \{Q1(x_1)\}_e \tag{6.13}$$

Hence, only a one-dimensional cardinal basis is required; the solution domain is $\Omega \equiv R^1 \times x_1$, for $x_1 \geqslant x_1^0$; and R^1 spans $0 \leqslant x_2 < \alpha\ \delta(x_1)$, where $\alpha \geqslant 1$ is a parameter dependent upon the specific boundary condition (6.10) or (6.11). [Eventually, a grid stretching transformation will be employed to compensate for R^1 growing like $\delta(x_1)$, or (6.2)-(6.3), can be transformed using the von-Mises or Levy-Lees formulations (Blottner, 1970)]. Since parameters are interpolated using the dependent variable construction, then also

$$v^h(\mathbf{x}) \equiv \sum_{e=1}^{M} \{N_k(x_2)\}^T \{Q2(\mathbf{x}_1)\}_e \tag{6.14}$$

$$\frac{1}{\rho_0}\frac{dp^h(\mathbf{x})}{dx_1} \equiv p_I'(x_1) \tag{6.15}$$

With the definitions (6.13)-(6.15), the construction of the finite-element algorithm statement for (6.3) is identical to that in Secs. 4.3 or 5.4, with time t replaced by the x_1 coordinate. The sole gradient boundary condition (6.11) is homogeneous, and $\beta_1 \equiv 0$ is consistent with the boundary layer ordering [see (5.47)]. Therefore, the sole constraint is orthogonality of the semidiscrete approximation error $L(q^h)$, that is,

$$\int_{R^1} \{N_k\}\, L(q_1^h)\, d\tau \equiv \{0\} \tag{6.16}$$

As before, (6.16) is evaluated on the discretization $\cup R_e^1$ of R^1 and the element contributions assembled using the operator S_e. Furthermore, the Green-Gauss theorem is used to transform the diffusion term in (6.3). Independent of the degree k of the basis $\{N_k\}$, (6.16) is the system of ordinary differential equations

$$[C]\,\{Q1\}' + [U+K]\,\{Q1\} + \{b\} = \{0\} \tag{6.17}$$

where C denotes the capacity matrix, U and K the convection and diffusion matrices, and $\{b\}$ contains all other nonhomogeneities. Defining the θ-implicit integration algorithm produces the algebraic system

$$\{F1\} = \{Q1\}_{j+1} - \{Q1\}_j - h[\theta\,\{Q1\}_{j+1}' + (1-\theta)\{Q1\}_j'] = \{0\} \tag{6.18}$$

In (6.18), the appropriate spatial derivatives are given by (6.17), j is the x_1-station index, $h = \Delta x_1$ is the integration step, and $J = 1$ denotes the elements of q_1^h at the nodal coordinates of $\cup R_e^1$. The Newton algorithm for (6.18) is

$$[J(F1)_{j+1}^p]\,\{\delta Q1\}_{j+1}^{p+1} = -\{F1\}_{j+1}^p \tag{6.19}$$

where the dependent variable is the iteration vector, and

$$\{Q1\}_{j+1}^{p+1} = \{Q1\}_{j+1}^{p} + \{\delta Q1\}_{j+1}^{p+1} \tag{6.20}$$

Evaluation of $\{F1\}$ in (6.18) requires knowledge of $p_I'(x_1)$ and the nodal array of transverse velocity $\{V(x_1)\}$. The former is available from the exterior potential solution. The latter must be determined as a function of $\{Q1(x_1)\}'$ using the continuity equation (6.2). As a consequence of the definitions (6.13)-(6.14), the x_1 functional dependence in (6.2) has become parameterized, yielding

$$L^b(v^h) = \frac{d\{V(x_1)\}}{dy} + \frac{d}{dx}\{U(x_1)\} = \{0\} \tag{6.21}$$

where superscript b denotes that (6.21) is the boundary layer form of (6.2). Equation (6.21) is in the standard form of an ordinary differential equation, the solution for which is simply

$$\begin{aligned}\{F2\} &= \{V\}_{j+1} - \{V\}_j - h[\theta\{V\}_{j+1}' + (1-\theta)\{V\}_j'] \\ &= \{V\}_{j+1} - \{V\}_j + h[\theta\{U\}_{j+1}' + (1-\theta)\{U\}_j'] \equiv \{0\}\end{aligned} \tag{6.22}$$

The final form of (6.22) was obtained using (6.21); θ is the implicitness factor; and $h = y_{j+1} - y_j$ $(=\Delta_e)$ is the integration step size (which is identical to the distribution of the measure Δ_e of $\cup R_e^1$). The elements of $\{U\}'$ are the nodal values of the x_1 derivative of $u^h(\mathbf{x})$. In principal these can be evaluated from (6.17) by premultiplication by $[C]^{-1}$. Alternatively, they can be determined using a finite-difference formula. For example, the second-order accurate backward difference expression on a nonuniform (x_1) grid spacing is

$$\begin{aligned}\{U(x_p)\}' \approx \frac{1}{h_p h_{p-1}(h_p + h_{p-1})} &[h_{p-1}(2h_p + h_{p-1})\{U\}_p \\ &- (h_p + h_{p-1})^2\{U\}_{p-1} + (h_p)^2\{U\}_{p-2}]\end{aligned} \tag{6.23}$$

where h_p and h_{p-1} are the current and immediate-past Δx_1 integration step sizes used in the solution of (6.18), i.e.,

$$h_p \equiv x_p - x_{p-1} \qquad h_{p-1} \equiv x_{p-1} - x_{p-2} \tag{6.24}$$

Problem

1 Verify the order of accuracy of (6.23).

6.4 THEORETICAL ANALYSIS, ACCURACY AND CONVERGENCE

Oden and Reddy (1976) developed the theoretical statement of convergence for the linear parabolic equation (6.17) (see Sec. 4.8). Recalling that x_1 is now the time-like coordinate, and using the fully explicit ($\theta = 0$) integration algorithm, (4.133) takes the form

$$\|\epsilon^h(n\,\Delta x\|_{H^m} \leqslant C_1\,\Delta_e^{(k+1-m)}\|q(n\,\Delta x)\|_{H^{k+1}} + C_5\,\Delta x\|Q_0\|_{H^m} \tag{6.25}$$

Recall that the C_α are constants, and $\|Q_0\|_{H^m}$ is the H^m norm of the initial distribution.

A convergence statement similar to (6.25) is not available for the nonlinear, initial-value problem statement for the boundary layer u momentum equation. However, if the linear theory can be extended to the more general problem, then the convergence properties of the finite-element algorithm could be expressed in the form of (6.25). Assuming this may occur, (6.25) squared defines anticipated semidiscrete convergence in the energy norm for the boundary layer equation solution:

$$E(\epsilon^h(n\,\Delta x), \epsilon^h(n\,\Delta x)) \leqslant C_1\,\Delta_e^{2k}\|F(n\,\Delta x)\|_{H^0}^2 + C_5\,\Delta x^2\,\|u_0\|_{H^1}^2 \tag{6.26}$$

In (6.26), $\|F\|$ is the H^0 norm of the "data," which includes at least the freestream pressure gradient, i.e.,

$$\|F(n\,\Delta x)\| \equiv \left[\int_{R^1}\left(\frac{1}{\rho_0}\frac{dp_I}{dx}\right)^2 dy\right]^{1/2} \tag{6.27}$$

The form of the energy norm for the boundary layer equation system must be established. The inner product of a function set $v(x)$ and a differential equation $L(u(x))$, with boundary conditions $l(u(\bar{x}))$, is

$$E(v, L(u)) \equiv \int_{R^n} v(x)L(u(x))\,d\tau + \lambda\int_{\partial R} v(x)l(u(\bar{x}))\,d\sigma \tag{6.28}$$

From (6.3), letting $v=\frac{1}{2}u$ in (6.28), and using the subscript comma to denote partial derivative, (6.28) becomes

$$E\left(\frac{1}{2}u, L(u)\right) = \frac{1}{2}\int_{R^1} u\left[uu_{,x} + vu_{,y} + \frac{1}{\rho_0}p_I' - \frac{1}{\mathrm{Re}}(\nu u_{,y})_{,y}\right] dy$$

$$= \frac{1}{2}\int_{R^1}\left[u^2u_{,x} + \frac{1}{2}v(u^2)_{,y} + \frac{1}{\rho_0}up_I - \frac{u}{\mathrm{Re}}(\nu u_{,y})_{,y}\right] dy \tag{6.29}$$

The second term can be integrated by parts to yield

$$\int_{R^1}\tfrac{1}{2}v(u^2)_{,y}\,dy = \tfrac{1}{2}vu^2\Big|_0^{u_I} - \int_{R^1}\tfrac{1}{2}u^2v_{,y}\,dy = \tfrac{1}{2}v_Iu_I^2 - \int_{R^1}\tfrac{1}{2}u^2(-u_{,x})\,dy$$

using (6.2) and the no-slip wall boundary condition. The last term in (6.29) can also be integrated by parts to yield

$$\frac{1}{2\text{Re}} \int_{R^1} u(\nu u_{,y})_{,y}\, dy = \frac{1}{2\text{Re}}\, u\nu u_{,y} \Big|_0^{u_I} - \frac{1}{2\text{Re}} \int_{R^1} u_{,y}\, \nu u_{,y}\, dy$$

The first term vanishes at both limits. Combining, (6.29) becomes

$$E\left(\frac{1}{2}\, u,\, L(u)\right) = \frac{1}{2} \int_{R^1} \left[\frac{3}{2}\, u_{,x}(u)^2 + \frac{\nu}{\text{Re}}\, (u_{,y})^2\right] dy + \frac{1}{4}\, v_I u_I^2 + \frac{1}{\rho_0}\, p_I' \int u\, dy \tag{6.30}$$

In (6.30), two terms in the lead integral are quadratic in the dependent variable and its gradient. Hence, if $u_{,x}$ is considered a parameter, in the spirit of ν, the energy norm (6.26) is

$$E(u^h, u^h) = \sum_{e=1}^{M} \frac{1}{2} \int_{R_e^1} \left[\frac{3}{2}\, u_{,x}^h\, (u^h)^2 + \frac{\nu}{\text{Re}}\, (u_{,y}^h)^2\right] dy \tag{6.31}$$

and the third term in (6.30) is the specific form for the data of (6.27), i.e.,

$$\|F\| = \left[\int_{R^1} (\tfrac{1}{4}\, v_I u_I^2)^2\, dy\right]^{1/2} \tag{6.32}$$

An alternative expression for E can be derived. The first term in (6.30) can be reexpressed as

$$\tfrac{3}{2}\, u_{,x}\, (u)^2 = \tfrac{1}{2}\, (u^3)_{,x}$$

Since this nonlinearity has lost its quadratic character, the energy norm for (6.30) would then be

$$E(u^h, u^h) = \sum_{e=1}^{M} \frac{1}{2} \int_{R_e^1} \frac{\nu}{\text{Re}} \left(\frac{\partial u^h}{\partial y}\right)^2 dy \tag{6.33}$$

In this instance, (6.33) is identical with the energy norm used to quantize convergence for the linear transient problem.

Accuracy and convergence may as well be measured using the familiar boundary layer integral parameters of displacement (δ^*) and momentum (θ) thickness, defined as

$$\delta^*(x) \equiv \int_0^\infty \left[1 - \frac{u(x, y)}{u_I(x)}\right] dy \tag{6.34}$$

$$\theta(x) \equiv \int_0^\infty \frac{u(x, y)}{u_I(x)} \left[1 - \frac{u(x, y)}{u_I(x)}\right] dy \tag{6.35}$$

A convenient norm is shape factor H,

$$H \equiv \frac{\delta^*}{\theta} \tag{6.36}$$

Skin friction is an engineering measure of drag, hence, the distribution of viscosity induced shear stress. The skin friction coefficient C_f is a useful error measure, and is defined as

$$C_f \equiv \frac{\tau_w}{(1/2)(\rho_I u_I^2)} \equiv \left(\frac{1}{2}\,\rho_I u_I^2\right)^{-1} \rho_w \nu_w \left.\frac{\partial u}{\partial y}\right|_w \tag{6.37}$$

The Ludwig-Tillmann formula for (6.37) is

$$C_f = 0.246(10)^{-0.678H}\mathrm{Re}_\theta^{-0.268} \tag{6.38}$$

where Re_θ is the Reynolds number based on θ, and H is given in (6.36) (see Ludwig and Tillmann, 1950).

Problem

1 Establish (6.29) in the form (6.30).

6.5 IMPLEMENTATION USING THE LINEAR BASIS

Independent of the degree k of the finite-element approximation (6.13), the hypermatrix equivalent form of the algorithm (6.16) is

$$S_e\left[\Delta_e \{U\}_e^T[A3000]\,\{U\}'_e + \Delta_e\left(\frac{\nu}{\mathrm{Re}}\,[A211] + \{V\}_e^T[A3001]\right)\{U\}_e + \Delta_e p'_I\{A10\}\right] \equiv \{0\} \tag{6.39}$$

where $p'_I \equiv (1/\rho_0)/(dp_I/dx_1)$ is a constant on R^1 [see (6.15)]. The standard matrices defined in (6.39), for $k = 1$ in (6.13)-(6.14), are

$$[A3000] = \frac{1}{12}\begin{bmatrix} \begin{Bmatrix} 3 \\ 1 \end{Bmatrix} & \begin{Bmatrix} 1 \\ 1 \end{Bmatrix} \\ \\ \begin{Bmatrix} 1 \\ 1 \end{Bmatrix} & \begin{Bmatrix} 1 \\ 3 \end{Bmatrix} \end{bmatrix} \tag{6.40}$$

$$[A3001] = \frac{1}{6}\begin{bmatrix} \begin{Bmatrix} -2 \\ -1 \end{Bmatrix} & \begin{Bmatrix} 2 \\ 1 \end{Bmatrix} \\ \\ \begin{Bmatrix} -1 \\ -2 \end{Bmatrix} & \begin{Bmatrix} 1 \\ 2 \end{Bmatrix} \end{bmatrix} \tag{6.41}$$

$$[A211] = \begin{bmatrix} -1 & 1 \\ 1 & -1 \end{bmatrix} \tag{6.42}$$

$$\{A10\} = \frac{1}{2}\begin{Bmatrix} 1 \\ 1 \end{Bmatrix} \tag{6.43}$$

Upon definition of $\theta = \frac{1}{2}$ in (6.18), the hypermatrix equivalent of (6.18) becomes

$$\begin{aligned}\{F1\} = S_e\Bigg[& \Delta_e \{\bar{U}\}_e^T[A3000](\{U\}^p_{j+1} - \{U\}_j) \\ & + \frac{h\,\Delta_e}{2}\Bigg[\left(\{V\}_e^T[A3001] + \frac{\nu}{\text{Re}}[A211]\right)\{U\}^p_{j+1} \\ & + \left(\{V\}_e^T[A3001] + \frac{\nu}{\text{Re}}[A211]\right)\{U\}_j + \{A10\}(p'_{j+1} + p'_j)\Bigg]\Bigg] \equiv \{0\}\end{aligned} \tag{6.44}$$

In (6.44), $\{\bar{U}\}_e \equiv \frac{1}{2}(\{U\}^p_{j+1} + \{U\}_j)$. Equation (6.22) gives the corresponding expression for $\{F2\}$.

For an implicit formulation, the jacobians $[J(FIJ)]$ for the Newton statement (6.19) are formed, using (6.44) and (6.22), as

$$\begin{aligned}[J(1,1)] \equiv \frac{\partial\{F1\}}{\partial\{Q1\}} = S_e\Bigg[& \Delta_e\{U^p_{j+1}\}^T[A3000] \\ & + \frac{h\,\Delta_e}{2}\left(\{V\}^T_{j+1}[A3001] + \frac{\nu}{\text{Re}}[A211]\right)\Bigg]\end{aligned} \tag{6.45}$$

$$[J(1,2)] \equiv \frac{\partial\{F1\}}{\partial\{Q2\}} = S_e\left[\frac{h\,\Delta_e}{2}\{U\}^T_{j+1}[A3100]\right] \tag{6.46}$$

$$[J(21)] = \frac{\partial\{F2\}}{\partial\{U\}'}\,\frac{\partial\{U\}'}{\partial\{U\}} = \Delta_e f(h)[I] \tag{6.47}$$

$$[J(22)] = [I] \tag{6.48}$$

In (6.47)-(6.48), the function $f(h)$ is given by the first term in (6.23) and $[I]$ is the identity matrix.

For an explicit formulation, $\theta \equiv 0$ in (6.18), diagonalizing of the capacity matrix $\{U\}^T[A3000]$ is required for efficiency. Since this matrix is now explicitly nonlinear, several methods are available, as summarized by Popinski and Baker (1976). In particular, the matrix

$$[A3000]_3 \equiv \frac{1}{2}\begin{bmatrix} \begin{Bmatrix} 1 \\ 0 \end{Bmatrix} & \begin{Bmatrix} 0 \\ 0 \end{Bmatrix} \\ \begin{Bmatrix} 0 \\ 0 \end{Bmatrix} & \begin{Bmatrix} 0 \\ 1 \end{Bmatrix} \end{bmatrix} \tag{6.49}$$

upon premultiplication by $\{U\}_e$ and assembly, yields the Crank-Nicolson finite-difference recursion form

$$S_e[\Delta_e \{U\}_e^T[A3000]_3 \{U\}'_e] = \Delta_e \begin{bmatrix} \ddots & & \\ 0 & U & 0 \\ & & \ddots \end{bmatrix} \begin{Bmatrix} \vdots \\ U \\ \vdots \end{Bmatrix}' \Rightarrow \Delta U_j U_j' \tag{6.50}$$

assuming a uniform discretization. A second form results upon discarding of the off-diagonal entries in (6.40), and normalizing, as

$$[A3000]_2 \equiv \frac{1}{8}\begin{bmatrix} \begin{Bmatrix} 3 \\ 1 \end{Bmatrix} & \begin{Bmatrix} 0 \\ 0 \end{Bmatrix} \\ \begin{Bmatrix} 0 \\ 0 \end{Bmatrix} & \begin{Bmatrix} 1 \\ 3 \end{Bmatrix} \end{bmatrix} \tag{6.51}$$

Adding the off-diagonal entries to the diagonals and normalizing yields

$$[A3000]_1 \equiv \frac{1}{6}\begin{bmatrix} \begin{Bmatrix} 2 \\ 1 \end{Bmatrix} & \begin{Bmatrix} 0 \\ 0 \end{Bmatrix} \\ \begin{Bmatrix} 0 \\ 0 \end{Bmatrix} & \begin{Bmatrix} 1 \\ 2 \end{Bmatrix} \end{bmatrix} \tag{6.52}$$

It is left as an exercise to verify that the finite-difference recursion relation equivalents of (6.51)-(6.52) are

$$S_e[\Delta_e \{U\}_e^T[A3000]_2] \Rightarrow \frac{\Delta}{8}(U_{j-1} + 6U_j + U_{j+1})U_j' \tag{6.53}$$

$$S_e[\Delta_e \{U\}_e^T[A3000]_1] \Rightarrow \frac{\Delta}{6}(U_{j-1} + 4U_j + U_{j+1})U_j' \tag{6.54}$$

For comparison, using (6.40),

$$S_e[\Delta_e \{U\}_e^T[A3000]] \Rightarrow \frac{\Delta}{12}((U_{j-1} + U_j)U_{j-1}' + (U_{j-1} + 6U_j + U_{j+1})U_j' + (U_j + U_{j+1})U_{j+1}') \tag{6.55}$$

Comparing (6.50)–(6.55), the fullness of the hypermatrix [$A3000$] determines the extent of coupling of the velocity approximation U, and its x_1 derivative, in the nonlinear downstream convection term. The impact of the ad hoc operations on accuracy and convergence is summarized in the next section.

Problems

1 Verify the [$A3001$] transverse convection hypermatrix (6.41), for the $k = 1$ finite-element basis.

2 Using the definition for the jacobian, establish (6.45)–(6.48).

3 Verify the finite-difference recursion relations (6.50), (6.53)–(6.55).

6.6 ACCURACY AND CONVERGENCE, LAMINAR FLOW

The principal requirement is to quantize accuracy and convergence of the finite-element algorithm and of the various outlined formulational modifications in terms of the energy norm (6.26), as implemented using (6.31) and/or (6.33). Comparison of the results of closely controlled numerical experiments to the theory is reported by Soliman (1978) (see also Soliman and Baker, 1981a).

Following considerable numerical experimentation, including verification of the ability to reproduce the Blasius similarity solution, a linear-slug profile initial-condition for u^h was determined to be effective in eliminating the H^1 norm of the initial data [see (6.26)] as the dominant term setting the level of the energy norm. This profile is graphed in Fig. 6.2; maintaining the knee at $x_2 = 0.2$ provides a uniform evaluation of $\|Q_0\|_{H^1}$ for all k and all (nonuniform) discretizations. The transverse velocity was assumed identically zero, until four steps were taken in x_1, to permit an accurate evaluation of $\{U\}'$ using the backward difference formula

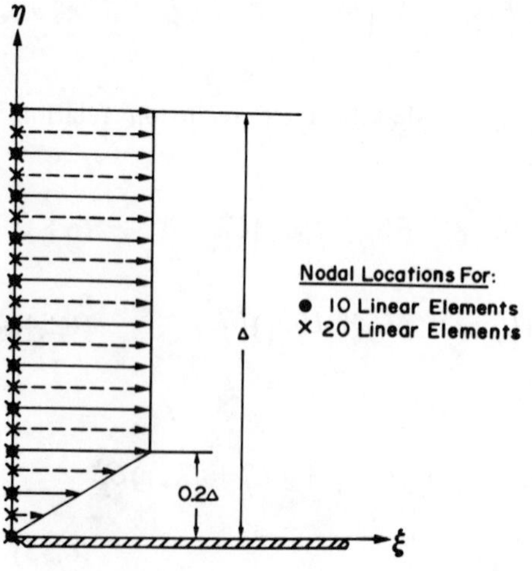

Figure 6.2 Graph of initial condition $u^h(x_2, x_1^0)$.

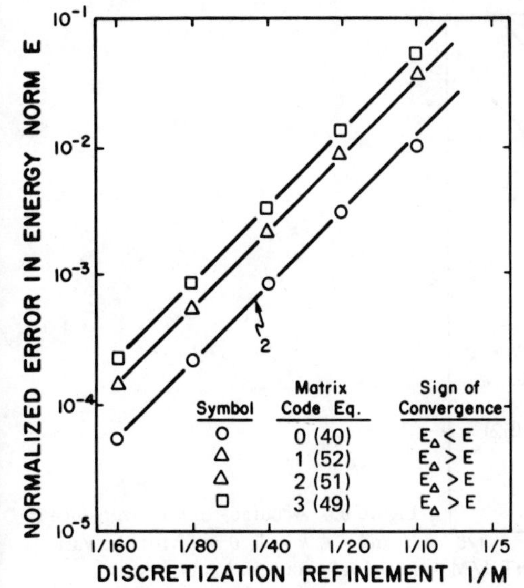

Figure 6.3 Accuracy and convergence in energy norm, $k = 1$, $\theta = \frac{1}{2}$, for the various initial-value matrix structures.

(6.23). The reported results were quantized at $\Delta x_1 = 0.8$ ft, for $\text{Re} = 0.7 \times 10^6$/ft, and a Richardson extrapolation was employed to verify that Δx_1 truncation error did not affect the significant digits in $E(\cdot, \cdot)$.

Figure 6.3 graphs the predicted accuracy and convergence for the $\theta = \frac{1}{2}$, $k = 1$ finite-element algorithm (6.17)–(6.22), using uniform discretization refinements of R^1, and for the four forms of the initial-value matrix (6.40), (6.49), (6.51), and (6.52). All converge quadratically, i.e., are accurately interpolated by the lines drawn at a slope of two, with negligible data scatter. Recall that the linear theory asserts that the finite-element solution will minimize the error in energy, in comparison to all other equivalently order-accurate solutions. The results in Fig. 6.3 thus indicate extension of the theory to this (milder) nonlinear application, since the results obtained using the finite-element derived matrix [$A3000$], (6.40), yield uniformly the smallest error, smaller by a factor of five than the Crank-Nicolson error in this norm. In further agreement with the linear theory, the finite-element solution convergence is from below, that is, $E^h < E$, where E is the estimated energy of the exact solution. This estimate, used to normalize E^h(E_Δ in the figure) is established assuming that convergence is indeed quadratic and extrapolating the data to very large M. All other forms for [$A3000$] yielded convergence from above, $E^h > E$; furthermore, the error associated with the two intermediate complexity matrix modifications, (6.51) and (6.52), was indistinguishable, and was a modest improvement over the Crank-Nicolson equivalent (6.49). The coarsest grid ($M = 10$) finite-element error is slightly lower than that predicted by strict adherence to the convergence curve, confirming the data of Popinski and Baker (1976). Convergence in the engineering norms H and C_f is also quadratic (Fig. 6.4), with negligible data scatter. The predicted differences in absolute accuracy for each M are negligibly small, except for the coarsest discretization. Importantly, however,

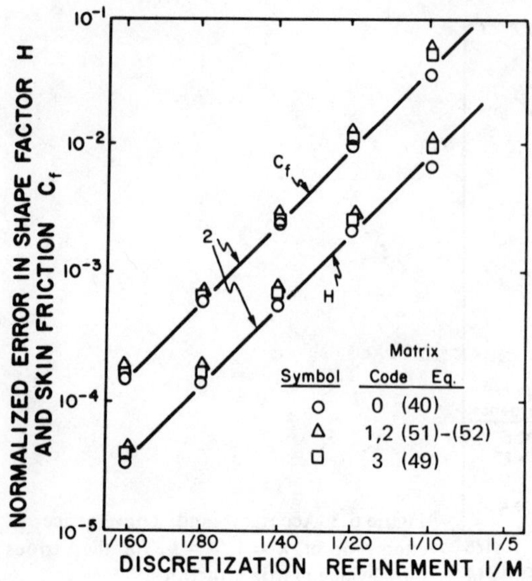

Figure 6.4 Accuracy and convergence in H and Cf, $k = 1$, $\theta = \frac{1}{2}$, for the various initial-value matrix structures.

the best absolute accuracy at each M accrues to the consistent finite-element algorithm solution.

The uniform grid accuracy and convergence assessment of the (consistent) finite-element algorithm, for the linear, quadratic and Lagrange cubic basis, $1 \leqslant k \leqslant 3$ in (6.13), is summarized in Fig. 6.5. The lines are at integer slope, and the numerically predicted convergence of the $k = 1$ solution, and the coarser grid $k = 2$ solutions, predict extension of the linear theory to the nonlinear equation

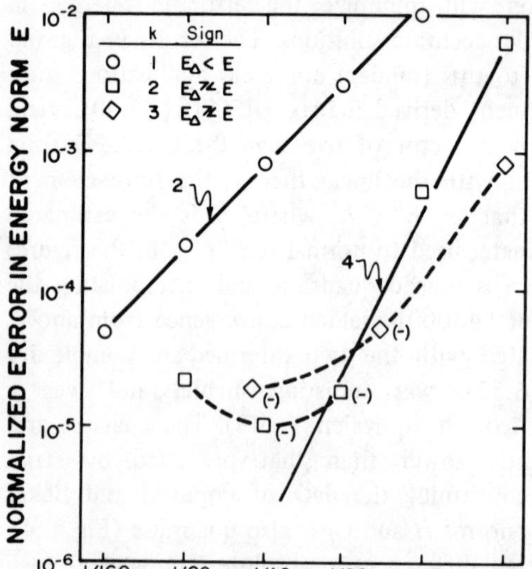

Figure 6.5 Accuracy and convergence in energy, linear, quadratic and cubic finite-element algorithm.

system. The finer grid $k = 2$ solutions fail to adhere to the convergence curve, for solution error in energy smaller than about 10^{-5}, which indicates an alternative error source has become dominant. The convergence of the $k = 3$ solutions is comparable to the quadratic, which is much poorer than the sixth degree predicted by the linear theory. Only for the $k = 1$ solution is convergence monotonic and from below, $E^h < E$. For $k = 2$ and $k = 3$, convergence is oscillatory and starts from below. The results of additional numerical experiments (Soliman, 1978), confirm that the coupling of the (second-order accurate) continuity equation solution algorithm [(6.22)-(6.23)] contributes significantly to the loss of accuracy of the quadratic algorithm for large M.

In actual engineering practice, boundary layer solutions are executed typically on nonuniform discretizations of R^1. The sole modification to the convergence statement (6.26) is replacement of Δ_e by $\Delta_e^{\max}$, the largest finite-element domain. A smooth progression of nonuniformity is desirable, with the smallest domains nearest the no-slip surface (especially for turbulent flows). A suitable procedure employs a geometric progression for Δ_e, that is, $\Delta_{j+1} \equiv \rho\, \Delta_j$ where $\rho \geqslant 1$ is the progression factor. The corresponding equation defining the node coordinates η_j of $\cup R_e^1$ is

$$\eta_{e+1} = \eta_e + \frac{R^1}{\sum_{j=1}^{M} \rho^{j-1}}\, \rho^{e-1} \qquad 1 \leqslant e \leqslant M \tag{6.56}$$

where η_{e+1} is the extremum nodal coordinate of Δ_e. Table 6.1 summarizes the useful range of ρ, and the corresponding value of M.

The $M = 80$ linear-element uniform discretization was selected (Soliman and Baker, 1981a), as the base case for comparison of all nonuniform solutions. The knee of the u^h initial profile (Fig. 6.2) was maintained at 20 percent of the domain span, such that $\|Q_0\|_{H^1}$ was a uniform constant for all nonuniform discretizations and all finite-element basis. Figure 6.6 summarizes computed $k = 1$ accuracy and

Table 6.1 Factors for geometric nonuniform discretization of R^1

Linear basis, $k = 1$		Quadratic basis, $k = 1$	
M	ρ	M	ρ
16	1.1917	8	1.4883
23	1.1008	11	1.2369
27	1.0726	16	1.1143
33	1.0509	24	1.0442
48	1.0202	40	1.0000
80	1.0000		

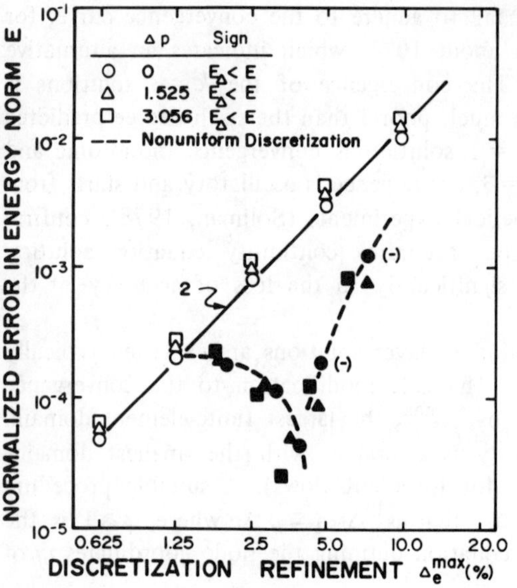

Figure 6.6 Accuracy and convergence in energy, boundary layer with pressure gradient, linear finite-element algorithm.

convergence for a range of pressure gradient p_I' [see (6.15)], which controlled solution energy level by ±50 percent compared to the initial profile energy. This corresponds to the norm $\|F(n\,\Delta x)\|_{H^0}$ of the data. The nonuniform grid solutions are the solid symbols, and the minus signs adjacent to the coarse grid symbols indicate the sign of the error changed, that is, $E^h > E$, where E is the estimated exact energy. The advantage of the nonuniform discretization is clearly evident, since the level of error is smaller for any (all) M (with smallest element adjacent to the wall). Furthermore, the dashed line interpolation of the nonuniform grid data passes through an absolute minimum (zero), at which $M \approx 27$, $\rho \approx 1.07$, which indicates existence of an optimum grid for the problem class. Existence of this optimum grid was confirmed in the engineering norms H and C_f, as well, although the impact of pressure gradient on absolute level of error was considerably larger. Since the data in E collapse to an essential universal curve, the energy norm does appear to be a preferred measure of accuracy.

The companion results for the comparison Crank-Nicolson algorithm form are summarized in Fig. 6.7. Contrary to the finite-element data, the error level changes substantially with pressure gradient. However, convergence remains nominally quadratic for both the uniform and geometrically nonuniform discretizations, with select data scatter and some evidence of coarse grid inaccuracy. The absolute level of improvement with nonuniform discretization is drastically reduced in comparison with the finite-element data, and there is only slight indication of existence of an optimum grid.

Soliman and Baker (1981a) also present data on accuracy and convergence in energy for the quadratic element algorithm (Fig. 6.8). Only for zero pressure gradient is the optimal fourth degree convergence confirmed on the coarser grids. This convergence rate is reduced considerably using a nonuniform grid, with the net

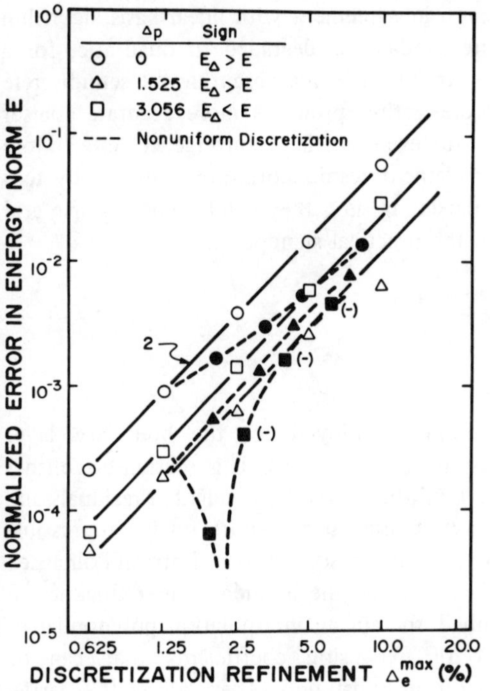

Figure 6.7 Accuracy and convergence in energy, boundary layer with pressure gradient, Crank-Nicolson finite difference form.

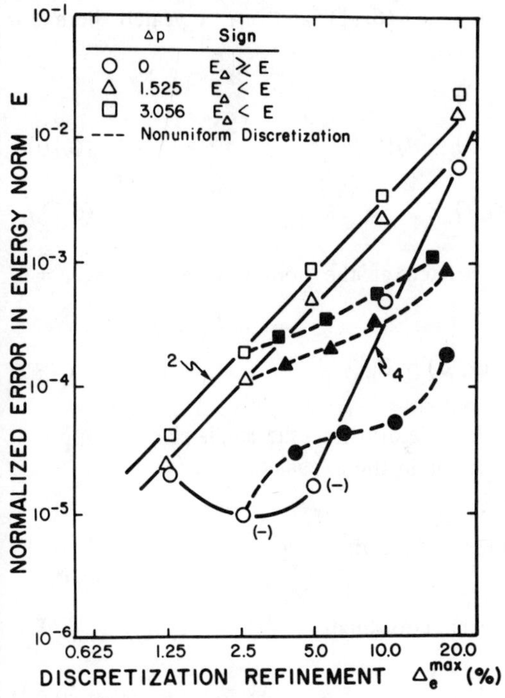

Figure 6.8 Accuracy and convergence in energy, boundary layer with pressure gradient, quadratic finite-element algorithm.

result being improved coarse grid accuracy in agreement with linear basis algorithm data. Convergence for nonzero pressure gradient is degraded to quadratic, for a uniform grid, indicating that alternative error sources are obscuring the semidiscrete error. Nevertheless, the nonuniform discretization produces more accurate coarser grid solutions, which correspond to an even smaller convergence rate. More correctly, however, these and the linear element results correspond universally to a lack of divergence with discretization coarsening, i.e., they exhibit good coarse grid accuracy, a highly desirable feature from the practical standpoint.

6.7 HIGH-DEGREE BASIS SINGLE-ELEMENT SOLUTION

Integral solution procedures are commonly employed for the boundary layer equations (Blottner, 1970, 1975; Cebeci and Smith, 1974). This section establishes an example procedure within the context of the method of weighted residuals and local finite-element interpolation. The earliest integral procedure for incompressible constant viscosity boundary layer flows is attributed to von Karman-Polhausen (Schlichting, 1979). Referring to Fig. 6.1, assume the boundary layer thickness δ spanned by a single finite element. Imbed therein an interpolation polynomial of one degree greater than the number of expansion coefficients that can be determined by the known boundary condition constraints. Then, recast the partial differential equation system (6.2)-(6.3) for solution of this parameter. Boundary conditions for use were presented as (6.8)-(6.11) and are repeated here for convenience

$$u(x, 0) = 0 \tag{6.8}$$

$$u(x, \delta) = u_I(x) \tag{6.10}$$

$$\frac{\partial}{\partial y} u(x, \delta) = 0 \tag{6.11}$$

In addition, comparing (6.7) to (6.3) written at the boundary layer edge $y = \delta$, yields

$$\frac{\partial^2}{\partial y^2} u(x, \delta) = 0 \tag{6.57}$$

With four constraints for the problem description, the single-element approximation function must then contain five terms in the expansion

$$u^h(x, y) \equiv \sum_{i=0}^{4} a_i(x)\eta^i \tag{6.58}$$

In (6.58), η is the nondimensional transverse coordinate

$$\eta \equiv \frac{y}{\delta(x)} \tag{6.59}$$

A parameter of the solution λ can be identified

$$\lambda \equiv -\frac{\delta^2}{\nu}\frac{du_I}{dx} \tag{6.60}$$

in terms of which the expansion coefficients in (6.58) can be evaluated. Differentiation of (6.58) twice, substitution of the results into (6.3) evaluated at the wall $y = 0$, and use of (6.2) yields

$$\frac{\delta^2}{u_I}\frac{\partial^2}{\partial y^2}u(x, 0) = 2a_2 = \frac{\delta^2}{u_I}\nu\frac{dp_I}{dx}$$

Using the identity in (6.7), equivalently, from (6.60),

$$2a_2 = -\frac{\delta^2}{\nu}\frac{du_I}{dx} = \lambda$$

Substitution of (6.58) into (6.8)–(6.11) yields the elements a_i of $\{a\}$ as

$$\{a\}^T = \tfrac{1}{6}\,\{0, \lambda + 12, 3\lambda, 3\lambda - 12, 6 - \lambda\} \tag{6.61}$$

Therefore, the single-element approximation function (6.58) becomes expressed in terms of λ as

$$u^h(x, y) = \left[2\eta - 2\eta^3 + \eta^4 + \frac{\lambda}{6}(\eta - 3\eta^2 + 3\eta^3 - \eta^4)\right]u_I(x) \tag{6.62}$$

The solution will become expressed in terms of λ, δ^*, and θ, and the boundary layer thickness δ. Substitution of (6.62) into (6.34)–(6.35) yields

$$\frac{\delta^*}{\delta} = \frac{3}{10} - \frac{\lambda}{120} \qquad \frac{\theta}{\delta} = \frac{37}{315} - \frac{\lambda}{945} - \frac{\lambda^2}{9072} \tag{6.63}$$

Similarly, for wall shear (6.37), using (6.62),

$$\tau_w = \mu_w \left.\frac{\partial u}{\partial y}\right|_{y=0} = \frac{\mu u_I}{\delta}\left(\frac{\lambda + 12}{6}\right) \tag{6.64}$$

Therefore, all integral parameters of an isoenergetic incompressible boundary layer are cast in terms of λ. Hence, within the context of weighted residuals, the von Karman-Pohlhausen algorithm is achieved by defining

$$\int_0^\delta L(u^h)\,dy \equiv 0 \tag{6.65}$$

Using (6.3), (6.65) becomes (deleting superscript h for clarity)

$$\int_0^\delta \left[u\frac{\partial u}{\partial x} + v\frac{\partial u}{\partial y} + \frac{1}{\rho}\frac{dp_I}{dx} - \frac{\partial}{\partial y}\left(\nu\frac{\partial u}{\partial y}\right)\right] dy = 0 \tag{6.66}$$

Integrating (6.2) directly,

$$v(y) = v_w - \int_0^y \frac{\partial u}{\partial x}\, dy \tag{6.67}$$

Furthermore, from (6.7)

$$\frac{1}{\rho_0}\frac{dp_I}{dx} = -u_I \frac{du_I}{dx} \tag{6.68}$$

Using (6.67)-(6.68), (6.66) becomes

$$\int_0^\delta u \frac{\partial u}{\partial x}\, dy + v_w \int_0^\delta \frac{\partial u}{\partial y}\, dy - \int_0^\delta \frac{\partial u}{\partial y} \int_0^y \frac{\partial u}{\partial x}\, d\bar{y}\, dy$$

$$- \int_0^\delta u_I \frac{du_I}{dx}\, dy - \int_0^\delta \frac{\partial}{\partial y}\left(\nu \frac{\partial u}{\partial y}\right) dy = 0 \tag{6.69}$$

Integrating the third term by parts yields

$$u \int_0^y \frac{\partial u}{\partial x}\, dy \Bigg|_0^\delta - \int_0^\delta u \frac{\partial u}{\partial x}\, dy$$

Noting that the second and fifth terms in (6.69) are integrals of perfect differentials,

$$v_w \int_0^\delta \frac{\partial u}{\partial y}\, dy = v_w u_I$$

$$\int_0^\delta \frac{\partial}{\partial y}\left(\nu \frac{\partial u}{\partial y}\right) dy = \frac{-1}{\rho}\, \tau_w$$

Combining these expressions with (6.69) then yields

$$\int_0^\delta \frac{1}{2}\frac{\partial}{\partial x}(u^2)\, dy - \int_0^\delta \frac{1}{2}\frac{d}{dx}(u_I^2)\, dy + v_w u_I - u_I \int_0^\delta \frac{\partial u}{\partial x}\, dy = \frac{-1}{\rho}\, \tau_w \tag{6.70}$$

Finally, noting that the derivative of the boundary layer thickness with respect to the longitudinal coordinate vanishes, the x derivatives in (6.70) can be extracted from inside the integrals to yield

$$\frac{d}{dx}\, u_I^2 \int_0^\delta \frac{u}{u_I}\left(1 - \frac{u}{u_I}\right) dy + \frac{du_I}{dx}\, u_I \int_0^\delta \left(1 - \frac{u}{u_I}\right) dy - v_w u_I = \frac{1}{\rho}\, \tau_w$$

Noting the definitions of displacement thickness δ^* and momentum thickness θ, (6.63), the final form for (6.65) is

$$(u_I^2\theta)' + u_I\delta^* u_I' - v_w u_I = \frac{1}{\rho}\tau_w \tag{6.71}$$

The single-element approximation function is written in (6.62) as a one-parameter function of λ, as are δ^* and θ. Equation (6.71) can be rearranged to expose λ. Expanding and multiplying through by $\theta/u_I\nu$, it is left as an exercise to show that (6.71) can be written as

$$\begin{aligned}\left(\frac{u_I}{\nu}\theta^2\right)' &= \frac{\theta^2}{\nu}u_I' - 2\left(2+\frac{\delta^*}{\theta}\right)\frac{\theta^2}{\nu}u_I' - \frac{v_w\theta}{\nu} + \theta\frac{\tau_w}{u_I\mu}\\ &= -\left(3\frac{\theta^2}{\delta^2} + \frac{2\delta^*\theta}{\delta^2}\right)\frac{\delta^2}{\nu}u_I' - \frac{v_w\theta}{\nu} + \theta\frac{\tau_w}{u_I\mu}\end{aligned} \tag{6.72}$$

Substituting the definition of λ (6.60) into (6.72) finally yields

$$\left(\frac{u_I}{\nu}\theta^2\right)' = 3\left(\frac{\theta}{\delta}\right)^2\lambda + 2\left(\frac{\delta^*}{\delta}\right)\left(\frac{\theta}{\delta}\right)\lambda + v_w\frac{\theta}{\delta}\frac{\lambda}{\delta u_I'} + \frac{\theta}{\delta}\frac{\lambda+12}{6} \equiv F(\lambda) \tag{6.73}$$

The second form occurs since θ/δ and δ^*/δ are specified functions of λ. The numerical solution of (6.73) then provides determination of the evolution of $\theta(x)$. It fundamentally is a function of u_I' assuming $v_w(x)$ is known.

For the case of zero mass flux at the wall, the solution of (6.72)–(6.73) can be developed further. Define

$$K \equiv \frac{-\theta^2}{\nu}u_e' = \frac{\theta^2}{\delta^2}\lambda \tag{6.74}$$

For (6.72) and $v_w = 0$, using (6.74)

$$\left(\frac{u_I}{\nu}\theta^2\right)' = K - 2\left(2+\frac{\delta^*}{\theta}\right)K + \frac{\theta\tau_w}{u_I\mu} \tag{6.75}$$

From the definitions (6.60) and (6.74),

$$\frac{\delta^*}{\theta} \equiv f_1(K) \qquad \frac{\tau_w\theta}{u_I\mu} \equiv f_2(K)$$

Therefore, (6.75) becomes

$$\left(\frac{u_I}{\nu}\theta^2\right)' = K - 2[2 + f_1(K)]\,K + f_2(K) \approx 0.47 - 5K \tag{6.76}$$

expanding the definition expressions and dropping higher order terms. Then (6.75) becomes

$$\left(\frac{u_I\theta^2}{\nu}\right)' \approx 0.47 - 5\left(\frac{\theta^2}{\nu}u_I'\right)$$

or
$$\left(\frac{u_I\theta^2}{\nu}\right)' + \frac{5}{u_I}\frac{\theta^2 u_I}{\nu}u_I' \approx 0.47 \tag{6.77}$$

Multiplying through by u_I^5 allows the left side to be cast as a perfect differential as

$$\left(u_I^5\,\frac{u_I\theta^2}{\nu}\right)'$$

Integrating this expression from the stagnation point forward then yields

$$\theta^2(x) \approx \frac{0.47\nu}{u_I^6(x)}\int_0^x u_I^5(\xi)\,d\xi \tag{6.78}$$

The solution of (6.78) yields $\theta(x)$; therefore, from (6.74) we determine K, and then λ in concert with (6.63). We then have the necessary information to solve (6.63) for δ and δ^* and subsequently (6.64) for τ_w.

As an example, consider the previously discussed case of boundary layer flow over a flat plate with zero-pressure gradient. Hence, $u_I(x) = U_\infty =$ constant, and (6.78) yields

$$\theta(x) \approx \sqrt{\frac{0.47\nu x}{U_\infty}} = 0.686\sqrt{\frac{\nu x}{U_\infty}} \tag{6.79}$$

The exact similarity (Blasius) solution (Schlichting, 1979) predicts

$$\theta_B(x) = 0.664\sqrt{\frac{\nu x}{U_\infty}}$$

Therefore, (6.79) is only about 3 percent in error for this simple case; more importantly, it displays the correct functional dependence. Continuing, from (6.74), $K = 0 = \lambda$, and from (6.63)

$$\delta = \frac{315}{37}\,\theta = 5.840\sqrt{\frac{\nu x}{U_\infty}}$$

For comparison, the Blasius solution yields

$$\delta_B \approx 5.0\sqrt{\frac{\nu x}{U_\infty}}$$

Therefore, the boundary layer thickness is overestimated by approximately 16 percent. From (6.63), for the displacement thickness comparison

$$\delta^*(x) = \frac{3}{10}\,\delta \approx 1.752\sqrt{\frac{\nu x}{U_\infty}}$$

The exact solution is

$$\delta_B^*(x) = 1.72\sqrt{\frac{\nu x}{U_\infty}}$$

and the one-element solution is in error by less than 2 percent. Finally, for skin friction, from (6.64),

$$\frac{\tau_W}{\rho u_I^2} = 0.342 \sqrt{\frac{1}{\text{Re } x}}$$

By comparison, the Blasius solution yields

$$0.332 \sqrt{\frac{1}{\text{Re } x}}$$

showing that the single-element solution is only 3 percent in error for shear stress.

Thus observe that a high degree single finite-element solution of the boundary layer equations has resulted in a readily evaluable determination capability for the important engineering parameters. Furthermore, for the simple case for which a comparison similarity solution exists, the solution accuracy in terms of the boundary layer parameters is quite acceptable for engineering purposes.

Problems

1 Determine the single-element approximation function for u^h (6.62) in terms of λ and η, using the boundary conditions and definition (6.60).

2 Determine the functional relationships (6.63) between δ^*, θ, and δ in terms of λ.

3 Obtain the form (6.72) from the parent differential equation (6.71).

4 Solve (6.78) for the case of stagnation point flow where $u_I(x) = U_\infty x$. Determine the functional forms and solve for the engineering parameters δ, δ^*, θ, and τ_W.

6.8 TURBULENT BOUNDARY LAYER EQUATION SYSTEM

The two-dimensional turbulent flow boundary layer equations are obtained by time-averaging the parent Navier-Stokes equations and then performing the boundary layer order of magnitude analysis (Cebeci and Smith, 1974). For steady mean flows, the instantaneous velocity vector $\mathbf{u}(x_i, t)$ is assumed expressible in terms of an average steady flow component $\bar{\mathbf{u}}(x_i)$, and a fluctuation $\mathbf{u}'(x_i, t)$ about that mean value, as

$$\mathbf{u}(x_i, t) \equiv \bar{\mathbf{u}}(x_i) + \mathbf{u}'(x_i, t) \tag{6.80}$$

Time-averaging is expressed as

$$\overline{\mathbf{u}(x_i, t)} \equiv \lim_{T\to\infty} \frac{1}{T} \int_{t_0}^{t_0+T} \mathbf{u}(x_i, t)\, dt \equiv \bar{\mathbf{u}}(x_i) \tag{6.81}$$

where the second form is the definition of $\bar{\mathbf{u}}$. By direct substitution into (6.81),

$$\bar{\mathbf{u}}' = 0$$

The time-averaging of products of scalar components of velocity, as occurs in the convective acceleration term in the Navier-Stokes equations, yields, for example,

$$\overline{u(x_i, t)v(x_i, t)} = \overline{uv} + \overline{u'v'} \tag{6.82}$$

Time-averaging the Navier-Stokes equations and applying the boundary layer order-of-magnitude analysis yields the boundary layer equations for turbulent flow as

$$L(\rho_0) \equiv \frac{\partial \bar{u}}{\partial x} + \frac{\partial \bar{v}}{\partial y} = 0 \tag{6.83}$$

$$L(\bar{u}) = \bar{u}\frac{\partial \bar{u}}{\partial x} + \bar{v}\frac{\partial \bar{u}}{\partial y} + \frac{1}{\rho_0}\frac{dp_I}{dx} - \frac{\partial}{\partial y}\left(\frac{\nu}{\text{Re}}\frac{\partial \bar{u}}{\partial y} - \overline{u'v'}\right) = 0 \tag{6.84}$$

$$L(v) = \frac{\partial}{\partial y}(\bar{p} + \rho_0\overline{v'v'}) = 0 \tag{6.85}$$

Comparing (6.83)-(6.85) to the laminar flow form, (6.2)-(6.4), confirms the continuity equation unchanged for the mean-flow velocity, and the addition of the Reynolds shear stress $-\overline{u'v'}$ to the x momentum equation. In addition, (6.85) indicates a first-order balancing of the pressure distribution through δ with the Reynolds normal stress component $-\overline{v'v'}$. This linear equation is directly integrated yielding

$$\bar{p}(x, y) = p_I(x)[1 + \rho_0\overline{v'v'}(y)] \tag{6.86}$$

where $p_I(x_1)$ is the inviscid freestream flow pressure distribution.

Equations (6.83)-(6.84) define a well-posed initial-boundary value problem for **u**(x), upon identification of correlation equations for the Reynolds stresses. Two closure models are in common practice. The basic assumption is definition of a "turbulent" kinematic viscosity ν^t, such that

$$-\overline{u'v'} \equiv \nu^t \frac{\partial \bar{u}}{\partial y} \tag{6.87}$$

Dimensional homogeneity dictates ν^t be the product of a scale velocity and scale length, i.e.,

$$\nu^t \equiv ul \tag{6.88}$$

where u and l are measures on the scale of fluctuating velocity correlations. For the turbulence kinetic energy (TKE) model,

$$u \equiv \tfrac{1}{2}(\overline{u'u'} + \overline{v'v'} + \overline{w'w'}) \equiv k \tag{6.89}$$

i.e., the kinetic energy (k) of the fluctuating velocity correlation. The corresponding dissipation length scale l_d is defined as

$$l \equiv \frac{\omega^b C_\nu k^{3/2}}{\epsilon} \equiv l_d \tag{6.90}$$

where ϵ is the isotropic turbulence dissipation function:

$$\epsilon \equiv \frac{2\nu}{3} \overline{\frac{\partial u_i'}{\partial x_j} \frac{\partial u_i'}{\partial x_k}} \delta_{jk} \tag{6.91}$$

Summation over the tensor index pairs is implied in (6.91). Furthermore, in (6.90), C_ν is a correlation constant and ω is a specified function of x_2 that accounts for wall proximity damping effects on the scale length. Hence, (6.88) takes the specific form, for the TKE closure model,

$$\nu^t \equiv \omega^b C_\nu \frac{k^2}{\epsilon} \tag{6.92}$$

For the Prandtl mixing length (MLT) closure model (Cebeci and Smith, 1974), the length scale l_m is defined as

$$l_m \equiv \begin{cases} \kappa y & 0 \leqslant y \leqslant \dfrac{\lambda\delta}{\kappa} \\ \lambda\delta & y > \dfrac{\lambda\delta}{\kappa} \end{cases} \tag{6.93}$$

where $\delta(x)$ is the boundary layer thickness, and κ and λ are constants (typically 0.435 and 0.09, respectively). The scale velocity u is selected as the magnitude of the mean flow strain rate; hence, (6.88) takes the form

$$\nu^t \equiv (\omega l_m)^2 \left| \frac{\partial \bar{u}}{\partial y} \right| \tag{6.94}$$

where ω is the van Driest damping function

$$\omega \equiv 1 - e^{-y/A} \tag{6.95}$$

In (6.95), A is a complex function of many factors influencing flow phenomena near the surface, including axial pressure gradient and normal mass flow. The form of Cebeci and Smith (1974) serves to unify the many formulations as

$$A \equiv A^+ \nu N^{-1} \left(\frac{\tau_w}{\rho_w}\right)^{-1/2} \left(\frac{\rho}{\rho_w}\right)^{1/2} \tag{6.96}$$

where $$N^2 \equiv \frac{\nu}{\nu_I} \left(\frac{\rho_I}{\rho_w}\right)^2 \frac{p^+}{v^+} \left[1 - \exp\left(11.8 \frac{\nu_w}{\nu} v^+\right)\right] + \exp\left(11.8 \frac{\nu_w}{\nu} v^+\right) \tag{6.97}$$

All variables are time-averaged steady components; subscripts I and w refer to freestream and wall values, respectively; A^+ is a constant (25.3); and τ_w is the skin friction. Pressure gradient and mass addition effects are accounted for accordingly as

$$p^+ \equiv \left(\frac{\nu_I u_I}{u_\tau^3}\right) \frac{du_I}{dx} \tag{6.98}$$

$$v^+ \equiv u_\tau^{-1} v_w \tag{6.99}$$

where u_I is the freestream axial velocity, v_w is the specified velocity normal to the surface, if present, and u_τ is the shear velocity

$$u_\tau \equiv \left(\frac{\tau_W}{\rho_W}\right)^{1/2} \tag{6.100}$$

The shear stress τ_W is defined as

$$\tau_W \equiv \rho_W \nu_W \left.\frac{\partial \bar{u}}{\partial y}\right|_w \tag{6.101}$$

It can be evaluated using a difference formula for $\partial\bar{u}/\partial y$ or from the Ludwig-Tillmann equation for skin friction

$$C_f \equiv \frac{\tau_W}{(1/2)(\rho_I u_I^2)} \equiv 0.246 \times 10^{-0.678H} \mathrm{Re}_\theta^{-0.268} \tag{6.102}$$

Therefore, once the parameters are specified for a solution and the mean flow velocity distribution $\bar{u}$ is determined, ν^t can be evaluated and the problem definition is closed.

Equations (6.92) or (6.94), coupled with (6.87) complete the closure. Defining the effective viscosity,

$$\nu^e \equiv \frac{\nu}{\mathrm{Re}} + \nu^t \tag{6.103}$$

Eq. (6.84) takes the nonlinear parabolic form

$$L(\bar{u}) = \bar{u}\,\frac{\partial \bar{u}}{\partial x} + \bar{v}\,\frac{\partial \bar{u}}{\partial y} - \frac{\partial}{\partial y}\left(\nu^e\,\frac{\partial \bar{u}}{\partial y}\right) + \frac{1}{\rho_0}\,\frac{d\bar{p}}{dx} = 0 \tag{6.104}$$

The boundary layer form of the additional differential equations for the TKE closure (Cebeci and Smith, 1974) are also parabolic:

$$L(k) = \bar{u}\,\frac{\partial k}{\partial x} + \bar{v}\,\frac{\partial k}{\partial y} - \frac{\partial}{\partial y}\left(\frac{\nu^e}{C_k}\,\frac{\partial k}{\partial y}\right) - \nu^t\left(\frac{\partial \bar{u}}{\partial y}\right)^2 + \epsilon = 0 \tag{6.105}$$

$$L(\epsilon) = \bar{u}\,\frac{\partial \epsilon}{\partial x} + \bar{v}\,\frac{\partial \epsilon}{\partial y} - \frac{\partial}{\partial y}\left(\frac{\nu^t}{C_\epsilon}\,\frac{\partial \epsilon}{\partial y}\right) - C_\epsilon^1 \epsilon k^{-1} \nu^t \left(\frac{\partial u}{\partial y}\right)^2 + C_\epsilon^2 \epsilon^2 k^{-1} = 0 \tag{6.106}$$

where the various C_β^α are model constants (Hanjalic and Launder, 1972). The MLT closure requires no additional equations. Since (6.104)-(6.106) are parabolic, two boundary conditions and an initial distribution are required. At an impervious surface, all variables vanish:

$$\begin{aligned} \bar{u}(x, 0) &= 0 = \bar{v}(x, 0) \\ k(x, 0) &= 0 = \epsilon(x, 0) \end{aligned} \tag{6.107}$$

At the freestream, $y > \delta(x)$, all dependent variables merge smoothly with vanishing y derivative into their freestream levels, i.e.,

$$\frac{\partial \bar{u}}{\partial y} = \frac{\partial k}{\partial y} = \frac{\partial \epsilon}{\partial y} = 0 \tag{6.108}$$

Furthermore, by definition, $k = 0 = \epsilon$ in the freestream and $\bar{u}(x, y > \delta)$ equals the freestream inviscid velocity u_I. Again, (6.83) is solved directly for $\bar{v}(x, y)$ as a pure initial-value problem with $\bar{v}(x, 0) \equiv 0$ for no mass addition.

Initial distributions for $\bar{u}$, k and ϵ at (x_0, y) are required to initialize the solution of (6.104)-(6.106). In the absence of experimental data (the usual case), Cole's law (Cebeci and Smith, 1974) can be utilized to compute $u(x_0, y < \delta)$ based on $u_I(x_0)$ and $\delta(x_0)$. This is sufficient information for an MLT solution initialization. Should a TKE solution be required, the availability of the MLT computed ν^t, (6.94), coupled with (6.90) and (6.92) can be used to establish $k(x_0, y)$, and $\epsilon(x_0, y)$, assuming a relationship exists between l_d and l_m. From numerical experimentation, a useful form is

$$l_d \equiv C^{-1/2} \omega^a l_m \tag{6.109}$$

where C and a are parameters to be determined. Combining (6.88), (6.89), and (6.109) then yields

$$k(x_0, y) = C\omega^{2(2-a)} l_m^2 \left| \frac{\partial \bar{u}}{\partial y} \right| \tag{6.110}$$

Finally, substituting (6.109)-(6.110) into (6.90) yields

$$\epsilon(x_0, y) = \frac{C^{1/2} \omega^{b-a} C_\nu k^{3/2}}{l_m} \tag{6.111}$$

Equations (6.109)-(6.111) have been determined (Baker et al., 1982) to yield initial distributions that converge to solutions of (6.105)-(6.106), for a range of problem specifications. Typical values for the model constants $\{a, b, C, C_\nu\}$ are $\{1.0, 2.0, 3.0, 0.068\}$.

As a final step, a coordinate transformation is usually employed to account for boundary layer growth. A suitable elementary form is the grid-stretching transformation

$$\xi = x \qquad \eta = \frac{y}{f(x)} \tag{6.112}$$

illustrated in Fig. 6.9, where $f(x) \geqslant \delta(x)$ is at least piecewise continuous. Using the chain rule,

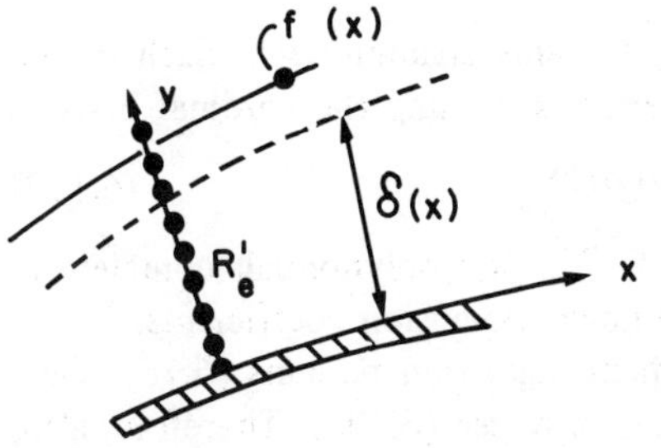

Figure 6.9 Illustration of boundary layer domain parameters.

$$\frac{\partial}{\partial x} = \frac{\partial}{\partial \xi}\frac{d\xi}{dx} + \frac{\partial}{\partial \eta}\frac{d\eta}{dx} = \frac{\partial}{\partial \xi} - \eta\frac{f'}{f}\frac{\partial}{\partial \eta} \tag{6.113}$$

where superscript prime denotes the ordinary derivative. Denoting $h \equiv f'/f$, the final form of (6.83), (6.104)-(6.106) for the turbulent boundary layer description is

$$L(\bar{v}) = \left(\frac{\partial}{\partial \xi} - \eta h\frac{\partial}{\partial \eta}\right)\bar{u} + \frac{\partial \bar{v}}{\partial \eta} = 0 \tag{6.114}$$

$$L(\bar{u}) = \bar{u}\left(\frac{\partial}{\partial \xi} - \eta h\frac{\partial}{\partial \eta}\right)\bar{u} + \bar{v}\frac{\partial \bar{u}}{\partial \eta} - \frac{\partial}{\partial \eta}\left(\frac{\nu^e}{f}\frac{\partial \bar{u}}{\partial \eta}\right) + \frac{1}{\rho_0}\frac{dp_I}{d\xi} = 0 \tag{6.115}$$

$$L(k) = \bar{u}\left(\frac{\partial}{\partial \xi} - \eta h\frac{\partial}{\partial \eta}\right)k + \bar{v}\frac{\partial k}{\partial \eta} - \frac{\partial}{\partial \eta}\left(\frac{\nu^e}{fC_k}\frac{\partial k}{\partial \eta}\right) - \nu^t\left(\frac{\partial \bar{u}}{\partial \eta}\right)^2 + \epsilon = 0 \tag{6.116}$$

$$L(\epsilon) = \bar{u}\left(\frac{\partial}{\partial \xi} - \eta h\frac{\partial}{\partial \eta}\right)\epsilon + \bar{v}\frac{\partial \epsilon}{\partial \eta} - \frac{\partial}{\partial \eta}\left(\frac{\nu^t}{fC_\epsilon}\frac{\partial \epsilon}{\partial \eta}\right) - C_\epsilon^1\frac{\epsilon\nu^t}{k}\left(\frac{\partial \bar{u}}{\partial \eta}\right)^2 + C_\epsilon^2\frac{\epsilon^2}{k} = 0 \tag{6.117}$$

Problems

1 Prove the relationship (6.82).

2 Derive (6.110)-(6.111).

3 Verify (6.113).

6.9 FINITE-ELEMENT SOLUTION ALGORITHM ADDITIONS

The finite-element solution algorithm for the form of (6.115)-(6.117) has been given in (6.16)-(6.20). The necessary generalization is to the vector-valued dependent variable set $q_j(\mathbf{x}) = \{\bar{u}, k, e, \bar{v}\}$. As before, the finite-element approximation $q_j^h(\mathbf{x})$ to $q_j(\mathbf{x})$ is defined in terms of the elemental solutions q_j^e as,

$$q_j(\mathbf{x}) \approx q_j^h(\mathbf{x}) \equiv \sum_{e=1}^{M} q_j^e(\mathbf{x}) \tag{6.118}$$

where M equals the number of finite-element domains spanning R^1. Each of the solution elemental variables and parameters is expressed using the cardinal basis as

$$q_j^e(\mathbf{x}) = \{N_k(\eta)\}^T\{QJ(\xi)\}_e \tag{6.119}$$

for the transformation (6.112). The elements of $\{N_k\}$ are polynomials complete to degree k, and the elements of $\{QJ\}_e$ are the unknown expansion coefficients.

The theoretical statement of the finite-element algorithm remains (6.16), since only homogeneous gradient boundary constraints exist, see (6.108). Therefore, also,

(6.17)–(6.20) is generalized to $\{FJ\}$ and $\{QJ\}$. The hypermatrix statement of the finite-element algorithm for (6.115)–(6.117) is, therefore,

$$S_e[\Delta_e \{U\}_e^T[A3000]\,\{QJ\}'_e - \Delta_e(\{U\}_e^T[A40010]\,h\,\{ETA\}_e - \{V\}_e^T[A3001])\{QJ\}_e + \Delta_e f^{-1}\,\{XNUE\}_e^T[A3011]\,\{QJ\}_e + \Delta_e\,\{SORCJ\}_e] \equiv \{0\} \tag{6.120}$$

The elements of the matrix $\{ETA\}_e$ are the (stationary) nodal coordinates of the finite-element discretization of R^1, while those of $\{SORCJ\}_e$ are the source/sink terms distinctive for each identification of q_j. From (6.115),

$$\{SORC1\}_e = p'_I\{A10\} \tag{6.121}$$

which is independent of e since p'_I is element independent. For $q_2 = k$, referring to (6.116)

$$\int_{R_e} \nu^t\left(\frac{\partial \bar{u}}{\partial \eta}\right)^2 d\eta = \{XNUT\}_e^T \int_{R_e^1} \{N_k\}\,\{U\}_e^T\,\{N_k\}'\,\{N_k\}'^T\{U\}_e\,\{N_k\}\,d\eta$$

$$= \Delta_e\,\{XNUT\}_e^T([A40011]\,\{U\}_e)\{U\}_e \tag{6.122}$$

In (6.122), $[A40011]$ is a hypermatrix of order $k+2$, where k is the degree of the finite-element basis, and each matrix element is a square matrix of the same order. Hence, the source term for k becomes

$$\{SORC2\}_e = -\{XNUT\}_e^T([A40011]\,\{U\}_e)\{U\}_e + [A200]\,\{EPS\}_e \tag{6.123}$$

where the braces emphasize that the inner matrix product must be performed first.

The source term for ϵ in (6.117) involves the irrational function ϵ/k. Since both ϵ and k are interpolated to the same degree over R_e^1, an element average can be employed, yielding

$$\{SORC3\}_e \equiv -C_\epsilon^1\,\overline{\epsilon/k}\,\{XNUT\}_e^T([A40011]\,\{U\}_e)\{U\}_e + C_\epsilon^2\,\overline{\epsilon/k}\,[A200]\,\{EPS\}_e \tag{6.124}$$

The solution statement for v^h remains (6.21)–(6.22), and the algorithm statement is completed by the initial condition definition,

$$\{QJ(\xi_0)\} \leftrightarrow q_j(x_0, y) \tag{6.125}$$

the mapping of the initial conditions onto the nodal coordinates of Ω_e^0.

No additional comments in (6.26) are required regarding anticipated accuracy and convergence of the semidiscrete solution, except that the energy norm is now a strongly nonlinear function of the solution through ν^t; see (6.92) and (6.94). The finite-element evaluation of E is

$$E(q_j^h, q_j^h) \equiv \frac{1}{2}\sum_{e=1}^{M}\int_{R_e^1}\left(\frac{\nu}{\mathrm{Re}} + \nu^t\right)\frac{\partial q_j}{\partial \eta}\frac{\partial q_k}{\partial \eta}\,\delta_{jk}\,d\eta \tag{6.126}$$

$$E(q_j^h, q_j^h) = \frac{1}{2} \sum_{e=1}^{M} \Delta_e \{QJ\}_e^T (\{XNUE\}_e^T [A3011]) \{QK\} \delta_{JK} \qquad \text{(6.126 Cont.)}$$

The structure of the jacobian $[J]$ for the θ-implicit algorithm using the TKE closure is now block four diagonal. The specific components of $[J(FIJ)]$ are constructed from (6.120), using (6.121)-(6.124), in the manner illustrated by (6.45)-(6.46). The continuity equation algorithm jacobians (6.47)-(6.48) are unchanged.

Problems

1 Verify (6.120).
2 Construct the jacobians $[J(FIJ)]$ for (6.120).

6.10 ACCURACY AND CONVERGENCE, TURBULENT FLOW

The requirement is to confirm the exponent $2k$ in the convergence statement (6.26) for error in the semidiscrete approximation. Soliman and Baker (1981b) report these results for a flat-plate turbulent boundary layer flow, using a fixed-grid, MLT closure and the slug profile for $\bar{u}^h(x_2, x_1^0)$ shown in Fig. 6.2. The nodal coordinates of $\cup R_e^1$, for the nonuniform discretization, were generated using (6.56). Table 6.2 summarizes the range of ρ and M employed for the study. The span of the element directly adjacent to the wall was a uniform constant for all M, as was the number of elements between the plate and the knee of the slug velocity profile (one-sixth the total number of elements spanning the solution domain). No turbulence transition model was employed; computational transition from laminar to MLT turbulent flow was specified to occur when the shape factor H achieved 90 percent of the fully developed value for laminar boundary layer flow.

Figure 6.10 presents the determination of accuracy and convergence in energy for the $k = 1$ and $k = 2$ finite-element algorithm statement. The solid lines, drawn

Table 6.2 Discretization data for turbulent boundary layer flow

Linear basis, $k = 1$		Quadratic basis, $k = 2$	
M	ρ	M	ρ
12	1.627	6	2.814
24	1.222	12	1.510
36	1.125	18	1.271
48	1.083	24	1.176
60	1.061	30	1.110

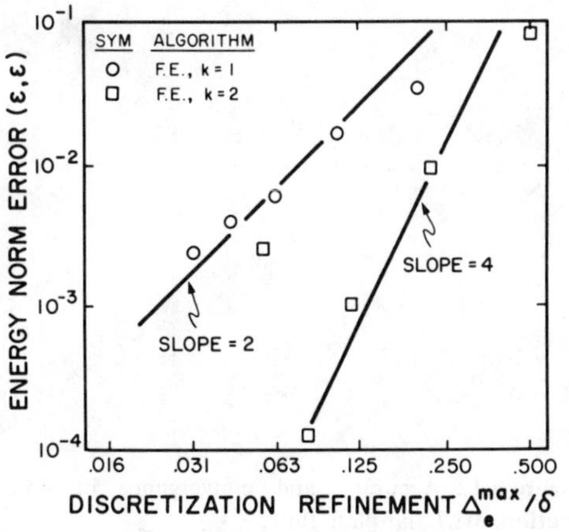

Figure 6.10 Accuracy and convergence in energy, MLT flat-plate boundary layer.

at integer slopes of two and four, essentially interpolate the numerical data, indicating the validity of the exponent $2k$ in (6.26). Both solution forms exhibit coarse grid accuracy superior to strict adherence to the convergence curve. As occurred in the laminar flow convergence studies, the $k = 2$ results for the finest discretization show a significantly larger absolute error, which is interpreted as indication of the limit of practically useful discretizations regarding control of error sources other than that due to the semidiscrete approximation. The absolute accuracy of the $k = 2$ element solution can be a factor of 50 improvement over the corresponding linear element case, for the same minimum element span.

Figures 6.11-6.12 present the evaluation of corresponding error in the engineering norms H and C_f as a function of discretization refinement. Convergence is oscillatory for the $k = 2$ solutions, as experienced with the laminar flow studies (Sec. 6.6), and essentially fourth degree to the practical limit of accuracy. The absolute error for the $k = 2$ solutions on the finer discretizations is disproportionally large, confirming the experience in the energy norm. Convergence in C_f is quadratic for the $k = 1$ algorithm solution, but nonexistent for the shape

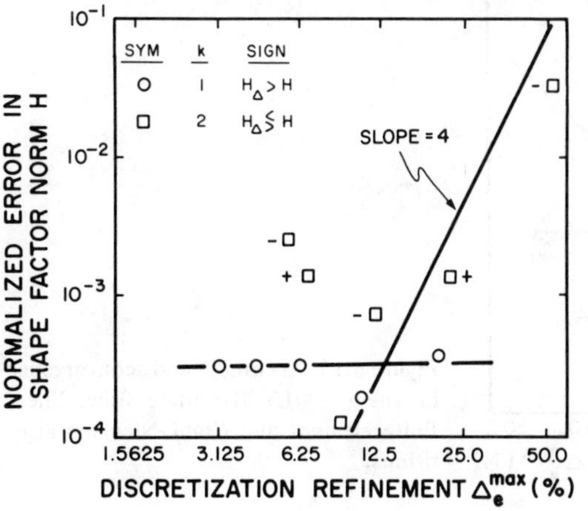

Figure 6.11 Accuracy and convergence in shape factor, MLT flat-plate flow.

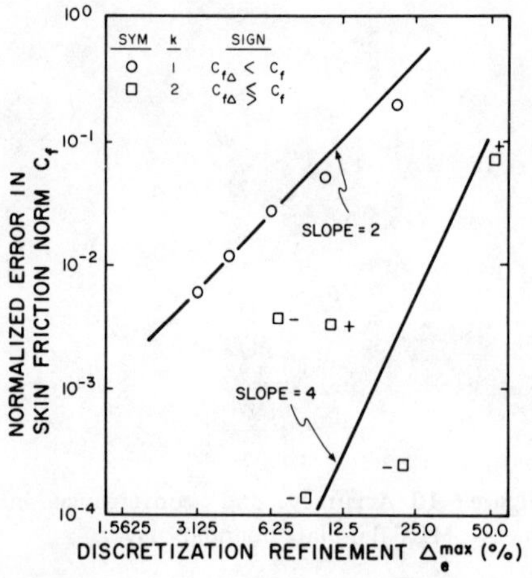

Figure 6.12 Accuracy and convergence in skin friction, MLT flat-plate flow.

factor H, which was interpreted as a problem sensitivity for this specific norm. These results further confirm the utility of the energy norm in quantizing the semidiscrete accuracy.

A necessary comparison is the $k = 1$ finite-element algorithm solution results with those generated using the various capacity matrix condensations; see (6.49), (6.51)-(6.52). Figure 6.13, from Soliman and Baker (1981b), graphs the accuracy and convergence curves in energy as obtained for the MLT flat-plate turbulent boundary layer test case. The line slope equal to two interpolates the data and, again, semidiscrete error of the consistent finite-element algorithm is the minimum for all M. Further, superior accuracy is again exhibited for the coarsest grid solution. While these differences are small, importantly they predict extension of the linear equation theory to this important, highly nonlinear problem class.

Soliman and Baker (1981b) document turbulent boundary layer prediction accuracy in comparison to the data set for the Bradshaw relaxing boundary layer experiment, IDENT 2400 in the Stanford Conference Proceedings (Coles and Hirst,

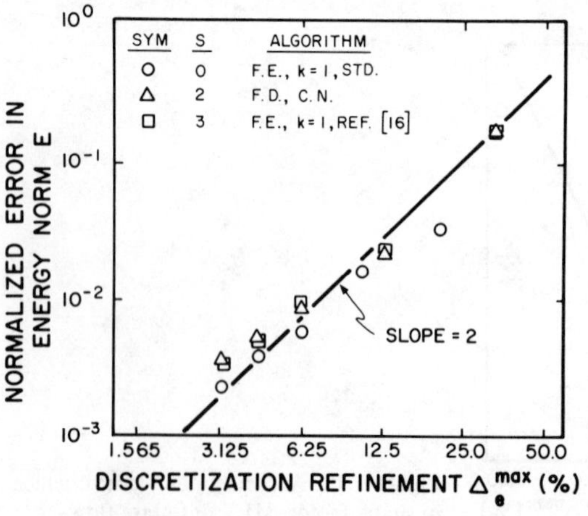

Figure 6.13 Accuracy and convergence in energy, MLT flat plate flow, linear finite element and Crank-Nicolson algorithms.

1968; Kline et al., 1968). This experiment corresponds to evolution of a non-equilibrium, incompressible turbulent boundary layer flow induced by abrupt removal of an adverse pressure gradient. Nominal freestream velocity (U_∞) is 33.5 m/s, wind tunnel background turbulence level was less than 0.1 percent, and the reference unit Reynolds number is 2.38×10^7 m^{-1}. The test case is considerably demanding since nonequilibrium phenomena are involved in the relaxation process.

For the $\theta = \frac{1}{2}$, $k = 1$ algorithm formulation, these numerical experiments confirm that a $M \approx 50$ finite-element discretization is required for adequate solution accuracy using the TKE turbulence closure model and resolving the sublayer region using boundary conditions (6.107). An $M = 30$ discretization spanning $0 \leqslant y/\delta \leqslant 1.2$ is adequate for a MLT solution, which is obtained by specifying $\rho \approx 1.2$ (see Table 6.2). This produces an extremum element aspect ratio $\Delta_\delta^{\max}/\Delta_1^{\min} \approx 0.01$. Consequently, $\Delta_1^{\min}/y^+ \approx 0.2$ where $y^+ \equiv u_\tau y/\nu$ is the wall shear Reynolds number, which yields an adequate resolution of near wall phenomena. Recall (6.100) defines u_τ, which was evaluated using (6.102) and the definition $C_f \equiv \tau_\omega/\frac{1}{2}\rho u_\infty^2$.

Figures 6.14–6.15 summarize solution accuracy compared with the published

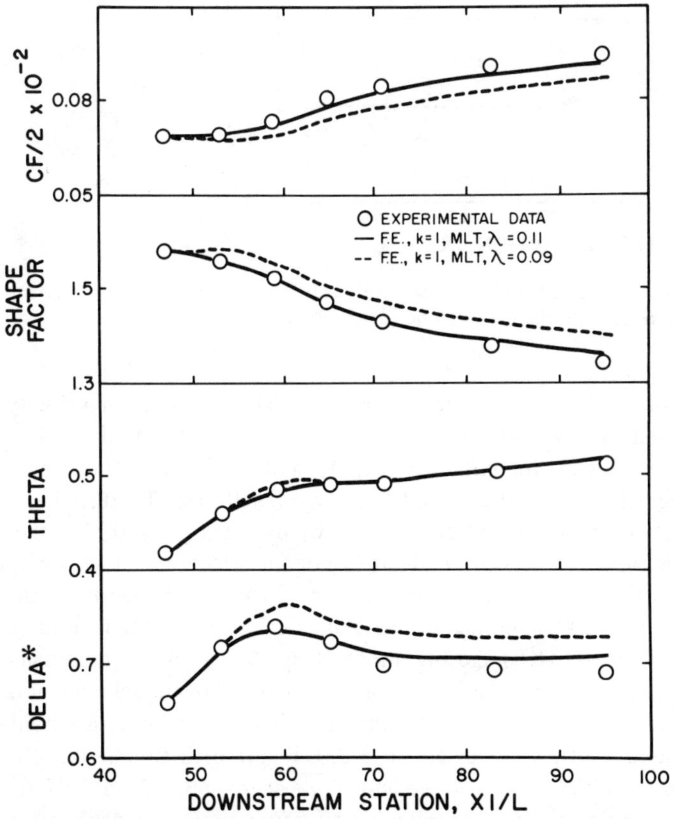

Figure 6.14 Computed boundary layer integral parameter distributions for Bradshaw relaxing flow, linear finite-element algorithm, mixing length closure model.

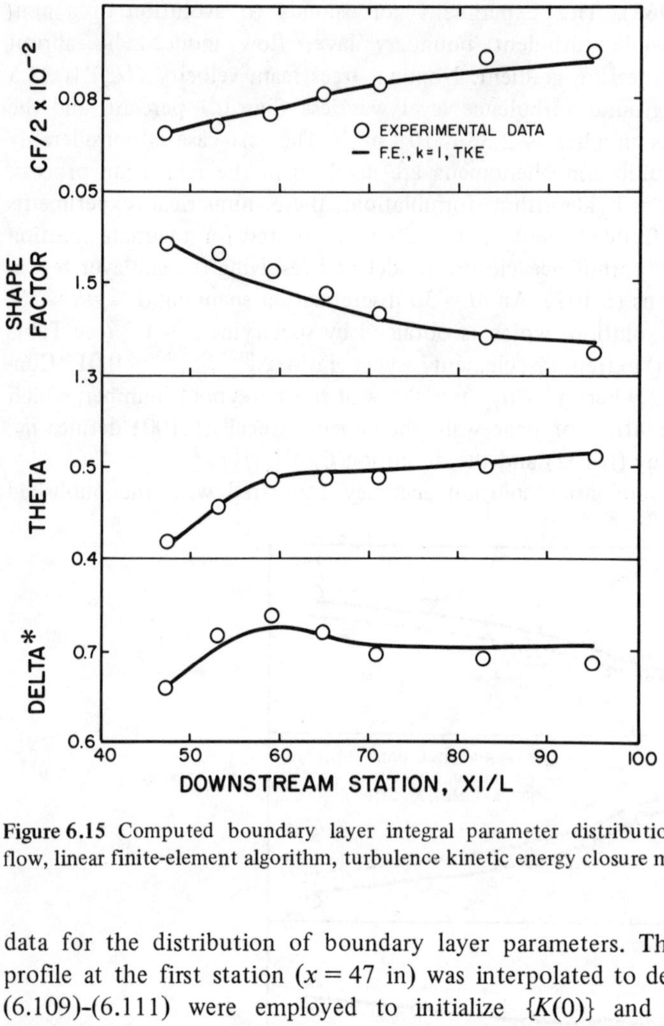

Figure 6.15 Computed boundary layer integral parameter distributions for Bradshaw relaxing flow, linear finite-element algorithm, turbulence kinetic energy closure model.

data for the distribution of boundary layer parameters. The published $\bar{u}$ velocity profile at the first station ($x = 47$ in) was interpolated to define $\{U(0)\}$. Equations (6.109)-(6.111) were employed to initialize $\{K(0)\}$ and $\{EPS(0)\}$. The finite-element solution agreement using the Prandtl mixing length (MLT) turbulence closure model (Fig. 6.14) was improved for δ^* and C_f by setting $\lambda = 0.11$ rather than the standard value $\lambda = 0.09$ [see (6.93)]. It is not unexpected that the MLT algebraic (point function) model would experience some difficulty in describing the nonequilibrium (path function) phenomena. The numerical results obtained using the turbulence kinetic energy (TKE) closure model (Fig. 6.15) are of nominally identical accuracy, and were obtained using the published standard model constants ($C_k = 1.0$, $C_\epsilon = 1.3$, $C_\epsilon^1 = 1.44$, $C_\epsilon^2 = 1.92$) and the low turbulence Reynolds number model constants $a = 1.0$, $b = 2.0$, and $C = 3.0$. Figure 6.16 summarizes the TKE computed solution profiles for $\bar{u}$, k, ϵ, and $\overline{u_1' u_2'}$ at $x = 53$, 72, and 94 in, (recall $x_0 = 47$ in). The action of the grid stretching transformation is evident in the plot growth. The experimental data for $\bar{u}$ are plotted on Fig. 6.16*a* and agreement is excellent. Note the nearly singular behavior in ϵ near the wall, Fig. 6.16*c*; actually, the sharp spike is interpolated over approximately six elements and the solution is smooth with $\epsilon \equiv 0$ at the wall. Adequate grid resolution of this region is mandatory for acceptable accuracy. The computed profiles for k are smooth, and both k and $\overline{u'v'}$ indicate the downstream decay in turbulence levels, even though the wall level of shear stress increases uniformly (see C_f in Fig. 6.15).

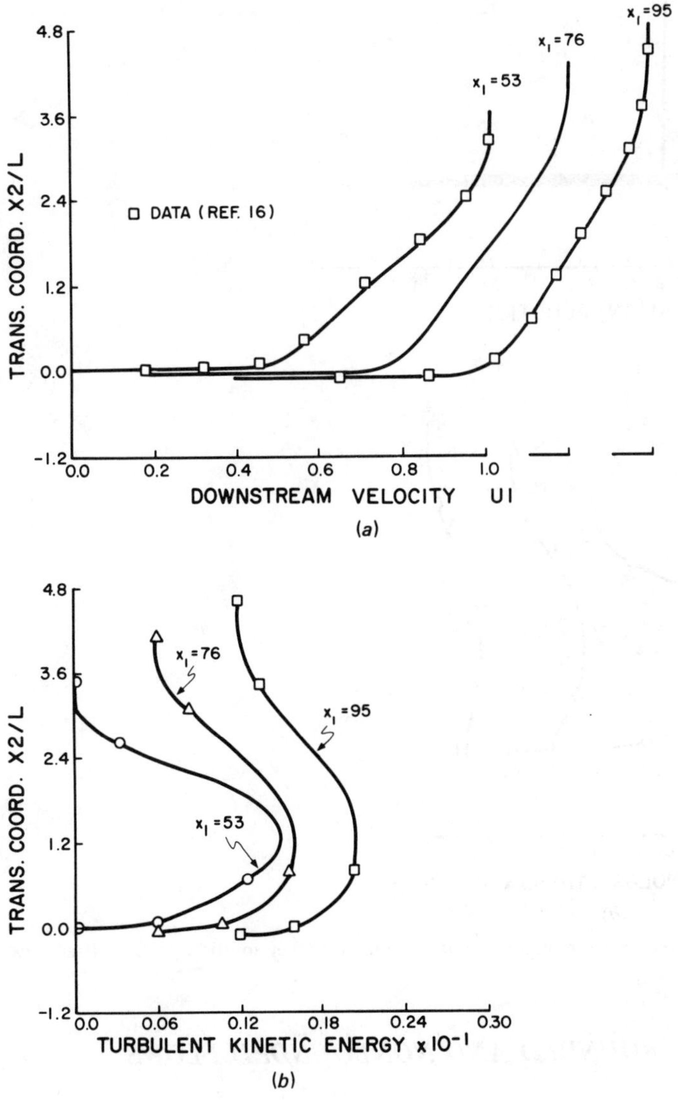

Figure 6.16*a* and *b* Computed turbulent boundary layer solution profiles, Bradshaw relaxing flow.

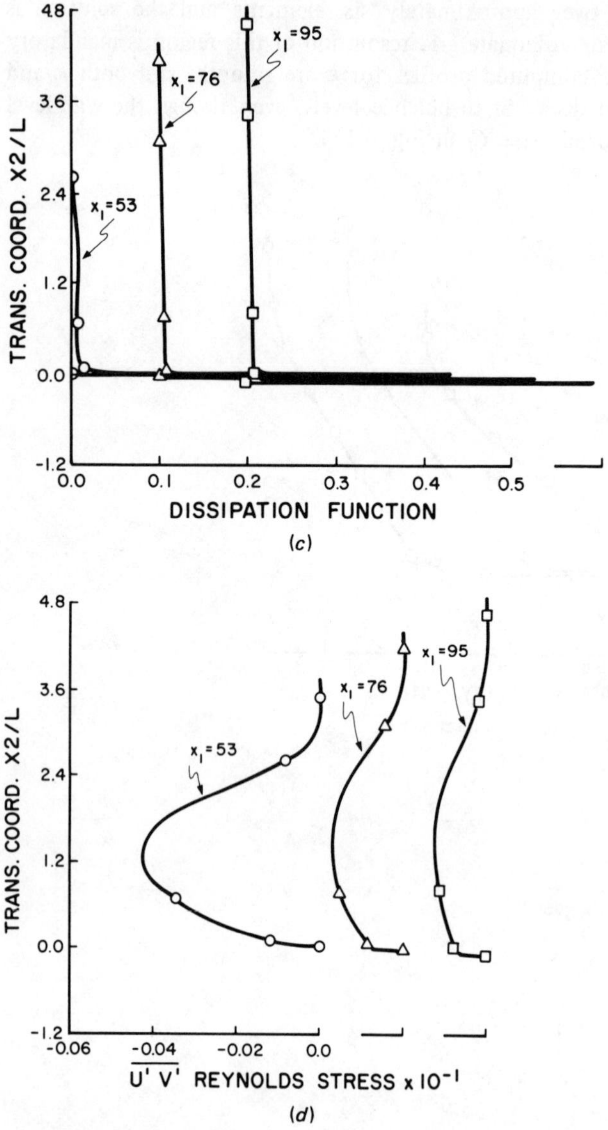

Figure 6.16*c* **and** *d* (*Continued*) Computed turbulent boundary layer solution profiles, Bradshaw relaxing flow.

B. FULLY BOUNDED AND NONBOUNDED FLOWS

6.11 ORDERED DIFFERENTIAL EQUATION SYSTEM

Part A of this chapter has detailed the finite-element algorithm for solution of the two-dimensional parabolic Navier-Stokes equation (2DPNS) in semibounded domains for laminar flow, (6.2)-(6.5), and turbulent flow, (6.114)-(6.117). In both cases, the boundary condition specification (6.8)-(6.11) or (6.107)-(6.108) permitted direct solution of the continuity equation as an initial-value problem for v^h on R^1.

Figure 6.17 illustrates two unidirectional flow geometries where this boundary layer solution procedure for 2DPNS fails. In Fig. 6.17*a*, the flow is bounded on two sides by solid walls, hence the boundary conditions

$$v(x, -h) = 0 = v(x, h) \tag{6.127}$$

must be satisfied by v^h. Correspondingly, in Fig. 6.17*b*, no boundary conditions on $v(x, y/h \gg 1)$ are known. Factually, since a design requirement of the illustrated jet flow is to entrain mass from the far field, the distribution of $v(x, y/h \gg 1)$ is to be determined from the 2DPNS solution. In each cited instance, the boundary data rule out direct solution of the continuity equation for v^h. The requirement is therefore to structure the 2DPNS equation system to render it well posed for a semidiscrete approximation procedure.

Equations (6.83)-(6.85) are the 2DPNS system governing first order $[O(1)]$ phenomena in a unidirectional flow field. No terms have been discarded as higher order in (6.83), and the significant $O(\delta)$ term discarded in (6.84) was $\partial(\overline{u_1' u_1'})/\partial x_1$. The $O(\delta)$ terms discarded in (6.85) constitute the essence of the transverse momentum equation, i.e.,

$$L^\delta(\bar{v}) = \bar{u}\,\frac{\partial \bar{v}}{\partial x_1} + \bar{v}\,\frac{\partial \bar{v}}{\partial x_2} + \frac{\partial}{\partial x_1}\,(\overline{u'v'}) - \frac{\nu}{\mathrm{Re}}\,\frac{\partial^2 \bar{v}}{\partial x_2^2} = 0 \tag{6.128}$$

Importantly, (6.128) exhibits the two-point (parabolic) boundary value specification, for which (6.127) is a well-posed constraint. Furthermore, (6.128) contains the initial-value term that facilitates marching the solution for $\bar{v}$ parallel to x_1.

Therefore, the requirement is to construct a solution algorithm for the 2DPNS equation system (6.84), (6.85), and (6.128), subject to the constraint that (6.83) is satisfied. This is an example of the classical problem of constrained extremization, discussed in Chap. 5 in the context of the incompressible Navier-Stokes equations.

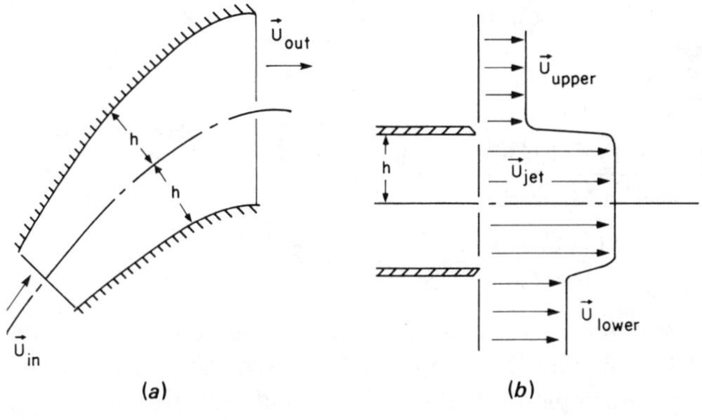

Figure 6.17 Illustration of nonboundary layer 2DPNS flow configurations. (*a*) Fully bounded flow; (*b*) nonbounded flow.

The semidiscrete solution approximation procedure is therefore based upon construction of a penalty function formulation of the finite-element algorithm.

The 2DPNS form of the transverse momentum equation, combining (6.85) and (6.128), and embedding the grid-stretching coordinate transformation (6.112), is

$$L^p(\bar{v}) = \bar{u}\left(\frac{\partial}{\partial \xi} - \eta h \frac{\partial}{\partial \eta}\right)\bar{v} + \bar{v}\frac{\partial \bar{v}}{\partial \eta} + \left(\frac{\partial}{\partial \xi} - \eta h \frac{\partial}{\partial \eta}\right)\overline{u'v'}$$

$$- \frac{\partial}{\partial \eta}\left(\frac{\nu}{f\,\mathrm{Re}}\frac{\partial \bar{v}}{\partial \eta}\right) + \frac{\partial}{\partial \eta}\left(\frac{\bar{p}}{\rho_0} + \overline{v'v'}\right) = 0 \tag{6.129}$$

The superscript p in (6.129) signifies the 2DPNS form, the last term is $O(1)$, while the remainder are all $O(\delta)$ or smaller. Equation (6.87) provides the definition of the Reynolds shear stress, i.e.,

$$-\overline{u'v'} = \frac{\nu^t}{f}\frac{\partial \bar{u}}{\partial \eta} \tag{6.130}$$

where ν^t is the kinematic turbulence viscosity [see (6.92) or (6.94)]. The Reynolds normal stress $-\overline{v'v'}$ is required defined for solution of (6.129). As expanded in detail in Sec. 7.3, using tensor field theory and the parabolic ordering analysis, the first- and second-order terms in a Reynolds normal stress constitutive equation are

$$\overline{u'u'} = \overbrace{C_1 k - C_2 C_4 \frac{k^3}{f^2 \epsilon^2}\left(\frac{\partial \bar{u}}{\partial \eta}\right)^2}^{O(\delta)} \overbrace{- 2C_4 \frac{k^2}{\epsilon}\left(\frac{\partial}{\partial \xi} - \eta h \frac{\partial}{\partial \eta}\right)\bar{u}}^{O(\delta^2)} \tag{6.131}$$

$$\overline{v'v'} = C_3 k - C_2 C_4 \frac{k^3}{f^2 \epsilon^2}\left(\frac{\partial \bar{u}}{\partial \eta}\right)^2 - 2C_4 \frac{k^2}{f\epsilon}\frac{\partial \bar{u}}{\partial \eta} \tag{6.132}$$

$$\overline{w'w'} = C_3 k \tag{6.133}$$

In (6.131)-(6.133), the C_α, $1 \leqslant \alpha \leqslant 4$ are constants defined by Launder et al. (1975) as

$$\begin{aligned}
C_1 &\equiv \frac{22(C_{01} - 1) - 6(4C_{02} - 5)}{33(C_{01} - 2C_{02})} \\
C_2 &\equiv \frac{4(3C_{02} - 1)}{11(C_{01} - 2C_{02})} \\
C_3 &\equiv \frac{22(C_{01} - 1) - 12(3C_{02} - 1)}{33(C_{01} - 2C_{02})} \\
C_4 &\equiv \frac{44C_{02} - 22C_{01}C_{02} - 128C_{02} - 36C_{02}^2 + 10}{165(C_{01} - 2C_{02})^2}
\end{aligned} \tag{6.134}$$

In (6.134), C_{01} and C_{02} are universal empirical constants; suggested values are $C_{01} \approx 2.8$ and $C_{02} \approx 0.45$ (Hanjalic and Launder, 1972). The variables k and ϵ are turbulence kinetic energy and isotropic dissipation [(6.89) and (6.91)], and $\overline{w'w'}$ is required to be defined for (6.89).

The final formulational step is construction of a suitable replacement solution form for (6.85), the first-order transverse momentum equation. One approach (Baker and Orzechowski, 1981), is differentiation of (6.129) with respect to η to yield a Poisson equation for $\bar{p}(\mathbf{x})$. Returning to tensor notation, adding (6.128) and (6.85), and differentiating on x_2 yields, for $1 \leqslant j \leqslant 2$,

$$L^p(\bar{p}) = \frac{1}{\rho_0}\frac{\partial^2 \bar{p}}{\partial x_2^2} + \frac{\partial^2}{\partial x_2\, \partial x_j}\left(\bar{u}_2\bar{u}_j + \overline{u_2' u_j'} - \delta_{j2}\frac{\nu}{\text{Re}}\frac{\partial \bar{v}}{\partial x_2}\right) = 0 \qquad (6.135)$$

Equation (6.135) defines a pseudolinear Poisson equation for determination of the pressure field $\bar{p}(\mathbf{x})$ as a two-point boundary value problem on R^1 with parametric dependence on x_1. The semidiscrete approximate solution to (6.135) is assumed constituted of *complementary* and *particular* solutions, i.e.,

$$p^h(\mathbf{x}) \equiv p_c(\mathbf{x}) + p_p(\mathbf{x}) \qquad (6.136)$$

The complementary solution satisfies the homogeneous form of (6.135)

$$L^p(p_c) \equiv \frac{\partial^2 p_c}{\partial x_2^2} \equiv 0 \qquad (6.137)$$

subject to Dirichlet boundary conditions known at the boundary ∂R of R^1. For the nonbounded flow case (Fig. 6.16*b*), these data are provided by the exterior (potential) flow solution. For the fully bounded case (Fig. 6.16*a*), the pressure gradient correction algorithm of Patankar and Spalding (1972) can provide the data. Integrating the $\bar{u}$ momentum equation (6.84) over a control volume spanning the duct cross section, $-h \leqslant x_2 \leqslant h$, yields the approximation to the x_1 pressure gradient

$$\frac{dp^*}{dx_1} = \frac{1}{A}\left(F - 2\tilde{u}\frac{d\tilde{m}}{dx_1} + \frac{\tilde{m}\tilde{u}}{A}\frac{dA}{dx_1}\right) \qquad (6.138)$$

In (6.138), the superscript tilde denotes the cross-sectional integration, where

$$\tilde{m} \equiv \rho_0 \tilde{u} \equiv \int_{R^1} \rho_0 \bar{u}(x_2)\, dx_2 \qquad (6.139)$$

$A(x_1)$ is the duct cross-sectional area distribution and $F(x_1)$ is the wall friction. The numerical evaluation of the right side of (6.138) determines the approximation dp^*/dx, which is then adjusted to conserve the numerical measure of $\tilde{m}$. Integration of (6.138) downstream yields

$$p^*(x_1) \approx \bar{p}_{\text{in}} + \int_0^{x_1} \frac{dp^*}{dx_1}\, dx_1 \qquad (6.140)$$

Equation (6.140) provides an estimate of a level of $p_c(x_1)$ somewhere on the duct cross section. It is logical to assume this is at the duct centerline, that is, $p_c(x_1, 0) \equiv p^*(x_1)$. Since (6.137) is a potential description, the absence of constraints on $p_c(x_1, \pm h)$ indicates the appropriate boundary condition is (homogeneous) Neumann. Therefore, (6.137) is solved on each duct half-width subject to a vanishing derivative at the boundary intersection with the wall. For a straight centerline, therefore, $p_c(x_1, x_2) = p^*(x_1)$ yields a uniform distribution across the cross section. For curved ducts, the laplacian in (6.137) will pick up first order derivatives in x_2 (e.g., polar coordinates), hence $p_c(x_1, x_2)$ will become distributed on the cross section.

Returning to (6.136), the particular pressure p_p is any solution to (6.135) subject to homogeneous Dirichlet boundary conditions at locations on ∂R whereupon p_c is known. For the nonbounded case, $p_p(x_1, x_2/h \gg 1) = 0$. For the fully bounded case, assuming p_c is known on the centerline, (6.85) defines the nonhomogeneous Neumann constraint on ∂R. As an alternative, since $\bar{u}_i$ and $\overline{u_i' u_j'}$ both vanish on ∂R, $p_p \equiv 0$ on ∂R is also admissible.

6.12 FINITE-ELEMENT PENALTY FUNCTION ALGORITHM

The 2DPNS differential equation system governing unidirectional flows on fully bounded and nonbounded (and semibounded!) domains R^2 has been identified. For the dependent variable set $q_j(x_i) \equiv \{\bar{u}, \bar{v}, k, \epsilon, p_c, p_p, \overline{u_i' u_j'}\}$, the equation set includes (6.115)-(6.117), (6.129)-(6.133), (6.135), and (6.137). In addition, the continuity equation (6.114) must be satisfied by the computed mean velocity field $\bar{\mathbf{u}}(x_i)$. This defines the requirement that the resultant semidiscrete approximation solution statement belongs to a class of constrained extremization. Since no variational boundary value statement exists for the highly nonlinear 2DPNS equation system, the theoretical approach is the penalty function method presented in Sec. 5.10.

Baker and Orzechowski (1982a, b) derive and implement a penalty function 2DPNS solution algorithm statement, wherein the penalty measure is the harmonic solution $\phi_n(\mathbf{x})$ to the Poisson equation

$$L^P(\phi_n(\mathbf{x})) \equiv \frac{\partial^2 \phi_n}{\partial x_2^2} - \nabla \cdot \mathbf{u}_n^h = 0 \tag{6.141}$$

The boundary conditions for ϕ_n are homogeneous Dirichlet and/or Neumann, dependent upon the domain boundedness. In the limit, as $\mathbf{u}_n^h \Rightarrow \mathbf{u}^h$, (6.141) becomes homogeneous, and $\|\delta\phi_n^h\| \Rightarrow |0|$ as a consequence of the boundary conditions. Therefore, the penalty term, analogous to extremization of $(\lambda_n/2) \int_{R^2} (\nabla \cdot \mathbf{u}_n)^2$ in (5.128), is the form

$$\lambda_n \int_{R^1} \hat{\mathbf{j}} \cdot \nabla \{N_k\} L^P(\phi_n^h) \, d\tau \tag{6.142}$$

which becomes applied (only) to the finite-element solution algorithm statement for $L^P(v_n^h)$; see (6.129).

With (6.141), the differential equation system for 2DPNS is complete. The four equations (6.115)-(6.117) and (6.129), written on $\bar{u}$, $\bar{v}$, k, and ϵ, are each initial-value, parabolic specifications of the general form

$$L^P(q_j(\eta)) = \bar{u}\frac{\partial q_j}{\partial \xi} + f(\bar{u}, \bar{v}, h)\frac{\partial q_j}{\partial \eta} - \frac{\partial}{\partial \eta}\left(\nu_j \frac{\partial q_j}{\partial \eta}\right) + s_j = 0 \tag{6.143}$$

In (6.143), the lead (downstream convection) term permits space marching, the second is the common lateral convection term, the third corresponds to lateral diffusion, where $\nu_j = \nu_j(q_j)$, and the last is the source/sink term specific for each $1 \leqslant j \leqslant 4$. The domain for (6.143) is $\Omega \equiv R^1 \times x_1$, with boundary $\partial\Omega \equiv \partial R \times x_1$, whereupon the various cited boundary conditions belong to the general statement

$$l(q_j(\eta)) = a_j^1 q_j + a_j^2 \frac{\partial q_j}{\partial \eta_2} + a_j^3 = 0 \tag{6.144}$$

where a_j are specified functions of ξ for each $1 \leqslant j \leqslant 4$. In addition, an initial condition on $\Omega_0 \equiv R^1 \times x_1^0$ must be defined as

$$q_j(\xi^0, \eta) \equiv q_j^0(\eta) \tag{6.145}$$

There are also three parabolic two-point boundary value problem specifications for the members $q_j = \{p_C, p_P, \phi\}$ of the 2DPNS dependent variable set [see (6.135), (6.137), and (6.141). The general form is

$$L^P(q_j(\eta)) \equiv \frac{\partial^2 q_j}{\partial \eta_2} + s_j(q_j) = 0 \tag{6.146}$$

and (6.144) contains the appropriate boundary condition constraints. Note that (6.146) is simply a special case of (6.143) with unit diffusion coefficient. The 2DPNS dependent variable set definition statement is completed by (6.130)-(6.133) for components of $\overline{u_i'u_j'}$.

The finite-element solution algorithm for the 2DPNS equation system (6.143)-(6.146) follows the established procedure. The dependent variable set $q_j(\eta) \equiv \{\bar{u}, \bar{v}, k, \epsilon, p_C, p_P, \overline{u_i'u_j'}, \phi\}$ is represented by the semidiscrete approximation

$$q_j(\eta) \approx q_j^h(\eta) = \sum_{e=1}^{M} q_j^e(\eta) = \sum_{e=1}^{M} \{N_k(\eta)\}^T \{QJ(\xi)\}_e \tag{6.147}$$

where $1 \leqslant (j, J) \leqslant 11$ is a free index denoting members of the set $q_j(\eta)$. As before, the elements of the cardinal basis $\{N_k(\eta)\}$ are kth degree polynomials on η, while those of $\{QJ(\xi)\}_e$ are the nodal values of q_j^e on R_e^1. Identifying the Lagrange multiplier set β_i, the orthogonalization of the semidiscrete approximation error in (6.143), (6.144), and (6.146), plus the penalty constraint (6.142), yields the weighted residuals algorithm statement

$$\int_{R^1} \{N_k\} L^P(q_j^h)\, d\tau + \beta_1 \int_{\partial R} \{N_k\}\, l(q_j^h)\, d\sigma + \beta_2 \cdot \int_{R^1} \nabla\{N_k\} L^P(\phi_n^h)\, d\tau\, \delta_{j2} \equiv \{0\} \tag{6.148}$$

where δ_{j2} is the Kronecker delta and $\beta_2 \equiv \lambda_n \hat{\mathbf{j}}$; see (6.142).

As occurred in the boundary layer equation solution formulation for 2DPNS [see (6.16)], (6.148) is a system of coupled ordinary differential and algebraic equations of the form

$$[C]\{QJ\}' + [U + K]\{QJ\} + \{SJ\} = \{0\} \tag{6.149}$$

inferring a one-to-one correspondence with terms in (6.143) and (6.146), as augmented by (6.144) and (6.142). The θ-implicit integration algorithm applied to (6.149) yields the uniformly nonlinear algebraic equation system

$$\{FJ\} \equiv \{QJ\}_{j+1} - \{QJ\}_j - [\theta\{QJ\}'_{j+1} + (1-\theta)\{QJ\}'_j] \tag{6.150}$$

The Newton iteration algorithm for solution of (6.150) is

$$[J(FJ)]^p_{j+1}\{\delta QJ\}^{p+1}_{j+1} = -\{FJ\}^p_{j+1} \tag{6.151}$$

where the dependent variable is related to the solution in the usual manner;

$$\{QJ\}^{p+1}_{j+1} \equiv \{QJ\}^p_{j+1} + \{\delta QJ\}^{p+1}_{j+1} \tag{6.152}$$

The elements of the jacobian $[J]$ in (6.151) are defined as

$$[J(FJ)] \equiv \frac{\partial\{FJ\}}{\partial\{QI\}} \tag{6.153}$$

6.13 THEORETICAL ANALYSIS, ACCURACY AND CONVERGENCE

Only minor additional comments are required on this basis topic, as presented in Secs. 6.4 and 3.3. For those members of $q_j^h(\eta)$ that are solutions to the initial value problem statement (6.143), the error ϵ_j^h in the semidiscrete approximation (6.147) can be expected to be bounded in H^1 in the form

$$\|\epsilon_j^h(n\,\Delta\xi)\|_{H^1} \leqslant C_1\,\Delta_m^k\,\|q_j(n\,\Delta\xi)\|_{H^{k+1}} + C_2\,\Delta\xi\,\|q_j^0\|_{H^1} \tag{6.154}$$

for $1 \leqslant j \leqslant 4$. Recall that C_α are constants, Δ_m is the extremum measure of the discretization $\cup R_e^1$, and $\Delta\xi$ is the downstream integration step size. For those members of $q_j^h(\eta)$ that are solutions to the parabolic equation (6.146), the accuracy and convergence statement (3.27) takes the form

$$\|\epsilon_j^h(n\,\Delta\xi)\|_{H^1} \leqslant C_3\,\Delta_m^k\,\|q_j(n\,\Delta\xi)\|_{H^{k+1}} \tag{6.155}$$

The energy norm for estimation of the semidiscrete approximation error (recall Secs. 6.4 and 6.10) is of the form

$$E(q_j^h(\xi), q_j^h(\xi)) = \frac{1}{2}\sum_{e=1}^{M}\int_{R_e^1} \nu_j^e\,\frac{\partial q_j^e}{\partial\eta}\,\frac{\partial q_j^e}{\partial\eta}\,d\eta = \frac{1}{2}\sum_{e=1}^{M}\{QJ\}_e^T(\{XNUE\}_e^T[A3011])\{QJ\}_e \tag{6.156}$$

with no summation on j implied.

Based upon the convergence results documented in Chap. 2, and thus far in this chapter, (6.154)-(6.156) can be anticipated to characterize the basic character of the 2DPNS algorithm for nonbounded and fully bounded flows. However, viewing the difficulties encountered in firmly quantizing the exponent k in (6.154) for the elementary MLT boundary layer solutions (Secs. 6.6 and 6.10), little prospect exists for a repeat performance for the current dependent variable set $q_j(\eta)$ containing eleven elements! Therefore, the quantization of performance rests principally on verification that the 2DPNS formulation algorithm can reproduce the boundary layer solutions on a semibounded solution domain to acceptable accuracy. Further, this process can yield determination of an optimal form for β_2, and the specific implementation of the penalty constraint term in (6.148).

Baker (1981) documents these data for the 2DPNS finite-element solution for laminar boundary layer flow in zero pressure gradient, i.e., the Blasius case, for the $\theta = \frac{1}{2}$ linear-basis algorithm, $k = 1$ in (6.147). Following extensive numerical experimentation, the implementation of the penalty term (6.148) that yields excellent accuracy, iteration convergence in (6.150)-(6.153), and stability, defines $\beta_2 \equiv \Delta\xi\hat{\mathbf{j}}$; hence $\lambda_n \equiv \Delta\xi$ is independent of n and equal to the downstream integration step size. Concurrently, the evaluation of $\int_{R^1} \nabla\{N_k\}L^P(\phi_n^h)\, d\tau$ in (6.148), which forms a contribution to $\{Q2\}_{j+1}'$ in (6.150), is accumulated into a column matrix during the iteration at ξ_{j+1}. Denoting this matrix as $\{GQ2/PHI\}$, at the pth iteration at step ξ_{j+1}, the solution ϕ_n^h yields the penalty term evaluation (6.142) in the form

$$\{GQ2/PHI\}_{j+1}^n \equiv S_e[\Delta_e[A210]\{PHI\}_{j+1}^p] \tag{6.157}$$

This determination is algebraically summed with the previous $p-1$ evaluations, and multiplied by a diagonal matrix with elements $\{Q1\}_{j+1}^p$, i.e., U^h, yielding

$$\{GQ2\}_{j+1}^p \equiv [Q1]_{j+1}^p \sum_{n=1}^{p} \{GQ2/PHI\}_{j+1}^n \tag{6.158}$$

Then, $\{F2\}$ in (6.150) takes the form

$$\{F2\}_{j+1}^p = S_e[\Delta_e\{\bar{U}\}_e^T[A3000]\{V_{j+1}^p - V_j\} + \cdots] + \Delta\xi\{GQ2\}_{j+1}^p \tag{6.159}$$

Thus, each successive solution ϕ_n^h, $n = 1, 2, \ldots, p$ is applied in a manner that corrects the action of each previous solution, such that $\|\delta\phi_n^h\| \Rightarrow 0$ as p increases without bound.

The Blasius laminar boundary layer test case is quite definitive for the 2DPNS algorithm. Referring to Fig. 6.18, the freestream level $u(\xi, \eta/\delta > 1)$ is invariant with ξ, yet the 2DPNS solution for $V^h(\xi, \eta/\delta > 1)$ must decrease as $\xi^{-1/2}$; that is, the action of the continuity equation is global, not local. Furthermore, the 2DPNS algorithm must produce $\partial V^h(\xi, 0)/\partial\eta = 0$, since $\partial\bar{u}(\xi, 0)/\partial\xi = 0$; see (6.8). Neither of these actions can be enforced directly, but must be predicted.

The 2DPNS finite-element penalty algorithm is a robust solution procedure for

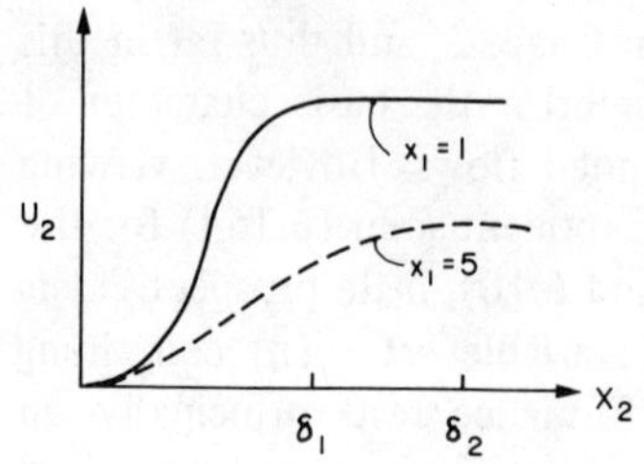

Figure 6.18 Essential features of Blasius check case.

this problem specification (Baker, 1981), specifying $\partial\phi(\xi, 0)/\partial\eta = 0$ and $\phi(\xi, \eta/\delta > 1) = 0$. Plotted on any reasonable scale, the velocity solutions $\mathbf{u}^h(\eta)$ from the boundary layer (2DBL) algorithm (6.16)–(6.22) and the 2DPNS algorithm (6.148), (6.157)–(6.159), are identical. Table 6.3 summarizes the comparison for $V^h(\xi = 5, \eta)$, for $k = 1$ solutions initialized at $\xi = 1$ on a geometrically nonuniform (optimum) $M = 32$ discretization (see Fig. 6.6), and grid stretching of 50 percent on $\Delta\xi = 4$. The digits of significance range over 10^7, the 2DBL and 2DPNS distributions agree almost identically, and the 2DPNS approximation to $\partial V^h(\xi, 0)/\partial\eta = 0$ is excellent. For iteration convergence set at $\{|\delta QJ|\}_{j+1}^{p+1} \leqslant 10^{-5}$, the energy comparison for $u^h(\xi = 5)$ is $E(\cdot, \cdot)_{2\text{DBL}} = 7.3685$ and $E(\cdot, \cdot)_{2\text{DPNS}} = 7.3532$, which is a negligible

Table 6.3 Transverse velocity distributions $V^h(\xi = 5, \eta) \times 10^3$ laminar incompressible boundary layer flow

Coordinate (x_2/δ)	Boundary layer solution	Continuity constraint solution
0.0	0.0	0.0
0.0009	0.0000011	0.0000001
0.0021	0.0000054	0.0000030
0.0035	0.0000149	0.0000114
⋮	⋮	⋮
0.0095	0.00011	0.00011
⋮	⋮	⋮
0.031	0.00118	0.00118
⋮	⋮	⋮
0.10	0.0128	0.0127
⋮	⋮	⋮
0.67	0.139	0.138
⋮	⋮	⋮
1.0	0.218	0.218

Table 6.4 2DPNS penalty function algorithm convergence laminar incompressible boundary layer flow

Iteration (n)	Energy norm, $E(\partial\phi_n^h, \partial\phi_n^h)$
1	0.69432 E(−9)
2	0.30670 E(−9)
3	0.15692 E(−9)
4	0.08028 E(−9)

difference. The intrinsic norm for ϕ_n^h is also energy; for comparison, at the 2DPNS solution final station, $E(\partial\phi_p^h, [\![\phi_p^h) = 0.8 \times 10^{-10}$, which is eleven orders of magnitude smaller than $E(u^h, u^h)$. Furthermore (see Table 6.4), $E(\partial\phi_n^h, \partial\phi_n^h)$ decreases by a nominal factor of two during each iteration of the Newton algorithm, as a consequence of the formulation (6.157)-(6.159).

An additional factor affecting solution accuracy and acceptability is the possible emergence of spurious $2\,\Delta x$ waves in the 2DPNS solution for $v^h(\eta)$. As discussed in Chap. 5, the action of the continuity penalty function is mod $|\nabla^h|$, which for the $k = 1$ linear basis algorithm enforces essentially a central difference approximation. Therefore, should a mechanism initialize this error mode in ϕ_n^h, the 2DPNS computed transverse velocity field will eventually exhibit the same character. The $2\,\Delta x$ error can be efficiently filtered during construction of V^h by averaging the Newton iteration dependent variable $\{\delta Q2\}_{j+1}^{p+1}$, that is,

$$\{\delta Q2\}_{j+1}^{p+1} \equiv S_e[[A200]\,\{\delta Q2\}_{j+1}^{p+1}] \qquad (6.160)$$

Should V^h by some means have already taken on the $2\,\Delta x$ error mode, periodic application of the operation (6.160) to the actual solution $\{Q2\}_{j+1}^{p+1}$ can filter the error and restore smoothness. Additional results (Baker and Orzechowski, 1982b), document similar 2DPNS algorithm performance for turbulent boundary layer flow prediction, using both the MLT and TKE turbulence closure models.

6.14 TURBULENT FLOW IN VARIABLE CROSS-SECTIONAL DUCT

Baker and Orzechowski (1981) document application of the developed 2DPNS finite-element penalty algorithm to predict turbulent flow in a two-dimensional duct of variable cross section. In this case, the boundary condition for all members of $q_j^h(\eta)$ including ϕ is homogeneous Dirichlet at both walls. Figure 6.19 illustrates the

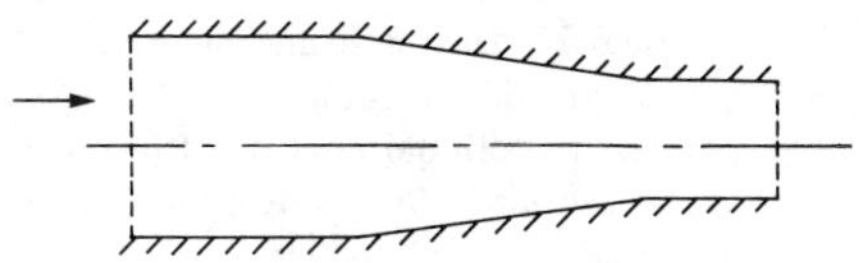

Figure 6.19 Variable cross-sectional duct geometry.

duct geometry, constructed as a symmetric plane wall transition between a uniform cross-sectional inlet and outlet with a 20 percent difference in area. Running the flow from left to right induces a favorable pressure gradient, computed to conserve mass flux using (6.138). Conversely, an adverse pressure gradient is induced by running the flow from right to left. A geometrically nonuniform discretization, containing $M = 60$ elements spanned by the $k = 1$ basis was employed, with the finer discretization located adjacent to each wall. The initial condition for $\bar{u}_1^0(\eta)$ is a turbulent boundary layer profile, obtained by using Coles law reflected about the symmetry line. Equations (6.110)-(6.111) were employed to initialize k^0 and ϵ^0; $\bar{u}_2^0$ was generated from ϕ_n^h following 10 integration steps downstream (to smooth the error distribution in the initial profiles k^0 and ϵ^0). The Reynolds number based on duct half-width was $\text{Re} \equiv U_\infty H_f/\nu_\infty = 0.2 \times 10^5$, and tests were run for $0 < M_\infty \leqslant 0.5$.

Figures 6.20-6.23 summarize the $M_\infty = 0.1$ solutions for the initial-valued members of $q_j^h(\eta)$. The duct transition was defined on $4 \leqslant \xi/H_f \leqslant 12$, where H_f is the duct half-width. For direct comparison, the results for the diverging duct (*a* in each figure), are plotted for flow from left to right. Part *b* of each figure shows the

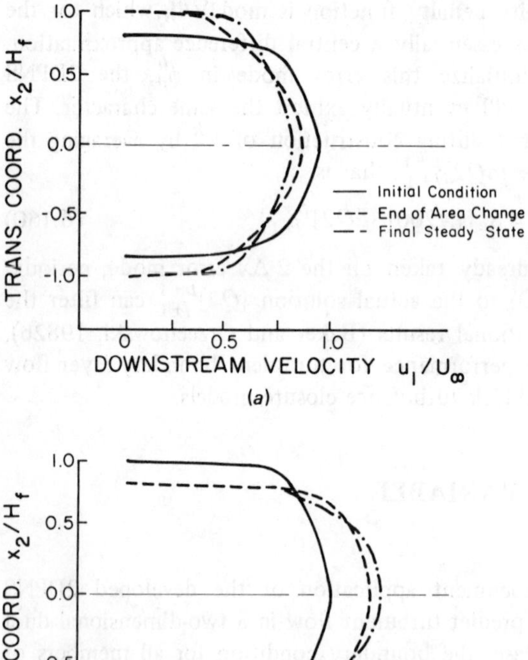

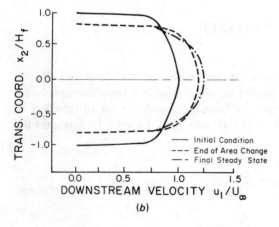

Figure 6.20 Downstream mean velocity $\bar{u}_1$ profiles, turbulent flow in variable cross-sectional duct. (*a*) Diverging cross section; (*b*) converging cross section.

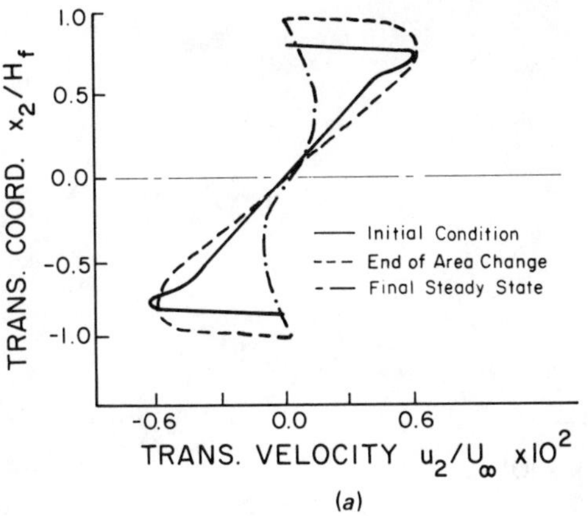

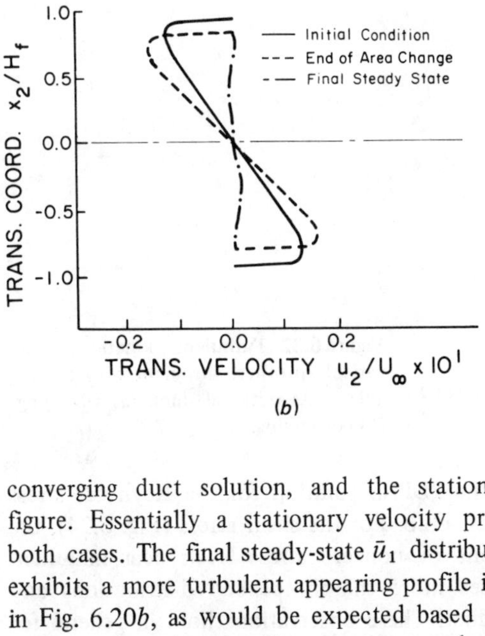

Figure 6.21 Transverse mean velocity $\bar{u}_2$ profiles, turbulent flow in variable cross section duct. (*a*) Diverging; (*b*) converging.

converging duct solution, and the station plot symbols are recorded in each figure. Essentially a stationary velocity profile is predicted by $x_1/H_f = 20.0$ for both cases. The final steady-state $\bar{u}_1$ distribution for the diverging duct (Fig. 6.20*a*), exhibits a more turbulent appearing profile in comparison to the corresponding data in Fig. 6.20*b*, as would be expected based upon the pressure gradient. Figure 6.21 exhibits the corresponding transverse velocity distributions $\bar{u}_2$, and considerably larger transitional magnitudes are recorded for the converging duct. Note also the opposing senses computed for $\bar{u}_2$ during duct transition, and the persistence of this sign in the steady-state profiles. In Figs. 6.22–6.23, the solution for k and ϵ are both characterized by extremely steep gradients adjacent to the walls, which places a significant demand on grid resolution, hence algorithm performance. From nominally identical initial k distributions, the diverging duct flattens and broadens the distributions, while the converging duct generates lower mid-duct levels and sharply accentuates the peaks adjacent to the walls. The largest distinction between diverging and converging geometry occurs for ϵ, wherein the steady-state extremum levels at the wall differ by a factor of about four (Fig. 6.23).

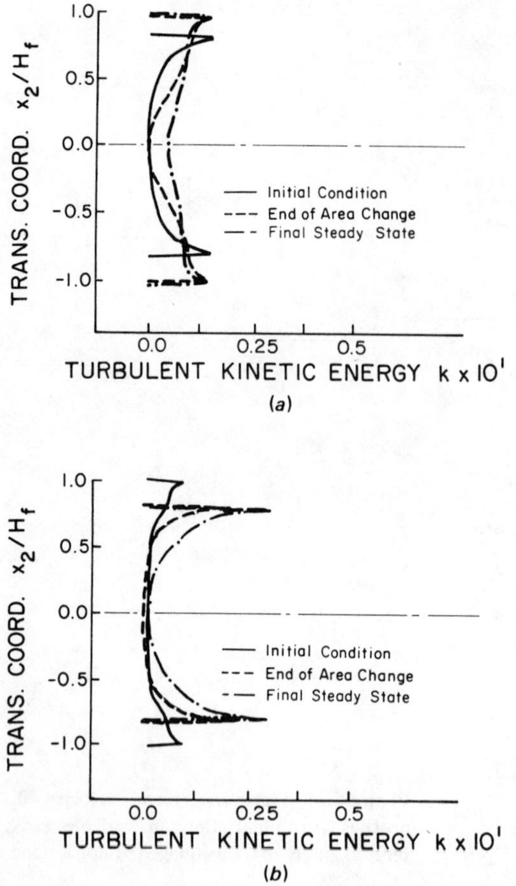

Figure 6.22 Turbulent kinetic energy variable profiles, turbulent flow in variable cross-sectional duct. (*a*) Diverging; (*b*) converging.

The distributions computed from the 2DPNS solution for the Reynolds stress tensor $-\overline{u_i'u_j'}$ are summarized in Figs. 6.24–6.26. For the shear stress (Fig. 6.24), the diverging duct has induced a filling out of nonzero stress levels near mid-duct. Conversely, the converging duct induces more sharply peaked distributions and proportionally smaller levels near mid-duct. These observations hold in general for the normal stresses $-\overline{u_1'u_1'}$ and $-\overline{u_2'u_2'}$ (Figs. 6.25–6.26). Note that the computational variable k differs from one-half the trace of the Reynolds stress tensor $\frac{1}{2}\overline{u_i'u_i'}$ by the low turbulence Reynolds number function ω [see (6.90)–(6.95)] in the immediate vicinity of the wall. The nominally zero initial levels at the duct center, which are induced by the initialization of k°, respond directly to the duct specification. On the centerline, $\overline{u_1'u_1'} \approx 0.0005$ at ξ_0 in both cases. At $x_1/H_f = 20.0$, centerline levels are 0.0036 for the diverging case and 0.0009 for the converging duct. The predictions for $\overline{u_2'u_2'}$ follow a similar trend. For both geometries, the extremum level for each stress component occurred within the interval $10 < y^+ \leqslant 50$. Assuming $\overline{u_3'u_3'} \approx \overline{u_2'u_2'}$, [see (6.133)], the corresponding extremum levels for turbulent kinetic energy $\frac{1}{2}\overline{u_i'u_i'}$, are 0.010 and 0.006 for the converging and diverging duct, respectively.

No experimental data are published to corroborate these predictions. The trends exhibited by the solutions do appear plausible, however, and the results of the next section do have a quantitative basis for comparison.

6.15 TURBULENT AERODYNAMIC TRAILING EDGE WAKE FLOW

The 2DPNS equation system and finite-element penalty function algorithm are applicable to prediction of flow-field evaluation, in the wake downstream of a sharp trailing edge airfoil (see Fig. 6.27). For the special case of a symmetric airfoil at zero angle of attack, the 2DBL equation system is also applicable. An algorithm for prediction of laminar boundary layer merging downstream of a flat plate is reported by Veldman (1975). Melnik and Chow (1975) document a laminar flow theoretical model using matched asymptotic expansions and a triple deck structure. For turbulent flows, Melnik and Chow (1976) document a generalization of the triple deck analysis, and Bradshaw (1970), Smith and Cebeci (1973), and Cebeci et al. (1979) present numerical algorithms for the 2DBL equation forms. The application

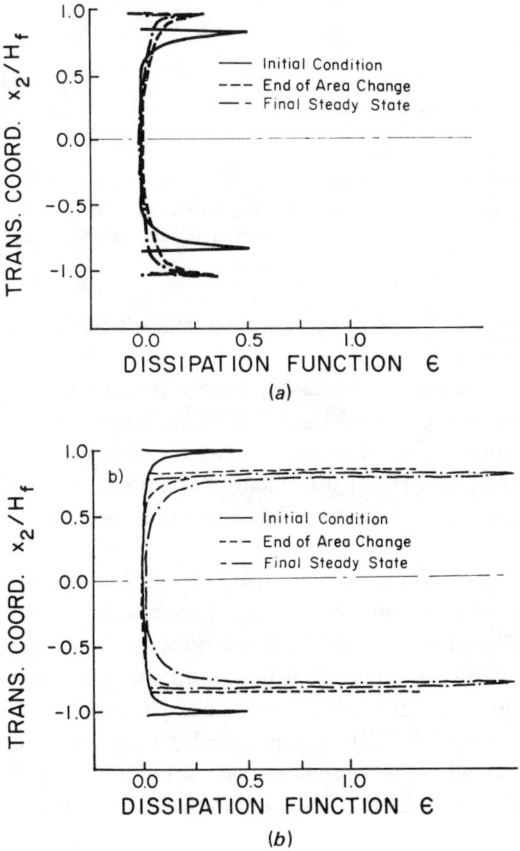

Figure 6.23 Turbulent dissipation variable profiles, turbulent flow in variable cross-sectional duct. (*a*) Diverging; (*b*) converging.

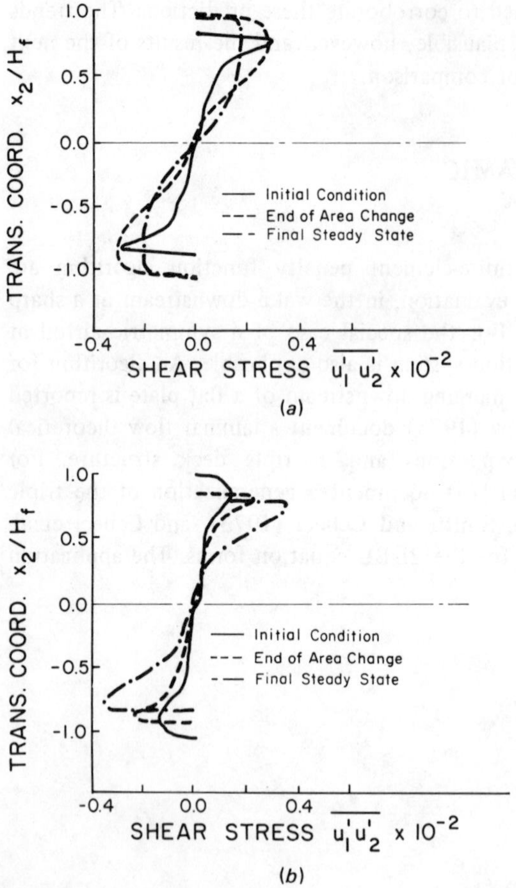

Figure 6.24 Reynolds shear stress $\overline{u_1' u_2'}$ profiles, turbulent flow in variable cross-sectional duct. (*a*) Diverging; (*b*) converging.

of each is strictly limited to the symmetric wakes produced by symmetric airfoils at zero angle of attack.

The developed 2DPNS equation statement, when interactively coupled with a viscous augmented exterior two-dimensional potential flow (2DPHI) solution, can be used to predict the turbulent wake evolution downstream of arbitrary, sharp-trailing edge airfoils at angle of attack. Baker et al. (1982) document the application to a NACA 63-012 wake flowfield, and compare results to detailed distributions of high quality experimental data.

This airfoil wake specification corresponds to a mixed semibounded and unbounded domain prediction, i.e., upstream and downstream, respectively, of the trailing edge plane (see Fig. 6.27). The 2DBL (or 2DPNS) solutions on the upper and lower airfoil surfaces, on $0.9 \leqslant \xi/C \leqslant 1.0$, where C is the airfoil chord, provide the initial conditions $q_j^h(\xi = 1, \eta)$ for the 2DPNS solution on $\xi/C > 1.0$. The boundary conditions for the p_C solution, (6.137), are provided by the exterior potential flow solution, which interacts with the viscous domain solutions through the efflux velocity distribution u^1; see (3.5). The iteration loop between

2DBL/2DPNS, and the 2DPHI solution, is cycled until $p_I(\xi)$ and $\bar{p}(\eta)$ become stationary; see (6.136).

The initial estimate of the viscous displacement surface for the 2DPHI solution can be economically obtained by iteration with the solution to the integral turbulent boundary layer equation analogous to (6.77), as

$$L(\theta) = \frac{d\theta}{d\xi} + \frac{\theta}{u_I}(H + 2)\frac{du_I}{d\xi} - \frac{1}{2}C_f = 0 \tag{6.161}$$

The variables θ, H, u_I, and C_f are the usual boundary layer parameters.

During the 2DPNS iteration with 2DPHI, the application of the $p_p(\eta)$ solution to the $\bar{u}(\eta)$ equation solution is retarded by one interaction step, to avoid numerical violation of the parabolic assumption. The second and third interaction 2DPNS solutions for $p(\eta)$ were reported nominally identical, yielding convergence for $\bar{p}(\eta)$. Additional detail is presented in the cited reference.

An important problem aspect is initialization of the computational experiment sufficiently close to the actual physical experiment. Equations (6.109)–(6.111) were

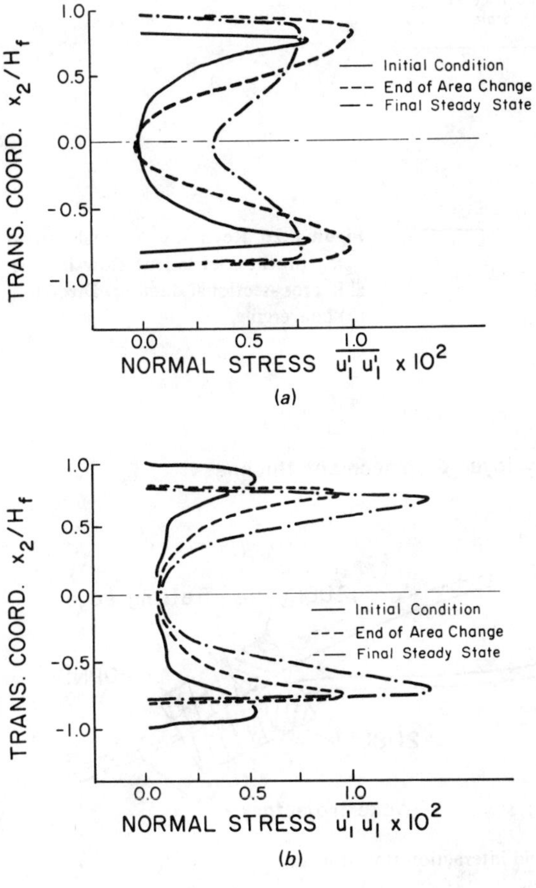

Figure 6.25 Reynolds normal stress $\overline{u_1' u_1'}$ profiles, turbulent flow in variable cross-sectional duct. (*a*) Diverging; (*b*) converging.

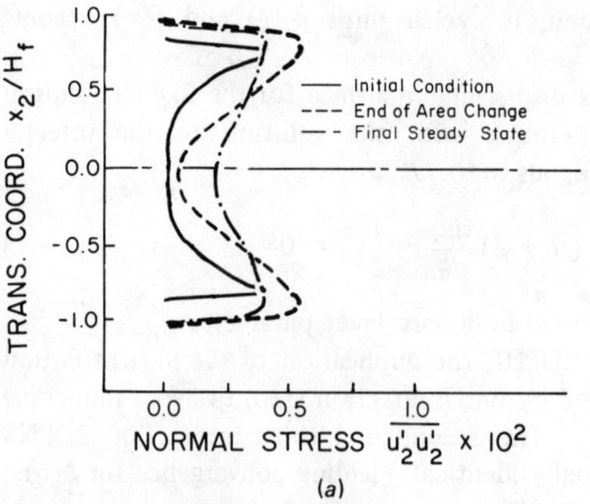

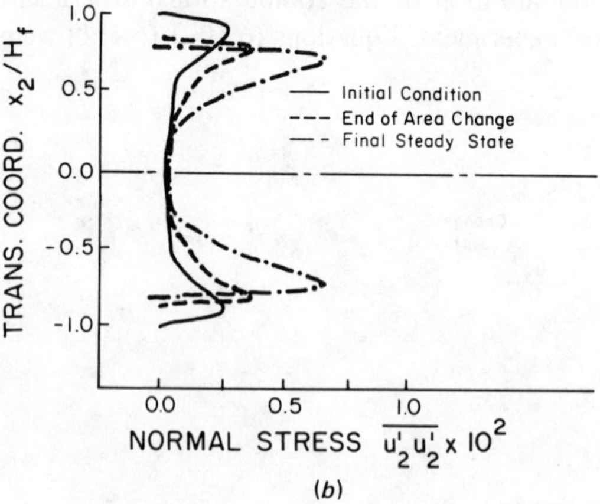

Figure 6.26 Reynolds normal stress $\overline{u_2'u_2'}$ profiles, turbulent flow in variable cross-sectional duct. (*a*) Diverging; (*b*) converging.

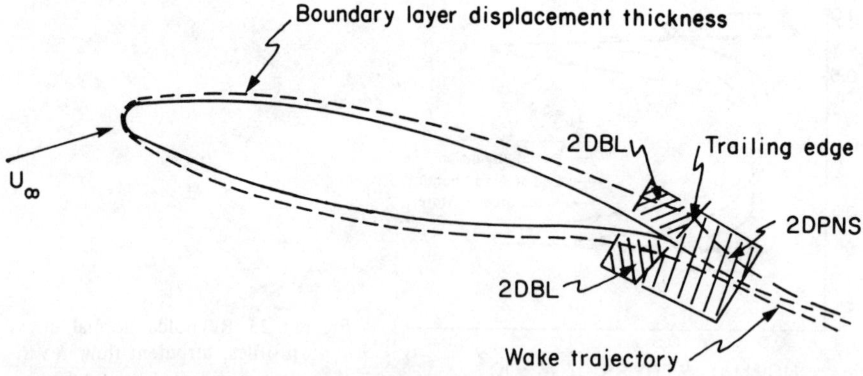

Figure 6.27 Graph of airfoil viscous-inviscid interaction flow domain.

employed in regions of the 2DBL domain devoid of experimental data. Elsewhere, where the experimental data were available, the initial distributions were established assuming $\overline{u_1'} \approx \sqrt{C_1 k}$ that is, neglecting the two other terms in $\overline{u_1' u_1'}$ (6.131). Thus,

$$k_0 \equiv \frac{\overline{u_1'^2}}{C_1} \tag{6.162}$$

$$\epsilon_0 \equiv \frac{\omega^b C_4 k^{3/2}}{l_d} \tag{6.163}$$

$$l_d \geqslant \frac{\sqrt{C_1}\ \overline{u_1' u_2'}}{\overline{u_1'}\,|\partial \bar{u}_1/\partial x_2|} \tag{6.164}$$

The form of (6.164) avoids division by products of small numbers, yielding l_d a constant on $x_2/\delta > 0.9$. Hence, both k and ϵ may go to zero in the freestream.

Figure 6.28 summarizes the converged interaction algorithm 2DBL solution distributions for mean and fluctuating velocity correlation on the upstream trailing edge region $0.9 < \xi_1/C \leqslant 1.0$, for flow on the airfoil underside. Each curve is shifted in plotting to avoid overlap, and the symbols are experimental data. The sole purpose in the 2DBL solution is to ensure that initialization of the 2DPNS wake computational experiment corresponds to the physical experiment to the maximum extent possible. The close agreement between data and the 2DBL solution confirms the high degree of compatibility achieved. The last three curves in each plot are computational predictions on $0.99 \leqslant \xi/C \leqslant 1.0$, with excellent agreement with data.

Figure 6.29 summarizes the 2DBL solution for dissipation function and particular pressure p_p [see (6.85)], on $0.9 \leqslant x_1/C \leqslant 1.0$. The region where ϵ is highly spiked, inside $y^+ \approx 30$, is essentially dominated by the low-turbulence Reynolds number wall model. In distinction, the plots of p_p are smooth in this region, as is, therefore, the turbulence kinetic energy distribution. Repeating the 2DBL solution with a doubling of the computational grid refinement does not affect the solutions on the scale of these plots.

Figure 6.30 summarizes the converged interaction algorithm 2DPNS solution in the wake of the NACA 63-012 airfoil at zero angle of attack. The left curve in each plot is the 2DPNS solution at $x_1/C = 1.00002$ after the first step. Sixty integration steps $\Delta\xi$ were taken to obtain the solution at $x_1/C = 1.0027$, the location of the first experimental data station. In comparison, only 130 integration steps were used to complete the 2DPNS solution on $1.0027 < x_1/C \leqslant 1.10$. The agreement between the data and the numerical prediction is generally excellent at all stations. The $\bar{u}_1$ minimum in the defect region is underpredicted by 8 percent at $x_1/C = 1.0027$; this is reduced to 5 percent at $x_1/C = 1.10$, which is the experimental confidence. The computed spike in $(\overline{u_1' u_1'})^{1/2}$ is sharper than data at $x_1/C = 1.0027$; thereafter, the 2DPNS solution exhibits the double maxima and overall spreading rate of the data. At $x_1/C = 1.10$, the local extremum disparity with data is 9 percent. The same comparison is exhibited for $\overline{u_1' u_2'}$. The computed spike exceeds data by 60 percent at $x_1/C = 1.0027$; thereafter, overall agreement with peaks and spreading rate is

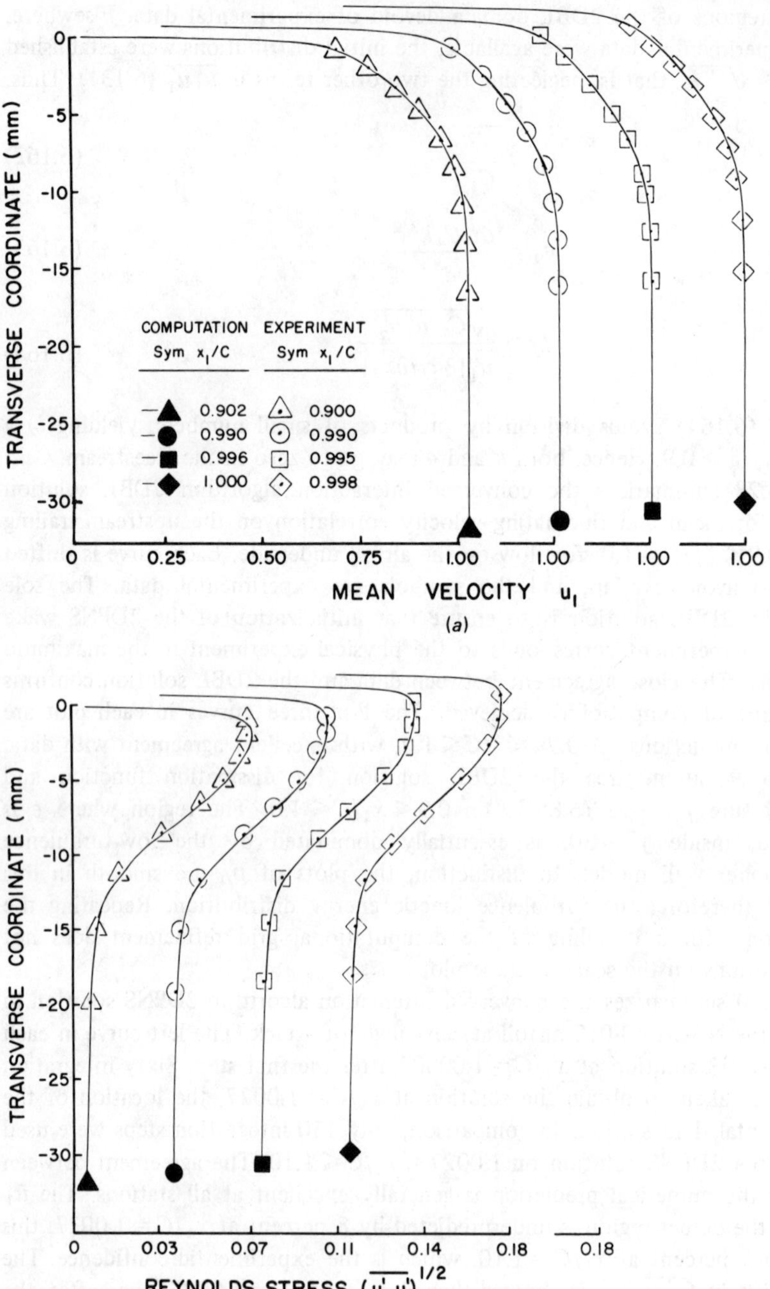

Figure 6.28 Interaction algorithm 2DBL solution comparison to data, $0.902 \leqslant x_1/C \leqslant 1.000$, NACA 63-012, $\alpha = 0°$. (*a*) Mean velocity $\bar{u}_1$; (*b*) Reynolds normal stress $\sqrt{\overline{u_1' u_1'}}$.

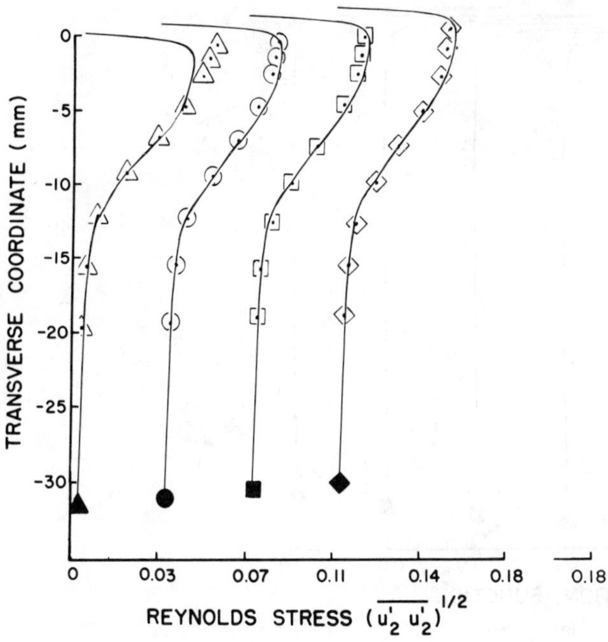

(c)

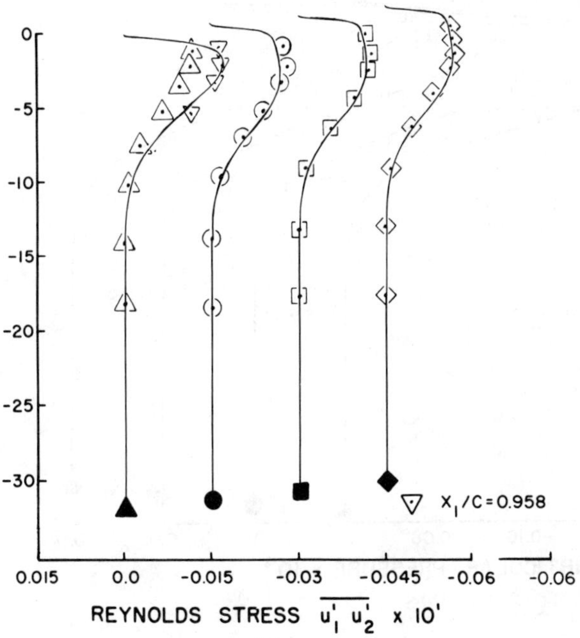

(d)

Figure 28 (*Continued*) Interaction algorithm 2DBL solution comparison to data, $0.902 \leqslant x_1/C \leqslant 1.000$, NACA 63-012, $\alpha = 0°$. (*c*) Reynolds normal stress $\sqrt{\overline{u'_2 u'_2}}$; (*d*) Reynolds shear stress $\overline{u'_1 u'_2}$.

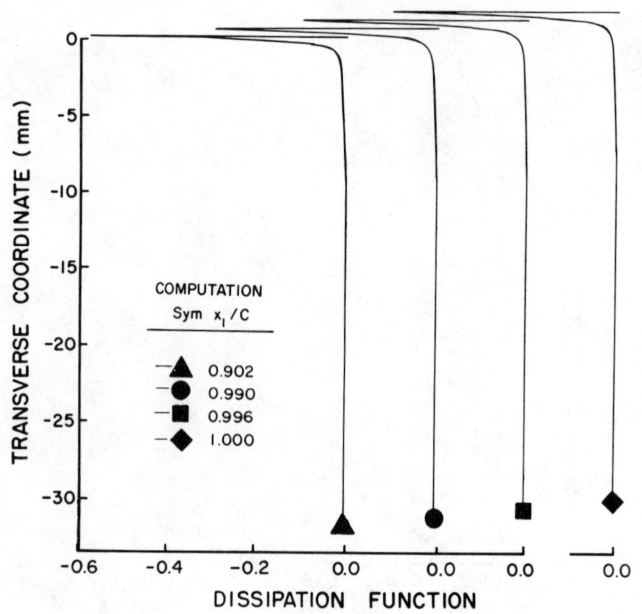

(a)

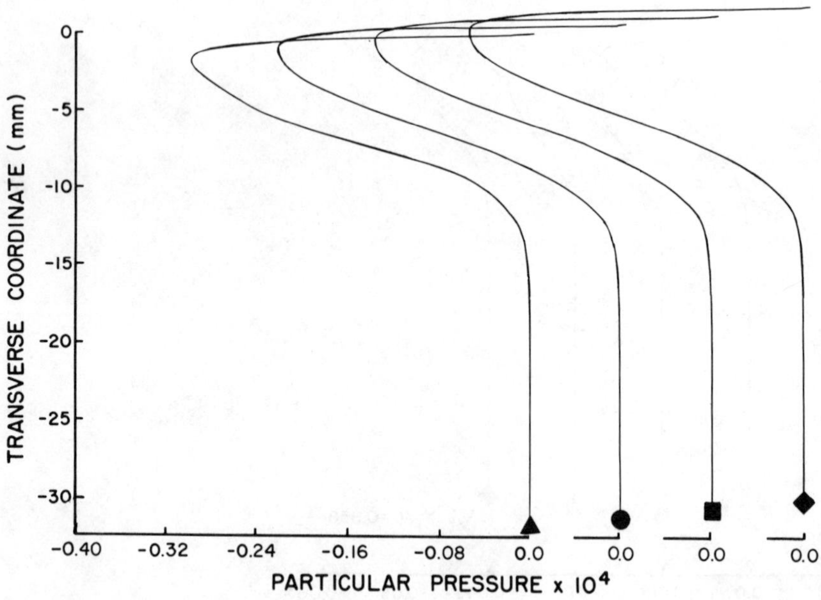

(b)

Figure 6.29 Interaction algorithm 2DBL solution for dissipation and pressure particular solution $0.9 \leqslant x_1/C \leqslant 1.0$, NACA 63-012, $\alpha = 0°$. (*a*) Dissipation function ϵ; (*b*) pressure particular solution p_p.

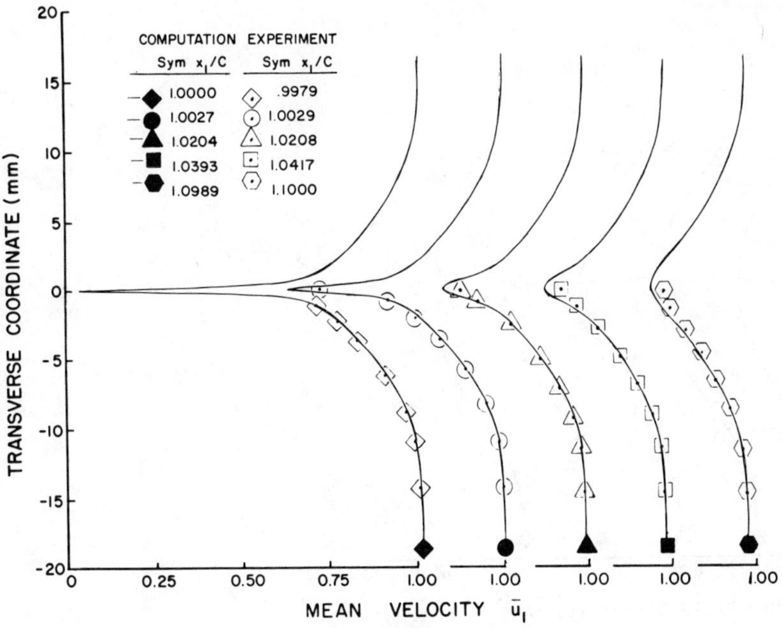

(*a*)

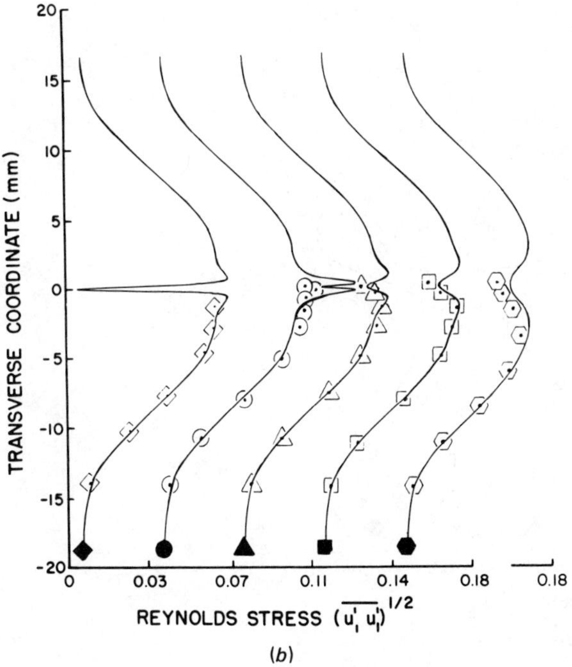

(*b*)

Figure 6.30 Interaction algorithm 2DPNS solution comparison to data, $1.0 \leqslant x_1/C < 1.10$, NACA 63-012, $\alpha = 0°$. (*a*) Mean velocity $\bar{u}_1$; (*b*) Reynolds normal stress $\sqrt{\overline{u_1' u_1'}}$.

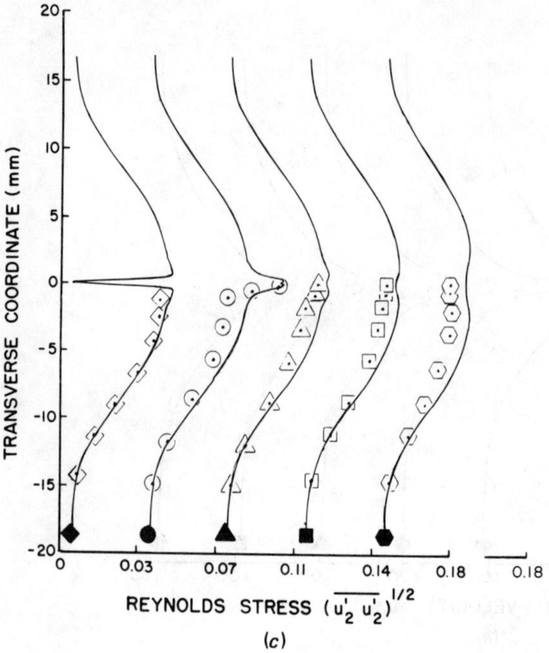

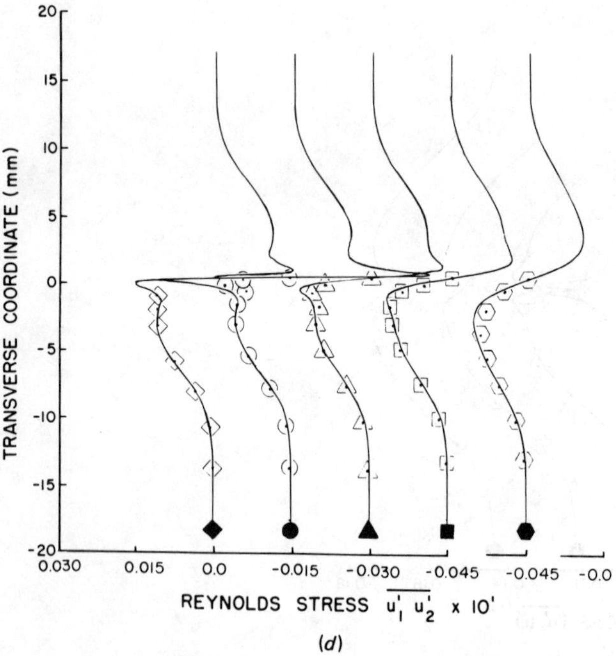

Figure 6.30 (*Continued*) Interaction algorithm 2DPNS solution comparison to data, $1.0 \leqslant \underline{x_1/C} \leqslant 1.10$, NACA 63-012, $\alpha = 0°$. (*c*) Reynolds normal stress $\sqrt{\overline{u_2' u_2'}}$; (*d*) Reynolds shear stress $\overline{u_1' u_2'}$.

generally excellent. The extremum shear stress at $x_1/C = 1.10$ is underpredicted by 10 percent, which is the experimental confidence.

An anomaly exists in the experimental data for $(\overline{u_2'u_2'})^{1/2}$, in that the downstream level decreased abruptly by 30 percent compared with the upstream data. Hence, the numerical predictions lie above the data. Aside from this, the computed spike at $x_1/C = 1.0027$ and the overall spreading and decay rates exhibit trends in good agreement with data. Note in particular the numerical confirmation of a single extremum, in marked distinction to the double extremum for $(\overline{u_1'u_1'})^{1/2}$. This distinction is due solely to the difference in the sign of the $O(\delta^2)$ term in the tensor expansion for $\overline{u_i'u_i'}$; see (6.132). Its significance is the major distinction in the normal stress distributions, as confirmed by the experimental data.

Figure 6.31 summarizes the 2DPNS solution distribution for particular pressure p_P, (6.135), and dissipation function. A large favorable x_1 pressure gradient is predicted in the momentum-defect core, between the trailing edge and $x_1/C = 1.0027$. Thereafter, it turns modestly adverse before essentially vanishing on $x_1/C > 1.02$. The initial zero levels for ϵ near the wake centerline rapidly decrease in concert with reduction of the wall induced spike on $1.0 < x_1/C \leqslant 1.02$. Thereafter, dissipation function decays to a nominally null but importantly nonzero distribution level.

Viewing these results, the consequential relaxation of the turbulent layers is completed within the first fraction of a percent chord into the wake, i.e., $\Delta x_1/C \leqslant 0.003$. Even though a large particular pressure gradient was therein computed, its inclusion into the composite pressure field on the sequential algorithm passes increased $\bar{u}_1(x_1/C = 1.0027)$ by only about 2 percent, due primarily to the extremely short distance involved. Hence, the near-field acceleration appears primarily responsive to the rate of turbulence mixing, coupled with the effects of continuity.

The 2DPNS solution depends most critically on an initial condition specification that is a solution to the equation system, prior to extinction of the no-slip wall boundary condition. From this standpoint, the low-turbulence Reynolds number model, permitting solution of the k and ϵ equations through the sublayer region, was most crucial to the success of the computational experiment. With this confidence, the interaction algorithm can be applied to analysis of trailing edge flows at nonzero angle of attack, even though no experimental data are available for comparison. For example, Fig. 6.32 compares the computational experiment solution at $x_1/C = 1.10$ at $\alpha = 0°$ and $\alpha = 6°$. The nonsymmetries and level changes induced by angle of attack appear plausible, and are clear indicators of the trends to be expected in data from a physical experiment.

6.16 FREE JET TURBULENT MIXING

The 2DPNS algorithm is equally applicable to this problem class, in which enhanced entrainment of mass from the far field by turbulent mixing in the region of large shear stress may be the design goal. The application aspects of the algorithm are

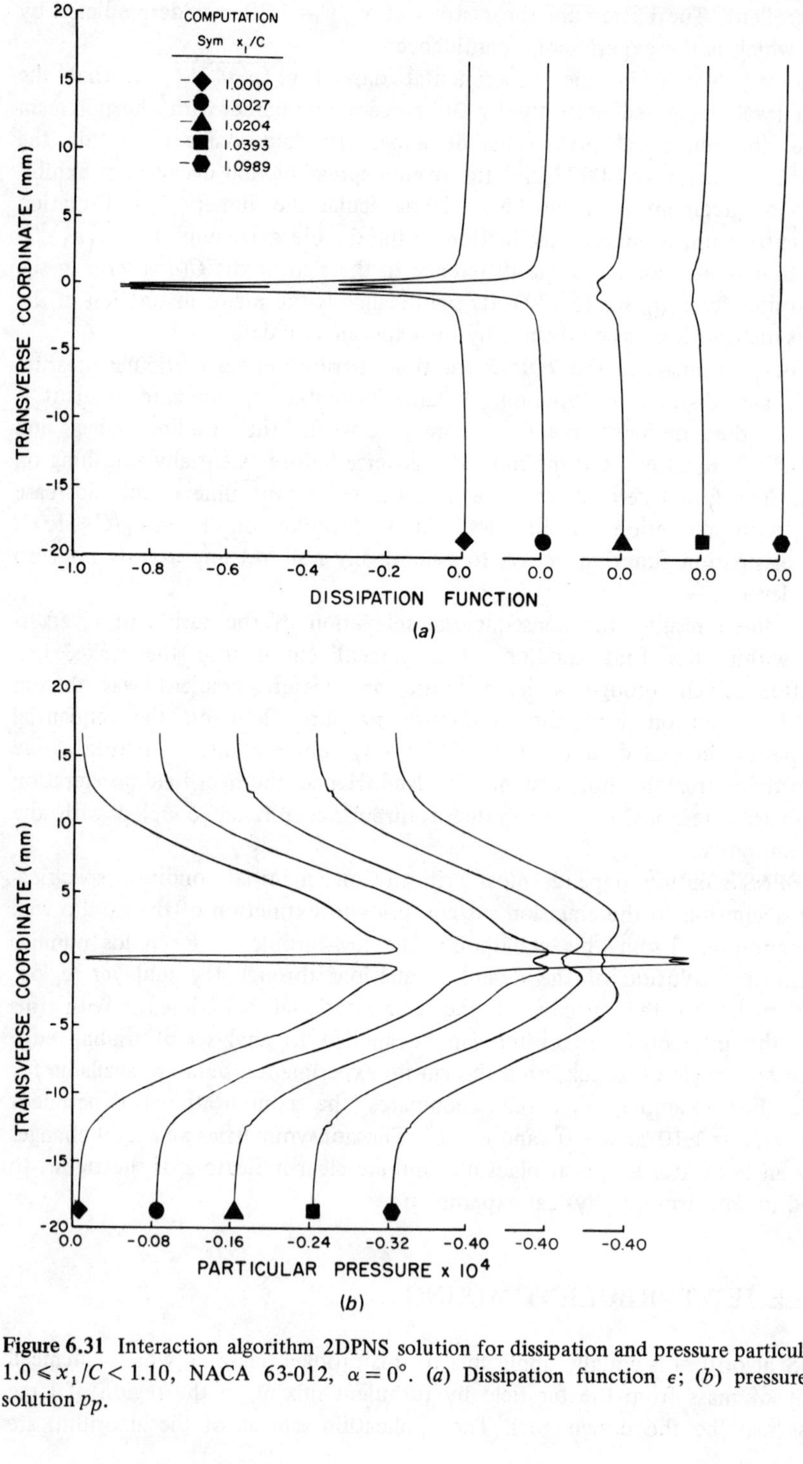

Figure 6.31 Interaction algorithm 2DPNS solution for dissipation and pressure particular solution, $1.0 \leqslant x_1/C < 1.10$, NACA 63-012, $\alpha = 0°$. (*a*) Dissipation function ϵ; (*b*) pressure particular solution p_p.

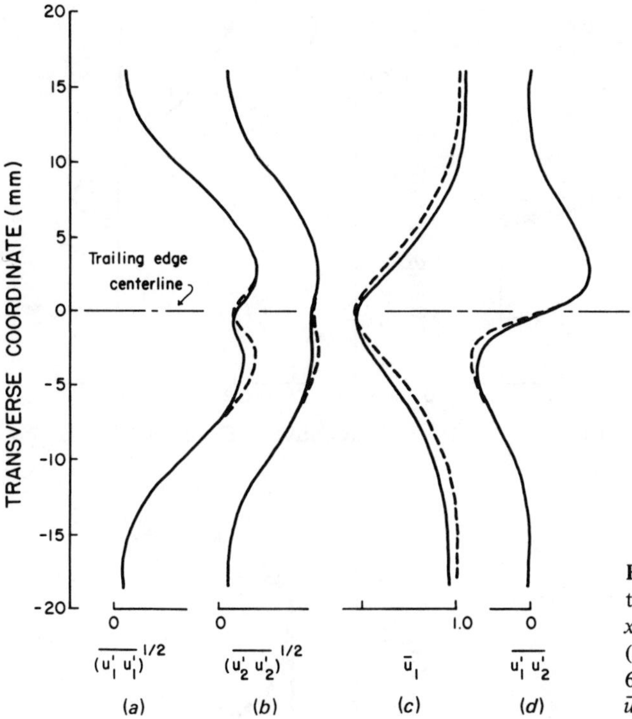

Figure 6.32 Comparison between 2DPNS solutions at $x_1/C = 1.10$, NACA 63-012, (- - -) $\alpha = 0°$ and (——) $\alpha = 6°$. (*a*) $\sqrt{\overline{u_1' u_1'}}$; (*b*) $\sqrt{\overline{u_2' u_2'}}$; (*c*) $\bar{u}_1$; (*d*) $\overline{u_1' u_2'}$.

similar to those presented in the previous two sections. Baker et al. (1982b) document a 2DPNS experiment to verify the algorithm application to turbulent mixing of a jet issued from a slot into a quiescent chamber (see Fig. 6.17*b*).

Figure 6.33*a*–*d* summarizes the solution of the initial-valued variables $\{\bar{u}_1, \bar{u}_2, k, \epsilon\}$ on $0 \leqslant \xi/H_f \leqslant 1.0$, where H_f is the slot jet half-width. The boundary conditions are vanishing normal gradients at both the centerline and the far field for all variables except ϕ, which was set to zero on the far-field boundary. The characteristic actions in turbulent jet mixing are clearly illustrated by the 2DPNS solution. The jet potential core is progressively eroded by turbulent mixing (Fig. 6.33*a*). Starting from a zero initial level for transverse velocity, the penalty algorithm clearly predicts entrainment (negative $\bar{u}_2$) from the far field (Fig. 6.33*b*), with $\bar{u}_2$ remaining nominally zero in the potential core region. The profiles for k and ϵ rapidly broaden to fill the region of strong turbulent mixing (Fig. 6.33*c*–*d*), while remaining nominally zero in the far field and within the potential core. While no experimental data are available for comparison to this specific case, these results are in qualitative agreement with anticipated behavior.

6.17 CLOSURE

This chapter presents the finite-element penalty function solution algorithm for the nonlinear partial differential equation systems governing laminar and turbulent

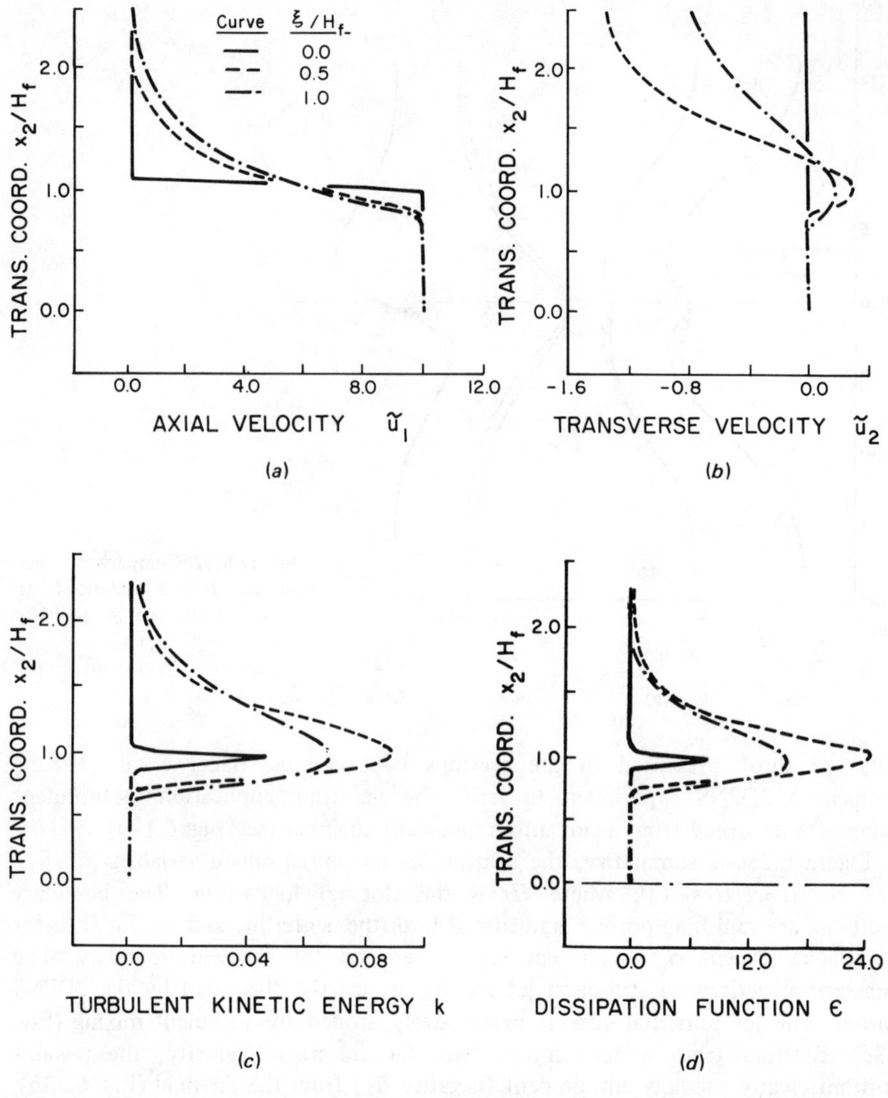

Figure 6.33 2DPNS computed solution field, turbulent rectangular slot jet flow. (*a*) axial velocity $\bar{u}_1$; (*b*) transverse velocity $\bar{u}_2 \times 10$; (*c*) turbulent kinetic energy k; (*d*) dissipation function ϵ.

two-dimensional parabolic flows. Development of the procedures has amply illustrated the great versatility built into the finite-element solution concept. The numerical results attest to the capability to solve complex nonlinear equations, as well as firmly document basic concepts of accuracy and convergence. The following chapter expands the penalty function algorithm concept to three-dimensional parabolic flows, as a modest theoretical but comprehensively detailed extension of the developed ideas.

REFERENCES

Baker, A. J. (1981). Research on Numerical Algorithms for the Three-Dimensional Navier-Stokes Equations, II. Dissipative Finite Element, U.S.A.F. Rept. AFWAL-TR-80-3157.

Baker, A. J. and Orzechowski, J. A. (1981). A Continuity-Constraint Finite Element Algorithm for Three-Dimensional Parabolic Flow Prediction, *Proceedings ASME-AIAA Symposium on Computers in Flow Prediction and Experiments*, ASME/WAM, pp. 103–107.

Baker, A. J. and Orzechowski, J. A. (1982a). A Viscous-Inviscid Interaction Algorithm for Three-Dimensional Turbulent Subsonic Aerodynamic Juncture Region Flow, AIAA Paper No. 82-0100.

Baker, A. J. and Orzechowski, J. A. (1982b). A Penalty Finite Element Method for Parabolic Flow Prediction, ASME, App. Mech. Div., AMD-Vol. 51, pp. 137–142.

Baker, A. J., Yu, J. C., Orzechowski, J. A., and Gatski, T. B. (1982). Prediction and Measurement of Incompressible Turbulent Aerodynamic Trailing Edge Flows, *AIAA J.*, vol. 20, no. 1, pp. 51–59.

Blottner, F. G. (1970). Finite Difference Methods of Solution of the Boundary Layer Equations, *AIAA J.*, vol. 8, no. 2, pp. 192–205.

Blottner, F. G. (1975). Computational Techniques for Boundary Layers, NATO/AGARD Lecture Series No. 73, *Computational Methods for Inviscid and Viscous Two- and Three-Dimensional Flow Fields*, pp. 1–51.

Blottner, F. G. and Flugge-Lotz, I. (1963). Finite Difference Computation of the Boundary Layer with Displacement Thickness Iteration, *J. Mechan.*, vol. 2, no. 4, pp. 397–423.

Bradshaw, P. (1970). Prediction of the Turbulent Near Wake of a Symmetrical Airfoil, *AIAA J.*, vol. 8, no. 8, pp. 1507–1508.

Cebeci, T. and Smith, A. M. O. (1974). *Analysis of Turbulent Boundary Layers*, vol. 2, Academic Press, New York.

Cebeci, T., Thiele, F., Williams, P. G., and Stewartson, K. (1979). On the Calculation of Symmetric Wakes, I. Two-Dimensional Flows, *J. Numer. Heat Trans.*, vol. 2.

Coles, D. A., Hirst, E. A. (eds.) (1968). *AFOSR-IFP-Stanford Conference on Computation of Turbulent Boundary Layers*, Vol. II, Thermosciences Division, Department of Mechanical Engineering, Stanford University, California.

Hanjalic, K. and Launder, B. E. (1972). A Reynolds Stress Model of Turbulence and Its Application to Thin Shear Flows, *J. Fluid Mech.*, vol. 52, pt. 4, pp. 609–638.

Kline, S. J., Sovran, G., Morkovan, M. V., Cockrell, D. J. (eds.) (1968). *AFOSR-IFP-Stanford Conference on Computation of Turbulent Boundary Layers*, vol. I, Thermosciences Division, Department of Mechanical Engineering, Stanford University, California.

Launder, B. E., Reece, G. J., and Rodi, W. (1975). Progress in the Development of a Reynolds-Stress Turbulence Closure, *J. Fluid Mech.*, vol. 68, pt. 3, pp. 537–566.

Lee, J. R., Sears, F. W., and Turcotte, D. L. (1963). *Statistical Thermodynamics*, Addison-Wesley, Reading, Mass.

Ludwig, H. and Tillmann, W. (1950). Untersuchungen über die Wandschubspannung in turbulenten Reibungsschichten, *Ing. Arch.*, vol. 17, pp. 288–299, Engl. transl. NACA TM 1825.

Melnik, R. E. and Chow, R. (1975). Asymptotic Theory of Two-Dimensional Trailing-Edge Flows, NASA Rept. SP-347, pp. 177–249.

Melnik, R. E. and Chow, R. (1976). Turbulent Interaction at Trailing Edges, NASA Rept. CP-2001, pp. 1423–1425.

Oden, J. T. and Reddy, J. N. (1976). *Introduction to Mathematical Theory of Finite Elements*, Wiley, New York.

Patankar, S. V. and Spalding, D. B. (1967). *Heat and Mass Transfer in Boundary Layers*, Morgon-Grompian, London.

Patankar, S. V. and Spalding, D. B. (1972). A Calculation Procedure for Heat, Mass and Momentum Transfer in Three-Dimensional Parabolic Flows, *Int. J. Heat Mass Transfer*, vol. 15, pp. 1787–1806.

Popinski, Z. and Baker, A. J. (1976). An Implicit Finite Element Algorithm for the Boundary Layer Equations, *J. Comput. Phys.*, vol. 21, no. 1, pp. 55–84.

Schlichting, H. (1979). *Boundary Layer Theory*, McGraw-Hill, New York.

Smith, A. M. O. and Cebeci, T. (1973). Remarks on Methods for Predicting Viscous Drag, NATO/AGARD Conf. Publ. No. CP-124.

Soliman, M. O. (1978). Accuracy and Convergence of a Finite Element Algorithm for Computational Fluid Dynamics, Ph.D. Dissertation, ESM Rept. 78-1, University of Tennessee, Knoxville.

Soliman, M. O. and Baker, A. J. (1981a). Accuracy and Convergence of a Finite Element Algorithm for Laminar Boundary Layer Flow, *J. Comput. and Fluids,* vol. 9, pp. 43–62.

Soliman, M. O. and Baker, A. J. (1981b). Accuracy and Convergence of a Finite Element Algorithm for Turbulent Boundary Layer Flow, *Comp. Methods Appl. Mech. Eng.*, vol. 28, pp. 81–102.

Tennekes, H. and Lumley, J. L. (1974). *A First Course in Turbulence,* The MIT Press, Cambridge, Mass.

Veldman, A. E. P. (1975). A New Calculation of the Wake of a Flat Plate. *J. Eng. Math.*, vol. 9, pp. 65–70.

Wornom, S. G. (1978). Application of Higher-Order Numerical Methods to the Boundary Layer Equations, in *Numerical Methods in Laminar and Turbulent Flows,* Pentech Press, London, pp. 387–398.

CHAPTER

SEVEN

THREE-DIMENSIONAL PARABOLIC FLOW

7.1 INTRODUCTION

The parabolic approximation to the steady three-dimensional Navier-Stokes equation system is a highly useful method for generating three-dimensional bounded and unbounded flow fields. The system is a generalization of the two-dimensional parabolic equations developed in Chap. 6. This chapter presents the theoretical development and finite-element algorithm for solution of the three-dimensional parabolic Navier-Stokes equations governing the steady, unidirectional laminar and turbulent flow of a compressible multispecies fluid.

The three-dimensional parabolic Navier-Stokes equations (3DPNS) are derived from the parent three-dimensional Navier-Stokes system using order of magnitude analyses. The assumption that a predominant flow direction persists is a key assumption. Patankar and Spalding (1970) pioneered in development of the 3DPNS equation system for incompressible flow, and introduced the concept of resolution of the pressure field into an axial uniform gradient and a distribution in the plane transverse to the predominant flow direction (Patankar and Spalding, 1972). Briley (1974) derived a 3DPNS algorithm, for laminar incompressible flows, by identification of an irrotational perturbation velocity field to conserve mass and a two-dimensional Poisson equation for transverse plane pressure distribution. Ghia et al. (1976) presented additional results for laminar incompressible nonrectangular duct flows. Dodge (1976) extended the irrotational velocity perturbation to three-dimensions, to provide a pseudoelliptic coupling in pressure, and presented results for turbulent incompressible flows in a modestly nonrectangular duct geometry.

Briley and McDonald (1979) document prediction of vortex roll-up in the transverse plane for laminar flow in a curved duct of nominal rectangular cross section, using a parabolic Navier-Stokes algorithm and assuming an a priori potential flow pressure field. Resolution of the transverse plane velocity vector into potential and rotational components yields intrinsic enforcement of the continuity equation, and a noniterative, split linearized block implicit matrix solution algorithm was employed. Pratap and Spalding (1975) report an attempt for turbulent flow prediction in the same geometry using a partially parabolic Navier-Stokes alogrithm. Even though a turbulent kinetic energy-dissipation closure model was utilized, they suggest their Reynolds stress model as the cause of discrepancy with data. An additional error source could be poor satisfaction of continuity. Levy et al. (1980) also report results for turbulent flow prediction in a curved duct of nominal circular cross section, utilizing the algorithm of Briley and McDonald (1979). Essential agreement is achieved with one experimental data pattern for axial velocity isovels, utilizing an elementary mixing length turbulence closure model. No transverse plane velocity comparisons are presented, although one would infer that the basic momentum sources are present.

A pressure-velocity formulation is probably preferred for an algorithm to predict ducted turbulent flows. While definition of transverse plane potential function automatically satisifes the continuity equation, the elimination of transverse pressure gradients comes at the expense of definition and use of vorticity. The acknowledged weakness of a vorticity formulation is the kinematic boundary condition statement. The existence of a very large mean flow strain rate at a wall for turbulent flow serves to further complicate this basic weakness. Conversely, in a physical variable formulation, an algorithm must be developed to construct an overall parabolic, i.e., initial-value, elliptic boundary value statement for transverse plane phenomena. A careful order of magnitude analysis of the transverse plane momentum equation indicates that pressure variation will balance convection and/or turbulence effects to first order, and that overall this balance is of higher order effects than controlled by the continuity equation. Since the continuity equation is not parabolic for subsonic flow, the construction of a suitable transverse plane equation system is required and presented herein.

The second key requirement for prediction of turbulent three-dimensional flows is an adequate turbulence closure model. In this regard, the problem of exterior subsonic axial corner flow (Fig. 7.1) has received considerable theoretical and

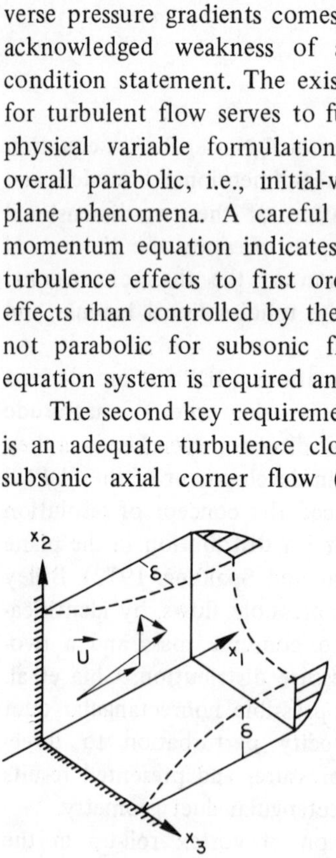

Figure 7.1 Visualization of subsonic axial corner flow.

experimental study. Rubin and coworkers (Rubin, 1966; Pal and Rubin, 1971; Rubin and Grossman, 1971; Weinberg and Rubin, 1972) pioneered in formulation and analysis of the laminar problem. Tokuda (1972) documents an extension of the analysis and compares predictions to the data of Zamir and Young (1970). Bragg (1969) analyzed the corresponding turbulent flow case and determined the corner distribution of the downstream Reynolds normal stress $\overline{u'_1 u'_1}$. The salient feature of the turbulent flow case is a persistent axial vorticity component. Various causal mechanisms have been theorized, including transverse pressure waves (Eichelbrenner and Preston, 1971), Reynolds shear stress gradients along the corner bisector (Gessner, 1973), and/or nonisotropy of the Reynolds stress tensor (Gessner and Emery, 1976). Quality experimental data for a confined corner flow (Melling and Whitelaw, 1976) indicates a primary mechanism to be nonisotropy of $\overline{u'_i u'_j}$.

The essential character in the idealized corner region flow appears to be the result of a delicate balance between turbulence phenomena and the induced secondary mean flow velocity field. These mechanisms represent a balancing of basically higher order effects however, as they can be readily dominated by flow-field curvature induced vorticity (Shabaka and Bradshaw, 1981). Nevertheless, an adequate stress closure model is required; one has been proposed by Baker and Orzechowski (1981). The six components of the (symmetric) Reynolds stress tensor are determined by using a constitutive equation formulation requiring solution of parabolized forms of the transport equations for turbulent kinetic energy (k) and isotropic dissipation function (ϵ). The stress constitutive equation includes a low-turbulence Reynolds number length scale model to permit solution of the (k, ϵ) equation system directly to a no-slip wall. Hence, the boundary conditions for k and ϵ are identical, vanishing at surfaces where the mean flow velocity vector vanishes.

The pressure-velocity form (Baker and Orzechowski, 1982) is used to develop the 3DPNS algorithm for subsonic steady turbulent flow prediction in semibounded and bounded domains. Persistence of a predominant component of the time-averaged, mean flow velocity permits an order of magnitude analysis yielding the parabolic approximation to the governing three-dimensional time-averaged Navier-Stokes equations. Using the same procedure for components of the Reynolds stress tensor, the balancing of lowest order terms in the transverse momentum equations yields a pressure Poisson equation. An algorithm for this equation is derived in terms of complementary and particular solution fields. The complementary solution enforces global conservation of mass. The particular solution refines this pressure field to account for Reynolds stress and transverse velocity fields. The particular solution is enforced in a retarded manner to update the three-dimensional pressure field, yielding an iterative interaction algorithm. Algorithm convergence occurs when this composite pressure solution becomes stationary. As a consequence of the ordering analysis, and since first order effects are contained within the (non-parabolic) continuity equation, a transverse momentum equation solution statement is constructed wherein the first-order effects due to satisfaction of the continuity equation are enforced as a differential constraint.

7.2 PARABOLIC NAVIER-STOKES EQUATIONS

The three-dimensional parabolic Navier-Stokes (3DPNS) equations are a simplification of the steady, three-dimensional time-averaged Navier-Stokes equations. In cartesian tensor notation, with superscript tilde and bar denoting mass-weighed and conventional time-averaging, respectively (Cebeci and Smith, 1974), the conservative equation form for a compressible, heat-conducting fluid is

$$L(\bar{\rho}) = \frac{\partial}{\partial x_j}(\bar{\rho}\tilde{u}_j) = 0 \tag{7.1}$$

$$L(\bar{\rho}\tilde{u}_i) = \frac{\partial}{\partial x_j}(\bar{\rho}\tilde{u}_i\tilde{u}_j + \bar{p}\delta_{ij} + \bar{\rho}\overline{u_i'u_j'} - \bar{\sigma}_{ij}) = 0 \tag{7.2}$$

$$L(\bar{\rho}\tilde{H}) = \frac{\partial}{\partial x_j}(\bar{\rho}\tilde{H}\tilde{u}_j - \tilde{u}_i\bar{\sigma}_{ij} + \bar{\rho}\overline{H'u_j'} - \overline{u_i'\sigma_{ij}'} + \bar{g}_j) = 0 \tag{7.3}$$

$$L(\bar{\rho}k) = \frac{\partial}{\partial x_j}\left[\bar{\rho}\tilde{u}_j k + \left(C_k\frac{k}{\epsilon}\,\overline{\rho u_i'u_j'} - \bar{\mu}\delta_{ij}\right)\frac{\partial k}{\partial x_i}\right] + \overline{\rho u_i'u_j'}\,\frac{\partial\tilde{u}_i}{\partial x_j} + \bar{\rho}\epsilon = 0 \tag{7.4}$$

$$L(\bar{\rho}\epsilon) = \frac{\partial}{\partial x_j}\left(\bar{\rho}\tilde{u}_j\epsilon + C_\epsilon\frac{k}{\epsilon}\,\overline{\rho u_i'u_j'}\,\frac{\partial\epsilon}{\partial x_j}\right) + C_\epsilon^1\,\overline{u_i'u_j'}\,\frac{\epsilon}{k}\frac{\partial\tilde{u}_i}{\partial x_j} + C_\epsilon^2\,\frac{\bar{\rho}\epsilon^2}{k} = 0 \tag{7.5}$$

In (7.1)–(7.3), $\bar{\rho}$ is density, $\tilde{u}_j$ is the mean velocity vector, $\bar{p}$ is pressure, δ_{ij} is the Kronecker delta, and $\tilde{H}$ is stagnation enthalpy. The Stokes stress tensor $\bar{\sigma}_{ij}$ and heat flux vector $\bar{q}_j$ are defined as

$$\bar{\sigma}_{ij} = \bar{\rho}\bar{\nu}\,\frac{\tilde{E}_{ij} - (2/3)\delta_{ij}\tilde{E}_{kk}}{\mathrm{Re}} \tag{7.6}$$

$$\bar{q}_j = \bar{\kappa}\,\frac{\partial\tilde{H}}{\partial x_j} \tag{7.7}$$

where $\mathrm{Re} = \bar{U}_\infty L/\bar{\nu}_\infty$ is the Reynolds number and $-\rho\,\overline{u_i'u_j'}$ is the Reynolds stress tensor. The essential decoupling of density and velocity fluctuations for Mach numbers below high supersonic (Morkovin, 1964) has been used to simplify (7.6)–(7.7); $\bar{\nu}$ and $\bar{\kappa}$ are fluid kinematic viscosity and heat conductivity, respectively, and $\tilde{E}_{ij}$ is the mean flow strain rate tensor

$$\tilde{E}_{ij} \equiv \frac{\partial\tilde{u}_i}{\partial x_j} + \frac{\partial\tilde{u}_j}{\partial x_i} \tag{7.8}$$

Equations (7.4)–(7.5) are the transport equations for turbulent kinetic energy and isotropic dissipation function, as obtained using the closure model of Launder et al. (1975) for the pressure-strain and triple correlations, and

$$k \equiv \tfrac{1}{2}\,\overline{u_i'u_i'} \tag{7.9}$$

$$\epsilon \equiv \frac{2\bar{\nu}}{3}\left(\overline{\frac{\partial u_i'}{\partial x_j}\frac{\partial u_i'}{\partial x_k}}\right)\delta_{jk} \tag{7.10}$$

The various coefficients C_β^α are model constants (Hanjalic and Launder, 1972).

The parabolic Navier-Stokes equation set is derived from (7.1)–(7.5) assuming the ratio of transverse mean velocity components to downstream component is less than unity, and further assuming that

1. The downstream velocity component suffers no reversal,
2. Diffusive transport processes in the downstream direction are higher-order, hence negligible, and
3. The overall elliptic character of the parent three-dimensional Navier-Stokes equation can become enforced through construction of a suitable pressure field.

Assume the x_1 (curvilinear) coordinate direction parallel to the predominant mean flow direction with scalar velocity component $\tilde{u}_1$ of order unity, that is, $O(1)$. Further assume $O(\tilde{u}_2) \approx O(\delta) \approx O(\tilde{u}_3)$, and that $O(\delta) < O(1)$. In agreement with boundary layer theory, the continuity equation (7.1) confirms that downstream variation in $\tilde{u}_1$ is of order equal to appropriate transverse plane variations of $\tilde{u}_2$ and $\tilde{u}_3$; hence for $\partial/\partial x_1 \approx O(1)$, $\partial/\partial x_2 \approx O(\delta^{-1}) \approx \partial/\partial x_3$.

Determination of the relative order of terms in the momentum equation (7.2) is straightforward. For the $\tilde{u}_1$ equation, since $O(\overline{\rho u_i' u_j'})$ must be essentially $O(\delta)$, the term $\partial(\overline{\rho u_1' u_1'})/\partial x_1$ is higher order and can be discarded. The assumption that the x_1-diffusion is negligible permits setting $\partial(\tilde{E}_{11})/\partial x_1 \equiv 0$, hence $O(\mathrm{Re}^{-1}) \leqslant O(\delta)$. Therefore, the terms in $\bar{\sigma}_{12}$ and $\bar{\sigma}_{13}$ involving $\tilde{u}_2$ and $\tilde{u}_3$, that is,

$$\frac{\partial}{\partial x_2}\frac{\partial \tilde{u}_2}{\partial x_1} \quad \text{and} \quad \frac{\partial}{\partial x_3}\frac{\partial \tilde{u}_3}{\partial x_1}$$

are both $O(\delta)$ or smaller and hence negligible. Deletion of these terms is the fundamental step to the parabolic approximation, since their elimination removes the elliptic boundary value character in the downstream direction. The retaining of $\partial(\bar{\rho}\tilde{u}_1\tilde{u}_1)/\partial x_1$ instills the initial value form for the resultant equation, hence, permits marching the solution for $\tilde{u}_1$ in the downstream direction. The final 3DPNS form, denoted $L^P(\cdot)$, is

$$L^p(\bar{\rho}\tilde{u}_1) \equiv \frac{\partial}{\partial x_j}(\bar{\rho}\tilde{u}_1\tilde{u}_j) + \frac{\partial \bar{p}}{\partial x_1} + \frac{\partial}{\partial x_2}(\overline{\rho u_1' u_2'} - \bar{\sigma}_{12}) + \frac{\partial}{\partial x_3}(\overline{\rho u_1' u_3'} - \bar{\sigma}_{13}) = 0 \tag{7.11}$$

which is thoroughly familiar. As a final note, should x_j correspond to a curvilinear coordinate description, the derivatives expressed in (7.11) are interpreted as covariant derivatives. The 3DPNS form of the energy equation (7.8) is similarly constructed as

$$L^p(\bar{\rho}\tilde{H}) = \frac{\partial}{\partial x_1}(\bar{\rho}\tilde{u}_1\tilde{H}) + \frac{\partial}{\partial x_l}(\bar{\rho}\tilde{H}\tilde{u}_1 - \tilde{u}_i\bar{\sigma}_{il} + \overline{\rho H' u_l'} - \overline{u_i'\sigma_{il}'} + \bar{q}_l) = 0 \tag{7.12}$$

Equation (7.12) introduces as well the 3DPNS limited index summation convention $1 \leqslant (i, j) \leqslant 3$ and $2 \leqslant l \leqslant 3$.

In agreement with boundary layer concepts, the order of pressure variation in the transverse plane is assumed determined by the lowest order terms appearing in (7.2) written on $\tilde{u}_2$ and $\tilde{u}_3$. Each transverse derivative of $\overline{\rho u_2' u_j'}$ and $\overline{\rho u_3' u_j'}$ is $O(1)$, while all other terms are $O(\delta)$ and higher. For example, for a two-dimensional boundary layer (see Sec. 6.8),

$$L(\bar{\rho}\tilde{u}_2) \approx \frac{\partial}{\partial x_2} (\bar{p} + \overline{\rho u_2' u_2'}) = 0 \tag{7.13}$$

The solution is trivial; $\bar{p}$ differs from the inviscid flow edge pressure by a constant, equal to a fraction of the freestream turbulence (k) level, and is distributed through the boundary layer in proportion to $\overline{\rho u_2' u_2'}$. The initial value character, exhibited by the three-dimensional PNS approximation to (7.2), for $\tilde{u}_2$ and $\tilde{u}_3$, can be recast into a more tractible form by taking the divergence. Retaining the higher-order convection and diffusion terms for generality, the appropriate 3DPNS form for the two transverse momentum equations is

$$L(\bar{p}) = \frac{\partial^2 \bar{p}}{\partial x_l^2} + \frac{\partial^2}{\partial x_j \partial x_l} (\bar{\rho}\tilde{u}_l\tilde{u}_j + \overline{\rho u_l' u_j'} - \bar{\sigma}_{lj}) = 0 \tag{7.14}$$

Equation (7.14) defines an elliptic boundary value problem for determination of pressure distributions in the transverse plane. The pressure field that satisfies this Poisson equation consists of complementary and particular solutions,

$$\bar{p}(x_i) = p_c(x_i) + p_p(x_i) \tag{7.15}$$

The complementary solution satisfies the homogeneous portion of (7.14),

$$L(p_c) = \frac{\partial^2 p_c}{\partial x_l^2} = 0 \tag{7.16}$$

subject to the Dirichlet boundary condition known for $\bar{p}(x_1, x_l)$. Elsewhere, an appropriate boundary condition for p_c is homogeneous Neumann.

The particular pressure is any solution to (7.14) subject to homogeneous Dirichlet boundary conditions on boundary segments where p_c is known. Elsewhere, at a no-slip wall for example, the nonhomogeneous Neumann constraint is provided by the inner product of (7.2) with the local outward pointing unit normal $\hat{\eta}_l$,

$$l(p_p) = L(\bar{\rho}\tilde{u}_i) \cdot \hat{\eta}_l = 0 \tag{7.17}$$

Since the convection terms vanish at a wall, and since $\hat{\eta}_l$ possesses no component parallel to the x_1 direction, (7.17) becomes

$$l(p_p) = \frac{\partial p_p}{\partial x_l} \cdot \hat{\eta}_l + \frac{\partial}{\partial x_j} (\overline{\rho u_l' u_j'} - \bar{\sigma}_{lj}) \cdot \hat{\eta}_l = 0 \tag{7.18}$$

The critical issue with the pressure field resolution is knowledge of boundary values of $\bar{p}(x_i)$, the existence of which is assured via assumption 3 of the 3DPNS argument. For a semibounded flow field (for example, a subsonic aerodynamic wing-body juncture region), the PNS boundary values of $\bar{p}$ are provided by a full three-dimensional potential flow solution on the effective viscous-displacement surface distribution (Baker et al., 1982). The viscous-inviscid interaction is enforced by iteration between the PNS determination of the potential flow onset-velocity boundary condition, and the resultant three-dimensional potential solution modification to the boundary values of $\bar{p}(x_i)$.

This situation is not as well defined for a fully bounded, i.e., ducted, flow problem. The upstream initial condition for $\tilde{u}_1$ defines the axial mass flow rate through the duct, which is insensitive to downstream pressures. The inlet level of $\bar{p} \equiv \bar{p}_r$ is also specified. Casting (7.1) into a control-volume form confirms that the axial mass flow rate is conserved (assuming nonporous walls). This led Patankar and Spalding (1972) to formulate a pressure-gradient correction algorithm that numerically conserves axial mass flow rate. Integrating (7.2) for $\tilde{u}_1$, over a control volume spanning the duct cross section, yields

$$\frac{dp^*}{dx_1} = \frac{1}{A}\left[F - 2\bar{u}\,\frac{d\bar{m}}{dx_1} + \overline{mu}\left(\frac{1}{A}\,\frac{dA}{dx_1} + \frac{1}{\bar{\rho}}\,\frac{d\bar{\rho}}{dx_1}\right)\right] \tag{7.19}$$

In (7.19), the bar denotes a cross-sectional integration

$$\bar{\rho} \equiv \int_{R^2} \rho(x_l)\, dx_l \qquad \bar{m} \equiv \int_{R^2} \rho u_1(x_l)\, dx_l \qquad \bar{u} \equiv \frac{\bar{m}}{\bar{\rho}} \tag{7.20}$$

$A(x_1)$ is the duct cross-sectional area distribution, and $F(x_1)$ is the wall friction. The numerical evaluation of the right side of (7.19) yields dp^*/dx_1, which is then adjusted to conserve the numerical measure of $\bar{m}$. The downstream integration then yields an elementary estimate of a (any) value of $\bar{p}(x_1)$, that is,

$$p^*(x_1) \approx \bar{p}_r + \int_0^{x_1} \frac{dp^*}{dx_1}\, dx_1 \tag{7.21}$$

This estimate for $\bar{p}(x_1)$ is logically assigned to the duct centerline. The boundary condition for (7.16) is thus homogeneous Neumann, and the solution is trivial; $p_c(x_1) \equiv p^*(x_1)$.

An improved estimate for p_c boundary conditions requires a more complete accounting of the geometric factors defining the duct. Specifically, for a substantially curved duct centerline, the first-level improved estimate is provided by the full three-dimensional solution for potential flow in the duct. Under the pseudonym "parabolic," this concept has been employed in a noniterative manner for analysis of curved-duct flows. The inclusion of a sequence of iterations between the full three-dimensional inviscid flow, and the PNS viscous solution, has been termed "partially parabolic" (see Patankar, 1980), and is required for an accurate prediction in nonelementary geometries.

7.3 REYNOLDS STRESS CLOSURE MODEL

A closure model for the kinematic Reynolds stress $-\overline{u_i' u_j'}$, appearing in (7.2)-(7.5), is required to complete the 3DPNS order of magnitude analysis. A considerable insight is provided by the construction of a stress-strain rate constitutive equation. The existence of this relationship is assured at sufficient distances from boundaries in space (and time) (see Lumley, 1970).

Using the results of order of magnitude analysis, and simplified lower-dimensional forms, Baker et al. (1979) established the lead terms of the kinematic form appropriate for 3DPNS analyses as

$$-\overline{u_i u_j} = -k\alpha_{ij} + C_4 \frac{k^2}{\epsilon} \tilde{E}_{ij} + C_2 C_4 \frac{k^3}{\epsilon^2} \tilde{E}_{ik}\tilde{E}_{kj} + \cdots \tag{7.22}$$

$\tilde{E}_{ij}$ remains the symmetric mean flow strain-rate tensor given in (7.8). This expansion results from reexpression of triple correlations within the Reynolds stress transport equation using the model of Launder et al. (1975). It is a generalization of the original analysis by Gessner and Emery (1976). In (7.22), α_{ij} is a diagonal tensor in principal coordinates

$$\alpha_{ij} \equiv \frac{1}{3k} (\overline{u_k' u_k'}) a_{\underline{i}} \delta_{ij} \tag{7.23}$$

The a_i are coefficients admitting anisotropy, where $a_1 \equiv C_1$, and $a_2 \equiv C_3 \equiv a_3$. The C_α are defined as (Launder et al., 1975)

$$\begin{aligned} C_1 &\equiv \frac{22(C_{01} - 1) - 6(4C_{02} - 5)}{33(C_{01} - 2C_{02})} \\ C_2 &\equiv \frac{4(3C_{02} - 1)}{11(C_{01} - 2C_{02})} \\ C_3 &\equiv \frac{22(C_{01} - 1) - 12(3C_{02} - 1)}{33(C_{01} - 2C_{02})} \\ C_4 &\equiv \frac{44C_{02} - 22C_{01}C_{02} - 128C_{02} - 36C_{02}^2 + 10}{165(C_{01} - 2C_{02})^2} \end{aligned} \tag{7.24}$$

In (7.24), C_{01} and C_{02} are universal empirical constants; suggested values are $C_{01} \approx 2.8$ and $C_{02} \approx 0.45$ (Hanjalic and Launder, 1972). The variables k and ϵ are turbulence kinetic energy and isotropic dissipation [see (7.9)-(7.10)].

The order of terms appearing in (7.22) can be estimated for the standard values $C_\alpha = \{0.94,\ 0.067,\ 0.56,\ 0.068\}$. For significance in (7.2), recall the requirement $O(\overline{u_i' u_j'}) = O(\delta)$. For an elementary two-dimensional flow, and for $i = 1$, and $j = 2$, (7.22) yields the familiar form

$$-\overline{u_1' u_2'} = C_4 \frac{k^2}{\epsilon} \frac{\partial \tilde{u}_1}{\partial x_2} \tag{7.25}$$

Hence, $O(C_4 k^2/\epsilon) = O(\delta^2)$. Further for $i = 1 = j$ in (7.22), and neglecting the second two terms, $O(k) = O(\delta)$. Combining, $O(C_4/\epsilon) = O(1)$; hence, $O(C_2/\epsilon) = O(1)$. Thus, $O[C_2 C_4 (k^3/\epsilon^2)] = O(k^3) = O(\delta^3)$. Therefore, in rectangular cartesian coordinates for illustration, the six components of the kinematic Reynolds stress tensor are, retaining terms of the first two orders of significance,

$$\begin{aligned}
&\qquad\qquad\qquad\qquad \overbrace{\qquad\qquad\qquad\qquad\qquad}^{O(\delta)} \qquad\qquad\qquad \overbrace{\qquad\qquad\qquad}^{O(\delta^2)}\\
\overline{u_1'u_1'} &= C_1 k - C_2 C_4 \frac{k^3}{\epsilon^2}\left[\left(\frac{\partial \tilde{u}_1}{\partial x_2}\right)^2 + \left(\frac{\partial \tilde{u}_1}{\partial x_3}\right)^2\right] - 2C_4 \frac{k^2}{\epsilon}\left[\frac{\partial \tilde{u}_1}{\partial x_1}\right]\\
\overline{u_2'u_2'} &= C_3 k - C_2 C_4 \frac{k^3}{\epsilon^2}\left[\frac{\partial \tilde{u}_1}{\partial x_2}\right]^2 - 2C_4 \frac{k^2}{\epsilon}\left[\frac{\partial \tilde{u}_2}{\partial x_2}\right]\\
\overline{u_3'u_3'} &= C_3 k - C_2 C_4 \frac{k^3}{\epsilon^2}\left[\frac{\partial \tilde{u}_1}{\partial x_3}\right]^2 - 2C_4 \frac{k^2}{\epsilon}\left[\frac{\partial \tilde{u}_3}{\partial x_3}\right]\\
\overline{u_1'u_2'} &= -C_4 \frac{k^2}{\epsilon}\left[\frac{\partial \tilde{u}_1}{\partial x_2}\right] - C_2 C_4 \frac{k^3}{\epsilon^2}\left[\frac{\partial \tilde{u}_1}{\partial x_3}\left(\frac{\partial \tilde{u}_2}{\partial x_3} + \frac{\partial \tilde{u}_3}{\partial x_2}\right)\right.\\
&\qquad \left. + 2\frac{\partial \tilde{u}_1}{\partial x_2}\left(\frac{\partial \tilde{u}_1}{\partial x_1} + \frac{\partial \tilde{u}_2}{\partial x_2}\right)\right]\\
\overline{u_1'u_3'} &= -C_4 \frac{k^2}{\epsilon}\left[\frac{\partial \tilde{u}_1}{\partial x_3}\right] - C_2 C_4 \frac{k^3}{\epsilon^2}\left[\frac{\partial \tilde{u}_1}{\partial x_2}\left(\frac{\partial \tilde{u}_2}{\partial x_3} + \frac{\partial \tilde{u}_3}{\partial x_2}\right)\right.\\
&\qquad \left. + 2\frac{\partial \tilde{u}_1}{\partial x_3}\left(\frac{\partial \tilde{u}_1}{\partial x_1} + \frac{\partial \tilde{u}_3}{\partial x_3}\right)\right]\\
\overline{u_2'u_3'} &= -C_2 C_4 \frac{k^3}{\epsilon^2}\left[\frac{\partial \tilde{u}_1}{\partial x_2}\frac{\partial \tilde{u}_1}{\partial x_3}\right] - C_4 \frac{k^2}{\epsilon}\left(\frac{\partial \tilde{u}_2}{\partial x_3} + \frac{\partial \tilde{u}_3}{\partial x_2}\right) \qquad (7.26)
\end{aligned}$$

Two key points regarding (7.26) should be noted. The terms that would provide an elliptic boundary value definition to the direct integration of (7.2), for $\tilde{u}_2$ and $\tilde{u}_3$, are indeed $O(\delta^2)$, in agreement with the ordering arguments leading to (7.14). Secondly, the terms of $O(\delta^2)$ in (7.26) should not be arbitrarily neglected, as demonstrated for the aerodynamic trailing edge wake analysis (Sec. 6.15). Recall that for this incompressible two-dimensional problem, the last term in the expression for $\overline{u_1'u_1'}$ can be changed to $+2C_4 k^2/\epsilon(\partial \tilde{u}_2/\partial x_2)$ using the continuity equation. Thus, the sign of this higher-order term is the sole consequential difference between $\overline{u_1'u_1'}$ and $\overline{u_2'u_2'}$ in (7.26). The favorable comparison of 2DPNS prediction with data verifies the importance of this term.

With this development, the ordering of terms in (7.4)–(7.5) can be completed to establish the appropriate 3DPNS approximation as

$$L^p(k) = \frac{\partial}{\partial x_i}(\bar{\rho}\tilde{u}_i k) + \frac{\partial}{\partial x_i}\left[\bar{\rho}\left(C_k \frac{k}{\epsilon}\overline{u_i' u_l'} - \bar{\nu}\delta_{il}\right)\frac{\partial k}{\partial x_l}\right] + \bar{\rho}\overline{u_1' u_l'}\frac{\partial \tilde{u}_1}{\partial x_l} + \bar{\rho}\epsilon = 0 \tag{7.27}$$

$$L^p(\epsilon) = \frac{\partial}{\partial x_i}(\rho\tilde{u}_i\epsilon) + \frac{\partial}{\partial x_i}\left(C_\epsilon \frac{k}{\epsilon}\overline{u_i' u_l'}\frac{\partial \epsilon}{\partial x_l}\right) + C_\epsilon^1 \overline{\rho u_1' u_l'}\frac{\epsilon}{k}\frac{\partial \tilde{u}_1}{\partial x_l} + C_\epsilon^2 \bar{\rho}\frac{\epsilon^2}{k} = 0 \tag{7.28}$$

using the limited summation convention, $1 \leqslant i \leqslant 3$, $2 \leqslant l \leqslant 3$.

Definition of boundary conditions for (7.27)-(7.28) requires addressing the issue of what constitutes sufficient distance for validity of (7.22). The standard approach for two-dimensional flows employs similarity arguments to assign values to k and ϵ at some distance from the wall, e.g., on $10 < y^+ < 50$, where $y^+ \equiv u_\tau x_2/\bar{\nu}$ is a turbulence Reynolds number based on wall shear velocity $u_\tau \equiv \sqrt{\tau_w/\bar{\rho}}$. Extension of this concept to a three-dimensional flow is suspect, but has been attempted (Pratap and Spalding, 1975). One alternative, Rodi (1981), suggests modifying the constants C_β^α appearing in (7.27)-(7.28) and integrating directly through the low-turbulence wall region with $k \equiv 0 \equiv \epsilon$ as boundary conditions.

An alternative approach was employed by Baker and Orzechowski (1981), based upon modification of the Reynolds stress constitutive equation to account for low-turbulence levels in the wall region. Equation (7.25) also defines the turbulent eddy viscosity $\nu^t \equiv C_4 k^2/\epsilon$. From dimensional arguments, recall ν^t can be constructed using a scale velocity and scale length, typically,

$$\nu^t \equiv k^{1/2} l_d \tag{7.29}$$

Comparison with (7.25) yields the familiar relationship

$$l_d \equiv C_4 \frac{k^{3/2}}{\epsilon} \tag{7.30}$$

Recalling the van Driest damping function ω, used to control evolution of the Prandtl mixing length scale, (7.30) can be multiplied by ω yielding (7.25) in the form

$$-\overline{u_1' u_2'} = \omega C_4 \frac{k^2}{\epsilon}\frac{\partial \tilde{u}_1}{\partial x_2} \tag{7.31}$$

The conventional form for ω, modified for a variable length scale damping, is

$$\omega \equiv 1 - \exp\frac{-by}{A} \tag{7.32}$$

where $A = A^+\nu(\tau_w/\rho)^{-1/2}$, $A^+ = 26$, and $b > 0$ is to be determined. Numerical studies (see Sec. 6.10) yielded $b = 2.0$ as a suitable specification. Hence, each of the coefficients C_α in (7.24) is premultiplied by ω, producing the required modification to the Reynolds stress equation (7.22) [see also (7.26)]. Finally, C_ϵ^2 in (7.28) is also multiplied by ω. The wall boundary conditions for (7.27)-(7.28) are then $k \equiv 0$ and $\epsilon \equiv 0$.

Problem

1 Expand (7.22) to obtain the form of (7.26).

7.4 FINITE-ELEMENT SOLUTION ALGORITHM

The consistently ordered 3DPNS equation system has been identified. For the dependent variable set $q_j(x_i) \equiv \{q\} = \{\bar{\rho}, \tilde{u}_1, \tilde{u}_2, \tilde{u}_3, \tilde{H}, \bar{p}, k, \epsilon, \overline{u_i'u_j'}\}^T$, the available equation system includes (7.1), (7.11), (7.12), (7.14), (7.22), (7.27), and (7.28) and an equation of state $\bar{\rho} = \bar{\rho}(\bar{p}, \tilde{H})$. At least one additional differential equation is required to close the system, since in three dimensions there are 14 unknowns and only 13 equations. This construction forms the heart of the continuity constraint algorithm concept, wherein the continuity equation solution becomes embedded (replaced, in a sense) within the higher-order transverse momentum equation solutions (Sec. 6.12). Equations (7.11), (7.12), (7.27), and (7.28) of the 3DPNS set contain the initial-value term that facilitates the space-marching discussed at length in Chap. 6. Equation (7.14) exhibits an elliptic boundary value description with parametric initial-value dependence. The continuity equation (7.1) will become recast as a differential constraint. The generalized form for the 3DPNS description is

$$L^p(q_j) = \frac{\partial}{\partial x_1}(\bar{\rho}\tilde{u}_1 q_j) + \frac{\partial}{\partial x_l}(\bar{\rho}\tilde{u}_l q_j + f_{lj}) + s_j = 0 \tag{7.33}$$

For (7.33), f_{lj} and s_j are specified nonlinear functions of their arguments, as determined by the selection of index j. This three-dimensional partial differential equation is defined on the euclidian space R^3 spanned by the x_i coordinate system. The solution domain Ω is defined as the product of R^2 and x_1, for all elements of x_1 belonging to the open interval measured from $x_1(0)$, that is,

$$\Omega \equiv R^2 \times x_1 = \{(x_l, x_1): x_l \epsilon R^2 \text{ and } x_1 \epsilon [x_1(0), x_1)\} \tag{7.34}$$

The boundary $\partial\Omega$ of the solution domain is the product of the boundary of R^2 and x_1, that is, $\partial\Omega \equiv \partial R \times x_1$. Thereupon, the generalized form for the differential boundary constraint is

$$l(q_j) = a_1 q_j + a_2 \frac{\partial}{\partial x_i} q_j \hat{n}_i + a_3 = 0 \tag{7.35}$$

In (7.35), the a_i are specified coefficients and $\hat{\mathbf{n}}_i$ is the outward pointing unit normal vector. Finally, an initial distribution for q_j on $\Omega_0 \equiv R^2 \times x_1(0)$ is required

$$q_j(x_l, x_1) \equiv q_j^0(x_l) \tag{7.36}$$

The finite-element numerical solution for (7.33)–(7.36) follows the well-developed procedures. The approximation $q_j^h(x_l, x_1)$ to the (unknown) exact solution $q_j(x_l, x_1)$ is constructed from members of a convenient finite-dimensional subspace of $H_0^1(\Omega)$, the Hilbert space of all functions possessing square integrable first derivatives and satisfying the boundary condition (7.35). The usual practice is to employ elementary polynomials, defined on disjoint interior subdomains Ω_e, the union of which forms the discretization of Ω. Hence,

$$q_j(x_l, x_1) \approx q_j^h(x_l, x_1) \equiv \sum_{e=1}^{M} q_j^e(x_l, x_1) \tag{7.37}$$

The elemental approximation is the familiar form

$$q_j^e(x_l, x_1) \equiv \{N_k(x_l)\}^T \{QJ(x_1)\}_e \tag{7.38}$$

In (7.37)-(7.38), $j(J)$ is a free index denoting members of $\{q^h\}$, and sub- or superscript e denotes pertaining to the eth finite element, $\Omega_e \equiv R_e^2 \times x_1$. The elements of the row matrix $\{N_k(x_l)\}^T$ are polynomials on x_l, $2 \leqslant l \leqslant 3$, complete to degree k and constructed to form a cardinal basis.

The functional requirement of the (any) solution algorithm is to render the error in q_j^h minimum in some norm. This is accomplished with the finite-element algorithm by requiring the error in (7.33) and (7.35), that is, $L^p(q_j^h)$ and $l(q_j^h)$, to be orthogonal to the function space employed to define q_j^h. The form of (7.33) will also be appropriate for the 3DPNS determination of $\tilde{u}_2$ and $\tilde{u}_3$, as well, wherein the discrete approximation $L^p(\bar{\rho}^h)$ to the continuity equation (7.1) will be enforced as a differential constraint. Identifying the (Lagrange) multiplier set β_i, these independent constraints are linearly combined to form the theoretical statement of the finite-element solution algorithm [recall (6.148)].

$$\int_{R^2} \{N_k\} L^p(q_j^h)\, d\mathrm{x} + \beta_1 \int_{\partial R} \{N_k\}\, l(q_j^h)\, d\mathrm{x} + \beta_2 \cdot \int_{R^2} \nabla \{N_k\}\, L^p(\bar{\rho}^h)\, d\mathrm{x} \equiv \{0\} \tag{7.39}$$

Upon selection of k in (7.38), (7.39) defines a system of ordinary differential equations on x_1

$$[C]\{QJ\}' + [U]\{QJ\} + [FLJ]\{QL\} + \{SJ\} = \{0\} \tag{7.40}$$

A one-to-one correspondence of terms in (7.40) and (7.33) is inferred, with matrices augmented for the various additional terms introduced through $\beta_i \neq 0$ in (7.39). An efficient and accurate integration algorithm for (7.40) is the trapezoidal rule. Hence,

$$\{FJ\} \equiv \{QJ\}_{j+1} - \{QJ\}_j - \frac{\Delta x_1}{2}\left[\{QJ\}'_{j+1} + \{QJ\}'_j\right] \equiv \{0\} \tag{7.41}$$

defines a system of nonlinear algebraic equations for determination of the elements of $\{QJ(x_1)\}$. The Newton iteration algorithm for [7.41) is

$$[J(FJ)]_{j+1}^{p} \{\delta QJ\}_{j+1}^{p+1} = -\{FJ\}_{j+1}^{p} \tag{7.42}$$

The dependent variable in (7.42) is the iteration vector $\{\delta QJ\}$, related to the solution in the conventional manner

$$\{QJ\}_{j+1}^{p+1} \equiv \{QJ\}_{j+1}^{p} + \{\delta QJ\}_{j+1}^{p+1} \tag{7.43}$$

The jacobian $[J]$ is formed as the derivative of (7.41) with respect to each member of $\{QJ\}_{j+1}$,

$$[J(FJ)] = \frac{\partial \{FJ\}}{\partial \{QI\}} \tag{7.44}$$

The nonparabolic continuity equation (7.1) governs first-order effects for the mean velocity field $\tilde{u}_i$. Since the 3DPNS equation (7.11) is written on $\tilde{u}_1$, $\tilde{u}_k \equiv \{\tilde{u}_2, \tilde{u}_3\}$ is required determined from the solution of (7.1). This is accomplished by enforcing a measure of the solution of (7.1) as a penalizing differential constraint on the solution of the (higher-order) 3DPNS approximation to (7.2) for $\tilde{u}_l$. Retaining the highest two orders of terms, the 3DPNS order of magnitude analysis of (7.2) yields

$$L^p(\bar{\rho}\tilde{u}_k) = \frac{\partial}{\partial x_1}(\bar{\rho}\tilde{u}_1\tilde{u}_k + \overline{\rho u_1' u_k'}) + \frac{\partial}{\partial x_l}(\bar{\rho}\tilde{u}_l\tilde{u}_k + \overline{\rho u_l' u_k'} + \bar{p}\delta_{kl} - \bar{\sigma}_{kl}) = 0 \tag{7.45}$$

Note that (7.45) is of the form (7.33), and employs the 3DPNS limited index $2 \leqslant k \leqslant 3$. The middle two terms in the second bracket are $O(\delta)$, while the remaining terms are all $O(\delta^2)$. The boundary condition statement (7.35) is appropriate for (7.45), upon retention of terms of $O(\delta^2)$ in the Reynolds stress equation, e.g., (7.26). The initial condition statement for (7.45) is (7.36).

The finite-element algorithm statement for (7.45) is (7.39), on specification of the form of the term modified by β_2. The theoretical concept, as presented in Chap. 6 and borrowed from the variational calculus, is to enforce a measure of the continuity equation (solution) as a differential constraint on solution of the transverse momentum equations. This solution measure must span R^2 and must vanish as continuity becomes satisfied. As before, an appropriate measure is the harmonic function $\phi(x_l)$, the solution to the Poisson equation

$$L^p(\phi) \equiv \frac{\partial^2 \phi}{\partial x_l^2} - \frac{\partial}{\partial x_i}(\bar{\rho}\tilde{u}_i) \equiv 0 \tag{7.46}$$

subject to homogeneous Neumann boundary conditions on ∂R, and setting $\phi = 0$ at one location at least on ∂R. Thus, (7.46) becomes homogeneous when the continuity equation is identically satisfied, and ϕ becomes null as a consequence of the boundary condition specifications.

The algorithmic embodiment of the differential constraint concept employs a sequential summation for the penalty term $\beta_2 \cdot \int \nabla\{N_k\} L^p(\bar{\rho}^h)\, dx$ in (7.39). The β_2 coefficient is redefined as the diagonal matrix $C\Delta x[U1]\{\hat{\mathbf{j}}, \hat{\mathbf{k}}\}$, where $\hat{\mathbf{j}}$ and $\hat{\mathbf{k}}$ are unit vectors parallel to x_l. As discussed in Chap. 6, $[U1]$ is a diagonal matrix containing the nodal values of the $\tilde{u}_1$ velocity component, C is a constant of order unity, and Δx_1 is the integration step size. For the $\tilde{u}_2$ equation, for example, this term corresponds to a column matrix, say $\{G2PHI\}$. The solution algorithm for (7.46) is the conventional finite-element procedure (Chap. 3). Letting $\{PHI\}_{j+1}^n$ denote the solution at iteration n, then

$$\{G2PHI\}_{j+1}^{n} \equiv S_e\left[\hat{\mathbf{j}}\cdot\int_{R_e^2} \nabla\{N_k\}\{N_k\}^T\{PHI\}_{j+1}^{n}\,d\mathbf{x}\right] \tag{7.47}$$

This contribution is then summed with the previous p evaluations to converge to the action of the differential constraint term for step $(\Delta x_1)_{j+1}$, that is,

$$\{GU2\}_{j+1}^{p} \equiv C\,\Delta x_1\,[U1]_{j+1}^{p}\sum_{n=1}^{p-1}\{G2PHI\}_{j+1}^{n} \tag{7.48}$$

Thus, each successive determination of $\{PHI\}$ corrects the action of all previous solution iterates. Hence, as the algorithm converges at step Δx_{j+1}, the Newton algorithm iterate $\{\delta PHI\}_{j+1}^{p} \to |\epsilon|$, where $|\epsilon| > 0$ is an acceptable discrete level of computed zero, in the limit as p increases without bound.

Problem

1 Derive (7.45) using the 3DPNS order of magnitude analysis.

7.5 GRID-STRETCHING TRANSFORMATION FOR VARIABLE GEOMETRY

Elementary grid-stretching coordinate transformations can be efficiently utilized within the framework and ordering simplification of the PNS equation system. A more general curvilinear transformation would be required to accurately describe highly nonregular duct geometries with large curvature. For elementary cross-sectional variations, the generalization of the 2DPNS transformation (see Chap. 6) that normalizes transverse spans, with boundaries f_{li}, $2 \leqslant l \leqslant 3$, $1 \leqslant i \leqslant 3$, is

$$\{\eta_i\} \equiv \left\{\begin{matrix} x_1 \\[1ex] \dfrac{x_2 - f_{21}(x_1)}{[f_{22}(x_1) - f_{21}(x_1)]/f_2} \\[2ex] \dfrac{x_3 - f_{31}(x_1)}{[f_{32}(x_1) - f_{31}(x_1)]/f_3} \end{matrix}\right\} \tag{7.49}$$

The $f_{li}(x_1)$ are assumed to be piecewise continuous and the f_l are normalizing coefficients. Using the chain rule, differentiation on x_1 introduces additional derivatives on η_l:

$$\begin{aligned} \frac{\partial}{\partial x_1} &= \frac{\partial}{\partial \eta_1} - (h_{22} + \eta_2 h_{23})\frac{\partial}{\partial \eta_2} - (h_{32} + \eta_3 h_{33})\frac{\partial}{\partial \eta_3} \\ \frac{\partial}{\partial x_2} &= h_{21}\frac{\partial}{\partial \eta_2} \end{aligned} \tag{7.50}$$

$$\frac{\partial}{\partial x_3} = h_{31} \frac{\partial}{\partial \eta_3} \tag{7.50 (Cont.)}$$

The functions h_{li}, $1 \leqslant i \leqslant 3$, are defined as

$$\{h_{li}\} \equiv \begin{Bmatrix} f_l(f_{l2} - f_{l1})^{-1} \\ h_{l1} f'_{l1} \\ h_{l1} f_l^{-1}(f'_{l2} - f'_{l1}) \end{Bmatrix} \tag{7.51}$$

The superscript prime denotes the (ordinary) derivative with respect to x_1, and the η_i coordinate system is fixed in the transform space.

7.6 ALGORITHM IMPLEMENTATION USING THE LINEAR NATURAL BASIS

Implementation of the 3DPNS finite-element algorithm is most easily illustrated using the linear cardinal basis $\{N_1(\zeta)\}$. The intrinsic operation is integration of products of the elements of the cardinal basis and the associated (gradient) derivative $\partial\{N_1(\zeta)\}/\partial x_l$ on the discretization of R^2 formed by the union of triangles. The master element is graphed in Fig. 7.2, which also illustrates the various coordinate systems including the natural coordinate system ζ_i. Recall that the elements of $\{N_1\}$ are identical to ζ_i, and that

$$\int_{R_e^2} \zeta_1^p \zeta_2^q \zeta_3^r \, d\mathbf{x} = \frac{A_e}{2} \frac{p!\,q!\,r!}{(2+p+q+r)!} \tag{7.52}$$

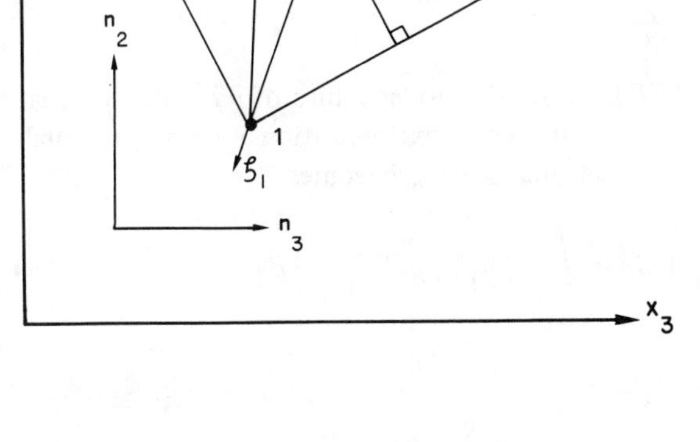

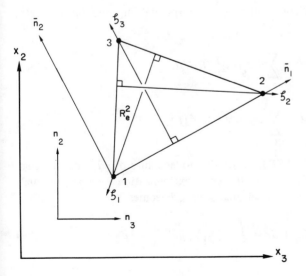

Figure 7.2 Coordinate system for master finite element R_e^2.

where A_e is the plane area of R_e^2. Furthermore,

$$\{\zeta\} = \begin{Bmatrix} 1 - \dfrac{\bar{\eta}_1}{\bar{\eta}_1^2} - \left(1 - \dfrac{\bar{\eta}_1^3}{\bar{\eta}_1^2}\right)\dfrac{\bar{\eta}_2}{\bar{\eta}_2^3} \\ \dfrac{\bar{\eta}_1}{\bar{\eta}_1^2} - \left(\dfrac{\bar{\eta}_1^3}{\bar{\eta}_1^2}\right)\dfrac{\bar{\eta}_2}{\bar{\eta}_2^3} \\ \dfrac{\bar{\eta}_2}{\bar{\eta}_2^3} \end{Bmatrix} \tag{7.53}$$

and $\bar{\eta}_l^\alpha$ denotes the $\bar{\eta}_l$ coordinate of node point α, for the sequencing defined in Fig. 7.2. The elementary transformation defining $\bar{\eta}_l = \bar{\eta}_l(\eta_k)$ is

$$\bar{\eta}_l = a_{lk}\,\eta_k \tag{7.54}$$

where a_{lk} are the direction cosines defining $\bar{\eta}_1$ as the line connecting nodes 1 and 2 of R_e^2. The derivatives of the elements of $\{N_1(\zeta)\}$ are formed using the chain rule and tensor index summation convention, as

$$\frac{\partial}{\partial x_l}\{N_1(\zeta)\} = \frac{\partial}{\partial \zeta_i}\{\zeta\}\,\frac{\partial \zeta_i}{\partial \bar{\eta}_j}\,\frac{\partial \bar{\eta}_j}{\partial \eta_k}\,\frac{\partial \eta_k}{\partial x_l} \tag{7.55}$$

Consider the first term of the 3DPNS generalized differential equation (7.33), wherein the elements of $q_j(x_i) = \{\tilde{u}_1, \tilde{u}_2, \tilde{u}_3, \tilde{H}, k, \epsilon\}^T$ are marched in the x_1 direction. For the coordinate transformation given by (7.49), and subtracting out the continuity equation (7.1), yielding the so-called nonconservative form, this term becomes

$$\bar{\rho}\tilde{u}_1\,\frac{\partial q_j}{\partial x_1} = \bar{\rho}\tilde{u}_1\left[\frac{\partial}{\partial \eta_1} - (h_{22} + \eta_2 h_{23})\,\frac{\partial}{\partial \eta_2} + (h_{32} + \eta_3 h_{33})\,\frac{\partial}{\partial \eta_3}\right] q_j \tag{7.56}$$

Employing the finite-element construction, to interpolate $\bar{\rho}\tilde{u}_1$ and $\eta_l(\zeta)$ on R_e^2, yields

$$(\bar{\rho}\tilde{u}_1)^h \equiv \sum_e \{N_1(\zeta)\}^T\{RHOU1\}_e \tag{7.57}$$

$$\eta_l^h \equiv \sum_e \{N_1(\zeta)\}^T\{ETAL\}_e \tag{7.58}$$

The elements of $\{RHOU1\}_e$ and $\{ETAL\}_e$ are the nodal values of $\bar{\rho}\tilde{u}_1$ and η_l. Then, the term corresponding to (7.56) within the error extremization weighted residuals statement (7.39), on rearrangement of selected scalars, becomes

$$\int_{R^2}\{N_1\}L(q_j^h)\,d\tau = \int_{R^2}\{N_1\}\left(\bar{\rho}\tilde{u}_1^h\,\frac{\partial q_j^h}{\partial x_1}\right)d\mathbf{x} \tag{7.59}$$

$$\int_{R^2} \{N_1\}L(q_j^h)\, d\tau = S_e\Bigg[\{RHOU1\}_e^T \int_{R_e^2} \{N_1\}\{N_1\}$$

$$\cdot\left(\{N\}^T\{QJ\}_e' - (h_{22} + h_{23}\{N_1\}^T\{ETA2\}_e)\frac{\partial\{N_1\}^T}{\partial\eta_2}\right.$$

$$\left. - (h_{32} + h_{33}\{N_1\}^T\{ETA3\}_e)\frac{\partial\{N_1\}^T}{\partial\eta_3}\right)d\eta\{QJ\}_e\Bigg]$$

(7.59)
(Cont.)

Equation (7.59) defines the global calculus operations, on $R^2 = UR_e^2$, as the matrix assembly (S_e) on the equivalent calculations performed on the master element. Consideration of the first term, and expansion in terms of $\{\zeta\}$ yields

$$\{RHOU1\}_e^T\int_{R_e^2}\{N_1\}\{N_1\}\{N_1\}^T d\eta\{QJ\}_e$$

$$= \{RHOU1\}_e^T\int_{R^2}\begin{Bmatrix}\zeta_1\\ \zeta_2\\ \zeta_3\end{Bmatrix}\begin{bmatrix}\zeta_1^2 & \zeta_1\zeta_2 & \zeta_1\zeta_3\\ & \zeta_2^2 & \zeta_2\zeta_3\\ (\text{sym}) & & \zeta_2^2\end{bmatrix}d\eta\{QJ\}_e'$$

$$\equiv A_e\{RHOU1\}_e^T[B3000]\ \{QJ\}_e' \tag{7.60}$$

In (7.60), recall that A_e is the element plane area, and $\frac{1}{60}$ is the normalizing coefficient of the integers constituting the master hypermatrix $[B3000]$. The grid-stretching coordinate transformation has introduced additional terms that involve derivatives of elements of $\{N_1(\zeta)\}$ on the η_k. Using (7.55),

$$\frac{\partial}{\partial\eta_l}\{N_1(\zeta)\} = h_{21}(x_1)\{B112\}_e\,\hat{e}_2 + h_{31}(x_1)\{B113\}_e\,\hat{e}_3 \tag{7.61}$$

The elements of $\{B11K\}_e$, 3×1 column matrices that are element dependent, are strictly a function of the node coordinates $\bar{\eta}_l^\alpha$ of R_e^2 and the set a_{lk} of direction cosines (7.54). The unit vectors $\hat{e}_k$ are parallel to the x_l coordinate system, and the metrics h_{k1} are functions of x_1 at most. Therefore, (7.61) is the matrix equivalent of the directional derivative with scalar components parallel to $\tilde{u}_l$. Then, on the master element, the second and third terms in (7.59) become

$$\{RHOU1\}_e^T\int_{R_e^2}\{N_1\}\{N_1\}(-h_{l2} - h_{l3}\{N_1\}^T\{ETAL\}_e)\frac{\partial\{N_1\}^T}{\partial\eta_l}d\eta\{QJ\}_e$$

$$= A_e\{RHOU1\}_e^T[(-h_{22}h_{21}[B200] - h_{23}h_{21}[B3000]\{ETA2\}_e)\{B112\}_e^T\{QJ\}_e$$

$$+ (-h_{32}h_{31}[B200] - h_{33}h_{31}[B3000]\{ETA2\}_e)\{B113\}_e^T\{QJ\}_e] \tag{7.62}$$

In distinction to the universality of the symbol $[B3000]$ for all $\{N_k\}$, the form of (7.62) must change if the elements of $\partial\{N_k\}/\partial\eta_l$ are functions of η_l. The generalized basis statement for (7.62) is

$$\int_{R_e^2} \{N_k\}\left(\bar{\rho}\tilde{u}_1^h \frac{\partial q_j^h}{\partial x_1}\right) d\mathbf{x} = A_e \{RHOU1\}_e^T [B30000]\ \{QJ\}_e'$$
$$+ A_e \{RHOU1\}_e^T (-h_{l2} h_{l1} [B300L]_e$$
$$- h_{l3} h_{l1} [B400L0]_e \{ETAL\}_e) \{QJ\}_e \qquad (7.63)$$

In (7.63), the index $l(L)$ is a tensor index that takes the values $2 \leqslant (l, L) \leqslant 3$. Furthermore, $[B400L0]$ is a hypermatrix of degree two; the first and last boolean indices (O) indicate $\{RHOU1\}_e$ and $\{ETAL\}_e$ are interpolated, and these (inner) multiplications must be performed prior to postmultiplication by $\{QJ\}_e$, which has been differentiated parallel to $\eta_l(L)$. The remaining terms in the finite-element algorithm statement (7.39) are formed in the same manner.

The second major formulational step is construction of the jacobian of the Newton iteration algorithm, (7.42)-(7.44). Continuing with the example of the downstream convection term, the specific form for the resultant expressions in $\{FJ\}$, (7.41), is

$$\{FJ\} = S_e\Big[A_e \{\overline{RHOU1}\}_e^T [B3000](\{QJ\}_{j+1}^p - \{QJ\}_j)$$
$$- \frac{\Delta x_1}{2}[A_e \{\overline{RHOU1}\}_e^T (h_{l2} h_{l1} [B300L]_e + h_{l3} h_{l1} [B400L0]_e \{ETAL\}_e)\{QJ\}$$
$$+ \cdot\cdot\cdot]_{j+1,j}\Big] \qquad (7.64)$$

In (7.64), $\{\overline{RHOU1}\}_e \equiv \frac{1}{2}(\{RHOU1\}_{j+1}^p + \{RHOU1\}_j)$, and $\Delta x_1 = x_{j+1} - x_j$, is the downstream marching step size. Furthermore, $\circ]_{j+1,j}$ indicates the algebraic average, and superscript p is the iteration index. For (7.44), the independent variable is $\{QJ\}_{j+1}^p$; therefore, the elemental contributions to $[J]$, from (7.64), become formed as

$$\frac{\partial\{FJ\}_e}{\partial\{QI\}_e} = A_e \{RHOU1\}_e^T [B3000]\,\delta_{JI} - \frac{\Delta x_1 A_e}{2} \{\overline{RHOU1}\}_e^T [h_{l2} h_{l1} [B300L]_e$$
$$+ h_{l3} h_{l1} [B400L0]\ \{ETAL\}_e]\,\delta_{JI} + \frac{\partial\{FJ\}}{\partial\{\overline{RHOU1}\}} \frac{\delta\{\overline{RHOU1}\}}{\partial\{QI\}} \qquad (7.65)$$

In (7.65), δ_{JI} is the discrete index Kronecker delta, which yields the self-dependence expressions, that is, $\partial\{FJ\}/\partial\{QJ\}$. Since $\bar{\rho}\tilde{u}_1^h$ (i.e., $\{RHOU1\}$), is a function of both $\bar{\rho}$ and $\tilde{u}_1$, which are dependent variables, the second term in (7.65) yields the nonself-coupling. The algebraic equation of state yields $\bar{\rho} = \bar{\rho}(\bar{p}, \bar{H})$; for subsonic flows, the density variation is weak and can be neglected in $[J]$. Using the chain rule, then

$$\frac{\partial\bar{\rho}\tilde{u}_1^h}{\partial q_i^h} \approx \bar{\rho}\delta_{1i} \qquad (7.66)$$

Hence, interchanging orientation in the hypermatrix formation, as required, yields

$$\frac{\partial\{FJ\}}{\partial\{\overline{RHOU1}\}}\frac{\partial\{\overline{RHOU1}\}}{\partial\{QI\}} = \frac{A_e\bar{\rho}_e}{2}\{QI\}_e^T[B3000]\,\delta_{J1}\delta_{I1}$$
$$-\frac{\Delta x_1 A_e\bar{\rho}_e}{4}\{QI\}_e^T(h_{l2}h_{l1}\,[B3000]$$
$$+\,h_{l3}h_{l1}\,[B4L00]\{ETAL\}_e)\delta_{J1}\delta_{I1} \qquad (7.67)$$

where $\bar{\rho}_e$ is defined as the element-average value of $\bar{\rho}$ on R_e^2.

Completion of the particular pressure solution algorithm statement is straightforward. Noting that (7.14) is the derivative on x_l of (7.45), the first two terms in the finite-element algorithm statement (7.39) for p_p yields

$$-\int_{R^2}\{N_k\}L^p(p_p)\,d\tau + \lambda\int_{\partial R}\{N_k\}l(p_p)\,d\sigma$$

$$= \int_{R^2}\frac{\partial}{\partial x_k}\{N_k\}L^p(\bar{\rho}\tilde{u}_k)\,d\tau - \oint_{\partial R}\{N_k\}L^p(\bar{\rho}\tilde{u}_l)\cdot\hat{\eta}_l\,d\sigma + \lambda\int\{N_k\}l(p_p)\,d\sigma$$

$$= \int_{R^2}\frac{\partial\{N_k\}}{\partial x_k}\left[\tilde{u}_k\frac{\partial\bar{\rho}\tilde{u}_1}{\partial x_1} + \bar{\rho}\tilde{u}_1\frac{\partial\tilde{u}_k}{\partial x_3} + \frac{\partial}{\partial x_1}(\overline{\rho u_1' u_l'}) + \tilde{u}_k\frac{\partial\bar{\rho}\tilde{u}_l}{\partial x_l} + \bar{\rho}\tilde{u}_l\frac{\partial u_k}{\partial x_l}\right.$$

$$\left.+\frac{\partial}{\partial x_l}(\overline{\rho u_k' u_l'}) + \frac{\partial\bar{p}_p}{\partial x_k} - \frac{\partial}{\partial x_l}(\bar{\sigma}_{kl})\right]d\tau - \oint_{\partial R}\{N_k\}L^p(\bar{\rho}\tilde{u}_l)\cdot\hat{\eta}_l\,d\sigma$$

$$+\,\lambda\int_{\partial R}\{N_k\}l(p_p)\,d\sigma = \{0\} \qquad (7.68)$$

From (7.17), the last two terms in (7.68) cancel identically upon the definition $\lambda \equiv 1$. Further, the first and fourth terms in the integral on R^2 sum to zero via continuity, (7.1). Therefore, the final form for the particular pressure solution algorithm statement, upon rearrangement of terms in (7.68), is

$$\int_{R^2}\frac{\partial\{N_k\}}{\partial x_l}\left[\frac{\partial p_p}{\partial x_l} + \bar{\rho}\tilde{u}_i\frac{\partial\tilde{u}_l}{\partial x_i} + \frac{\partial}{\partial x_i}(\overline{\rho u_i' u_l'}) - \frac{\partial}{\partial x_k}\bar{\sigma}_{kl}\right]d\tau \equiv \{0\} \qquad (7.69)$$

In (7.69), recall the tensor index summation convention $1 \leqslant i \leqslant 3$ and $2 \leqslant (k, l) \leqslant 3$. Further, the derivatives on x_i and x_k are defined by (7.50) when utilizing the grid-stretching transformation (7.49).

The evaluation of the finite-element matrices defined in (7.69), for the linear natural coordinate basis $\{N_1(x_l)\}$ construction, is straightforward. Neglecting the grid-stretching transformation, the matrix statement equivalent for (7.69) is

$$\int_{R^2} \frac{\partial \{N_1\}}{\partial x_l} [(\cdot)]\, d\tau = S_e\left[\int_{R_e^2} \frac{\partial \{N_1\}}{\partial x_l} [(\circ)_e]\, d\tau\right]$$

$$\begin{aligned}
&= S_e\,\{A_e(\{B112\}\{B112\}^T + \{B113\}\{B113\}^T)\{PP\}_e \\
&+ A_e(\{RHOU1\}^T[B200]\,\{U2\}'\{B112\} \\
&+ \{RHOU1\}^T[B200]\,\{U3\}'\{B113\}) \\
&+ A_e(\{B112\}(\{RHOU2\}^T\{B10\}\{B112\}^T\{U2\} \\
&+ \{RHOU3\}^T\{B10\}\{B113\}^T\{U2\}) \\
&+ \{B113\}(\{RHOU2\}^T\{B10\}\{B112\}^T\{U3\} \\
&+ \{RHOU3\}^T\{B10\}\{B113\}^T\{U3\})) \\
&+ A_e[\{B112\}\{B10\}^T\{\overline{RU'V'}\} + \{B113\}\{B10\}^T\{\overline{RU'W'}\}] \\
&+ A_e[\{B112\}(\{B112\}^T\{\overline{RV'V'}\} + \{B113\}^T\{\overline{RV'W'}\}) \\
&+ \{B113\}(\{B112\}^T\{\overline{RV'W'}\} + \{B113\}^T\{\overline{RW'W'}\})]\} = \{0\}
\end{aligned} \tag{7.70}$$

In (7.70), the elemental subscript e has been deleted for clarity. In addition, the contributions from the laminar flow Stokes stress tensor $\bar{\sigma}_{kl}$ have been omitted, since they are usually small compared to the Reynolds stress tensor. They can be easily included by defining the total stress tensor

$$\tau_{ij} \equiv \bar{\sigma}_{ij} - \overline{\rho u_i' u_j'}$$

using (7.6) and (7.22), and replacing the element nodal arrays $\{\overline{RUL'UJ'}\}_e$ with $\{TAULJ\}_e$.

There is an exacting amount of detail required to complete all aspects of the statement. However, the developed hypermatrix formalisms and master element concepts have produced a rigorous procedure to keep track of the details. The role of the tensor indices and matrix differential calculus are invaluable tools put to practical use. Finally, these equations become written in a pseudo-FORTRAN language, which yields coding that is identical in appearance to the theoretical statements.

Problems

1 Expand (7.55), hence obtain the evaluation of (7.61) for R_e^2 oriented (*a*) with one leg parallel to the x_3 axis (Fig. 7.2); (*b*) arbitrarily.

2 Verify (7.62) as a special case of (7.63).

3 Obtain (7.70) from (7.69).

4 Generalize (7.70) to include the terms resulting from the grid-stretching transformation (7.49).

7.7 THREE-DIMENSIONAL RECTANGULAR DUCT FLOW

A basic application of the 3DPNS algorithm, for a fully bounded flow geometry, is exemplified by flow in a straight duct of rectangular cross section (see Fig. 7.3*a*). Baker and Orzechowski (1981) document laminar and turbulent flow predictions, for a duct configuration and Reynolds number for which quality experimental data are available (Melling and Whitelaw, 1976). A nonuniform discretization, employing $M = 288$ triangular elements spanned by $\{N_1\}$, was defined for a symmetric quarter of the duct. The boundary condition specifications for both laminar and turbulent simulations are identical vanishing of all dependent variables on the (no-slip) walls, and vanishing normal derivatives on the symmetry planes, except for the appropriate components of $\tilde{u}_l = 0$ (see Fig. 7.3*b*). The initial condition for the laminar simulation is a slug profile for $u_1(x_l, x_1^0)$ and $u_l(x_l, x_1^0) \equiv 0$. For the turbulent simulation, the two-dimensional boundary layer initialization concepts discussed in Sec. 6.8 were extended to node columns to initialize $\tilde{u}_1$, k, and ϵ at x_1^0, while still assuming $\tilde{u}_l(x_l, x_1^0) \equiv 0$.

The principal requirement of the turbulent simulation, conducted at $\mathrm{Re} = 4.2 \times 10^4$ based upon hydraulic diameter D_h, is to assess the importance of $O(\delta)$ and $O(\delta^2)$ terms in the Reynolds stress tensor constitutive model (7.26). Since the turbulent flow initialization was rather inaccurate (no accounting for existence of the corner), the 3DPNS solution was executed to $x_1/D_h \approx 10$, solving only for $\tilde{u}_1$, k, ϵ and ϕ under the action of the Boussinesq eddy viscosity ν^t only [see (7.29)-(7.31). Figure 7.4*a* graphs the resultant computed transverse plane velocity distribution. The extremum ratio $\tilde{u}_l^m/u_\infty = 0.003$, to which the vector representation is scaled, is about half that reported by Melling and Whitelaw (1976) for their experiment. Importantly, no (artificial) initiation of a vortex pair roll-up is indicated.

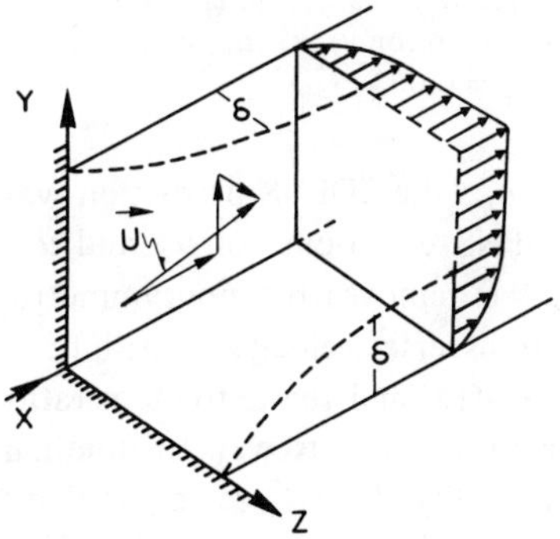

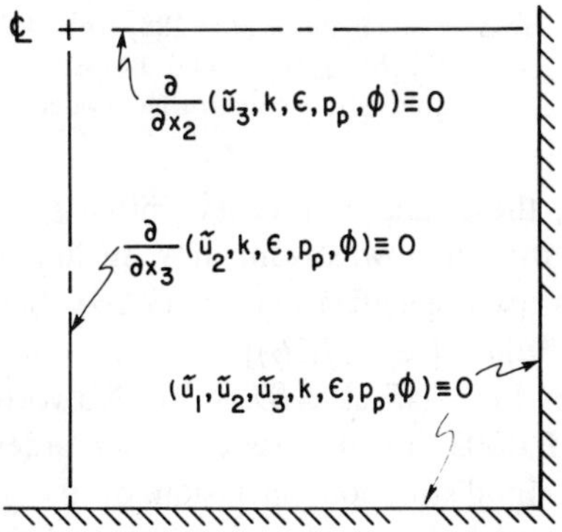

Figure 7.3 Flow in a straight, rectangular cross-sectional duct. (*a*) Geometric orientation; (*b*) 3DPNS boundary conditions.

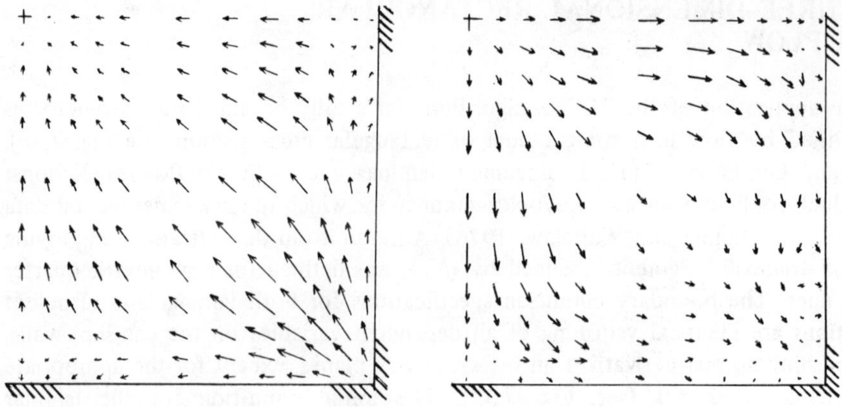

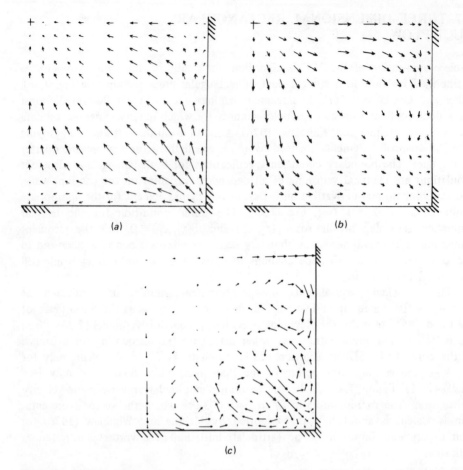

Figure 7.4 3DPNS computed transverse plane velocity $\tilde{u}_l$ distributions, turbulent flow in rectangular cross-sectional duct, $M = 288$, $\text{Re} = 4.2 \times 10^4$. (*a*) $x_1/D_h = 10.0$, initialization plane data, $\tilde{u}_l^m/u_\infty = 0.003$. (*b*) $x_1/D_h = 30.0$, Boussinesq eddy viscosity ν^t (only), $\tilde{u}_l^m/u_\infty = 0.0003$. (*c*) $x_1/D_h = 30.0$, Reynolds stress constitutive model (7.22), $\tilde{u}_l^m/u_\infty = 0.003$.

Using these data as the new initial specification q_j^0, the 3DPNS prediction was executed further downstream, now including the 3DPNS equations for $\tilde{u}_2$ and $\tilde{u}_3$, (7.45) for two specifications in (7.26). Setting $C_2 \equiv 0$ removes the nonsymmetric terms in $\overline{u_l' u_l'}$ [see (7.26)] and produces the transverse velocity distribution graphed in Fig. 7.4*b* at $x_1/D_h = 30$. No vortex is indicated, and the extremum ratio $\tilde{u}_l^m/u_\infty = 0.0003$ has decreased by an order of magnitude on its way to nominal vanishing. In distinction, inclusion of the terms multiplied by C_2, as required by invariance, and use of the identical initialization yields the results shown in Fig. 7.4*c* at $x_1/D_h = 30$. The axial vortex pair is clearly evident, and the extremum $\tilde{u}_l^m/u_\infty = 0.003$ is of the order of the initializing data.

This solution is in qualitative agreement with the experimental data reproduced as Fig. 7.5*a*. However, there are detailed inaccuracies, principally in the erroneous prediction of another vortex at the symmetry boundaries. Refined grid and full-duct turbulent flow solutions for the same experimental configuration are reported by Baker and Orzechowski (1982). Figure 7.5*b* graphs the refined grid ($M = 1052$) solution for the symmetric quarter duct. The qualitatively correct vortex patterns nearly fill the section, and $\tilde{u}_l^m/\tilde{u}_1 = 0.0043$ remains a factor of two lower than the experimental data. The erroneous vortices are still predicted to occur adjacent to both symmetry planes, but their size and magnitude is substantially reduced in comparison to the coarse grid solution. These two solutions indicate the mechanism causing this local pollution is a singularity in the boundary conditions for the conservation function $\phi^h(x_l)$. Since a velocity component is permitted (must occur) parallel to the symmetry plane, but not along the no-slip wall, the corner intersection corresponds to a switch from Dirichlet to Neumann boundary conditions.

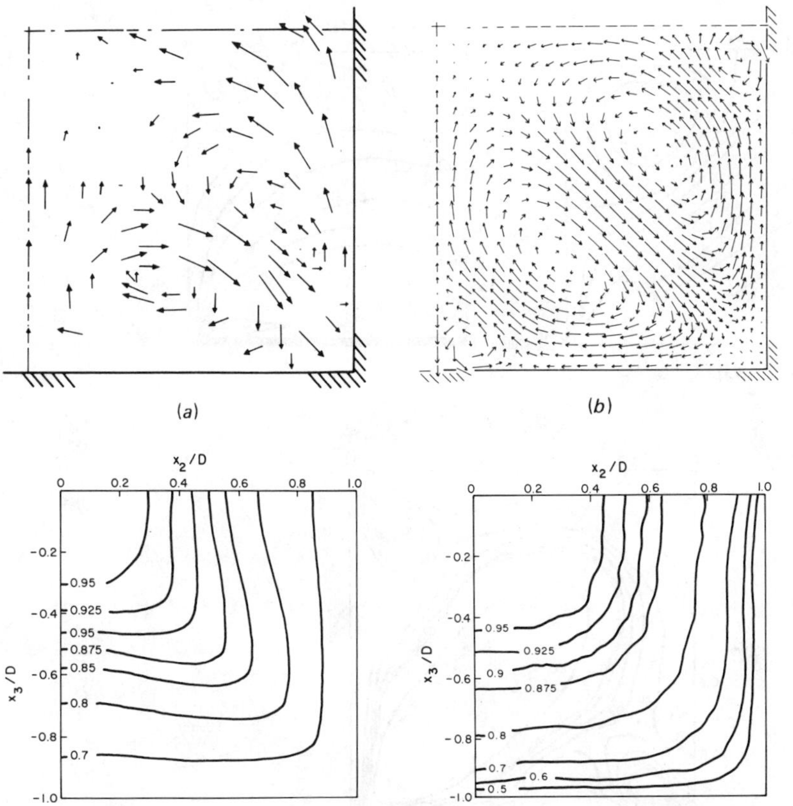

Figure 7.5 3DPNS and experimental mean velocity distributions, $\tilde{u}_l$ and $\tilde{u}_1$, turbulent flow in a rectangular cross-sectional duct, $x_1/D_h = 36.8$, $\mathrm{Re} = 4.2 \times 10^4$. (*a*) Experimental distribution, $\tilde{u}_l^m/u_\infty = 0.0086$. After Melling and Whitelaw (1976). (*b*) 3DPNS $\tilde{u}_l$ distribution, $M = 1052$, $\tilde{u}_l^m/u_\infty = 0.0043$. From Baker and Orzechowski (1982). (*c*) Experimental $\tilde{u}_1$ distribution. After Melling and Whitelaw (1976). (*d*) 3DPNS $\tilde{u}_1$ distribution, $M = 1052$. From Baker and Orzechowski (1982).

The 3DPNS solution on a coarse ($M = 1052$) grid discretization of the entire duct did not predict these spurious vortices. However, the solution on this grid remains too coarse for quantitative assessments. The quarter duct $M = 1052$ solution is of appropriate refinement, and since the pollution due to the singularity is rather localized, a quantitative comparison with data is reported by Baker and Orzechowski (1982). Figure 7.5*c* verifies the significant intrusion of the core velocity $\tilde{u}_1$ into the corner region, as induced by the vortex structure (Fig. 7.5*a*). The 3DPNS solution exhibits this character for $\tilde{u}_1 \leqslant 0.70$ only (Fig. 7.5*d*). The intersection of the 3DPNS $\tilde{u}_1 = 0.70$ isovel with the symmetry plane is in good agreement with experiment. Above this level, and on the symmetry planes, the intersection of 3DPNS levels for $\tilde{u}_1$ exceed data by $\Delta x_l \approx 15$ percent. Along the corner bisector, the levels are in better agreement.

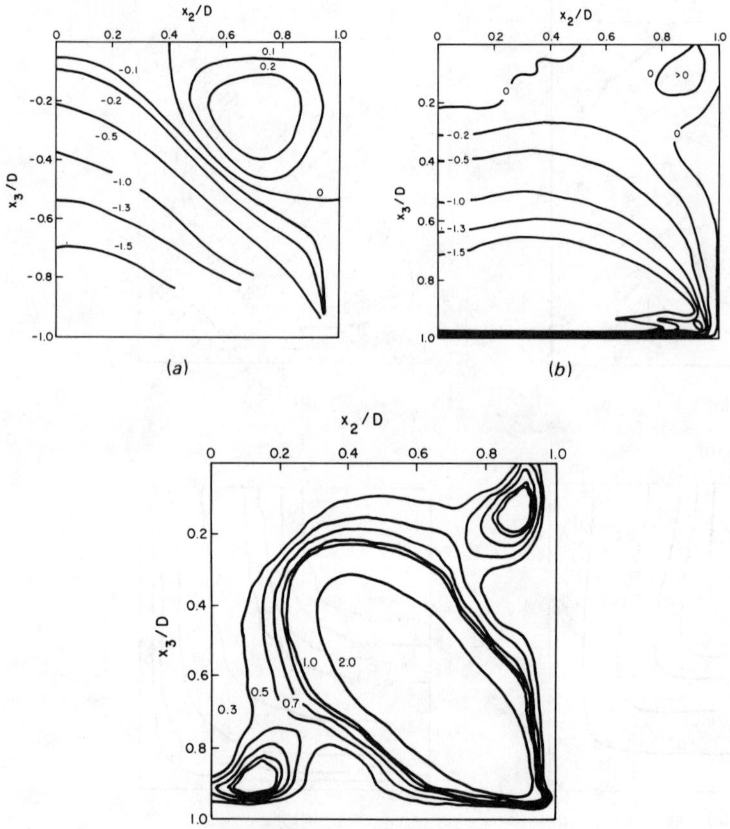

Figure 7.6 3DPNS and experimental Reynolds shear stress distributions, turbulent flow in rectangular cross-sectional duct, $x_1/D_h = 36.8$, $\mathrm{Re} = 4.2 \times 10^4$. (*a*) Experimental $-\overline{u'_1 u'_3} \times 10^3$ distribution. After Melling and Whitelaw (1976). (*b*) 3DPNS $-\overline{u'_1 u'_3} \times 10^3$ distribution. From Baker and Orzechowski (1982). (*c*) 3DPNS $-\overline{u'_2 u'_3} \times 10^4$ distribution. From Baker and Orzechowski (1982).

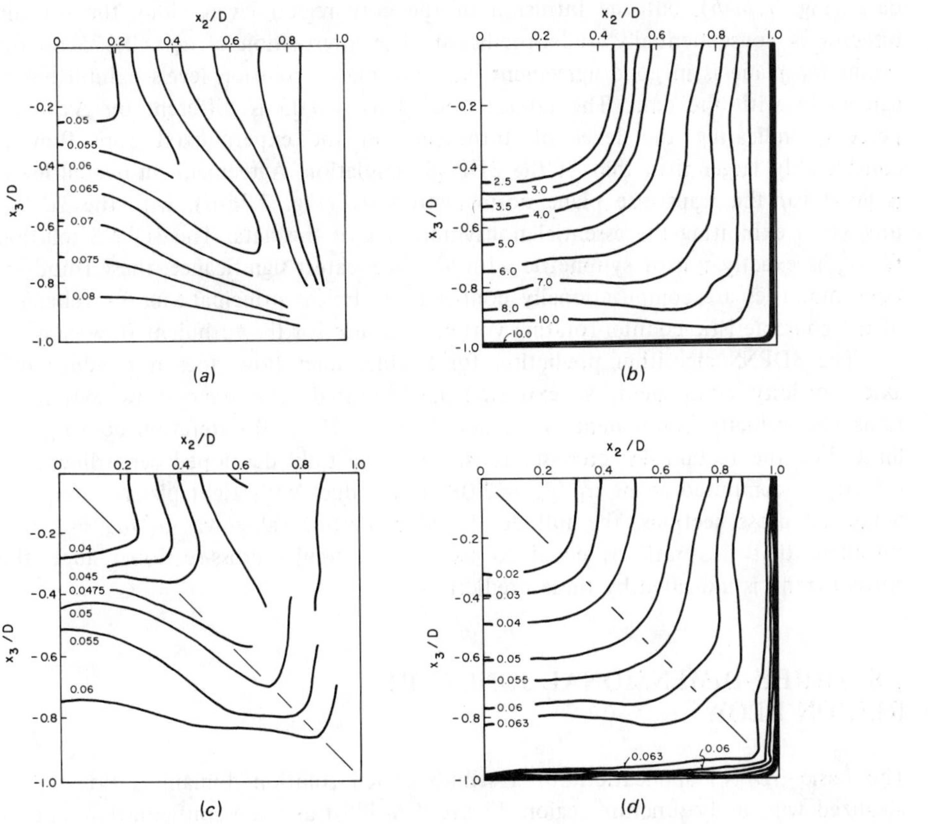

Figure 7.7 3DPNS and experimental Reynolds normal stress distributions, turbulent flow in rectangular cross-sectional duct, $x_1/D_h = 36.8$, Re $= 4.2 \times 10^4$. (*a*) Experimental $\sqrt{\overline{u_1' u_1'}}$ distribution. After Melling and Whitelaw (1976). (*b*) 3DPNS $\sqrt{\overline{u_1' u_1'}} \times 10^2$ distribution. From Baker and Orzechowski (1982). (*c*) Experimental $\sqrt{\overline{u_2' u_2'}}$ distribution. After Melling and Whitelaw (1976). (*d*) 3DPNS $\sqrt{\overline{u_2' u_2'}}$ distribution. From Baker and Orzechowski (1982).

Figure 7.6 compares the experimental and 3DPNS Reynolds principal shear stress distributions, $-\overline{u_1' u_3'}$. Essential agreement is indicated, as well as some detail of the contour shapes for the largest levels. The experimentally measured regions of small negative $-\overline{u_1' u_3'}$ (and small positive $-\overline{u_1' u_2'}$) shear stress result from the inflections in $\tilde{u}_1$ (Fig. 7.5*c*-*d*). The 3DPNS solution has correctly predicted this essential character, although the details are largely affected by the boundary condition singularity. This is clearly illustrated by the "ears" on the 3DPNS prediction of $-\overline{u_2' u_3'}$ (Fig. 7.6*c*). No experimental determination of this order of magnitude smaller shear stress component is reported.

Figure 7.7 summarizes the corresponding comparisons on the square root of Reynolds normal stresses. The overall agreement on level confirms the standard definitions for the constitutive equation model constants C_α, and the coefficients C_α^β in (7.27)-(7.28). The 3DPNS prediction for $\overline{u_1'}$ is symmetric, in agreement with data (Fig. 7.7*a-b*), but the intrusion of the core region levels along the domain bisector is consequentially under-predicted. The intersection of $\overline{u_1'} = 0.075$ on the symmetry plane is in good agreement, and the higher solution levels exhibit better agreement with the data. The intersection of $\overline{u_1'} = 0.05$ is different by $\Delta x_l \approx 20$ percent, indicating the level of turbulence in the experimental core flow is considerably larger than that of the 3DPNS simulation. Agreement on overall levels is good for the transverse plane normal stress $\overline{u_2'}$ (Fig. 7.7*c-d*), with the 3DPNS prediction exhibiting the essential nonsymmetries of the data. The 3DPNS solution for $\overline{u_3'}$ is exactly mirror symmetric with $\overline{u_2'}$. Of greatest significance, these (modest) nonsymmetries are computationally confirmed to be the principal causal mechanism of the characteristic counter-rotating vortex structure for the turbulent flow case.

The 3DPNS algorithm prediction for laminar duct flow does not induce this axial vorticity component, as expected and required. The steady-flow extremum transverse velocity component is smaller than $\epsilon = 10^{-4}$, the iteration convergence limit. For the rectangular cross-sectional duct, the fully developed centerline axial velocity is computed to be $u_1^m/u_\infty = 2.08$. For a duct with eight planar sides, i.e., octagonal cross sections, the full developed centerline value was $u_1^m/u_\infty = 2.025$. Recalling that this ratio is equal to two for a circular cross-sectional duct, the correct trend is indicated by these predictions.

7.8 THREE-DIMENSIONAL JUNCTURE REGION FLOW

The basic 3DPNS application for a semi-bounded solution domain is flow in an idealized wing-body juncture region. Figure 7.8*a* illustrates the configuration, and as noted in Sec. 7.1, the right angle juncture has received considerable theoretical analysis.

Baker and Orzechowski (1982) document the 3DPNS solution for laminar and turbulent flow in a juncture region, formed by the right intersection of two 10-percent thick parabolic arc airfoils with coincident leading edges. For zero angle of attack, the freestream Mach number was $M_\infty = 0.08$ ($U_\infty = 100$ f/s) and $\text{Re}/C = 0.6 \times 10^6$. A nonuniform discretization containing $M = 361$ triangular elements spanned by $\{N_1\}$ was employed. Figure 7.8*b* illustrates the grid and Table 7.1 lists the boundary condition specifications. The complementary pressure p_C boundary conditions for the 3DPNS solution were obtained using the Hess (1972) potential flow computer code for the parabolic arc juncture. Figure 7.9 shows spanwise distributions of $p_C(x_l)$ at station $x_1/C = 0.01$, 0.085, and 0.46. By symmetry, these pressures are appropriate for $x_1/C = 0.54$, 0.915, and 0.99. Therefore, a favorable x_1 pressure gradient is induced to midchord, and thereafter turns adverse. The strongest gradients occur in the immediate vicinity of the corner.

The initial conditions for $\tilde{u}_1(x_1 = 0.01)$ were established using Cole's law to interpolate a turbulent boundary layer profile onto "columns" of nodes and matching the freestream level for p_C. The transverse velocity $\tilde{u}_l$ was identically zero until four algorithm steps were executed [to compute a reasonable estimate of

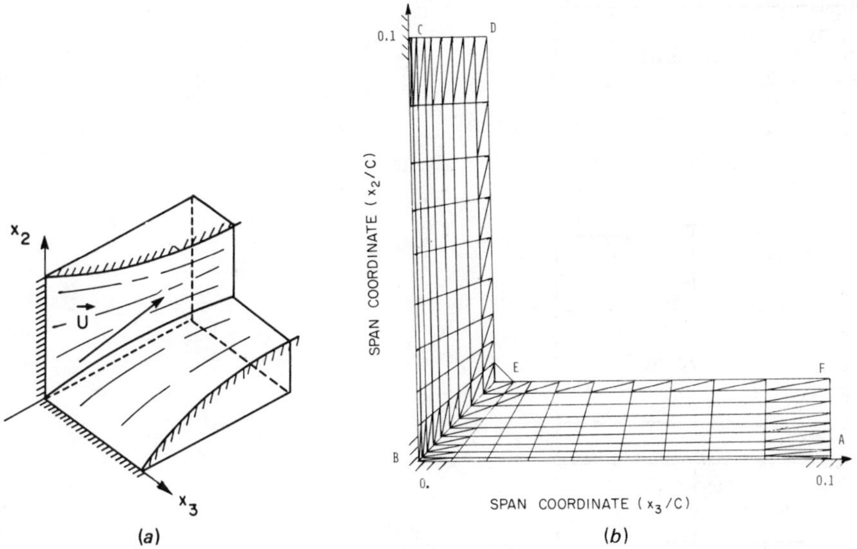

Figure 7.8 Characterization of 3DPNS solution specification for turbulent flow in a three-dimensional juncture region. (*a*) Juncture geometry; (*b*) 3DPNS domain discretization.

$\{U1\}'$ for (7.46)]. The initial distribution of k and ϵ were established using the mixing length-boundary layer concepts discussed in Chap. 6.

The pressure field $\bar{p}(x_1) = p_c + p_p$ [see (7.15)] converged to a stationary distribution on the third 3DPNS solution sweep for the turbulent flow solution. Figure 7.10 summarizes the solution in terms of transverse plane velocity vector plots on $0.01 < x_1/C < 0.50$. Only the spanwise half domain is shown, since the solution is exactly symmetric. Figure 7.10*a* confirms a large mass influx into the juncture corner, immediately upon starting of the transverse velocity algorithm as induced by the large favorable p_c pressure gradient. The largest scalar magnitude for $\tilde{u}_l$ is $\tilde{u}_l^m/u_\infty = 0.25$, corresponding to the largest arrow. By $x_1/C = 0.085$, the maximum ratio $\tilde{u}_l^m/u_\infty = 0.06$ is reduced by a factor of four (Fig. 7.10*b*). The dominant action is mass efflux along the span, in the lower reaches of the boundary layer, and formation of a very modest corner vortex. Near 20 percent chord (Fig. 7.10*d*), $\tilde{u}_l^m/u_\infty = 0.11$, the weak axial vortex pair is somewhat larger, very little

Table 7.1 PNS algorithm boundary conditions aerodynamic juncture region (Fig. 7.8*b*)

	Domain boundary segments	
Dependent variables	Dirichlet	Neumann
$\tilde{u}_i, k, \epsilon, p_p$	*A-B-C*	*C-D-E-F-A*
p_c, ϕ	*D-E-F*	*F-A-B-C-D*

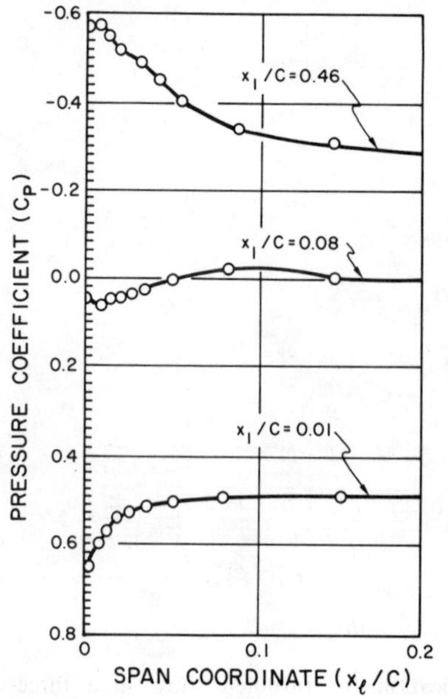

Figure 7.9 Three-dimensional potential flow boundary conditions for complementary pressure.

mass is being entrained from the free stream, and spanwise efflux is fully developed. The transverse flow field remains visually unchanged on $0.2 \leqslant x_1/C \leqslant 0.7$ (Fig. 7.10*e*–*f*), at which point $\tilde{u}_1$ separates at the node in the juncture corner, and the 3DPNS solution stops.

Figure 7.11*a* shows the companion laminar flow prediction of transverse plane velocity distribution at $x_1/C = 0.46$. In comparison to the turbulent case (Fig. 7.11*b*), $u_l^m/u_\infty = 0.06$ is half the value, the weak vortex pair is somewhat larger in extent, and reversal of the spanwise flow is indicated directly adjacent to the airfoil surface. For comparison to theory, Fig. 7.12 reproduces the composite laminar corner region solution of Rubin and Grossman (1971), which shows qualitative agreement in the corner layer region, except that the streamlines are not estimated to form closed circuits in the corner region. Figure 7.13 summarizes the laminar-turbulent boundary layer analysis of Shafir and Rubin (1976), which predicts the reversal of the laminar spanwise flow captured by the 3DPNS solution.

Figure 7.14 summarizes the turbulent juncture flow transverse plane distributions of $\tilde{u}_1$, $\overline{u_1'u_1'}$, $\overline{u_2'u_2'}$, and $\overline{u_1'u_2'}$ at $x_1/C = 0.46$. The displacement effect of corner geometry, and the action of the weak axial vortex pair is evident in Fig. 7.14*a*, as is the flow symmetry. Comparing to Fig. 7.5*d*, the semibounded character of the juncture region solution domain exerts a consequential impact. As further confirmation, the nonsymmetry in $\overline{u_2'u_2'}$ is just barely noticeable on the scale of Fig. 7.14*c* (compare Fig. 7.7*d*). The Reynolds shear stress $\overline{u_1'u_3'}$ would be a mirror reflection of $\overline{u_1'u_2'}$ about the corner bisector. For convergence set at $\epsilon = 3 \times 10^{-4}$, the 3DPNS algorithm averaged four iterations per space step. Satisfaction of continuity, as measured in the energy norm was maintained at $E(\delta\phi, \delta\phi) \leqslant 0.6 \times 10^{-5}$ at convergence.

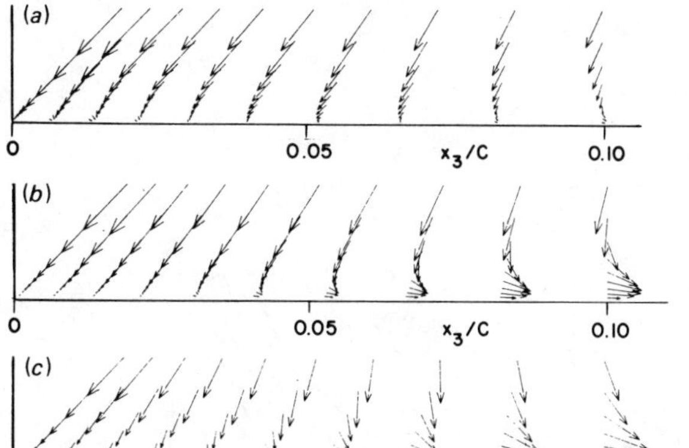

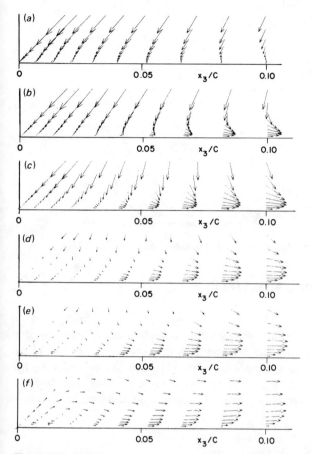

Figure 7.10 3DPNS transverse plane velocity distributions, turbulent flow, (*a*) $x_1/C = 0.021$, $\tilde{u}_l^m/u_\infty = 0.167$; (*b*) $x_1/C = 0.047$, $\tilde{u}_l^m/u_\infty = 0.072$; (*c*) $x_1/C = 0.081$, $\tilde{u}_l^m/u_\infty = 0.058$; (*d*) $x_1/C = 0.173$, $\tilde{u}_l^m/u_\infty = 0.112$; (*e*) $x_1/C = 0.349$, $\tilde{u}_l^m/u_\infty = 0.114$; (*f*) $x_1/C = 0.704$, $\tilde{u}_l^m/u_\infty = 0.097$.

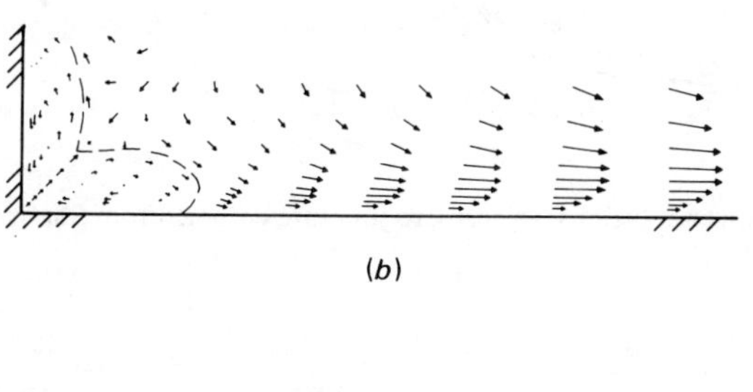

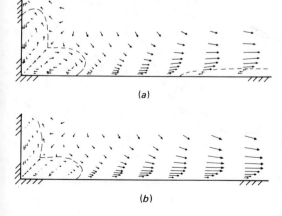

Figure 7.11 3DPNS transverse plane velocity distributions, laminar and turbulent flow in juncture region, $x_1/C = 0.46$. (a) Laminar flow, $\tilde{u}_l^m/u_\infty = 0.06$; (*b*) turbulent flow, $\tilde{u}_l^m/u_\infty = 0.10$.

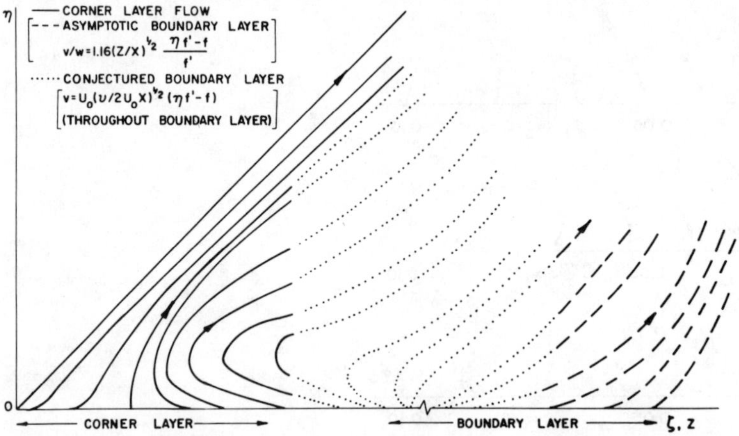

Figure 7.12 Composite laminar corner layer solution. From Rubin and Grossman (1971).

7.9 THREE-DIMENSIONAL MULTIPLE FREE JET FLOW

The 3DPNS equation system and solution algorithm is applicable to prediction of a wide variety of free jet flow fields. The problem class involves flow prediction in an unbounded solution domain. The corresponding far-field boundary condition on p_c is a homogeneous constant, hence $p_p = 0$ is the boundary constraint. The far-field boundary must be porous to transverse fluxes of mass and momentum, hence $\phi = 0$

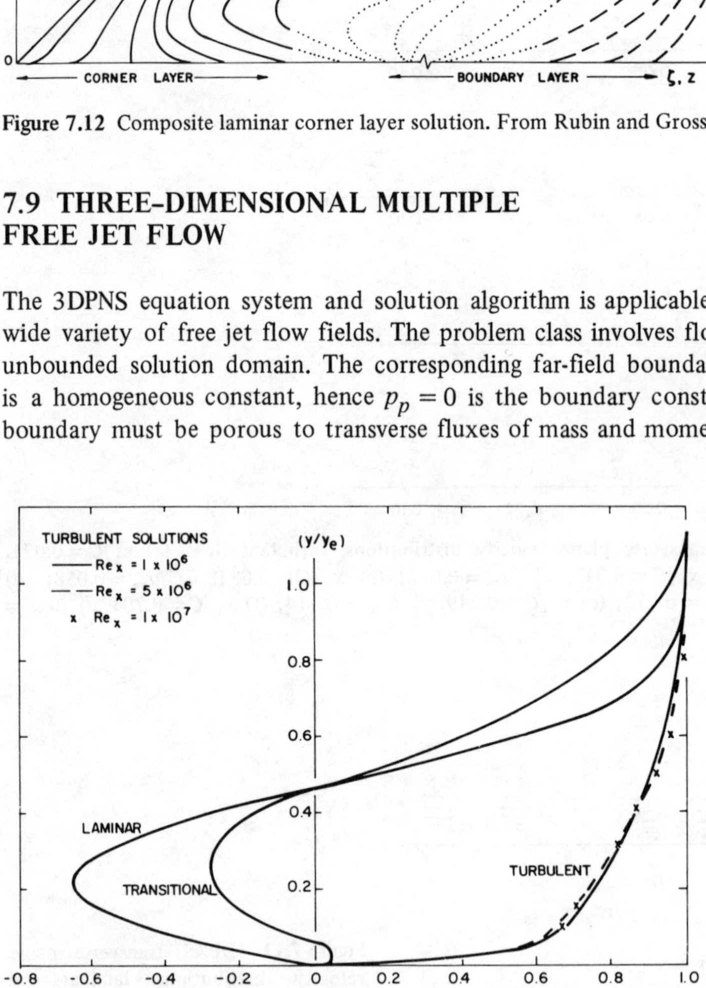

Figure 7.13 Laminar/turbulent boundary layer solutions adjacent to juncture corner. From Shafir and Rubin (1976).

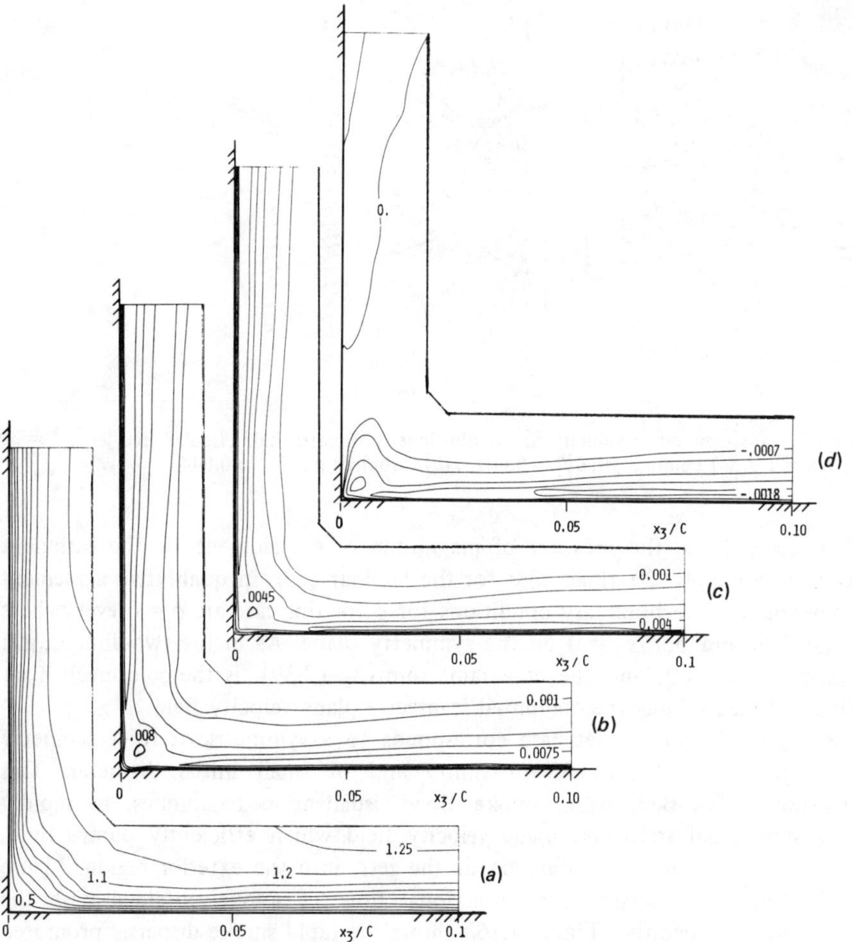

Figure 7.14 3DPNS solution for turbulent flow in juncture region, $\mathrm{Re}/C = 0.6 \times 10^6$, $M_\infty = 0.08$, $x_1/C = 0.46$. From Baker and Orzechowski (1982). *(a)* $\tilde{u}_1$; *(b)* $\overline{u'_1 u'_1}$; *(c)* $\overline{u'_2 u'_2}$; *(d)* $\overline{u'_1 u'_2}$.

is the appropriate far-field condition. The typical boundary condition specifications for $\tilde{u}_i$, k, and ϵ are vanishing derivatives normal to the domain boundary in the far-field.

Baker et al. (1983) document application of the 3DPNS algorithm to a multiple free-jet geometry at low Mach number. The basic preliminary test is the three-dimensional problem of a single free jet of initially circular cross section. Figure 7.15 summarizes the 3DPNS prediction of transverse half-plane velocity field at $x_1/D_h = 1.0$, where D_h is the initial jet diameter, for laminar flow and for turbulent flow with $\nu_t^0 = 10$. Both solutions exhibit the required symmetries and predict essentially radial entrainment. The plot length of each individual velocity vector is the measure of the relative magnitude of $\tilde{u}_l$, scaled to the local predicted extremum magnitude $\tilde{u}_l^m$. For laminar flow, $\tilde{u}_l^m/u_\infty = 0.0017$, while $\tilde{u}_l^m/u_\infty = 0.044$ for the

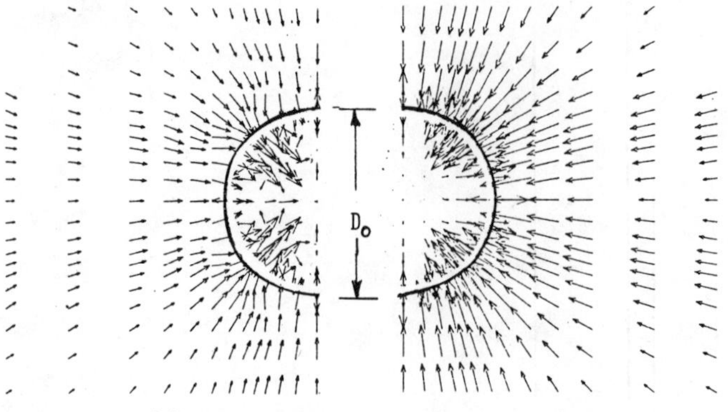

Figure 7.15 Transverse mean velocity $\widetilde{u}_l$ distributions, symmetric-half circular free jet, $\widetilde{u}_l^0 = 30$ m/s, $x_1/D_h = 1.0$. (*a*) Laminar jet, $\widetilde{u}_l^m = 0.0017$; (*b*) turbulent jet, $\widetilde{u}_l^m = 0.044$.

turbulent case. Thus, the measure of magnitude of entrainment for the turbulent case is approximately 20 times that for the laminar case, in qualitative agreement with experiment. The boundary conditions for ϕ for this case are $\phi = 0$ everywhere in the far-field and $\partial\phi/\partial x_3 = 0$ on the symmetry plane. As in the two-dimensional test (Chap. 6), $\widetilde{u}_l^0 \equiv 0$, and the constraint term β_2 (7.39), is the sole mechanism initiating and maintaining the computed transverse plane velocity field.

The reported multiple jet case corresponds to a symmetric four-jet geometry with the jets located in close proximity and of small initial diameter. This configuration is verified, using smoke flow visualization techniques, to rapidly induce a substantial transverse plane velocity field which efficiently pumps fluid, initially interior to the circumference of the jets, into the exterior region. Figure 7.16*a* illustrates the persistent unidirectional flow of smoke obtained with the multijet system inoperative. Figure 7.16*b* shows the rapid smoke dispersal promoted by the multiple jet system operating at design conditions. Figure 7.17 is a layout of

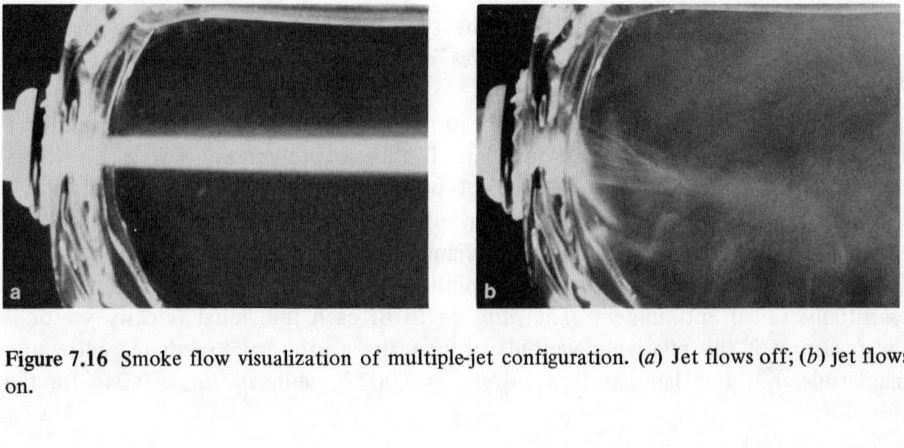

Figure 7.16 Smoke flow visualization of multiple-jet configuration. (*a*) Jet flows off; (*b*) jet flows on.

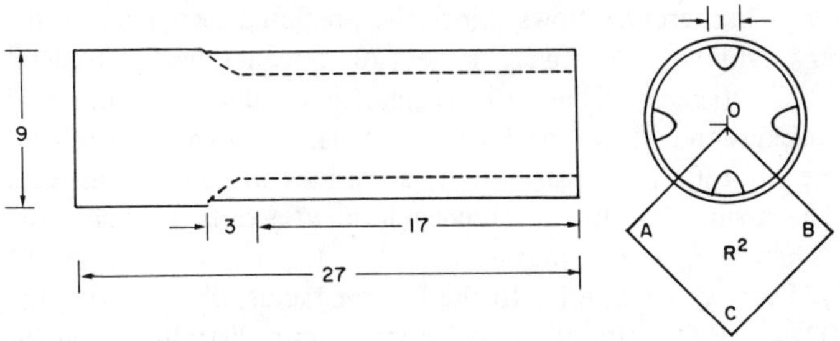

Figure 7.17 Layout of multiple jet geometry, dimensions in millimeters.

the device indicating characteristic dimensions. Operating on design, free air is induced to flow down each vent channel, of length 0.02 m, at a nominal velocity $\tilde{u}_j = 12$ m/s. The locator radius of the jets is $R = 0.004$ m, and the initial hydraulic diameter of each jet is $d_j = 0.001$ m. In the region interior to R, $\tilde{u}_1^0 \approx 0.02\,\tilde{u}_j^0$, while in the essentially unbounded exterior region $\tilde{u}_1^0 \approx 0$. The characteristic Reynolds number for the jet flow is $\text{Re} \approx 10^6$/m, and the vent channel walls are quite rough.

The symmetry of the geometry permitted calculations to be performed on the symmetric quarter domain with boundary *OACB* (Fig. 7.17). Figure 7.18 graphs the domain showing the nodal coordinates of the basic $M = 19 \times 19$ nonuniform discretization. The lateral extent spans twice the locator radius R, and segments *OA* and *OB* are symmetry planes upon which the normal component of velocity vanishes and all other variables possess vanishing normal derivatives. Boundary segment *ACB* was assumed sufficiently remote, such that all dependent variables have vanishing normal derivatives except ϕ, which vanishes identically.

For the base assessment, the specified initial conditions are $\tilde{u}_1^0(x_1^0, x_l)$, and the

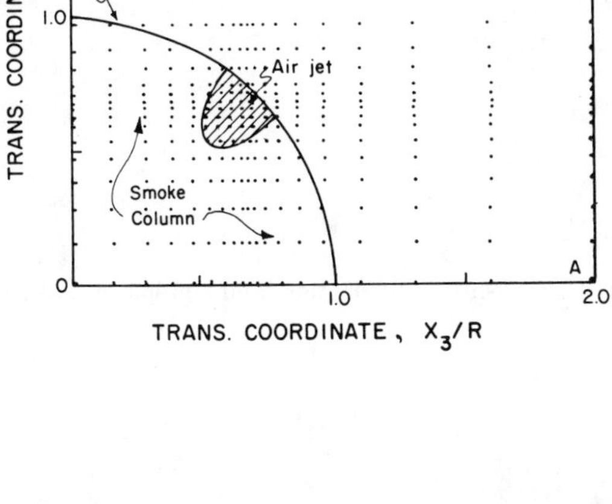

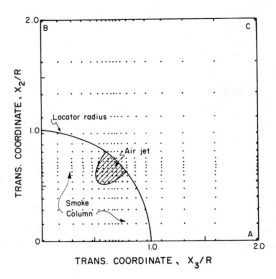

Figure 7.18 Solution domain for symmetric quarter plane prediction of four multiple jet configuration, including nodal coordinate distribution of $M = 19 \times 19$ discretization.

levels ν_t^0 in the air jet and background flows. Since the predicted secondary vortex flow field develops very rapidly, a relatively large (20 percent) background $\tilde{u}_1^0$ velocity field was used for efficiency. [The 3DPNS algorithm stability was marginal using a 10 percent background flow specification. Small, but not significant differences were predicted in $\tilde{u}_l(x_1, x_l)$ distributions at various stations downstream of the injector face. The assumed initial turbulence level ν_t^0 exerts a much more significant influence.] Therefore, within the air jet, $\tilde{u}_1^0 = 1.2\ u_\infty$. where $u_\infty = 12$ m/s, the design velocity. Everywhere exterior to the locator radius, $\tilde{u}_1^0 \equiv 0.2\ u_\infty$, the interior $\tilde{u}_1^0 \equiv (0.2 + 0.02)u_\infty$. Hence, the $\tilde{u}_1^0$ velocity strain rate distribution on the initial surface plane was on-design. Further, within the air jet $k^0 \equiv 0.005$, with ϵ^0 defined such that $\nu_t^0/\bar{\nu} \approx 35$. Everywhere exterior to the jet, $k^0 = 0.0001$ and $\nu_t^0/\bar{\nu} \approx 3$.

Figure 7.19 is a composite of the multiple vortex secondary velocity field predicted by the 3DPNS algorithm at $x_1/R = 1.5$, i.e., 6 mm downstream from the plane of solution initiation. Each velocity vector length is scaled to the extremum predicted level $(\tilde{u}_l/u_\infty)_{\max} \equiv \tilde{u}_l^m = 0.067$. The original location of each air jet coincides with the clustering of large radial velocities, and the net action of the four-jet device is to induce a system of eight symmetrically disposed, counter-

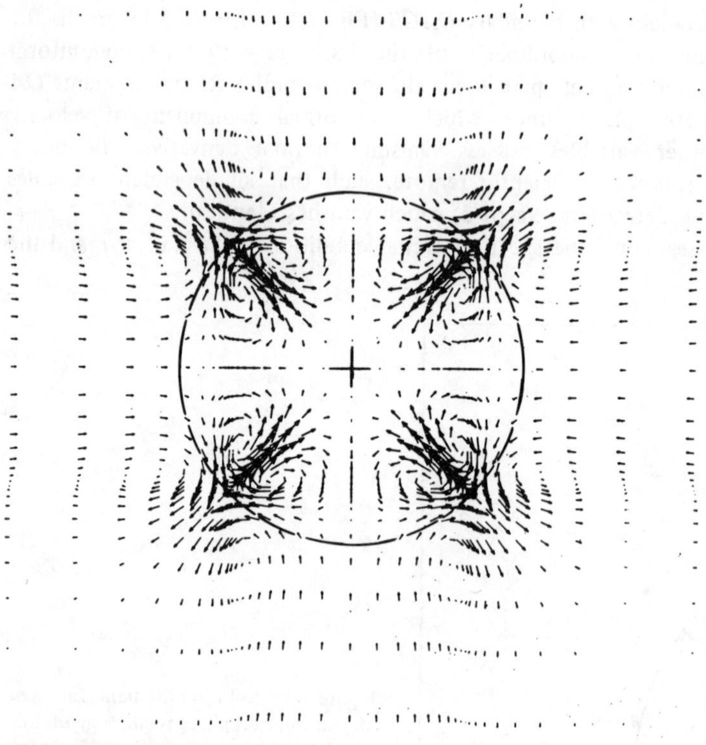

Figure 7.19 Computed composite transverse plane velocity $\tilde{u}_l$ distribution, four multiple jet geometry, $\tilde{u}_l^0 = 12$ m/s, $x_1/R = 1.5$.

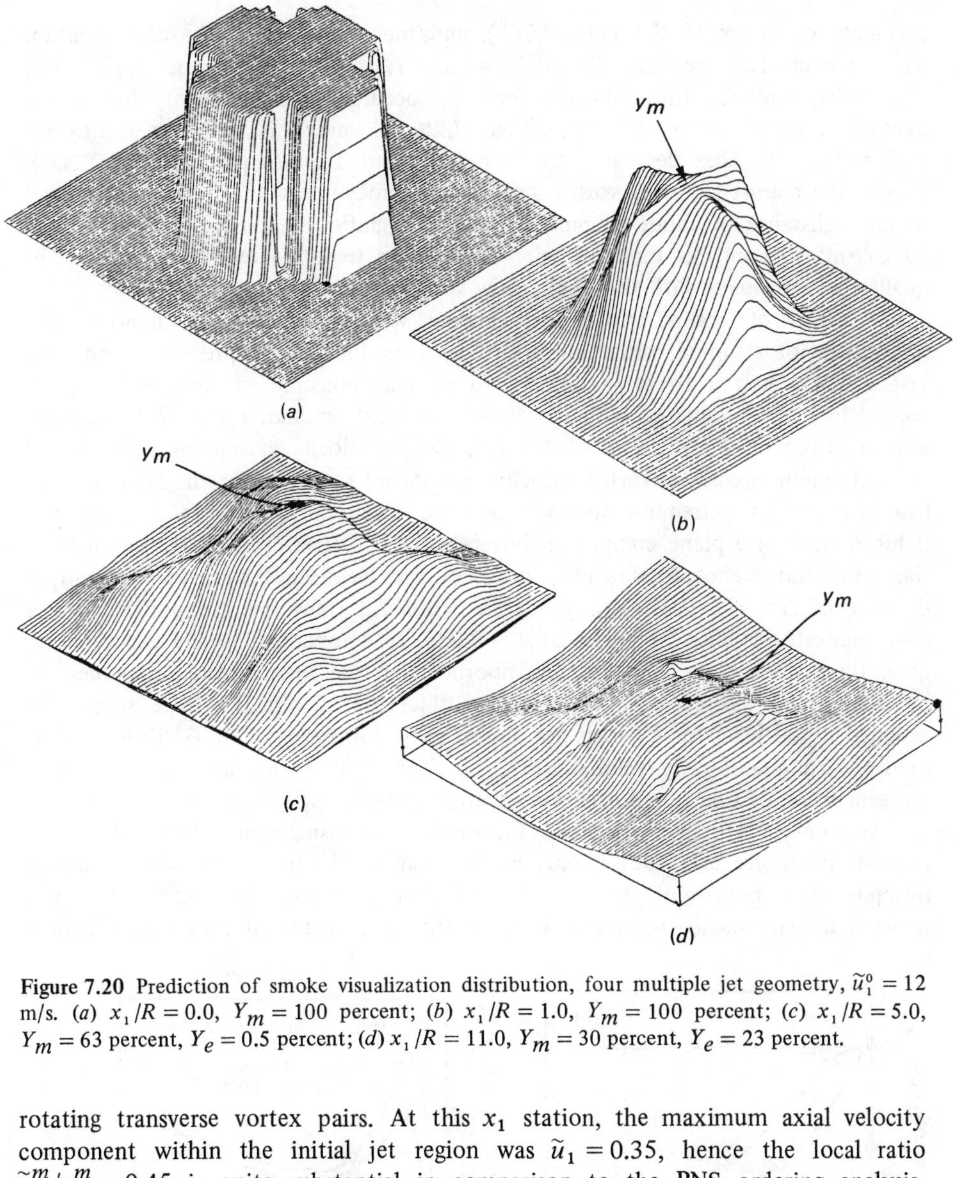

Figure 7.20 Prediction of smoke visualization distribution, four multiple jet geometry, $\tilde{u}_1^0 = 12$ m/s. (*a*) $x_1/R = 0.0$, $Y_m = 100$ percent; (*b*) $x_1/R = 1.0$, $Y_m = 100$ percent; (*c*) $x_1/R = 5.0$, $Y_m = 63$ percent, $Y_e = 0.5$ percent; (*d*) $x_1/R = 11.0$, $Y_m = 30$ percent, $Y_e = 23$ percent.

rotating transverse vortex pairs. At this x_1 station, the maximum axial velocity component within the initial jet region was $\tilde{u}_1 = 0.35$, hence the local ratio $\tilde{u}_l^m/u_1^m = 0.45$ is quite substantial in comparison to the PNS ordering analysis. Details on the evolution of this vortex flowfield are given in the cited reference. The visual appearance of the double counter-rotating vortex pattern persists essentially unchanged for distances up to $x_1/R = 11$ downstream of the initial condition plane.

A species continuity equation was added to the 3DPNS system to permit tracking the motion of fluid initially interior to the locator radius R. Figure 7.20*a* shows the $Y^0 = 100$ percent smoke distribution at the solution initiation plane; the four troughs correspond to the location of the four air jets. Diffusion processes dominate on $0 \leqslant x_1/R \leqslant 1$ (Fig. 7.20*b*), and the extremum smoke concentration Y_m remains 100 percent. By $x_1/R = 2.0$, $Y_m = 97$ percent, at $x_1/R = 3.0$, $Y_m = 84\%$, and the first non-zero level Y_e occurs at the boundary ∂R of the 3DPNS domain at $x_1/R = 5.0$ (Fig. 7.20*c*), where $Y_m = 63$ percent. By $x_1/R = 11.0$, Y_m has decreased to 30 percent and $Y_e = 23$ percent (Fig. 7.20*d*). Hence, the counter-rotating vortex system has homogenized the initial smoke level within a distance of about 44 mm. Of greatest significance, on ∂R at $x_1/R = 11.0$, $\partial Y/\partial x_j \cdot \hat{\mathbf{n}}_j > 0$ confirms that the material transport is dominated by convection, in qualitative agreement with the smoke flow visualization experimental data.

A series of computational experiments were conducted to ascertain the importance of assumed initial turbulence level on the 3DPNS prediction. For one test, k^0 was halved to $k^0 = 0.0025$ and ϵ^0 held constant, yielding $\nu_t^0/\nu = 9$. A second test was conducted with the air jets assumed laminar. Figure 7.21 summarizes these predictions in terms of decay of the jet velocity extremum, $\tilde{u}_1^m(x_1)$, and the extremum predicted vortex velocity component $\tilde{u}_l^m(x_1)$. For the laminar flow case, the air jet extremum does not decrease at all on $0 \leqslant x_1/R \leqslant 1.5$, and the induced transverse plane component hovers about $\tilde{u}_l^m \approx 0.01$. In distinction, halving the initial turbulence level simply displaces the jet decay curve to the right, a distance of $\Delta x_1/R \approx 0.25$, and yields an extremum transverse component that is only modestly smaller by about $\Delta\tilde{u}_l^m \approx 0.005$. In comparison to the experimental data, these predictions confirm the importance of the vent channel roughness in promoting the desired action of the multi-jet system. In the same sense, the assumed initial level for k^0 does not appear critical in terms of the 3DPNS solution predicting a qualitatively valid solution, provided ν_t^0 is sufficiently large to permit self-generation of solutions to the k-ϵ equation system.

As a computational experiment, the smoke flow visualization data indicate the multiple jet device efficiency is only modestly altered by partial blocking of one of the jets. This constraint destroys the inherent geometric symmetries, and the solution domain must encompass a region that is a factor of four larger. Figure

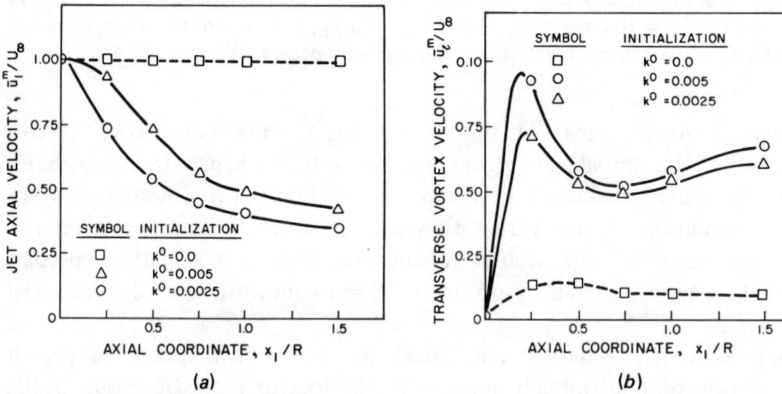

Figure 7.21 Summary of axial mean velocity $\tilde{u}_1$ and transverse plane velocity $\tilde{u}_l$ decay as function of jet initial turbulent kinetic energy level. (*a*) Jet velocity $\tilde{u}_1^m$; (*b*) transverse plane velocity $\tilde{u}_l^m$.

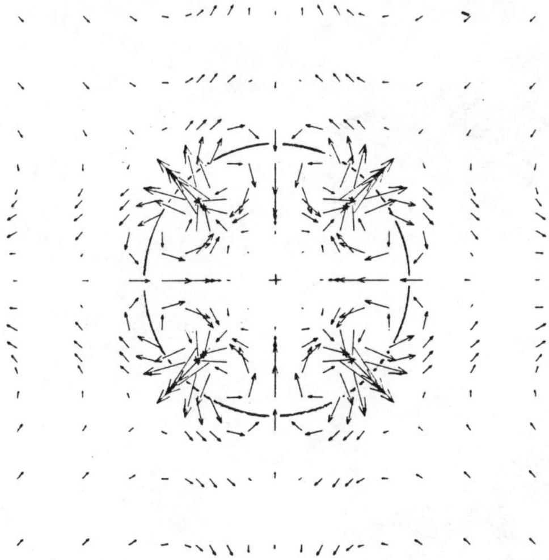

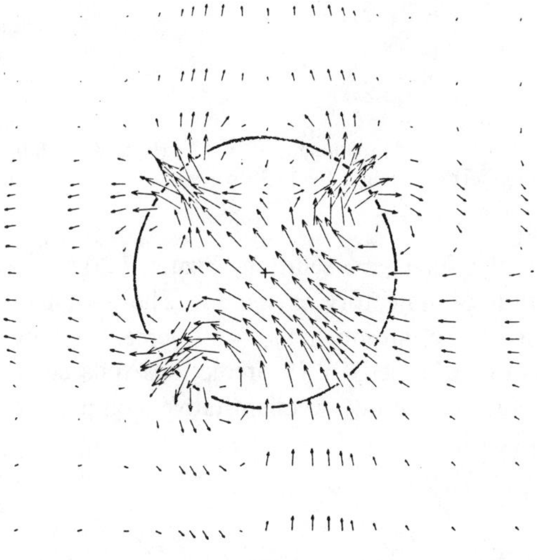

Figure 7.22 Transverse plane velocity $\tilde{u}_l$ distribution on half discretization of full solution domain, $\tilde{u}_1^0 = 12$ m/s, $x_1/R = 1.5$, $M = 19 \times 19$. (*a*) Four jets operating $\tilde{u}_l^m = 0.084$; (*b*) three jets operating $\tilde{u}_l^m = 0.126$.

7.22*a* graphs the transverse velocity distribution $\tilde{u}_l$ at $x_1/R = 1.5$ computed on the $M = 19 \times 19$, mesh that is twice as coarse as the base discretization (Fig. 7.18). Comparing Figs. 7.19 and 7.22*a* confirms that the coarse grid solution has captured the essential eight-vortex pair structure, and $\tilde{u}_l^m = 0.084$ is within 20 percent of the finer grid solution extremum.

Figure 7.22*b* graphs the 3DPNS predicted transverse plane velocity distribution $\tilde{u}_l$, at $x_1/R = 1.5$ obtained with the lower right jet completely shut off. A throughflow has resulted over the occluded jet, and the extremum level $\tilde{u}_l^m = 0.12$ is about 50 percent larger than the design configuration. Figure 7.23 compares the computed distributions of smoke density at $x_1/R = 6.0$ for both coarse grid

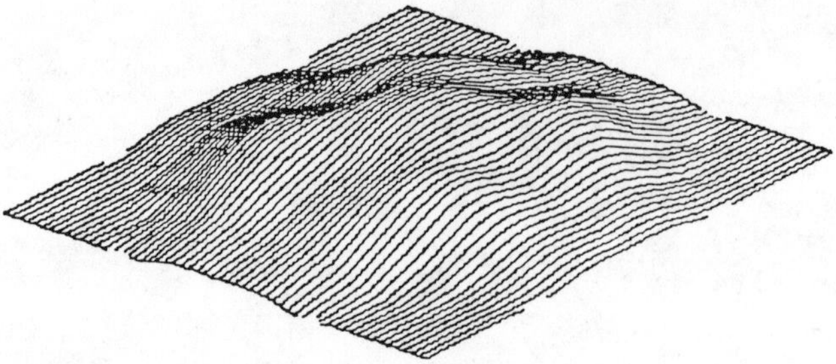

(a)

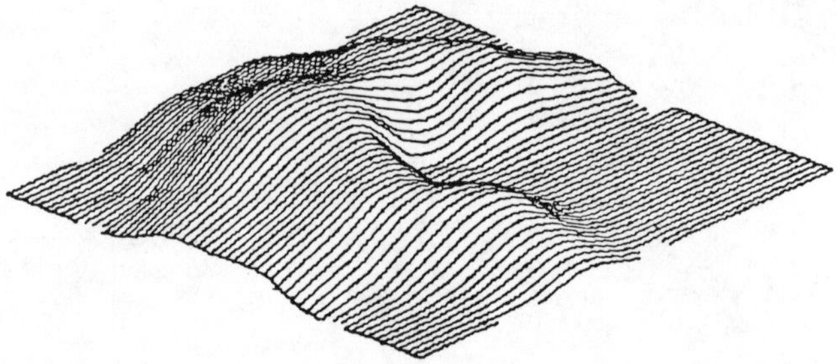

(b)

Figure 7.23 Smoke visualization distributions on full solution domain, $\tilde{u}_1^0 = 12$ m/s, $x_1/R = 6.0$. (*a*) Four jets operating, $Y_m = 53$ percent; (*b*) three jets operating, $Y_m = 59$ percent.

solutions. Figure 7.23*a* is comparable to the finer grid solution, Figure 7.20*c*, and $Y_m = 53$ percent lies on the interpolation of trajectory extremum. The action of the occluded vent is clearly evident in Fig. 7.23*b*, although $Y_m = 59$ percent is only 10 percent larger than the on-design solution. These 3DPNS predictions thus agree qualitatively with the field data, and further permit a quantitative comparison measure of the action of the design modification.

7.10 THREE-DIMENSIONAL DUCT MIXING AND COMBUSTION

Zelazny et al. (1976) document application of the 3DPNS algorithm to duct mixing and combustion of hydrogen is a supersonic air stream. Figure 7.24 shows the scramjet combustor model, used for wind tunnel testing (Beach, 1976), in place behind the Mach 2-6 nozzle. The primary requirement of a 3DPNS analysis is to quantize turbulent mixing and combustion of hydrogen injected perpendicular and parallel to the supersonic freestream. Figure 7.25 illustrates the two configurations and the finite-element coarse-grid discretizations of the corresponding 3DPNS solution domains. The shaded areas indicate the regions occupied by the 100 percent hydrogen jet in each case.

The parabolic Navier-Stokes equation system developed in Sec. 7.2 must be augmented for this analysis by a species continuity equation. Denoting $\tilde{Y}^\alpha$ as the mass fraction of species α, the 3DPNS form is

$$L^P(\bar{\rho}\tilde{Y}^\alpha) = \frac{\partial}{\partial x_1}(\bar{\rho}\tilde{u}_1\tilde{Y}^\alpha) + \frac{\partial}{\partial x_l}(\bar{\rho}\tilde{u}_l\tilde{Y}^\alpha + \overline{\rho u_l' Y^{\alpha\prime}}) + s^\alpha = 0 \qquad (7.71)$$

where s^α is a source term. The time-averaged correlation term is usually replaced, using the definition of an effective transport viscosity ν^e, in the form

$$\overline{\rho u_l' Y^{\alpha\prime}} \equiv \frac{\bar{\rho}}{\mathrm{Re}} \frac{\nu^e}{\mathrm{Sc}} \frac{\partial \tilde{Y}^\alpha}{\partial x_l} \qquad (7.72)$$

In (7.72), Re is the conventional Reynolds number and

$$\frac{\nu^e}{\mathrm{Sc}} \equiv \frac{\bar{\nu}}{\mathrm{Sc}^l} + \frac{\nu^t}{\mathrm{Sc}^t} \qquad (7.73)$$

where $\mathrm{Sc}^l = \overline{\rho\nu}_\infty/D$ (Sc^t) is the laminar (turbulent) Schmidt number for binary mixing with coefficient D. The stagnation enthalpy $\tilde{H}$ for the multispecies flow is defined as

$$\tilde{H} \equiv \sum_\alpha \tilde{h}^\alpha \tilde{Y}^\alpha + \tfrac{1}{2}\tilde{u}_i\tilde{u}_i \qquad (7.74)$$

where $\tilde{h}^\alpha$ is the mass-averaged enthalpy, defined to include the heat of formation h_0^α as

$$\tilde{h}^\alpha \equiv \int c_p \, dT + h_0^\alpha \qquad (7.75)$$

where c_p is the frozen specific heat and T is temperature. With these definitions, the 3DPNS energy equation (7.12) takes the specific form

$$L^P(\bar{\rho}\tilde{H}) = \frac{\partial}{\partial x_1}(\bar{\rho}\tilde{u}_1\tilde{H}) + \frac{\partial}{\partial x_l}\left[\bar{\rho}\tilde{u}_l\tilde{H} - \frac{\bar{\rho}\nu^e}{\mathrm{Re\,Pr}}\frac{\partial \tilde{H}}{\partial x_l} - \frac{U_\infty^2}{H_\infty}\frac{1-\mathrm{Pr}}{\mathrm{Pr}}\frac{\bar{\rho}\nu^e}{2\,\mathrm{Re}}\frac{\partial(\tilde{u}_i\tilde{u}_i)}{\partial x_l}\right.$$

$$\left. - \frac{\mathrm{Sc}-\mathrm{Pr}}{\mathrm{Sc\,Pr\,Re}}\bar{\rho}\nu^e \sum_\alpha \tilde{h}^\alpha \frac{\partial \tilde{Y}^\alpha}{\partial x_l}\right] \qquad (7.76)$$

where the effective Prandtl number Pr is defined according to the form of (7.73), and $\mathrm{Pr}^l \equiv c_p\overline{\rho\nu}/\kappa$. Finally, using Dalton's law and assuming each species behaves as a perfect gas, the gas constant $\bar{R}$ for the equation of state is defined as

$$\bar{R} \equiv R \sum_\alpha \frac{\tilde{Y}^\alpha}{W^\alpha} \qquad (7.77)$$

where R is the universal gas constant and W^α the molecular weight of the species α.

The analysis of a reacting flow requires a closure model for the chemical reactions. For the scram-jet combustor, Zelazny et al. (1976) conducted analyses using two models. The more complicated model assumes combustion is an equilibrium state among the reactions

$$\begin{aligned} &2H + O \rightleftharpoons H_2O \qquad 2H \rightleftharpoons H_2 \qquad 2O \rightleftharpoons O_2 \\ &H + O \rightleftharpoons OH \qquad N_2 + 2O \rightleftharpoons 2NO \end{aligned} \tag{7.78}$$

The equilibrium composition of the combustion by-products is determined by applying the law of mass action (Lee and Sears, 1978), to the equation system (7.78). This yields definition of a set of equilibrium constants κ, which for the elementary reaction $n\mathrm{A} + m\mathrm{B} \rightleftharpoons l\mathrm{C}$, are expressed in terms of mole fractions X^{α} as

$$\kappa \equiv \frac{[X^A]^n [X^B]^m}{[X^C]^l} \tag{7.79}$$

The combination of (7.78)-(7.79) with conservation of elemental and total mass yields a nonlinear algebraic equation system for solution of X^{α} as

$$[\mathrm{N}_{\alpha\beta}]\,\{X^{\alpha}\} = \{f_{\beta}\} \tag{7.80}$$

In (7.80), the elements of $[N_{\alpha\beta}]$ account for the distribution of the particular species mole fraction X^{α} containing the βth elemental constituent, e.g., O, H, and N. The elements of $\{f_{\beta}\}$ are constants, and (7.80) must be iteratively solved to convergence at every node coordinate of the discretization $\cup R_e^2$.

A much less expensive model, from the standpoint of computer CPU, employs the concept of complete combustion to the extinction of either reactant. This model, which yields an upper limit on the effect of heat release at the nodes of $\cup R_e^2$, replaces (7.78) with the elementary reaction

$$H_2 + \tfrac{1}{2}O_2 \rightarrow H_2O \tag{7.81}$$

Hence, H_2 reacts to the limit with the available O_2 to form water. Assuming the simple relationship for specific heat, $c_p = a + bT$, where a and b are coefficients dependent upon the specific heats of pure hydrogen and air, (7.75) can be solved directly for temperature in terms of $\widetilde{H}$ and $\bar{p}$.

Zelazny et al. (1976) report the pseudo-3DPNS solutions for the hydrogen fueled scram-jet configuration shown in Fig. 7.24. The elementary turbulent viscosity model (7.29)-(7.30) was utilized with the van Driest wall damping function. No computation of Reynolds stress was made, and the distribution of particular pressure was assumed null. Hence, the composite pressure field was constituted solely of p_c, which was approximated in a noniterative manner using (7.19)-(7.21). The continuity constraint algorithm form had not yet been derived; the continuity equation (7.1) was solved directly for $\tilde{u}_2$ and $\tilde{u}_3 \equiv 0$.

However, even with these consequential assumptions, the 3DPNS complete reaction simulations did provide detailed prediction of the turbulent mixing and reaction processes that were in qualitative agreement with the available experimental data. The solution domains are illustrated in Fig. 7.25, and the requirement was to assess the significant impact of perpendicular versus parallel hydrogen injection. No

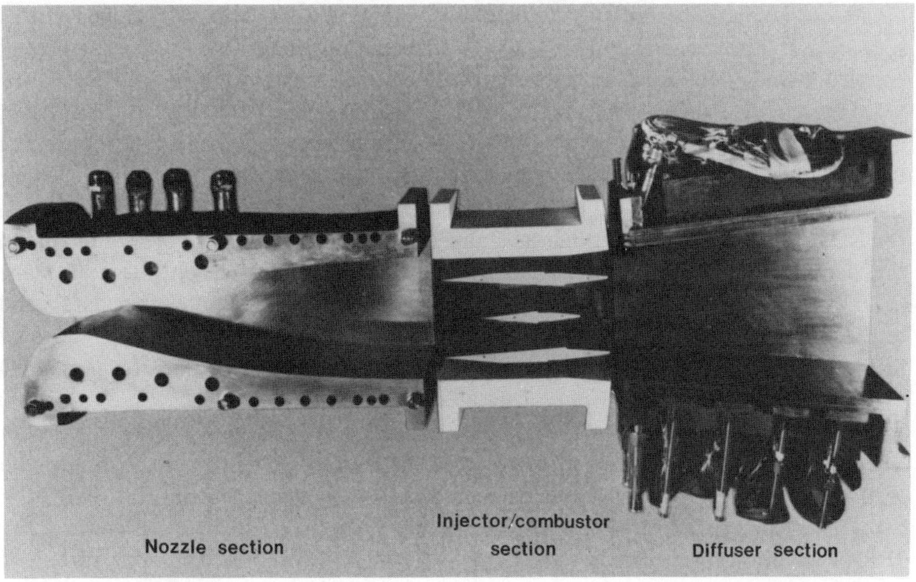

Figure 7.24 Scramjet combustor model.

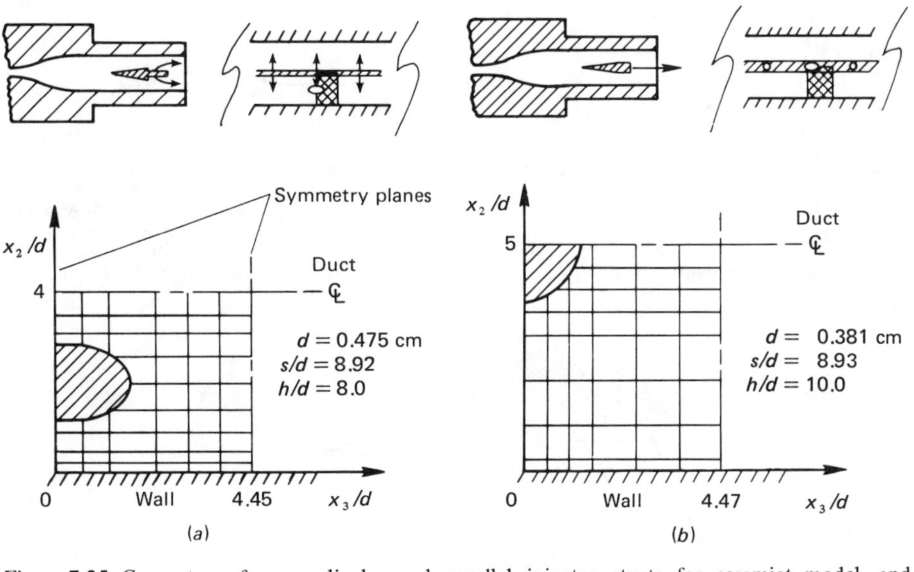

Figure 7.25 Geometry of perpendicular and parallel injector struts for scramjet model, and companion 3DPNS solution domains. (*a*) Perpendicular injection strut design; (*b*) parallel injection strut design.

data were available to initiate the solutions; therefore, the various developed virtual source and turbulent boundary layer initialization techniques were employed, coupled with model constant adjustment based upon comparison to cold flow data.

Figure 7.26*a* summarizes the 3DPNS solution, in terms of the traces of maximum hydrogen mass fraction downstream as a function of injection mode. The turbulent mixing, hence rate of combustion of hydrogen, is considerably slower for the parallel injection, as expected. Figure 7.26*b*–*c* compares the 3DPNS solution results to the available experimental data, limited to wall pressure measurements in the duct, and hydrogen equivalence ratio ϕ on the center line at the exit plane ($x_1/D = 150$) across one-half a jet. The solid symbols denote the data, and qualitative agreement with the predictions is indicated. In particular, the range of 3DPNS equivalence ratio computed for parallel injection is twice that for perpendicular, in agreement with the range of data.

Figure 7.27 illustrates the initial condition distributions, and maximum levels, for the 3DPNS perpendicular jet simulation, as surface elevations on the grid plane. Note the momentum defect and large gradients about the hydrogen core, and the existence of the (cold) wall. Figures 7.28–7.31 summarize the 3DPNS solutions for mean velocity $\tilde{u}_1$, hydrogen mass fraction Y^α turbulent

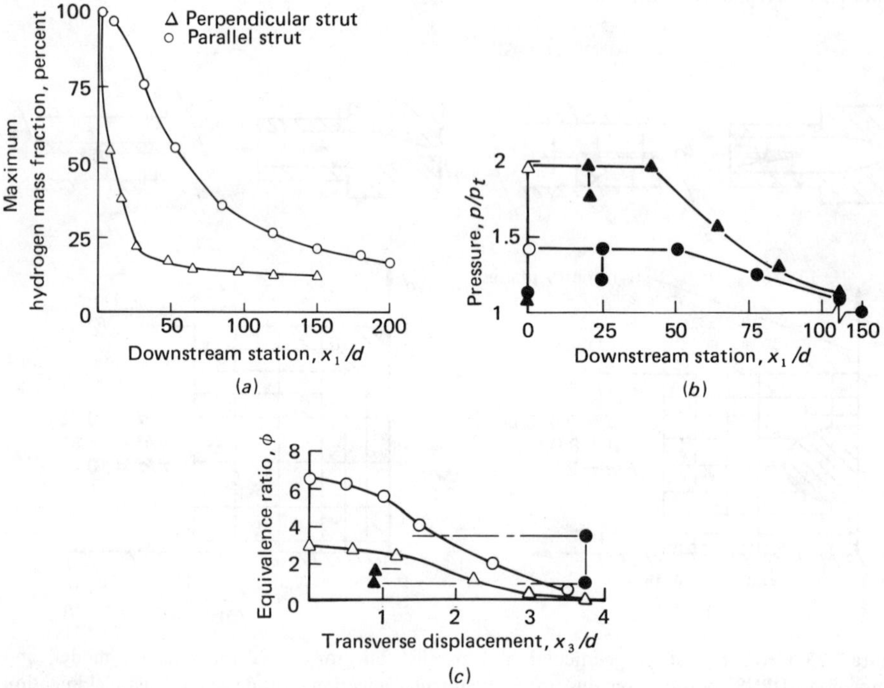

Figure 7.26 Summary of approximate 3DPNS solution for complete reaction hydrogen injection, parallel and perpendicular injectors, $M_\infty = 4.0$. (*a*) Trajectory of maximum hydrogen mass fraction; (*b*) pressure comparison; solid symbols are experimental data; (*c*) equivalence ratio comparison; solid symbols are experimental data.

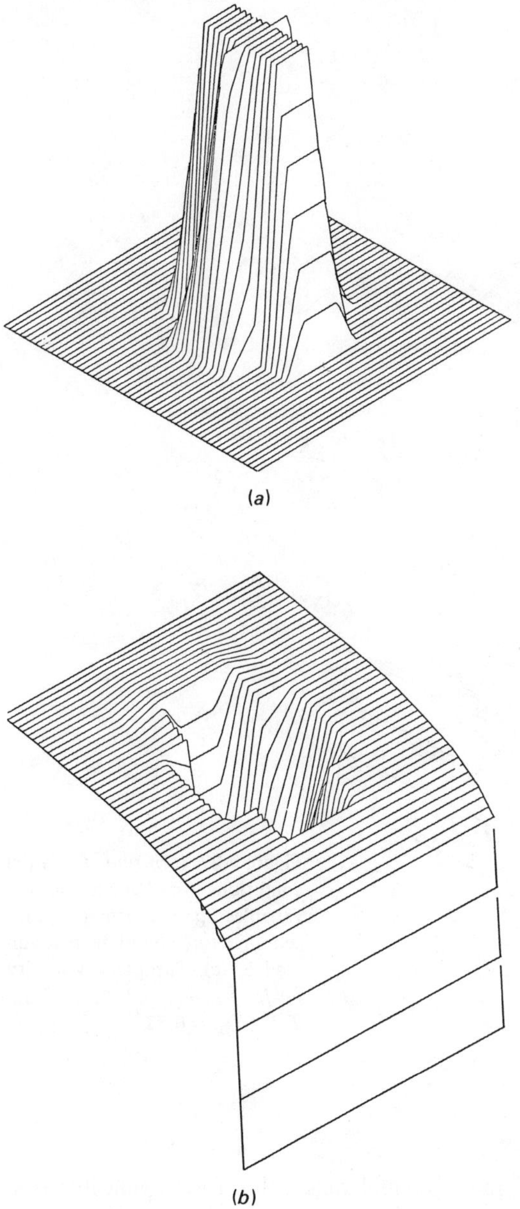

(a)

(b)

Figure 7.27 Initial conditions for 3DPNS solution variables, perpendicular hydrogen injector, complete reaction model. (*a*) Hydrogen mass friction $\widetilde{Y}^{\alpha}$; (*b*) downstream velocity $\widetilde{u}_1/u_{\infty}$.

viscosity $\bar{\rho}\nu_t$ and temperature T/T_0 at downstream stations $x_1/D = 10$ and $x_1/D = 40$. The high temperature region surrounding the fuel-rich core is clearly evident, as is the impact of the cold (water cooled) wall. While these results were obtained using a highly simplified version of the complete 3DPNS algorithm, they graphically illustrate the very complicated flow-field analysis amenable to a parabolized Navier-Stokes equation simulation.

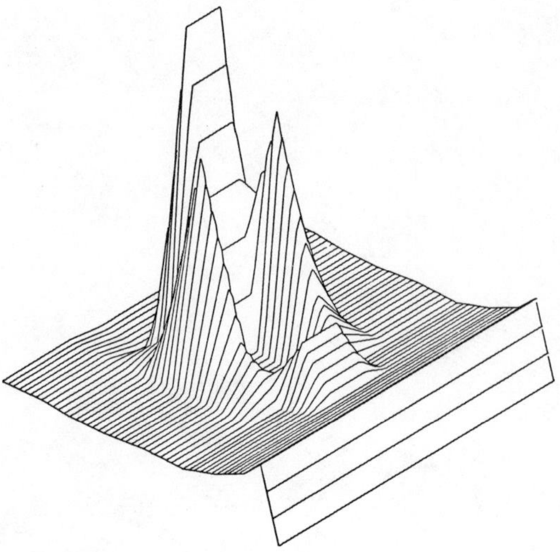

(c)

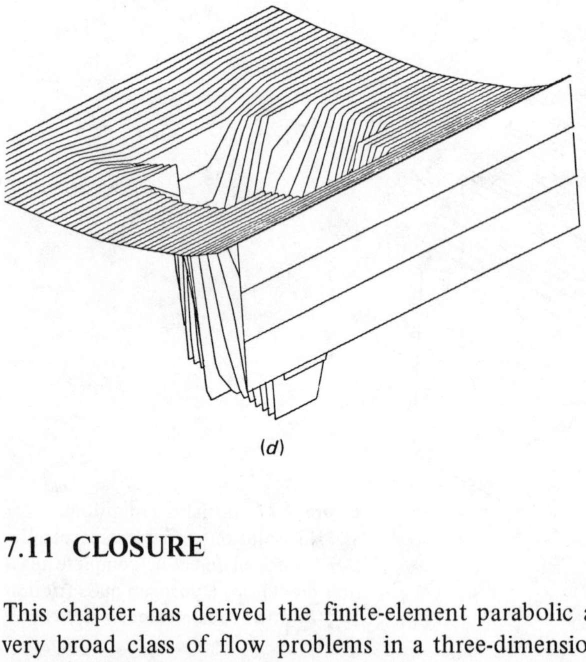

(d)

Figure 7.27 (*Continued*) Initial conditions for 3DPNS solution variables, perpendicular hydrogen injector, complete reaction model. (*c*) Turbulent viscosity $\bar{\rho}\nu^t/\rho_\infty\bar{\nu}_\infty; \bar{\rho}\nu^t_m = 10^4$. (*d*) Tem- T/T_0; $T_m = 0.52$.

7.11 CLOSURE

This chapter has derived the finite-element parabolic algorithm form applicable to a very broad class of flow problems in a three-dimensional specification. For the first time, a consequentially complete order of magnitude analysis exists to validate the concept and limitations of the parabolic analysis concept. The dominant first order effects of the nonparabolic continuity equation are cast into a mathematically robust algorithm formulation involving the concepts of a penalty function differential constraint. A Reynolds stress turbulence closure model is established and verified for the three-dimensional problem statement. The theoretical statements

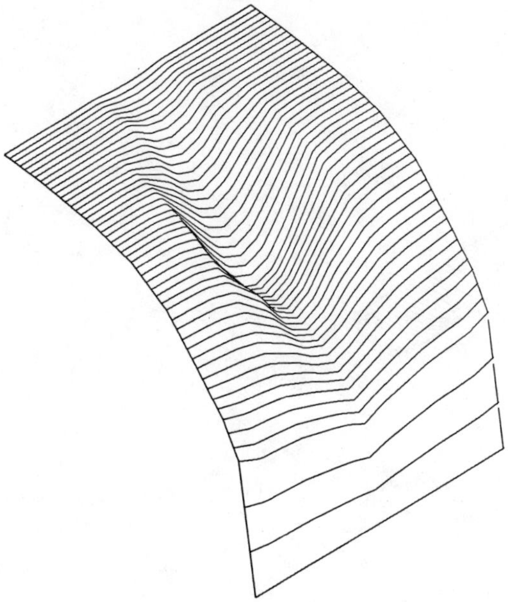

(a)

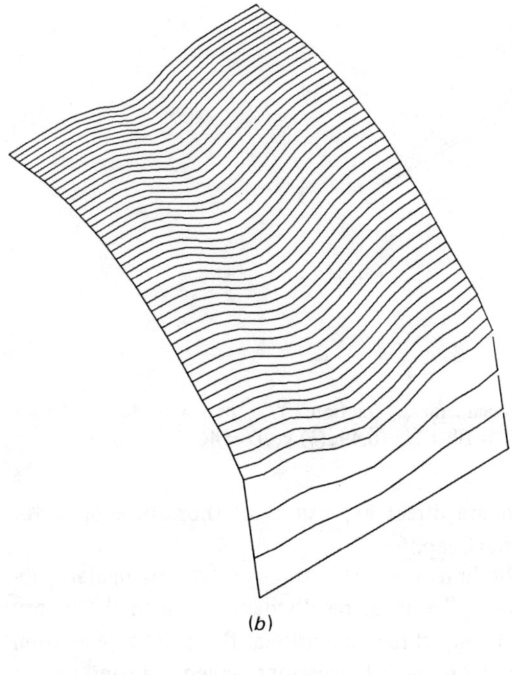

(b)

Figure 7.28 3DPNS solution distributions for mean velocity $\tilde{u}_1$, perpendicular hydrogen injection, complete reaction model. (*a*) $x_1/D = 10$, $\tilde{u}_1^m = 0.99$; (*b*) $x_1/D = 40$, $\tilde{u}_1^m = 0.98$.

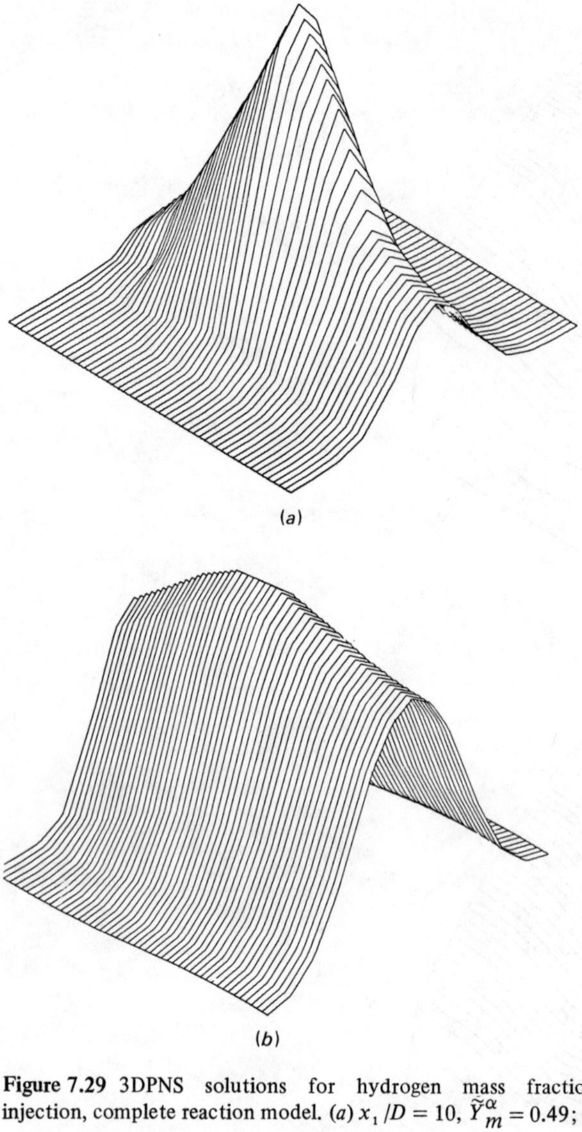

Figure 7.29 3DPNS solutions for hydrogen mass fraction $\widetilde{Y}^{\alpha}$, perpendicular hydrogen injection, complete reaction model. (*a*) $x_1/D = 10$, $\widetilde{Y}_m^{\alpha} = 0.49$; (*b*) $x_1/D = 40$, $\widetilde{Y}_m^{\alpha} = 0.19$.

underlying the algorithm formulation are direct extensions of those developed for the two-dimensional parabolic algorithm (Chap. 6).

Using the most elementary embodiment of the theory, i.e., triangular subdomains spanned by $\{N_1\}$, crucial proof-of-concept results have validated the theory and algorithm construction for several fully three-dimensional flows. The generation of axial vortex structures has occurred on several occasions, when appropriate for comparison to theory and/or experimental data. The algorithm is particularly robust concerning satisfaction of continuity, to the extent that analyses can be performed in fully, semi-, and nonbounded solution domains. Certainly, the next few years will see refinements of the basic algorithm concept, and a wide variety of applications to realistic problems. Our attention now turns to the complete Navier-Stokes equations.

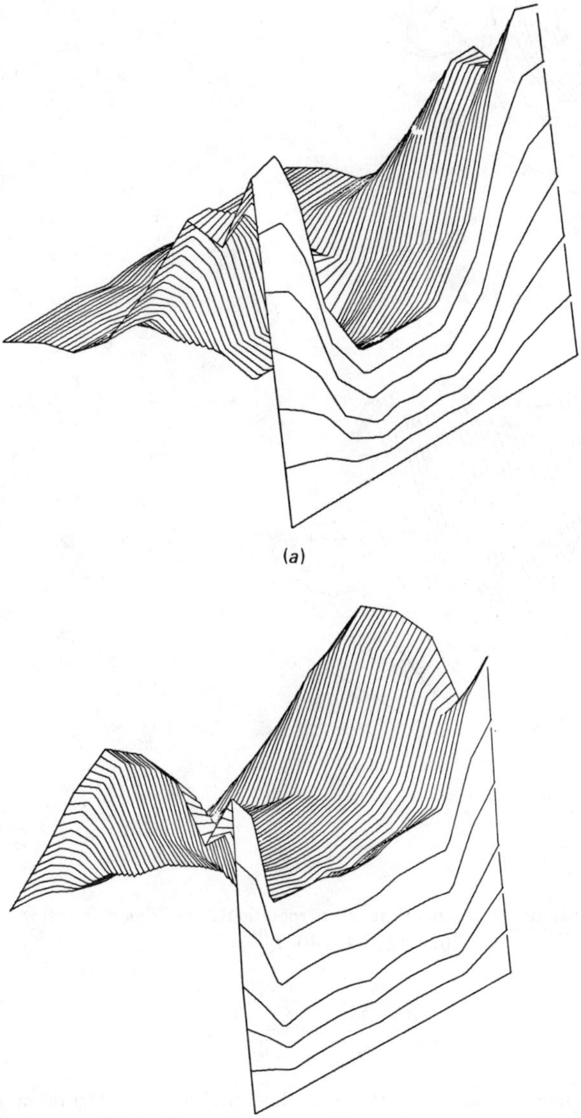

(a)

(b)

Figure 7.30 3DPNS solution distributions of turbulent viscosity $\bar{\rho}\nu^t$, perpendicular hydrogen injection, complete reaction model. (*a*) $x_1/D = 10$, $\bar{\rho}\nu^t_m = 2.6 \times 10^3$; (*b*) $x_1/D = 40$, $\bar{\rho}\nu^t_m = 10^3$.

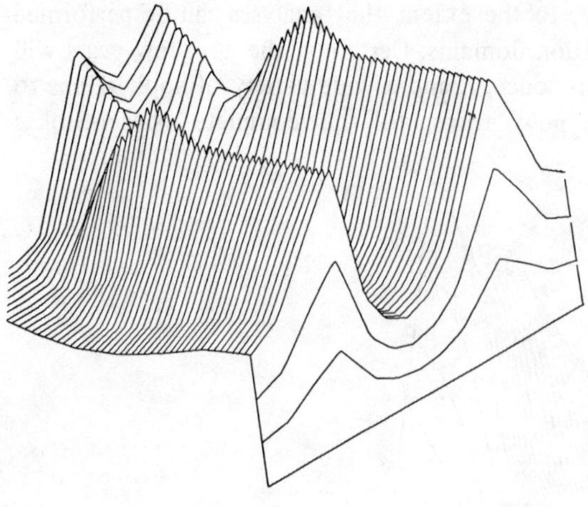

(*a*)

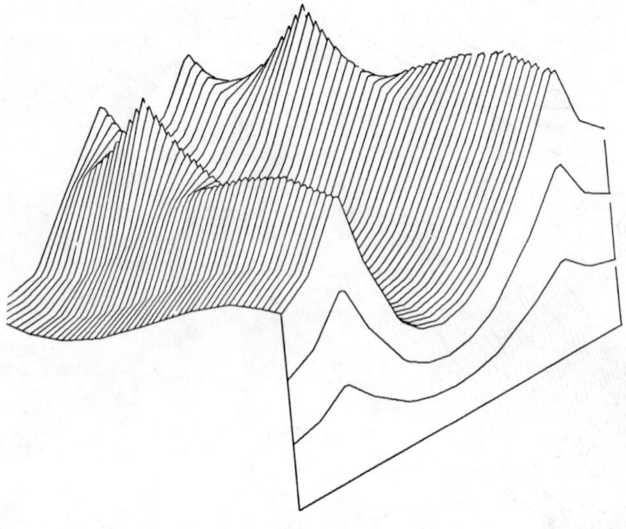

(*b*)

Figure 7.31 3DPNS solution distributions of temperature T, perpendicular hydrogen injection, complete reaction model. (*a*) $x_1/D = 20$, $T^m = 1.76$; (*b*) $x_1/D = 40$, $T^m = 1.92$.

REFERENCES

Baker, A. J., Manhardt, P. D., and Orzechowski, J. A. (1979). A Numerical Solution Algorithm for Prediction of Turbulent Aerodynamic Corner Flows, AIAA Paper No. 79-0073.

Baker, A. J., Yu, J. C., Orzechowski, J. A., and Gatski, T. B. (1982). Prediction and Measurement of Incompressible Turbulent Aerodynamic Trailing Edge Flows, *AIAA J.*, vol. 20, no. 1, pp. 51–59.

Baker, A. J. and Orzechowski, J. A. (1981). A Continuity Constraint Finite Element Algorithm for Three-Dimensional Parabolic Flow Prediction, ASME Publication, *Computers in Flow Predictions and Fluid Dynamics Experiments,* pp. 103–118.

Baker, A. J. and Orzechowski, J. A. (1982). A Numerical Interaction Algorithm for Three-Dimensional Subsonic Turbulent Juncture Region Flow, AIAA Paper No. 82-0100.

Baker, A. J., Orzechowski, J. A., and Stungis, G. E. (1983). Prediction of Secondary Vortex Flowfields Induced by Multiple Free-Jets Issuing in Close Proximity, AIAA Paper No. 83-0289.

Beach, H. L., Jr. (1976). Hydrogen-Fueled Scram-Jets: Potential for Detailed Combustor Analysis, NASA Rept. CP-2001, vol. 4, pp. 1629–1639.

Bragg, G. M. (1969). The Turbulent Boundary Layer in a Corner, *J. Fluid Mech.,* vol. 36, pt. 3, pp. 485–503.

Briley, W. R. (1974). Numerical Method for Predicting Three-Dimensional Steady Viscous Flow in Ducts, *J. Comp. Phys.,* vol. 14, pp. 8–28.

Briley, W. R. and McDonald, H. (1979). Analysis and Computation of Viscous Subsonic Primary and Secondary Flows, AIAA Paper No. 79-1453.

Cebeci, T. and Smith, A. M. O. (1974). *Analysis of Turbulent Boundary Layers,* Academic Press, New York.

Dodge, P. R. (1976). A Numerical Method for 2-D and 3-D Viscous Flows, AIAA Paper No. 76-425.

Eichelbrenner, E. A. and Preston, J. H. (1971). On a Role of Secondary Flow in Turbulent Boundary Layers in Corners (and Salients), *J. Meca.,* vol. 10, no. 1, pp. 91–112.

Gessner, F. B. (1973). The Origin of Secondary Flow in Turbulent Flow Along a Corner, *J. Fluid Mech.,* vol. 58, pt. 1, pp. 1–25.

Gessner, F. B. and Emery, A. F. (1976). A Reynolds Stress Model for Turbulent Corner Flows, I: Development of the Model, *J. Fluid Eng., Trans. ASME,* pp. 261–268.

Ghia, U., Ghia, K. N., and Studerus, C. J. (1976). A Study of Three-Dimensional Laminar Incompressible Flow in Ducts, AIAA Paper No. 76-424.

Hanjalíc, K. and Launder, B. E. (1972). A Reynolds Stress Model for Turbulence and Its Application to Thin Shear Flows, *J. Fluid Mech.,* vol. 52, pt. 4, pp. 609–638.

Hess, J. L. (1972). Calculation of Potential Flow About Arbitrary Three-Dimensional Lifting Bodies, McDonald Douglas Rept. MDC J5679-01.

Launder, B. E., Reece, G. J., and Rodi, W. (1975). Progress in the Development of a Reynolds-Stress Turbulence Closure, *J. Fluid Mech.,* vol. 68, pt. 3, pp. 537–566.

Lee, J. F. and Sears, F. W. (1978). *Thermodynamics,* Addison-Wesley, Reading, Ma.

Levy, R., McDonald, H., Briley, W. R., and Kreskovsky, J. P. (1980). A Three-Dimensional Turbulent Compressible Subsonic Duct Flow Analysis for Use with Constructed Coordinate Systems, AIAA Paper No. 80-1398.

Lumley, J. L. (1970). Toward a Turbulent Constitutive Relation, *J. Fluid Mech.,* vol. 41, pt. 2, pp. 413–434.

Melling, A. and Whitelaw, J. H. (1976). Turbulent Flow in a Rectangular Duct, *J. Fluid Mech.,* vol. 78, pt. 2, pp. 289–315.

Morkovin, M. V. (1964). Effects of Compressibility on Turbulent Flow, in Favre and Breach (eds.), *The Mechanics of Turbulence.*

Pal, A. and Rubin, S. G. (1971). Asymptotic Features of Viscous Flow Along a Corner, *Quart. Appl. Math.,* vol. 27, pp. 99–108.

Patankar, S. V. and Spalding, D. B. (1970). *Heat and Mass Transfer in Boundary Layers,* 2d ed., International Text, London.

Patankar, S. V. and Spalding, D. B. (1972). A Calculation Procedure for Heat, Mass and Momentum Transfer in Three-Dimensional Parabolic Flows, *Int. J. Heat Mass Transfer,* vol. 15, pp. 1787–1806.

Patankar, S. V. (1980). *Numerical Heat Transfer and Fluid Flow,* Hemisphere, Washington, D.C.

Pratap, V. S. and Spalding, D. B. (1975). Numerical Computations of the Flow in Curved Ducts, *Aero. Quart.,* vol. 26, pp. 12–22.

Rodi, W. (1981). Progress in Turbulence Modeling for Incompressible Flows, AIAA Paper No. 81-0045.

Rubin, S. G. (1966). Incompressible Flow Along a Corner, *J. Fluid Mech.*, vol. 26, pt. 1, pp. 97–110.

Rubin, S. G. and Grossman, B. (1971). Viscous Flow Along the Corner: Numerical Solution of the Corner Layer Equations, *Quart. Appl. Math.*, vol. 29, no. 2, pp. 169–186.

Schlichting, H. (1979), *Boundary Layer Theory,* 7th ed., McGraw-Hill, New York.

Shabaka, I. M. M. A. and Bradshaw, P. (1981). Turbulent Flow Measurement in an Idealized Wing/Body Juncture, *AIAA J.*, vol. 19, no. 2, pp. 131–132.

Shafir, M. and Rubin, S. G. (1976). The Turbulent Boundary Layer Near a Corner, *J. Appl. Mech.*, 76-APM-PP.

Schetz, J. A. (1980). *Injection and Mixing in Turbulent Flow, Progress in Astronautics and Aeronautics,* vol. 68, AIAA, New York.

Tokuda, N. (1972). Viscous Flow Near a Corner in Three Dimensions, *J. Fluid Mech.*, vol. 53, pt. 1, pp. 129–148.

Weinberg, B. C. and Rubin, S. G. (1972). Compressible Corner Flow, *J. Fluid Mech.*, vol. 56, pt. 4, pp. 753–774.

Zamir, M. and Young, A. D. (1970). Experimental Investigation of the Boundary Layer in a Streamwise Corner, *J. Aero. Quart.*, vol. 21, pp. 313–339.

Zelazny, S. W., Baker, A. J., and Rushmore, W. L. (1976). Modeling of Three-Dimensional Mixing and Reacting Ducted Flows, NASA Report No. CR-2661.

CHAPTER

EIGHT

GENERAL THREE-DIMENSIONAL FLOW

8.1 INTRODUCTION

The first seven chapters of this text examine the essential aspects of finite-element semidiscrete approximation procedures applied to progressively more complete differential equation descriptions in fluid mechanics. In each instance, the basic Navier-Stokes equation system, governing completely general flow fields in three-dimensional configurations, was simplified by enforcing assumptions that restricted certain physical and/or geometric aspects. This chapter presents the finite-element algorithm construction for the complete three-dimensional Navier-Stokes equations governing compressible, turbulent flow fields.

The discipline pacing the development of algorithms for computational fluid dynamics (CFD) applications, for the general problem description, has been aerodynamics. The true "workhorse" of the CFD aerodynamics community over the past decade has been the MacCormack algorithm, originally published in 1969 (MacCormack, 1969)–and variations thereof. This is due principally to the ultimate simplicity of this explicit, predictor-corrector algorithm, and its proven track record for prediction of compressible, supersonic inviscid flow fields. In the split-operator construction, the programming requirements are elementary, and the resultant code runs quite economically. The basic theoretical formulation enjoys continuing refinement, including application to the viscous Navier-Stokes equations (MacCormack, 1977, 1981). In this instance, the added discretization refinement required to resolve wall layers "stiffens" the resulting discretized equation system. For an elementary explicit algorithm (recall Chap. 4), the integration absolute stability interval is bounded by a multiple of the largest eigenvalue of the discretized system matrix, thus yielding the requirement to time march using a very small step size.

For this reason and for its own merit, recent CFD research has turned to development of implicit Navier-Stokes algorithms. Simply stated, one trades the small time-step restriction for the requirement to solve matrix equation systems. As a result, principal attention has focused on matrix factorization procedures that reduce large sparse matrices to block-banded forms, to permit running solutions on present computer systems. The approximate-factorization, implicit finite-difference (AFFD) Navier-Stokes algorithms of Beam and Warming (1978) and Briley and McDonald (1977) exemplify the concept. The numerics are typically second-order accurate in space, first order in (pseudo-) time, and may employ both implicit and/or explicit artificial diffusion to control perceived instabilities. In the favored noniterative *delta* formulation, the matrix solution procedure constitutes acceptance of the first iterate of the Newton algorithm, using an approximation to the true matrix system jacobian constructed upon addition of the identity matrix.

An integral ingredient of the AFFD algorithm construction has been definition and use of the "generalized coordinates" description. Basically, the divergence operator in the Navier-Stokes equation set is transformed into scalar components parallel to principal coordinates of a coordinate transformation "regularizing" the boundary ∂R of the solution domain R^n to the unit square (or cube, $n = 3$). Thompson and coworkers (Thames et al., 1977) pioneered the numerical transformation concept. Steger and Pulliam (1980) first reported results using the generalized coordinates AFFD algorithm concept for a two-dimensional cascade flow; topical results were recently summarized by Steger (1981).

In this chapter, we develop the finite-element algorithm for the problem class, that embraces as special cases the essential features of the AFFD algorithm. The basic finite-element theoretical statement is essentially identical to the dissipative, Galerkin weighted residuals algorithm derived in Chaps. 4 and 5, but generalized for a multidependent variable vector. The embedded dissipation parameter set β_α is generalized and optimized for the problem class. The entire algorithm statement is then recast into the generalized coordinates framework, which facilitates construction of the tensor matrix product approximation to the Newton iteration algorithm jacobian while retaining complete geometrical versatility. The remaining sections of this chapter quantize developmental aspects and document key numerical results regarding accuracy and convergence character.

8.2 THREE-DIMENSIONAL NAVIER-STOKES EQUATIONS

The partial differential equation set governing three-dimensional laminar and/or turbulent flow of a compressible, heat-conducting fluid is the familiar and very nonlinear Navier-Stokes system. In nondimensional divergence form, and using cartesian tensor summation notation, the equation set governing conservation of mass, momentum, and energy is

$$L(\rho) = \frac{\partial \rho}{\partial t} + \frac{\partial}{\partial x_j}(u_j \rho) = 0 \tag{8.1}$$

$$L(\rho u_i) = \frac{\partial(\rho u_i)}{\partial t} + \frac{\partial}{\partial x_j}(u_j \rho u_i + p\delta_{ij} - \sigma_{ij}) = 0 \tag{8.2}$$

$$L(\rho e) = \frac{\partial(\rho e)}{\partial t} + \frac{\partial}{\partial x_j}(u_j \rho e + u_j p - \sigma_{ij} u_i - q_j) = 0 \tag{8.3}$$

In (8.1)-(8.3), ρ is density, $\rho u_i \equiv m_i$ is the momentum vector, p is pressure, and e is mass specific total energy. The equation of state, for a polytropic gas $p = (\gamma - 1)\rho\epsilon$, is

$$L(p) = p - (\gamma - 1)(\rho e - \tfrac{1}{2} m_j u_j) = 0 \tag{8.4}$$

The Stokes viscous stress tensor σ_{ij}, and heat flux vector q_j in terms of the specific internal energy ϵ, are defined as

$$\sigma_{ij} = \frac{\mu}{\text{Re}}\left(\frac{\partial u_i}{\partial x_j} + \frac{\partial u_j}{\partial x_i}\right) - \frac{2\mu}{3\,\text{Re}}\frac{\partial u_k}{\partial x_k}\delta_{ij} \tag{8.5}$$

$$q_j = -\kappa \frac{\partial \epsilon}{\partial x_j} \tag{8.6}$$

$$\epsilon = e - \tfrac{1}{2} u_i u_i \tag{8.7}$$

where μ is the absolute viscosity, κ is the coefficient of heat conductivity, δ_{ij} is the Kronecker delta, and Re is the reference Reynolds number.

The Euler equations, governing three-dimensional inviscid flows, are contained within (8.1)-(8.4), i.e., (8.5)-(8.6) vanish identically. The equation set (8.1)-(8.4) is also representative of the mass-weighted, time-averaged Navier-Stokes equations for a turbulent flow (Cebeci and Smith, 1974, Chap. 2). The dependent variables are interpreted as descriptors of the time-averaged mean flow, and σ_{ij} is generalized to include nonvanishing correlations of subgrid scale phenomena. In this instance, the total stress tensor becomes

$$\sigma_{ij} \equiv \bar{\sigma}_{ij} - \overline{\rho u_i' u_j'} \tag{8.8}$$

where $-\overline{\rho u_i' u_j'}$ is the dynamic Reynolds stress tensor, and $\bar{\sigma}_{ij}$ denotes the time-averaged form of (8.5). The exact differential equation system governing the dynamic Reynolds stress tensor is (Marvin, 1982)

$$\begin{aligned} L(\overline{\rho u_i' u_k'}) = {} & \frac{\partial}{\partial t}(\overline{\rho u_i' u_k'}) + \frac{\partial}{\partial x_j}(\tilde{u}_j \overline{\rho u_i' u_k'}) + \overline{\rho u_i' u_j'}\frac{\partial \tilde{u}_k}{\partial x_j} + \overline{\rho u_k' u_j'}\frac{\partial \tilde{u}_i}{\partial x_j} + \frac{\partial}{\partial x_j}(\overline{\rho u_i' u_k' u_j'}) \\ & + \frac{\partial}{\partial x_k}(\overline{u_i' p}) + \frac{\partial}{\partial x_i}(\overline{u_k' p}) - \overline{p\left(\frac{\partial u_k'}{\partial x_i} + \frac{\partial u_i'}{\partial x_k}\right)} - \frac{\partial}{\partial x_j}(\overline{u_k' \sigma_{ij}}) \\ & - \frac{\partial}{\partial x_j}(\overline{u_i' \sigma_{kj}}) + \overline{\sigma_{ij}\frac{\partial u_k'}{\partial x_j}} + \overline{\sigma_{kj}\frac{\partial u_i'}{\partial x_j}} = 0 \end{aligned} \tag{8.9}$$

In (8.9), the mass weighted time-averaged velocity is defined as

$$\tilde{u}_i = \frac{\overline{\rho u_i}}{\bar{\rho}} \tag{8.10}$$

and the instantaneous velocity is assumed of the form

$$u_i(x_j, t) \equiv \tilde{u}_i(x_j, t) + u_i'(x_j, t) \tag{8.11}$$

The trace of the stress tensor $-\overline{\rho u_i' u_j'}$ defines the time-averaged turbulence kinetic energy $\bar{k}$

$$\bar{k} \equiv \frac{1}{2\bar{\rho}} \overline{\rho u_i' u_i'} \tag{8.12}$$

The corresponding transport equation for $\bar{k}$ is established from (8.9) as (Marvin, 1982)

$$L(\bar{\rho}\bar{k}) = \frac{\partial}{\partial t}(\bar{\rho}\bar{k}) + \frac{\partial}{\partial x_j}(\bar{\rho}\tilde{u}_j\bar{k}) + \overline{\rho u_i' u_k'} \frac{\partial \tilde{u}_i}{\partial x_k} + \frac{\partial}{\partial x_j}(\overline{\rho u_i' u_i' u_j'})$$
$$+ \frac{\partial}{\partial x_i}(\overline{u_i' p}) - \overline{p \frac{\partial u_i'}{\partial x_i}} - \frac{\partial}{\partial x_j}(\overline{u_i' \sigma_{ij}}) + \overline{\sigma_{ij} \frac{\partial u_i'}{\partial x_j}} = 0 \tag{8.13}$$

For flow fields with associated Mach numbers though modest supersonic, the larger scale motion is statistically coupled to the thermal field almost exclusively through mean values of density, viscosity, and conductivity (Morkovin, 1964). Hence, for many flows of practical interest, it may be sufficient to assume

$$\overline{\rho u_i' u_j'} \equiv \bar{\rho}\overline{u_i' u_j'} \tag{8.14}$$

Assuming the validity of (8.14), the corresponding differential equation for the kinematic Reynolds stress tensor $-\overline{u_i' u_j'}$ is established from (8.9) and (8.14) in the form

$$L(\overline{u_i' u_j'}) = \frac{\partial}{\partial t}(\overline{u_i' u_j'}) + \frac{\partial}{\partial x_k}(\tilde{u}_k \overline{u_i' u_j'}) + \left(\overline{u_j' u_k'} \frac{\partial \tilde{u}_i}{\partial x_k} + \overline{u_i' u_k'} \frac{\partial \tilde{u}_j}{\partial x_k}\right) + 2\bar{\nu}\, \overline{\frac{\partial u_i'}{\partial x_k}\frac{\partial u_j'}{\partial x_k}}$$
$$+ \overline{\frac{p}{\rho}\left(\frac{\partial u_i'}{\partial x_j'} + \frac{\partial u_j'}{\partial x_i}\right)} + \frac{\partial}{\partial x_k}\left[\overline{u_i' u_j' u_k'} - \nu \frac{\partial \overline{u_i' u_j'}}{\partial x_k} + \overline{\frac{p}{\rho}(\delta_{jk} u_i' + \delta_{ik} u_j')}\right] = 0$$
$$\tag{8.15}$$

where $\bar{\nu} \equiv \bar{u}/\bar{\rho}$ is the time-averaged kinematic viscosity.

The fourth term in (8.15) defines the mechanism for viscous dissipation of the kinematic Reynolds stress tensor. The scalar, formed by the contraction of this term, is defined as the isotropic dissipation function ϵ

$$\frac{2}{3}\delta_{ij}\epsilon \equiv 2\bar{\nu}\, \overline{\frac{\partial u_i'}{\partial x_k}\frac{\partial u_j'}{\partial x_k}} \tag{8.16}$$

The governing differential equation for the isotropic dissipation function ϵ is modeled after (8.15) (Tennekes and Lumley, 1974) as

$$L(\epsilon) = \frac{\partial \epsilon}{\partial t} + \frac{\partial}{\partial x_j}(\tilde{u}_j \epsilon) + 2\bar{\nu}\, \overline{\frac{\partial u_i'}{\partial x_k}\frac{\partial u_i'}{\partial x_l}\frac{\partial u_k'}{\partial x_l}} + 2\left(\nu \overline{\frac{\partial^2 u_i' u_i'}{\partial x_k \partial x_k}}\right)$$
$$+ \frac{\partial}{\partial x_k}\left(\overline{\bar{\nu} u_k' \frac{\partial u_i'}{\partial x_l}\frac{\partial u_i'}{\partial x_l}} + \overline{\frac{\nu}{\rho}\frac{\partial p}{\partial x_i}\frac{\partial u_k'}{\partial x_i}}\right) = 0 \tag{8.17}$$

The companion transport equation for turbulence kinetic energy function k,

$$k \equiv \tfrac{1}{2}\overline{u_i'u_i'} \tag{8.18}$$

is determined by contracting (8.15), yielding

$$L(k) = \frac{\partial k}{\partial t} + \frac{\partial}{\partial x_j}(\tilde{u}_j k) + \overline{u_i'u_j'}\frac{\partial \tilde{u}_i}{\partial x_j} + \epsilon + \left(\overline{\frac{p}{\rho}\frac{\partial u_i'}{\partial x_i}}\right)$$
$$+ \frac{\partial}{\partial x_j}\left(\overline{u_i'u_i'u_j'} - \nu\frac{\partial k}{\partial x_j} + \frac{\overline{pu_j'}}{\rho}\right) = 0 \tag{8.19}$$

Even with the simplification of (8.14), (8.15)-(8.19) contain more unknowns than available equations, since the various third order correlations are undefined. Additional differential equations could be derived, but each set in turn would contain fourth and higher order correlations as unknowns. Therefore, the typical practice is to model the highest order correlations in the set (8.9)-(8.19). For example, using the procedures of Launder et al. (1975) (see also Hanjalic and Launder, 1972), and assuming validity of (8.14), the two-equation closure system modeling of (8.17) and (8.19) produces the familiar k-ϵ system:

$$L(k) = \frac{\partial k}{\partial t} + \frac{\partial}{\partial x_j}\left[\tilde{u}_j k + \left(C_k\overline{u_i'u_j'}\frac{k}{\epsilon} - \bar{\nu}\delta_{ij}\right)\frac{\partial k}{\partial x_i}\right] + \overline{u_i'u_j'}\frac{\partial \tilde{u}_i}{\partial x_j} + \epsilon = 0 \tag{8.20}$$

$$L(\epsilon) = \frac{\partial \epsilon}{\partial t} + \frac{\partial}{\partial x_j}\left[\tilde{u}_j\epsilon + \left(C_\epsilon\overline{u_i'u_j'}\frac{k}{\epsilon}\right)\frac{\partial \epsilon}{\partial x_i}\right] + C_\epsilon^1\,\overline{u_i'u_j'}\,\frac{\epsilon}{k}\frac{\partial \tilde{u}_i}{\partial x_j} + C_\epsilon^2\frac{\epsilon^2}{k} = 0 \tag{8.21}$$

The standard values of the correlation coefficients C_k and C_ϵ^α, as determined by the analysis of Hanjalic and Launder (1972), are $C_k = 1.0$, $C_\epsilon = 1/1.3$, $C_\epsilon^1 = 1.52$, and $C_\epsilon^2 = 1.92$.

The solution to (8.20)-(8.21), coupled with appropriate boundary condition specifications, yields the distribution of the trace of the kinematic stress tensor $-\overline{u_i'u_j'}$ and ϵ. Therefore, an additional modeling is required to establish the relationship between k and ϵ and $-\overline{u_i'u_j'}$. As presented in Chaps. 6 and 7, one approach which encompasses the bousinesq eddy viscosity model as a special case is the tensor constitutive equation

$$\overline{u_i'u_j'} = C_{\underline{i}}k\delta_{ij} - C_\nu^1\frac{k^2}{\epsilon}\left(\frac{\partial \tilde{u}_i}{\partial x_j} + \frac{\partial \tilde{u}_j}{\partial x_i}\right) - C_\nu^2\frac{k^3}{\epsilon^2}\left(\frac{\partial \tilde{u}_i}{\partial x_l} + \frac{\partial \tilde{u}_l}{\partial x_i}\right)\left(\frac{\partial \tilde{u}_l}{\partial x_j} + \frac{\partial \tilde{u}_j}{\partial x_l}\right) + \cdots \tag{8.22}$$

The various correlations coefficients C_ν^α were defined in Sec. 7.3 [see (7.22)-(7.24)].

The boundary conditions for the equation set (8.1)-(8.22) are a general mixture of Dirichlet and Neumann specifications. On an inflow boundary segment, $\rho, \rho u_i, \rho e$, k, and ϵ are specified, and p is determined from (8.4). For an inviscid streamline (Euler equations on a far-field boundary), the normal derivative of the scalar variables vanish, and ρu_i is constrained to be parallel. For a no-slip aerodynamic surface, $\rho u_i, k$, and ϵ vanish identically, and the normal derivative of ρe is constrained (adiabatic or cooled wall). At an outflow boundary, typically, p is specified and the normal derivative of the remaining dependent variables is constrained.

Problems

1 Establish (8.13) from the trace of (8.9).
2 Derive (8.15) from (8.9) using (8.14).
3 Establish (8.19) using (8.15) and (8.18).

8.3 FINITE-ELEMENT SOLUTION ALGORITHM

Equations (8.1)-(8.22) constitute a general definition of the three-dimensional Navier-Stokes equations. In the limit $\mathrm{Re} \Rightarrow \infty$, (8.5) vanishes identically; assuming that the flow is nonturbulent, (8.1)-(8.4) reduce to the Euler equations governing an inviscid rotational flow. Specifying $m_i \equiv \rho u_i$, $g \equiv \rho e$, define the vector-valued dependent variable set as

$$q_\alpha(x_i, t) \equiv \{q_\alpha\} \equiv \{\rho, m_i, g, p, \sigma_{ij}, q_j, k, \epsilon\} \tag{8.23}$$

Equations (8.1)-(8.3), and (8.20)-(8.21) each constitute an initial-value description of the general form

$$L(q_\alpha) = \frac{\partial q_\alpha}{\partial t} + \frac{\partial}{\partial x_j}(u_j q_\alpha + f_{\alpha j}) + s_\alpha = 0 \tag{8.24}$$

In (8.24), $f_{\alpha j}(q_\beta)$ and $s_\alpha(q_\beta)$ are specific nonlinear functions of their argument, determined by inspection. The remaining algebraic and partial differential equations [cf. (8.4)-(8.7) and (8.22)] are each of the form

$$L(q_\alpha) = q_\alpha + f_\alpha(q_\beta) = 0 \tag{8.25}$$

where the f_α are also determined by inspection. Note in particular that (8.25) is simply a special form of (8.24).

The n-dimensional partial differential equation system (8.24)-(8.25) is defined on the euclidean space R^n, spanned by the $\mathbf{x}$ coordinate system with scalar components x_i, $1 \leqslant i \leqslant n$. The solution domain Ω is defined as the product of R^n and t, for all elements of $\mathbf{x}$ belonging to R^n and all elements of t belonging to the open interval measured from t_0, that is,

$$\Omega = R^n \times t = \{(\mathbf{x}, t) \colon x \in R^n \text{ and } t \in (t_0, t)\} \tag{8.26}$$

The boundary $\partial\Omega$ of the solution domain is the product of the boundary ∂R of R^n, spanned by $\underline{x}$, and t, i.e., $\partial\Omega = \partial R \times t$. Thereupon, the generalized form for a differential boundary constraint is

$$l(q_\alpha) = a_1^\alpha q_\alpha + a_2^\alpha \frac{\partial}{\partial x_j}(q_\alpha \hat{\mathbf{n}}_j) + a_3^\alpha = 0 \tag{8.27}$$

where the a_i^α are specified coefficients and $\hat{\mathbf{n}}_j$ is the outward pointing unit normal vector. Finally, an initial distribution for q_α on $\Omega_0 = R^n \times t_0$ is required; hence,

$$q_\alpha(\mathbf{x}, t_0) = q_\alpha^0(\mathbf{x}) \tag{8.28}$$

The finite-element algorithm for (8.24)-(8.27) is an extension of the original statement given in Secs. 4.10-4.11. The semidiscrete approximation $q_\alpha^h(\mathbf{x}, t)$ to the unknown exact solution $q_\alpha(\mathbf{x}, t)$ is constructed from members of a convenient finite-dimensional subspace of $H_0^1(R)$, the Hilbert space of all functions possessing square integrable first derivatives and satisfying the boundary conditions. The typical practice is to employ polynomials truncated to degree k, and defined on disjoint interior subdomains R_e^n, the union of which forms the discretization of $R^n \equiv \cup R_e^n$. Hence,

$$q_\alpha(\mathbf{x}, t) \approx q_\alpha^h(\mathbf{x}, t) = \sum_{e=1}^{M} q_\alpha^e(\mathbf{x}, t) \tag{8.29}$$

and

$$q_\alpha^e(\mathbf{x}, t) \equiv \{N_k(\mathbf{x})\}^T \{QI(t)\}_e \tag{8.30}$$

In (8.30), the semidiscrete free index "I" denotes q_α^h evaluated at the nodal coordinates of the discretization $\cup R_e^n$ at any time t. The sub- or superscript e denotes pertaining to the eth finite-element domain, $\Omega_e = R_e^n \times t$. The elements of the row matrix $\{N_k(\mathbf{x})\}^T$ are polynomials written on x_j, $1 \leqslant j \leqslant n$, complete to degree k, as discussed in Chap. 3.

The finite-element algorithm statement is the familiar form

$$\int_{R^n} \{N_k\} L(q_\alpha^h)\, d\mathbf{x} + \beta_1 \int_{\partial R} \{N_k\} l(q_\alpha^h)\, d\mathbf{x} + \beta_2 \cdot \int_{R^n} \{N_k\} \nabla L(q_\alpha^h)\, d\mathbf{x} \equiv \{0\} \tag{8.31}$$

Upon definition of k in (8.30), (8.31) is a mixed system of ordinary differential equations written on t, and algebraic equations of the form

$$[C]\{QI\}' + [U]\{QI\} + [FIJ]\{QJ\} + \{SI\} \equiv \{0\} \tag{8.32}$$

As discussed previously, the form of (8.32) suggests use of an implicit integration algorithm. The θ-implicit finite-difference algorithm, where $\theta = \frac{1}{2}$ yields the trapezoidal rule, yields

$$\{FI\} = \{QI\}_{j+1} - \{QI\}_j - \Delta t[\theta\{QI\}'_{j+1} + (1-\theta)\{QI\}'_j] \equiv 0 \tag{8.33}$$

and (8.32) provides the definition of the derivatives $\{QI\}'$. Upon substitution, and proceeding through the algebra, (8.33) becomes a nonlinear algebraic equation system written on $\{QI\}_{j+1}$. The Newton iteration algorithm solution statement is

$$[J(FI)]_{j+1}^p \{\delta QI\}_{j+1}^{p+1} = -\{FI\}_{j+1}^p \tag{8.34}$$

The dependent variable is the iteration vector $\{\delta QI\}$, yielding the solution in the conventional manner.

$$\{QI\}_{j+1}^{p+1} \equiv \{QI\}_{j+1}^p + \{\delta QI\}_{j+1}^{p+1} \tag{8.35}$$

The jacobian of the Newton algorithm is defined as

$$[J(FI)] \equiv \frac{\partial\{FI\}}{\partial\{QJ\}} \tag{8.36}$$

8.4 GENERALIZED COORDINATES FORMULATION

A principal requirement in three-dimensional problem descriptions is to accurately define domain boundary geometries $\partial\Omega$ that are nonregular and perhaps nonsmooth. The term *generalized coordinates* has gained acceptance in describing algorithm statements appropriate for use with regularizing boundary-fitted coordinate transformations, as discussed in Sec. 8.1. Many procedures are available to construct such transformations, including numerical solution of elliptic and hyperbolic partial differential equations, algebraic methods, and finite-element isoparametric interpolation (NASA, 1980).

The output of any of these procedures constitutes definition of the coordinate triples (pairs) on R^3 (R^2) that define the intersections of ∂R_e on Ω, called nodes. The generalized coordinates description requirement is to construct the local coordinate transformation, using these data, that maps $x^i \in R_e^n$ to a regularized domain spanned by an orthonormal coordinate system η_j. Figure 8.1 illustrates the concept, where (•) and (x) depict the nodal coordinates in both spaces. The coordinate transformation is

$$x_i = x_i(\eta_j) \tag{8.37}$$

The explicit form for (8.37) on R_e^n is constructed (recall Sec. 3.6) as

$$x_i = \{N_k^+(\eta)\}^T\{XI\}_e \qquad x_i \in R_e^n \tag{8.38}$$

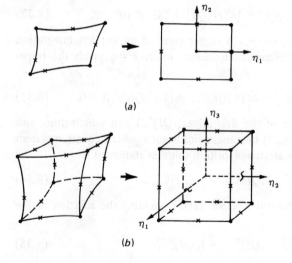

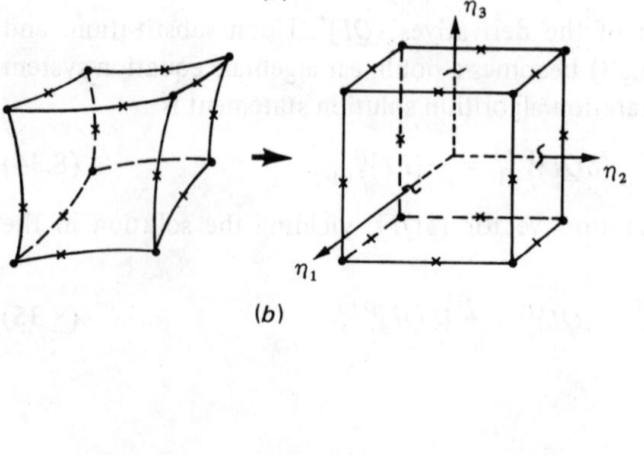

Figure 8.1 Biquadratic cardinal basis coordinate transformation. (*a*) Two-dimensional domain; (*b*) three-dimensional domain.

The elements of the column matrix $\{XI\}_e$ are the coordinates of the nodes of R_e^n, $1 \leqslant (i, I) \leqslant n$, hence $\cup R_e^n$, the global discretization. For convenience, recall on R^2,

$$\{N_1(\eta)\} = \frac{1}{4}\begin{Bmatrix} (1-\eta_1)(1-\eta_2) \\ (1+\eta_1)(1-\eta_2) \\ (1+\eta_1)(1+\eta_2) \\ (1-\eta_1)(1+\eta_2) \end{Bmatrix} \tag{8.39}$$

For a discretization on R^2 using curved-sided serendipity quadrilaterals,

$$\{N_2^+(\eta)\} = \frac{1}{4}\begin{Bmatrix} (1-\eta_1)(1-\eta_2)(-\eta_1-\eta_2-1) \\ (1+\eta_1)(1-\eta_2)(\eta_1-\eta_2-1) \\ (1+\eta_1)(1+\eta_2)(\eta_1+\eta_2-1) \\ (1-\eta_1)(1+\eta_2)(-\eta_1+\eta_2-1) \\ (1-\eta_1^2)(1-\eta_2) \\ (1+\eta_1)(1-\eta_2^2) \\ (1+\eta_1^2)(1+\eta_2) \\ (1-\eta_1)(1+\eta_2^2) \end{Bmatrix} \tag{8.40}$$

For discretization of R^3 employing planar-faced hexahedra,

$$\{N_1^+(\eta)\} = \frac{1}{8}\begin{Bmatrix} (1-\eta_1)(1-\eta_2)(1-\eta_3) \\ (1+\eta_1)(1-\eta_2)(1-\eta_3) \\ (1+\eta_1)(1+\eta_2)(1-\eta_3) \\ (1-\eta_1)(1+\eta_2)(1-\eta_3) \\ (1-\eta_1)(1-\eta_2)(1+\eta_3) \\ (1+\eta_1)(1-\eta_2)(1+\eta_3) \\ (1+\eta_1)(1+\eta_2)(1+\eta_3) \\ (1-\eta_1)(1+\eta_2)(1+\eta_3) \end{Bmatrix} \tag{8.41}$$

The basic issue for the generalized coordinates form of the finite element algorithm is transformation of the divergence operator in (8.24) i.e.,

$$\frac{\partial}{\partial x_j} = \frac{\partial \eta_i}{\partial x_j}\frac{\partial}{\partial \eta_i} \tag{8.42}$$

Recalling Sec. 3.6, the elements of the inverse jacobian $J^{-1} \equiv [\partial\eta_i/\partial x_j]$ are

$$\left[\frac{\partial \eta_i}{\partial x_j}\right] \equiv J^{-1} = \frac{1}{\det [J]}\,[\text{transformed cofactor of } J] \tag{8.43}$$

where J is the jacobian of the forward transformation (8.38). The differential element for (8.31) is

$$d\mathbf{x} = \det[J]\, d\eta \tag{8.44}$$

To illustrate the details, consider (8.31) written for the momentum equation (8.2). Using a Green-Gauss form of the divergence theorem, the first constraint term becomes

$$\begin{aligned}\int_{R^n} \{N\} L(\rho u_i^h)\, d\mathbf{x} = &\int_{R^n} \{N\} \frac{\partial \rho u_i^h}{\partial t} \det[J]\, d\eta \\ &+ \oint_{\partial R} \{N\}(u_j^h \rho u_i^h + p^h \delta_{ij} - \sigma_{ij}^h)\cdot \hat{\mathbf{n}}_j \det[J]\, d\sigma \\ &- \int_{R^n} \frac{\partial\{N\}}{\partial \eta_k}\left(\frac{\partial \eta_k}{\partial x_j}\right)(u_j^h \rho u_i^h + p^h \delta_{ij} - \sigma_{ij}^h) \det[J]\, d\eta\end{aligned} \tag{8.45}$$

Define the contravariant components of the convection velocity as

$$\bar{u}_k^h \equiv \det[J] \quad \frac{\partial \eta_k}{\partial x_j} \quad u_j^h \tag{8.46}$$

with scalar components parallel to the η_k coordinate system. Using the algebraic transformation (8.38), and (8.43), det $[J]$ cancels yielding

$$\bar{u}_k^h = [\text{Cof.}\, J] u_j^h \tag{8.47}$$

where [Cof. J] is the transformed cofactor matrix of $[J]$. Using (8.30) to interpolate the nodal distribution of $\bar{u}_k^h$ on R_e^n, (8.45) becomes

$$\begin{aligned}\int_{R^n} \{N\} L(\rho u_i^h)\, dx \equiv S_e \Bigg[&\int_{R_e^n} \{DET\}_e^T \{N\}\{N\}\{N\}^T \{RHOUI\}_e'\, d\eta \\ &- \int_{R_e^n} \{UBARK\}_e^T \{N\} \frac{\partial}{\partial \eta_k} \{N\}\{N\}^T \{RHOUI\}_e\, d\eta \\ &- \int_{R_e^n} \{ETAKI\}_e^T \{N\} \frac{\partial}{\partial \eta_k} \{N\}\{N\}^T \{P\}_e\, d\eta \\ &+ \int_{R_e^n} \{ETAKJ\}^T \{N\} \frac{\partial}{\partial \eta_k} \{N\}\{N\}^T \{SIGIJ\}_e\, d\eta \\ &+ \int_{\partial R_e \cap \partial R} [\{UBARK\}_e^T \{N\}\{N\}\{N\}^T \{RHOUI\}_e \\ &+ \{DET\}_e^T \{N\}\{N\}\{N\}^T (\{P\}_e \delta_{IK} - \{SIGIK\}_e)] \cdot \hat{\mathbf{n}}_k\, d\sigma \Bigg]\end{aligned} \tag{8.48}$$

where S_e is the matrix operator projecting element contributions to the corresponding global matrices. The determinant of J is interpolated on the element R_e^n using $\{N_k\}$ and the nodal values. Similarly, $\partial\eta_k/\partial x_i$ is interpolated as $\{ETAKI\}_e^T\{N_k\}$. Since the e-subscripted terms in (8.48) are independent of η_k, upon extraction from the integrand, the finite-element algorithm statement, expressed in terms of the standard hypermatrix definitions, is

$$\int_{R^n} \{N\}L(\rho u_i^h)\,dx = S_e[\{DET\}_e^T[M3000]\{RHOUI\}_e'$$
$$-\{UBARK\}_e^T[M30K0]\{RHOUI\}_e$$
$$-\{ETAKI\}_e^T[M30K0]\{P\}_e$$
$$+\{ETAKJ\}_e^T[M30K0]\{SIGIJ\}_e$$
$$+\hat{\mathbf{n}}_k(\{UBARK\}_e^T[N3000]\{RHOUI\}$$
$$+\{DET\}_e^T[N3000]\{P\}_e\delta_{IK} - \{DET\}_e^T[N3000]\{SIGIK\}_e)] \tag{8.49}$$

In (8.49), the indices K and L obey the tensor summation rule, I is the free index for ρu_i^h, and $[M30K0]$ is the element-independent hypermatrix equivalent of $\partial/\partial\eta_k$ integrated over R_e^n. The matrix $[N3000]$ results from interpolation integrals on the element-boundary intersection $\partial R_e \cap \partial R$ with outward normal $\hat{\mathbf{n}}_k$. For the coordinate transformation, $\{DET\}_e$ is the nodal distributions of components of J^{-1} on R_e^n. Within the generalized coordinates framework, therefore, the grid and metric data required for a numerical simulation are the nodal distributions of $J^{-1} = [\partial\eta_k/\partial x_j]$, and $\det[J] = \det[\partial x_i/\partial\eta_k]$. These data are strictly a function of the nodal coordinate distribution of the discretization $\cup R_e^n$, and may be generated using any coordinate transformation procedure.

As developed in Sec. 8.6, $\beta_2 \equiv \{DET\}_e \nu_{\alpha J}^\gamma$ is the functional form for the dissipation term in the finite-element algorithm statement (8.31). With this identification, the specific matrix forms of the algorithm statement $\{FI\} = \{0\}$, (8.33) can be expressed. The global matrix statement is always obtained using S_e on the sequence of elemental definitions, e.g.,

$$\{FI\} \equiv S_e[\{FI\}_e] \tag{8.50}$$

The elemental expression $\{FI\}_e$ is computed using the master hypermatrices $[M\cdots]$ contracted with element-dependent matrices. Denote the members of the discrete dependent variable set as $\{QI\}^T = \{R, M(I), G, P, S(I, J), Q(J), K, E\}$. The matrix algorithm statements $\{FI\}_e$, for arbitrary basis $\{N_k\}$ and dimension n, are:

$$\{FR\}_e = [\{DET\}^T[M3000] + \nu_{RJ}^1\{ETAKJ\}^T[M40K00]\{DET\}]\{R\}_{j+1}'$$
$$+\frac{\Delta t}{2}[-\{ETAKI\}^T[M30K0]\{MI\}$$
$$+\nu_{RJ}^2\{ETAKJ\}^T[M40KL0]\{UBARL\}\{R\}]_{j+1,j} \tag{8.51}$$

$$\{FMI\}_e = [\{DET\}^T [M3000] + \nu_{IJ}^1 \{ETAKJ\}^T [M40K00] \{DET\}] \{MI\}'_{j+1}$$
$$+ \frac{\Delta t}{2} [-\{UBARK\}^T [M30K0] \{MI\} - \{ETAKI\}^T [M30K0] \{P\}$$
$$+ \{ETAKJ\}^T [M30K0] \{SIGIJ\}$$
$$+ \nu_{IJ}^2 \{ETAKJ\}^T [M40KL0] \{UBARL\} \{MI\}]_{j+1,j} \tag{8.52}$$

$$\{FG\}_e = [\{DET\}^T [M3000] + \nu_{GJ}^1 \{ETAKJ\}^T [M40K00] \{DET\}] \{G\}'_{j+1}$$
$$+ \frac{\Delta t}{2} [-\{UBARK\}^T [M30K0] (\{G\} + \{P\}) + \{ETAKJ\}^T [M30K0] \{QJ\}$$
$$+ \{ETAKJ\}^T [M40K00] \{UL\} \{SIGLJ\}$$
$$+ \nu_{GJ}^2 \{ETAKJ\}^T [M40KL0] \{UBARL\} \{G\}]_{j+1,j} \tag{8.53}$$

$$\{FP\}_e = \{DET\}^T [M3000] \{P\} - (\gamma - 1)[\{DET\}^T [M3000] \{G\}$$
$$+ \tfrac{1}{2} \{DET\}^T [M40000] \{UJ\} \{MJ\}]_{j+1} \tag{8.54}$$

$$\{FSIJ\}_e = \{DET\}^T [M3000] \{SIGIJ\} - \frac{\mu}{\text{Re}} [\{ETAKJ\}^T [M30K0] \{UI\}$$
$$+ \{ETAKI\}^T [M30K0] \{UJ\} - \tfrac{2}{3} \delta_{IJ} \{ETAKL\}^T [M30K0] \{UL\}]_{j+1} \tag{8.55}$$

$$\{FQJ\}_e = \{DET\}^T [M3000] \{QJ\} - \kappa [\{ETAKI\}^T [M30K0] \{GSR\} - \{UJUJ\}]_{j+1} \tag{8.56}$$

$$\{FK\}_e = [\{DET\}^T [M3000] + \nu_{TJ}^1 \{ETAKJ\}^T [M40K00] \{DET\}] \{K\}'_{j+1}$$
$$+ \frac{\Delta t}{2} [-\{UBARK\}^T [M30K0] \{K\} + \{DET\}^T [M3000] \{E\}$$
$$+ \{ETAKJ\}^T [M400K0] \{UI\} \{SIJ\}$$
$$- \{ETAKJ\}^T (\{ETALI\}^T [M500K0L] \{KDIFIJ\}) \{K\}$$
$$+ \nu_{TJ}^2 \{ETAKJ\}^T [M40KL0] \{UBARL\} \{K\}]_{j+1,j} \tag{8.57}$$

$$\{FE\}_e = [\{DET\}^T [M3000] + \nu_{EJ}^1 \{ETAKJ\}^T [M40K00] \{DET\}] \{E\}'_{j+1}$$
$$+ \frac{\Delta t}{2} [-\{UBARK\}^T [M30K0] \{E\} + \{ESK\}^T [M40000] \{DET\} \{E\}$$
$$+ \{ETAKJ\}^T [M400K0] \{UI\} \{SIJ \cdot ESK\}$$
$$- \{ETAKJ\}^T (\{ETAKI\}^T [M500K0L] \{EDIFIJ\}) \{E\}$$
$$+ \nu_{EJ}^2 \{ETAKJ\}^T [M40KL0] \{UBARL\} \{E\}]_{j+1,j} \tag{8.58}$$

A few comments on notational structure for (8.51)-(8.58) are appropriate. For clarity, the subscript e has been deleted from each equation. The elemental hypermatrices $[M\cdots]$, for an n-dimensional problem description, are evaluated once and for all by integrals over a master finite-element domain R_e^n. For a one-dimensional domain R^1, that is, $[A\cdots]$, all matrices through $[A4\cdots]$ are listed in Appendix B.1, for both the linear ($k = 1$) and quadratic ($k = 2$) cardinal basis $\{N_k\}$. For two- and three-dimensional domains R^n, that is, $[B\cdots]$ and $[C\cdots]$, all element matrices through $[B4\cdots]$ and $[C2\cdots]$ are listed in Appendix B.2 and B.3, respectively, for the bilinear tensor product cardinal basis $\{N_1^+\}$. The discrete indices J, K, L, occurring in both matrix and variable (FORTRAN) names, are tensor summation indices with range $1 \leqslant (J, K, L) \leqslant n$. The multipole coefficient β_2 is expressed in terms of cartesian scalar components $v_{\alpha J}^{\gamma}$, with distinct values for each dependent variable.

The arrays $\{DET\}_e$ and $\{ETAKJ\}_e$ contain nodal values of the determinant J and elements of $\partial\eta_k/\partial x_j$. The nodal contravariant components of convection velocity $\bar{u}_k$, (8.47) are denoted $\{UBARK\}$, and $\{UBARL\}$ contains absolute values. The elements of $\{SIGIJ\}$ are nodal values of the stress tensor computed in principal coordinates in terms of $u_j = m_j/\rho$. Equation (8.55) is appropriate only for the laminar-flow Stokes stress tensor definition (8.5), and δ_{IJ} is the Kronecker delta. The additional terms resulting from inclusion of the Reynolds stress constitutive equation, (8.22), are readily evaluated using the illustrated expansions. In (8.56), $\{GSR\}$ denotes nodal values of $e \equiv g/\rho$, while $\{UIUI\}$ contains nodal values of the specific kinetic energy $\frac{1}{2}u_i u_i$. For (8.57)-(8.58), $\{KDIFIJ\}$ and $\{EDIFIJ\}$ contain as elements the nodal values of the "effective diffusion" coefficient tensors, $C_k \rho \overline{u_i' u_j'} k/\epsilon - \bar{\mu}\delta_{ij}$ and $C_\epsilon \rho \overline{u_i' u_j'} k/\epsilon$, respectively. Further, in (8.58), the elements of $\{ESK\}$ and $\{SIJ{\cdot}ESK\}$ are nodal values of $C_\epsilon^2 \epsilon/k$ and $C_\epsilon^1 \overline{u_i' u_j'} \epsilon/k$. In all equations, $\{\cdot\}'_{j+1}$ denotes $\{\cdot\}_{j+1}^p - \{\cdot\}_j$. The notation $]_{j+1,j}$ defines evaluation of the argument at t_{j+1}, and at t_j, followed by addition after multiplication by θ and $(1-\theta)$, see (8.33). Equations (8.51)-(8.58) are completed by addition of the appropriate boundary terms, recall (8.45)-(8.49).

Problems

1 Derive (8.51).

2 Derive (8.52).

3 Derive (8.53)-(8.54).

4 Derive (8.55)-(8.56).

5 Derive (8.57)-(8.58).

8.5 TENSOR MATRIX PRODUCT JACOBIAN

For efficiency, a suitable approximation to the Newton algorithm jacobian (8.34) is required (recall Chap. 4). The matrix tensor product construction (Halmos, 1958) can be achieved using the tensor product cardinal basis function set $\{N_k(\eta)\}$ spanning quadrilateral and hexahedra element domains R_e^2 and R_e^3, respectively (Sec. 4.10). The jacobian matrix $[J(FI)]$, (8.34) is replaced by the tensor (outer) product, defined as

$$[J(FI)] \Rightarrow [J_1] \otimes [J_2] \otimes [J_3] \tag{8.59}$$

Each component $[J_\eta]$ is constructed from its definition (8.36), assuming interpolation and differentiation are one-dimensional. Using (8.59), the Newton iteration algorithm statement (8.34) becomes replaced as

$$[J_1] \otimes [J_2] \otimes [J_3]\{\delta QI\}_{j+1}^{p+1} = -\{FI\}_{j+1}^p \tag{8.60}$$

Define
$$[J_2] \otimes [J_3]\{\delta QI\}_{j+1}^{p+1} \equiv \{P1\}_{j+1}^{p+1}$$
$$[J_3]\{\delta QI\}_{j+1}^{p+1} \equiv \{P2\}_{j+1}^{p+1} \tag{8.61}$$

Then, the operation defined in (8.60) is replaced by the sequence

$$\begin{aligned}[J_1]\{P1\}_{j+1}^{p+1} &= -\{FI\}_{j+1}^{p}\\ [J_2]\{P2\}_{j+1}^{p+1} &= \{P1\}_{j+1}^{p+1}\\ [J_3]\{\delta QI\}_{j+1}^{p+1} &= \{P2\}_{j+1}^{p+1}\end{aligned} \tag{8.62}$$

Obviously, other permutations of the index structure for $[J_\eta]$ could be utilized. The key aspect is replacement of the very large (albeit sparse) jacobian matrix $[J]$, with α-block-structured matrices $[J_\eta]$. The principal attributes are several orders of magnitude reduction in central memory requirements for the jacobian, and significantly reduced CPU for the LU decomposition and back substitution solution steps. The principal detraction is assured degradation of the quadratic convergence rate for the Newton iteration. This procedure in no way affects the formation of $\{FI\}$, (8.33), wherein lies the accuracy features intrinsic to the finite-element algorithm statement. Compromises in the evaluation of $\{FI\}$ will invariably produce inferior results for the Navier-Stokes equations.

The construction of the $[J_\eta]$ was introduced in Chap. 4 for a scalar equation. The procedures are directly extended to the present case. For example, the term in the jacobian corresponding to the initial-value term in the matrix statements (8.51)–(8.58) is

$$\frac{\partial\{FI\}}{\partial\{QJ\}} = S_e[\{DET\}_e^T[M3000]\,\delta_{IJ}] \equiv [JQQ] \tag{8.63}$$

where δ_{IJ} is the discrete index Kronecker delta. By definition, (8.63) is formed using S_e operating on the elemental definition

$$[JQQ]_e \equiv \{DET\}_e^T[M3000] \equiv \int_{R_e^n} \{DET\}_e^T\{N_k(\eta)\}\{N_k(\eta)\}\{N_k(\eta)\}^T\,d\eta \tag{8.64}$$

Assuming for exposition, $k = 1$, $n = 2$, and $\mathbf{x} \equiv \eta$ (the identity transformation), and recalling the definition $M \equiv B$ for $n = 2$, (8.64) becomes

$$\{DET\}_e^T[B3000] = \Delta_e[B200] \equiv \int_{R_e^2} \{N_1(\mathbf{x})\}\{N_1(\mathbf{x})\}^T\,d\mathbf{x} \tag{8.65}$$

Assuming the rectangular element domain R_e^2 described by measures l and ω, the evaluation of (8.65) yields

$$[JQQ]_e = \Delta_e[B200] = l\omega[B200] = \frac{l\omega}{36}\begin{bmatrix} 4 & 2 & 1 & 2\\ & 4 & 2 & 1\\ & & 4 & 2\\ (\mathrm{sym}) & & & 4\end{bmatrix} \tag{8.66}$$

The tensor product approximation to (8.63) involves evaluation of (8.65) on a one-dimensional domain. Recalling $M \equiv A$ for $n = 1$,

$$[JQQ_\eta]_e \equiv \Delta_n [A200] = \int_{R_e^1} \{N_1(x_1)\}\{N_1(x_1)\}^T \, dx_1 \tag{8.67}$$

and

$$[JQQ_1]_e = \frac{l}{6}\begin{bmatrix} 2 & 1 \\ 1 & 2 \end{bmatrix} \qquad [JQQ_2]_e = \frac{\omega}{6}\begin{bmatrix} 2 & 1 \\ 1 & 2 \end{bmatrix} \tag{8.68}$$

assuming $\Delta_1 = l$ and $\Delta_2 = \omega$. Accounting for entry locations in $[JQQ]$, (8.63), and using the assembly operator S_e, it is readily verified that

$$[JQQ] = S_e[[JQQ_1]_e \otimes [JQQ_2]_e] \tag{8.69}$$

By direct extension then, the tensor matrix product approximation of (8.63) on R^3 is

$$S_e[\{DET\}_e^T[M3000]] \Rightarrow S_e[\{DET1\}_e^T[A3000] \otimes \{DET2\}_e^T[A3000] \otimes \{DET3\}_e^T[A3000]] \tag{8.70}$$

where the tensor index $1 \leqslant K \leqslant 3$ on $\{DETK\}_e$ denotes the scalar component of the multidimensional measure parallel to η_K.

The second term in the typical jacobian [see (8.51)-(8.52)] is the matrix

$$S_e[\nu_{\alpha J}^1\{ETAKJ\}_e^T[M40K00]\{DET\}_e]$$

where $\nu_{\alpha J}^1$ results from definition of the explicit form for β_2, (8.31), and α denotes the specific dependent variable. The indices K, J are discrete tensor summation indices with range $1 \leqslant (K, J) \leqslant n$. $[M40K00]$ is a hypermatrix of degree two, i.e., it possesses elements which are themselves square matrices, which represents the integration over R_e^n of products of four cardinal basis sets $\{N_k(\eta)\}$, one of which is differentiated into scalar components parallel to η_K. The tensor product approximation is

$$S_e[\nu_{\alpha J}^1\{ETAKJ\}_e^T[M40K00]\{DET\}_e] \Rightarrow S_e[\nu_{\alpha J}^1\{ETA1J\}_e^T[A440100]\{DET1\}_e \otimes \{ETA2J\}_e^T[A440100]\{DET2\}_e \otimes \{ETA3J\}_e^T[A440100]\{DET\}_e] \tag{8.71}$$

where J is a discrete summation index with range $1 \leqslant J \leqslant n$, to be contracted with scalar components of $\nu_{\alpha J}^1$.

Equations (8.70)-(8.71) illustrate the construction of tensor matrix product components of $[J]$. Each one-dimensional component $[J_\eta]$ for any term is identical in appearance; note that $[A440100]$ appears in each term in (8.71). Therefore, the tensor product jacobian can be defined by a single term, retaining the index "K" to denote the component parallel to η_K. Equations (8.51)-(8.58) define the algorithm matrix expressions $\{FI\}_e$, which are analytically differentiable by members of $\{QJ\}_e$. The construction of certain terms involves differentiation with respect to the parameter $\bar{u}_k = \bar{m}_k/\rho$. Using the chain rule, and (8.46)-(8.47), as an exercise verify that

$$\frac{\partial}{\partial\{MI\}_e} = \frac{\partial}{\partial\{MI\}} + \frac{\partial}{\partial\{\bar{M}K\}}\frac{\partial\{\bar{M}K\}}{\partial\{MI\}} + \frac{\partial}{\partial\{\bar{U}K\}}\frac{\partial\{\bar{U}K\}}{\partial\{MI\}}$$
$$= \frac{\partial}{\partial\{MI\}} + \det J\frac{\partial\eta_k}{\partial x_i}\left[\frac{\partial}{\partial\{\bar{M}K\}} + \frac{1}{\bar{\rho}}\frac{\partial}{\partial\{\bar{U}K\}}\right] \tag{8.72}$$

$$\frac{\partial}{\partial\{R\}_e} = \frac{\partial}{\partial\{R\}} - \left(\frac{\bar{m}_K}{\bar{\rho}^2}\right)\frac{\partial}{\partial\{\bar{U}K\}} \tag{8.73}$$

Define the scalar $\bar{D}_{KI}$ to be the element average value of det $J(\partial\eta_k/\partial x_i)_e$ appearing in (8.72). Further define K to signify the discrete free index, i.e., *no* summation implied, corresponding to $\partial/\partial\eta_k$; (8.70)-(8.71). The nonempty tensor matrix product jacobians for the finite-element algorithm statement (8.51)-(8.56), suppressing the subscript e throughout, for clarity, are

$$[JRR]_e = \{DETK\}^T[A3000] + \nu^1_{RJ}\{ETAKJ\}^T[A40K00]\{DETK\}$$
$$+ \frac{\Delta t}{2}\nu^2_{RJ}\left[\{ETAKJ\}^T[M40KL0]\{UBARL\}\right.$$
$$\left. - \left(\frac{\bar{m}_L}{\bar{\rho}^2}\right)\{ETAKJ\}^T[M40K0L]\{R\}\right]$$

$$[JRMI]_e = \frac{\Delta t}{2}[-\{ETAKI\}^T[A30K0] + \nu^2_{RJ}\bar{D}_{KI}\{ETAKJ\}^T[A30KK]] \tag{8.74}$$
$$[JMIR]_e = \frac{\Delta t}{2}\left(\frac{\bar{m}_k}{\bar{\rho}^2}\right)[\{MI\}^T[A30K0] + \nu^2_{IJ}\{MI\}^T[A4KK00]\{ETAKJ\}]$$
$$[JMIMI]_e = \{DETK\}^T[A3000] + \nu^1_{IJ}\{ETAKJ\}^T[A40K00]\{DETK\}$$
$$+ \frac{\Delta t}{2}\left[-\{UBARK\}^T[A30K0] - \bar{D}_{KI}\{MI\}^T[A30K0]\frac{1}{\bar{\rho}}\right.$$
$$\left. + \nu^2_{IJ}(\{UBARK\}^T[A40KK0]\{ETAKJ\} + \frac{1}{\bar{\rho}}\{MI\}^T[A4KK00]\{ETAKJ\})\right]$$
$$[JMIMJ]_e = \frac{\Delta t}{2}\bar{D}_{KJ}\left(\frac{1}{\bar{\rho}}\right)[-\{MJ\}^T[A30K0] + \nu^2_{JL}\{MJ\}^T[A4KK00]\{ETAKL\}]$$
$$[JMIP]_e = -\frac{\Delta t}{2}\{ETAKI\}^T[A30K0]$$

$$[JMISIJ]_e = \frac{\Delta t}{2}\{ETAKJ\}^T[A40K00]\{DETK\} \tag{8.75}$$
$$[JGR]_e = \frac{\Delta t}{2}\left(\frac{\bar{m}_k}{\bar{\rho}^2}\right)[\{G+P\}^T[A30K0] + \nu^2_{GJ}\{G\}^T[A4KK00]\{ETAKJ\}]$$
$$[JGMI]_e = \frac{\Delta t}{2}\bar{D}_{KI}\left(\frac{1}{\bar{\rho}}\right)[-\{G+P\}^T[A30K0] + \nu^2_{GL}\{G\}^T[A4KK00]\{ETAKJ\}]$$
$$[JGG]_e = \{DETK\}^T[A3000] + \nu^1_{GJ}\{ETAKJ\}^T[A40K00]\{DETK\}$$
$$+ \frac{\Delta t}{2}[-\{UBARK\}^T[A30K0] + \nu^2_{GJ}\{UBARK\}^T[A40KK0]\{ETAKJ\}]$$

$$[JGP]_e = -\frac{\Delta t}{2}\{UBARK\}^T[A30K0]$$

$$[JGSIJ]_e = \frac{\Delta t}{2}\{ETAKJ\}^T[A40K00]\{UI\}$$

$$[JGQJ]_e = \frac{\Delta t}{2}\bar{D}_{LJ}\{ETAKL\}^T[A30K0] \tag{8.76}$$

$$[JPR]_e = -\left(\frac{\gamma-1}{2}\right)\left(\frac{\bar{m}_k}{\bar{\rho}^2}\right)\{DETK\}^T([A40000]\{MK\})$$

$$[JPMK]_e = \left(\frac{\gamma-1}{2}\right)\Big[\{DETK\}^T([A40000]\{UK\})$$
$$+\left(\frac{1}{\bar{\rho}}\right)\{DETK\}^T([A40000]\{MK\})\Big]$$

$$[JPG]_e = -(\gamma-1)\{DETK\}^T[A3000]$$
$$[JPP]_e = \{DETK\}^T[A3000] \tag{8.77}$$

$$[JSIJR]_e = \frac{\mu}{\bar{\rho}^2}[\bar{m}_i\{ETAKJ\}^T[A30K0] + \bar{m}_j\{ETAKI\}^T[A30K0]$$
$$-\tfrac{2}{3}\delta_{IJ}\bar{m}_l\{ETAKL\}^T[A30K0]]$$

$$[JSIJMI]_e = -\frac{\mu}{\bar{\rho}}[\{ETAKJ\}^T[A30K0] - \tfrac{2}{3}\delta_{IJ}\{ETAKL\}^T[A30K0]]$$

$$[JSIJSIJ]_e = \{DETK\}^T[A3000] \tag{8.78}$$

$$[JQIR]_e = \frac{\kappa}{\bar{\rho}^2}\left[\bar{g}\{ETAKI\}^T[A30K0] - \frac{\bar{m}_i^2}{\bar{\rho}}\{ETAKI\}^T[A30K0]\right]$$

$$[JQIMI]_e = \frac{\kappa\bar{m}_i}{\bar{\rho}^2}\{ETAKI\}^T[A30K0]$$

$$[JQIG]_e = -\frac{\kappa}{\bar{\rho}}\{ETAKI\}^T[A30K0]$$
$$[JQIQI]_e = \{DETK\}^T[A3000] \tag{8.79}$$

The scalars $\bar{m}_i$, $\bar{\rho}$, and $\bar{g}$ are element average values of $\{MI\}$, $\{R\}$, and $\{G\}$, respectively on R_e^1. In the formation of certain of these statements, the boolean index K in various A matrices has been permuted to facilitate differentiation by the last right contraction matrix. The elements of each jacobian are computed on each finite-element domain R_e^1, using the element matrices listed in Appendix B.1, and then assembled into the global form using the operator S_e. In actual practice, the column matrix $\{\delta QI\}$ is ordered on degrees of freedom at a node, for example $\{\ldots, \delta R_j, \delta U_j, \delta E_j, \delta P_j, \delta R_{j+1}, \ldots\}^T$. Hence, the global tensor jacobian $[J_\eta]$ (8.59), is α-block tridiagonal using the linear ($k = 1$) finite-element basis, and α-block pentadiagonal for the quadratic ($k = 2$) cardinal basis.

Problems

1 Verify (8.69) using (8.66)–(8.68).
2 Verify (8.72) and (8.73).
3 Derive (8.74).
4 Verify (8.75).
5 Verify (8.76).
6 Verify (8.77).

8.6 COMMENTS ON THE ALGORITHM

Equations (8.51)–(8.58) are an exact statement of the elemental matrix equivalent of the finite-element algorithm statement, which upon assembly on $\cup R_e^n$ yields (8.33). While the master hypermatrix symbology $[MP\cdots]_e$ is independent of the completeness of the semidiscrete approximation subspace, i.e., the degree k of $\{N_k(\eta)\}$ in (8.30), the order of each square matrix is $(k+1)^n$. In addition, since each master matrix is a hypermatrix of degree $P \geqslant 1$, there are $(k+1)^P$ entries for each element of each matrix $[MP\cdots]_e$.

The associated inner product DO-loop to form $\{FI\}$, especially for $k > 1$, is of excessive length on a scalar machine. The algorithm matrix statement can be simplified in this regard, with the commission of interpolation error only. Each boolean index "0" appearing in a hypermatrix $[MP\cdots]_e$ signifies the matrix inner product with the element-dependent column (row) matrix $\{\cdot\}_e$ corresponding to an interpolation on R_e^n. For example, the lead term in each matrix statement $\{FI\}$, (8.51)–(8.58), is $\{DET\}_e^T[M3000]_e$. In the instance of the linear transformation $\mathbf{x} = \eta$, the elements of $\{DET\}_e$ are each equal to a constant times the element measure. Hence, $\{DET\}_e^T = (DET)_e\{ONE\}^T$, where the elements of $\{ONE\}$ are unity, which yields

$$\{DET\}_e^T[M3000] = (DET)_e\{ONE\}^T[M3000] = (DET)_e[M200] \qquad (8.80)$$

where $(DET)_e$ is the scalar measure (area, volume) of the finite-element domain R_e^n. As presented in Sec. 8.9, for $k = 1, n = 2$, and a general quadrilateral domain R_e^n, the elements of $\{DET\}_e$ are each proportional to the element measure. Thus, defining the sum $(\overline{DET})_e \equiv \{DET\}^T\{ONE\}$, and for a "decent" element aspect ratio, (8.80) can be approximated as

$$\{DET\}_e^T[B3000] \approxeq (\overline{DET})_e[B200] \qquad (8.81)$$

with the commission of interpolation error only. This operation reduces by $(k+1)^P$ the number of multiplications required to form this term in $\{FI\}$.

Thus, in this context, every hypermatrix inner product in (8.51)–(8.58) is eligible for reduction of hypermatrix degree through element averaging. This is appropriate only for data that are sufficiently smooth, which in general rules out averaging of any dependent variable, since nonsmooth solutions must be admitted. However, for decent discretizations $\cup R_e^n$, the geometric data should be eligible for averaging on sufficiently refined grids. Therefore, in (8.52) for example,

$$\{ETAKJ\}_e^T [M40K00] \{DET\}_e \rightarrow (\overline{ETAKJ})_e (\overline{DET})_e [M2K0]$$
$$\{ETAKJ\}_e^T [M40KL0] \{UBARL\}_e \rightarrow (\overline{ETAKJ})_e \{UBARL\}_e^T [M30KL] \quad (8.82)$$

Further, in (8.57), for example,

$$\{ETAKJ\}_e^T (\{ETALI\}_e^T [M500K0L] \{KDIFIJ\}_e)$$
$$\rightarrow (\overline{ETAKJ})_e (\overline{ETAKL})_e \{KDIFIJ\}_e^T [M30KL] \quad (8.83)$$

Hence, no hypermatrix of degree $P > 1$ is required formed or stored, provided the discretization of R_e^n is of sufficient quality. The averaging of the grid data in the jacobian tensor matrix product formulation, (8.74)-(8.79) is thus also appropriate.

A second point in the finite-element formulation (8.51)-(8.58) is that definition and use of the stress tensor σ_{ij}, and heat flux vector q_j, as dependent variables has yielded an algorithm statement devoid of second order derivatives in the generalized coordinates framework. Hence, the troublesome, sometimes destabilizing, mixed spatial derivatives resulting from viscosity terms in the direct formulation are totally absent. The penalty for this dependent variable construction is a significant increase in the size of the α-block-banded tensor product jacobian. Conversely, a general turbulent flow prediction can ostensibly be handled with ease, by expansion of the defining equations for σ_{ij} and q_j. The fact that the algebraic "constitutive" equations for p, σ_{ij}, and q_j are handled directly within the weighted residuals algorithm framework lends an overall uniformity that simplifies construction.

Finally, a noniterative and direct steady-state form of the algorithm are each a special case of the presented formulation. The noniterative construction simply constitutes acceptance of the first solution $\{\delta QI\}_{j+1}^2$ of the Newton algorithm, using only evaluation of $\{FI\}_{j+1}^1$. Since the iteration index $p > 0$ by definition $\{QI\}_{j+1}^1 \equiv \{QI\}_j$. Therefore, $\{QI\}_{j+1}' = \{0\}$ throughout (8.51)-(8.58), and the corresponding expressions in brackets are not evaluated. Furthermore, $\Delta t/2 \rightarrow \Delta t$ and the evaluation $\cdot]_{j+1,j}$ reduces to $\cdot]_j$. Since the terms in $\{FI\}$ involving $\nu_{\alpha J}^1$ have been eliminated, so are the corresponding terms in the tensor product jacobians. The multiplier $\Delta t/2$ remains appropriate in $[J_\eta]$, and evaluations are made using $\{QI\}_{j+1}^1 \equiv \{QI\}_j$.

This noniterative procedure reduces the algorithm operations count by a significant factor, at the expense of removal of $\nu_{\alpha J}^1$ from the construction and acceptance of the first Newton iterate, obtained using an approximate jacobian. The direct steady-state algorithm is identical to the noniterative formulation except that $\Delta t/2 \rightarrow \Delta t$ in the jacobians. This multiplier, common to all elements of $\{FI\}$, can be divided out, yielding Δt^{-1} as a scalar multiplier on $\{DET\}^T [A3000]$ in the self-coupling jacobians $[JQQ]$ for the initial-value dependent variables. This yields the tensor matrix generalization of the "approximate factorization" procedures devised for finite-difference algorithms (Beam and Warming, 1978; Briley and McDonald, 1977; Steger, 1981).

8.7 THEORETICAL ANALYSIS, ACCURACY AND CONVERGENCE

As amply discussed and verified throughout this text, accuracy and convergence statements for finite-element algorithms are usually quantized as inequalities in Sobolev norms. The Navier-Stokes problem class for finite Reynolds number is nonlinear elliptic with initial-value character. For infinite Reynolds number (inviscid flow), the resulting (Euler) equation set is nonlinear hyperbolic. The available theoretical analyses are exact only for linear equations, and have already been presented; recall Secs. 2.8, 3.3, and 4.8. However, as presented in Chaps. 4 and 6, the convergence rates measured using controlled numerical experiments have provided indication that the linear theory is appropriate for nonlinear parabolic equations at least.

For a nonlinear, one-dimensional hyperbolic equation set (see Sec. 8.8), Baker (1982) measured convergence in H^1 and E for a shocked (nonsmooth) flow using the developed finite-element algorithm. Figure 8.2 summarizes the data, which indicate that in the semidiscrete approximation norms $\|q^h\|^2_{H^1}$ and $\|q^h\|_E$, the solutions converge monotonically with discretization refinement for $10 < M \leqslant 400$. A modest slope distinction is evidenced with α, the $k = 2$ data lies above the $k = 1$ results, but each appears consequentially independent of the degree of the approxima-

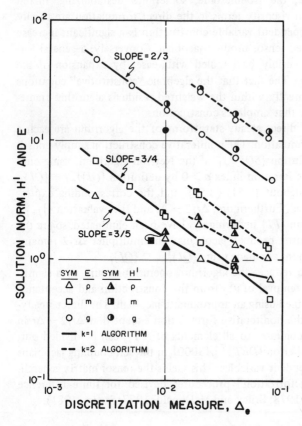

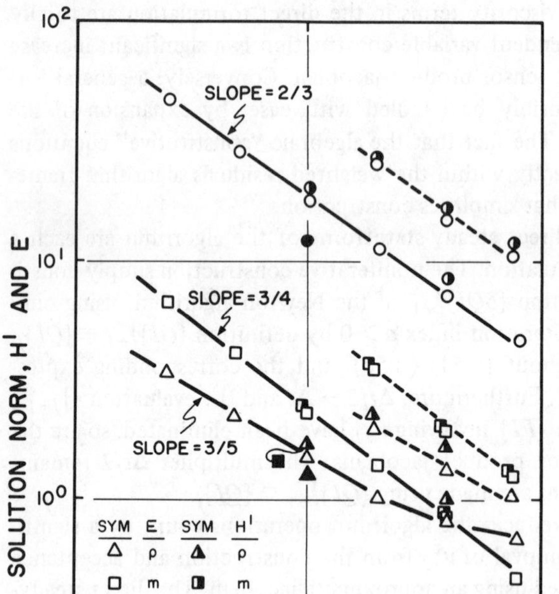

Figure 8.2 Semidiscrete approximation accuracy and convergence in $\|q^h\|^2_{H^1}$ and $\|q^h\|_E$, finite-element algorithm solution for Riemann shock tube. Solid symbols are Crank-Nicolson results, $M = 100$. From Baker (1982).

tion subspace $1 \leqslant k \leqslant 2$; see (8.30). This observation is in qualitative agreement with the theoretical convergence statement (4.136) for a linear hyperbolic equation. Furthermore, the $k = 1$ finite-element algorithm solution extremized each norm, in comparison to the Crank-Nicolson finite difference equivalent of the algorithm (recall Sec. 4.7), which considerably extends the problem class range over which this observation has been quantized. Viewing these data, the convergence character can be described in the form

$$\|q_\alpha^h\|_{H^1,E}^2 \leqslant C_1 \, \Delta^{p/(p+1)} + \cdots \tag{8.84}$$

which has been employed to define the order-of-accuracy (p) of a finite-difference scheme applied to nonsmooth solutions. As usual, C_1 is a constant independent of the (uniform) mesh measure Δ, and $p = 2$ from the data of Fig. 8.2, for the $1 \leqslant k \leqslant 2$ bases.

The principal control in the order of accuracy of the finite-element algorithm statement (8.31) lies in determination of the dissipation parameter set β_2. Recall in Sec. 4.11, the Fourier stability analysis applied to the one-dimensional form of (8.1). The Fourier decomposition of the semidiscrete approximation is

$$q^h(j\,\Delta x, t) = Q_0 \exp\left[i\omega(j\,\Delta x - \Gamma U_0 t)\right] \tag{8.85}$$

where $\Gamma \equiv \sigma + i\delta$, and σ and δ are real numbers; $i = \sqrt{-1}$; $\omega = 2\pi/\lambda$ is the wave number for Fourier mode of wavelength λ; and $x = j\,\Delta x$, $j = 0, 1, 2, \ldots$, is represented by discrete intervals of (uniform) measure Δx. For the definition $\beta_2 \equiv \nu\,\Delta x \hat{\mathbf{i}}$ in (8.31), where $\nu > 0$ is a scalar parameter, the Raymond and Garder (1976) analysis yielded the $k = 1$ algorithm expansions for σ and δ as [see (4.186)-(4.187)]

$$\sigma = 1 + \left(\frac{-1}{180} + \frac{\nu^2}{12}\right) d^4 + O(d^6) \tag{8.86}$$

$$\delta = -\frac{\nu}{12} d^3 + O(d^5) \tag{8.87}$$

where $d \equiv \omega\,\Delta x = 2\pi/n$, and n is the discrete Fourier mode index, $\lambda_n = n\,\Delta x$, and O indicates order. The semidiscrete solution q^h can be made a sixth-order accurate approximation by eliminating the $O(d^4)$ term in (8.86), yielding $\nu \equiv (15)^{-1/2}$. Correspondingly, $\delta < 0$ in (8.87) and an artificial dissipation mechanism becomes introduced.

The original analysis has been expanded (Baker, 1982) by redefining the dissipation parameter β_2 in the form

$$\beta_2 \equiv \Delta x(\nu^1 \delta_t + \nu^2 \delta_x)\hat{\mathbf{i}} \tag{8.88}$$

where δ_t and δ_x are Kronecker delta-type functions, yielding ν^1 operating on the time derivative, and ν^2 operating on the spatial derivative term only, in the one-dimensional form of (8.1). Proceeding through the substitutions yields, for the $k = 1$ algorithm,

$$\sigma = 1 - d^2(\nu^1 - \nu^2) + d^4\left[-\frac{1}{180} + \frac{\nu^1\nu^2}{12} + (\nu^1 - \nu^2)(\nu^1)^3\right] + O(d^6) \tag{8.89}$$

$$\delta = d(\nu^1 - \nu^2) - d^3\left[\frac{\nu^2}{12} - (\nu^1 - \nu^2)(\nu^1)^2\right] + O(d^5) \tag{8.90}$$

For the quadratic ($k = 2$) algorithm, the form for (8.89) is

$$\sigma = 1 - 4\nu^1\nu^2 + \frac{d^2[-14 + 184\nu^1\nu^2 - 60(\nu^1)^2 + 240\nu^2(\nu^1)^3]}{15}$$

$$+ d^4\left[\frac{2}{5} - \frac{542}{150}\nu^1\nu^2 + \frac{8}{3}(\nu^1)^2 - \frac{672}{15}\nu^2(\nu^1)^3 + 16(\nu^1)^4 - 64\nu^2(\nu^1)^5\right] + O(d^6) \tag{8.91}$$

Setting $\nu^1 \equiv \nu \equiv \nu^2$ in (8.89)–(8.90) yields the results of the original analysis. Enforcing sixth-order accuracy for (8.89)–(8.90) produces the constraint

$$\nu^2 = \frac{d^2[1/180 - (\nu^1)^4] + (\nu^1)^2}{d^2[\nu^1/12 - (\nu^1)^3] + \nu^1} \tag{8.92}$$

Figure 8.3 is a plot of (8.92) with n as a parameter. Sixth-order accuracy can be achieved only for $\nu^1 > 0$; for any level, ν^2 ranges over an order of magnitude dependent upon n, with the largest levels required for the shortest wavelengths. All data converge at the point $\nu^1 = (15)^{-1/2} = \nu^2$. Defining $\nu^1 \equiv 0$ in (8.89) or (8.91) renders both the $k = 1$ and $k = 2$ algorithm constructions, for the semidiscrete approximation q^h, a second-order accurate representation of the analytical solution for $\nu^2 \neq 0$.

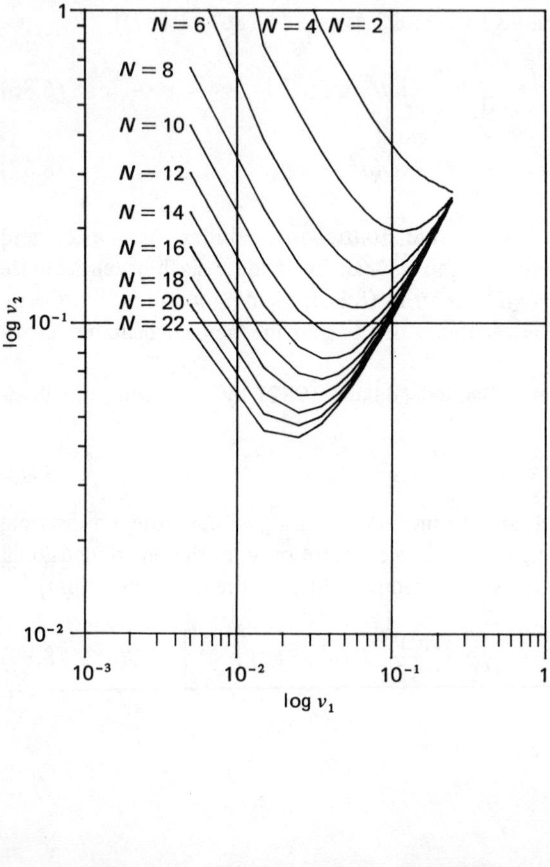

Figure 8.3 Distribution of solution to Eq. (8.92) for ν optimal. From Baker (1982).

The expansion of (8.88) for the multidimensional, multidependent variable, generalized coordinates definition for the dissipation parameter β_2^α is

$$\beta_2^\alpha \equiv (\det J)(\nu_\alpha^1 \delta_t + \nu_\alpha^2 \delta_x) \tag{8.93}$$

In (8.93), $\det J$ is the measure of R_e^n, subscript α denotes the appropriate member of q_α^h, and the parameter vectors ν_α^γ are expressed in terms of scalar components $\nu_{\alpha j}^\gamma$ in the x_j coordinate system.

Problems

1 Verify (8.86)–(8.87) (see Sec. 4.11).
2 Verify (8.89).
3 Verify (8.90).
4 Verify (8.92).

8.8 ALGORITHM CONSTRUCTION FOR QUASI-ONE-DIMENSIONAL FLOW

Most formulational aspects of the generalized coordinates, Navier-Stokes finite-element algorithm construction can best be exposed by examination of a quasi-one-dimensional inviscid flow. Defining the convection velocity $u \equiv m/\rho$, and the flow cross-sectional area as $A(x)$, we form from (8.1)–(8.4) the governing differential equation set

$$L(\rho) = \frac{\partial \rho}{\partial t} + \frac{\partial}{\partial x}[m] + \rho u \frac{d \ln A}{dx} = 0 \tag{8.94}$$

$$L(m) = \frac{\partial m}{\partial t} + \frac{\partial}{\partial x}[um + p] + mu \frac{d \ln A}{dx} = 0 \tag{8.95}$$

$$L(g) = \frac{\partial g}{\partial t} + \frac{\partial}{\partial x}[ug + up] + u(g + p)\frac{d \ln A}{dx} = 0 \tag{8.96}$$

$$L(p) = p - (\gamma - 1)[g - \tfrac{1}{2}um] = 0 \tag{8.97}$$

The algorithm statement requires the metric data $\{DET\}_e$ and $\{ETAKJ\}_e$. For the affine coordinate transformation $x_1 = \eta_1$, and with the η_1 origin at the element centroid, the members of the cardinal bases $\{N_k^+(\eta)\}$, $1 \leqslant k \leqslant 2$, are

$$\{N_1^+(\eta)\} = \frac{1}{2}\begin{Bmatrix} 1 - \eta \\ 1 + \eta \end{Bmatrix} \tag{8.98}$$

$$\{N_2^+(\eta)\} = \frac{1}{2}\begin{Bmatrix} -\eta(1 - \eta) \\ 2(1 - \eta)(1 + \eta) \\ \eta(1 + \eta) \end{Bmatrix} \tag{8.99}$$

By definition, $x_1 \equiv \{N_k(\eta)\}^T\{XI\}_e$, and $\det J = \det [\partial x_1/\partial \eta_1]$. Denoting the elements of $\{XI\}_e$ as the left (L), right (R) and middle (M) x_1 coordinates of R_e^1, where by definition $M \equiv \frac{1}{2}(R+L)$, then it is easy to verify that for

$$k=1: \qquad DET_e = \tfrac{1}{2}(R-L)$$

$$k=2: \qquad DET_e = \tfrac{1}{2}(R-L) - \eta(R+L-2M) \tag{8.100}$$

Since the element measure definition is $\Delta_e \equiv R-L$, then $\overline{DET}_e = \Delta_e/2$ for each basis. By the same procedures, the sole nonvanishing element of $\{ETAKJ\}_e$ is in the (1, 1) location with a value of unity.

Therefore, the finite-element algorithm statement becomes quite simplified for the quasi-one-dimensional situation. It is a suggested exercise to show that the algorithm statement (8.51)-(8.54) is

$$\begin{aligned}\{FR\}_e = {} & [\Delta_e[A200] + \nu_1^1[A210]]\{R\}'_{j+1} \\ & + \frac{\Delta t}{2}[[A210]\{M\} + \nu_1^2\{U\}^T[A3011]\{R\}] \\ & + \{A\}^T([A41000]\{U\})\{R\}]_{j+1,j} = \{0\}\end{aligned} \tag{8.101}$$

$$\begin{aligned}\{FM\}_e = {} & [\Delta_e[A200] + \nu_2^1[A210]]\{M\}'_{j+1} \\ & + \frac{\Delta t}{2}[\{V\}^T[A3010]\{M\} + [A210]\{P\} + \nu_2^2\{\bar{U}\}^T[A3011]\{M\} \\ & + \{A\}^T([A41000]\{U\})\{M\}]_{j+1,j} = \{0\}\end{aligned} \tag{8.102}$$

$$\begin{aligned}\{FG\}_e = {} & [\Delta_e[A200] + \nu_3^1[A210]]\{G\}'_{j+1} \\ & + \frac{\Delta t}{2}[\{U\}^T[A3010](\{G\} + \{P\}) + \nu_3^2\{\bar{U}\}^T[A3011]\{G\} \\ & + \{A\}^T([A41000]\{U\})(\{G\} + \{P\})]_{j+1,j} = \{0\}\end{aligned} \tag{8.103}$$

$$\{FP\}_e = \Delta_e[A200]\{P\} - \Delta_e(\gamma-1)[[A200]\{G\} - \tfrac{1}{2}\{U\}^T[A3000]\{M\}] = \{0\} \tag{8.104}$$

It is an elementary task to differentiate (8.101)-(8.104), to form the Newton algorithm jacobian contributions, (8.74)-(8.77), and to show that

$$\begin{aligned}\frac{\partial\{FR\}}{\partial\{R\}} \equiv [JRR]_e = {} & \Delta_e[A200] + \nu_1^1[A210] + \frac{\Delta t}{2}\Bigg[\nu_1^2\Bigg(\{\bar{U}\}^T[A3011] \\ & - \left(\frac{\bar{m}}{\bar{\rho}^2}\right)\{R\}^T[A3110]\Bigg) + \{A\}^T[A41000]\left(\{U\} - \frac{\bar{m}}{\bar{\rho}^2}\{R\}\right)\Bigg]_{j+1}^p\end{aligned}$$

$$[JRM]_e = \frac{\Delta t}{2}[[A210] + \nu_1^2[A211] + \{A\}^T[A3100]]_{j+1}^p$$

$$[JRG]_e = 0 = [JRP]_e \tag{8.105}$$

$$\frac{\partial\{FM\}}{\partial\{R\}} \equiv [JMR]_e = -\frac{\Delta t}{2}\left(\frac{\bar{m}}{\bar{\rho}^2}\right)\{M\}^T[[A3010] + \nu_2^2[A3110]$$
$$+ [A40001]\{A\}]_{j+1}^p$$
$$[JMM]_e = \Delta_e[A200] + \nu_2^1[A210]$$
$$+ \frac{\Delta t}{2}\{U\}^T[[A3010] + \nu_3^2[A3011] + [A40001]\{A\}]_{j+1}^p$$
$$+ \frac{\Delta t}{2}\left(\frac{1}{\bar{\rho}}\right)\{M\}^T[[A3010] + \nu_2^2[A3110] + [A40001]\{A\}]_{j+1}^p$$
$$[JMG]_e = [0]$$
$$[JMP]_e = \frac{\Delta t}{2}[A210] \qquad (8.106)$$

$$\frac{\partial\{FG\}}{\partial\{R\}} \equiv [JGR]_e = -\frac{\Delta t}{2}\left(\frac{\bar{m}}{\bar{\rho}^2}\right)[\{G\}^T([A3010] + \nu_3^2[A3110] + [A40001]\{A\})$$
$$+ \{P\}^T[A3010]]_{j+1}^p$$
$$[JGM]_e = \frac{\Delta t}{2}\left(\frac{1}{\bar{\rho}}\right)[\{G\}^T([A3010] + \nu_3^2[A3110] + [A40001]\{A\})$$
$$+ \{P\}^T[A3010]]_{j+1}^p$$
$$[JGG]_e = \Delta_e[A200] + \nu_3^1[A210]$$
$$+ \frac{\Delta t}{2}\{U\}^T[[A3010] + \nu_3^2[A3011] + [A40001]\{A\}]_{j+1}^p$$
$$[JGP]_e = \frac{\Delta t}{2}\{U\}^T[[A3010] + [A40001]\{A\}]_{j+1}^p \qquad (8.107)$$

$$\frac{1}{\Delta_e}\frac{\partial\{FP\}}{\partial\{R\}} \equiv [JPR]_e = -\left(\frac{\gamma-1}{2}\right)\left[\left(\frac{\bar{m}}{\bar{\rho}^2}\right)\{M\}^T[A3000]\right]_{j+1}^p$$
$$[JPM]_e = \frac{\gamma-1}{2}\left[\{U\}^T[A3000] + \left(\frac{1}{\bar{\rho}}\right)\{M\}^T[A3000]\right]_{j+1}^p$$
$$[JPG]_e = -(\gamma-1)[A200]$$
$$[JPP]_e = [A200] \qquad (8.108)$$

In (8.106)-(8.108), the superscript bar on m and ρ indicates the element average value, and absolute value when multiplied by ν_α^2. The elements of $\{A\}_e$ are the nodal values of $\ln A(x)$. The defined standard matrices and hypermatrices are listed in Appendix B.1 for both cardinal basis formulations, $1 \leqslant k \leqslant 2$.

It is important to detail the construction of the jacobian of the Newton iteration algorithm (8.34), especially since the multidimensional algorithm employs basically one-dimensional constructions in forming the matrix tensor product jacobian (8.59). Symbolically, using the assembly operator S_e, the Newton statement (8.34) is the form

$$S_e \begin{bmatrix} [JRR]_e & [JRM]_e & & \\ [JMR]_e & [JMM]_e & & [JMP]_e \\ [JGR]_e & [JGM]_e & [JGG]_e & [JGP]_e \\ [JPR]_e & [JPM]_e & [JPG]_e & [JPP]_e \end{bmatrix} \begin{Bmatrix} \delta R \\ \delta M \\ \delta G \\ \delta P \end{Bmatrix} = - \begin{Bmatrix} FR \\ FM \\ FG \\ FP \end{Bmatrix} \tag{8.109}$$

with the various element jacobians given by (8.105)-(8.108). In actual practice, to minimize bandwidth, the global vector $\{\delta QI\}$ is ordered by degrees of freedom at node points, e.g.,

$$\{\delta QI\}^T \Rightarrow \{\ldots\ldots, R_{j-1}, M_{j-1}, G_{j-1}, P_{j-1}, R_j, M_j, G_j, P_j, R_{j+1}, M_{j+1}, G_{j+1}, P_{j+1}, \ldots\ldots\} \tag{8.110}$$

For exposition, the lead matrix in each elemental jacobian of self-coupling $[JQQ]_e$ is $\Delta_e[A200]$. Assemblying over the element pair sharing node coordinate x_j, for the $\{N_1\}$ algorithm, yields the tridiagonal recursion relationship

$$S_e[\Delta_e[A200]] = S_e\left[\ldots, \frac{\Delta_{j-1}}{6}\begin{bmatrix} 2 & 1 \\ 1 & 2 \end{bmatrix}, \frac{\Delta_{j+1}}{6}\begin{bmatrix} 2 & 1 \\ 1 & 2 \end{bmatrix}, \ldots\right]$$

$$\Rightarrow \frac{1}{6}[\ldots, \Delta_{j-1}, 2(\Delta_{j-1} + \Delta_{j+1}), \Delta_{j+1}, \ldots] \tag{8.111}$$

assuming $\Delta_{j-1} \equiv (x_j - x_{j-1})$ and $\Delta_{j+1} \equiv (x_{j+1} - x_j)$ are distinct. Hence, define the elements of $S_e[JQQ]$ as

$$S_e[\Delta_e[A200]] \equiv [\ldots, 200_{j-1}, 200_j, 200_{j+1}, \ldots] \tag{8.112}$$

and the numerical values are given in (8.111). In a similar manner, noting the first term in $[JMR]_e$ involves $\{M\}_e^T[A3010]$, define the elements of the assembled form as

$$S_e\left[-\frac{\Delta t}{2}\left(\frac{\bar{m}}{\rho^2}\right)_e \{M\}_e^T[A3010]\right] \equiv [\ldots, M3010_{j-1}, M3010_j, M3010_{j+1}, \ldots] \tag{8.113}$$

Both forms (8.112) and (8.113) would extend to $(\cdot)_{j-2}$ and $(\cdot)_{j+2}$ should the $\{N_2\}$ basis be employed rather than $\{N_1\}$.

Using the definitions (8.112)-(8.113), the Newton algorithm statement (8.109) assembled on degrees of freedom at node coordinates, is the α-block partitioned matrix equation:

$$
\left[\begin{array}{cccc|cccc|cccc}
 & & & & & & & & & & & \\
\multicolumn{4}{c|}{\overbrace{\qquad\qquad\qquad}^{j-1}} & \multicolumn{4}{c|}{\overbrace{\qquad\qquad\qquad}^{j}} & \multicolumn{4}{c}{\overbrace{\qquad\qquad\qquad}^{j+1}} \\
\hline
200 & 210 & & & 200 & 210 & & & 200 & 210 & & \\
M3010 & 200 & & 210 & M3010 & 200 & & 210 & M3010 & 200 & & 210 \\
G3010 & G3010 & 200 & U3010 & G3010 & G3010 & 200 & U3010 & G3010 & G3010 & 200 & U3010 \\
M3000 & U3000 & 200 & 200 & M3000 & U3000 & 200 & 200 & M3000 & U3000 & 200 & 200 \\
\hline
 & & & & & & & & & & & \\
\end{array}\right]
\left\{\begin{array}{c}
\vdots \\ R_{j-1} \\ M_{j-1} \\ G_{j-1} \\ P_{j-1} \\ \hline R_j \\ M_j \\ G_j \\ P_j \\ \hline R_{j+1} \\ M_{j+1} \\ G_{j+1} \\ P_{j+1} \\ \vdots
\end{array}\right\} \equiv -\{FQ\}
\tag{8.114}
$$

In (8.114), each symbol corresponds to only the first term in any specific element jacobian (8.105)–(8.108). The prefixes M, G, U, on the 3010 and 3000 terms, indicate the occurrence of explicit nonlinearity in $[J\cdot\cdot]$. Note that the block structure is identical in appearance in each partition $[\cdot]_{j-1}$, $[\cdot]_j$, and $[\cdot]_{j+1}$. However, the entries are distinct, e.g.,

$$200_{j-1} = \Delta_{j-1} \qquad 200_j = 2(\Delta_{j+1} + \Delta_{j-1}) \qquad 200_{j+1} = \Delta_{j+1}$$

For the quadratic basis algorithm construction, the symbols in (8.114) extend to $j \pm 2$. The scalar bandwidth for the $\{N_1^+\}$ algorithm statement (8.114) is 12, since both the energy and pressure are fully coupled throughout the dependent variable set.

Problems

1 Derive (8.94)–(8.97) from (8.1)–(8.4).

2 Verify the one-dimensional basis $\{N_k^+(\eta)\}$ given in (8.98)–(8.99).

3 Verify (8.100).

4 Derive the algorithm statements (8.101)–(8.104).

5 Verify the algorithm jacobians (8.105)–(8.108).

6 Derive the elements of (8.114) using (8.111)–(8.113).

8.9 ACCURACY AND CONVERGENCE, MIXED ONE-DIMENSIONAL FLOWS

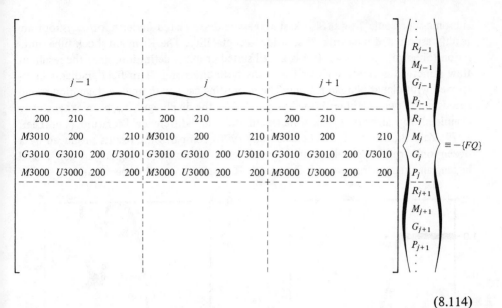

The principal requirement of any quasi, one-dimensional solution is to quantize accuracy and convergence performance of the finite-element algorithm for mixed subsonic-supersonic flows. Shock sharpness and associated undershoot/overshoot are readily assimilated measures of solution acceptability. The Riemann shock tube simulation (Shapiro, 1953, p. 1007) is a well-suited problem definition, since the resultant flow structure is richly endowed with discontinuities and sharp field gradients interspersed with planar plateau regions. The interesting case, with unique stagnation sound speeds in the two chambers initially separated by the diaphragm, has been exhaustively examined for algorithm performance in the finite-difference literature (van Leer, 1979; Zalesak, 1980). In particular, Sod (1978) compares the results produced by a dozen finite-difference algorithms, based selectively on both lagrangian and mixed lagrangian-eulerian frameworks, for a single Riemann shock tube specification.

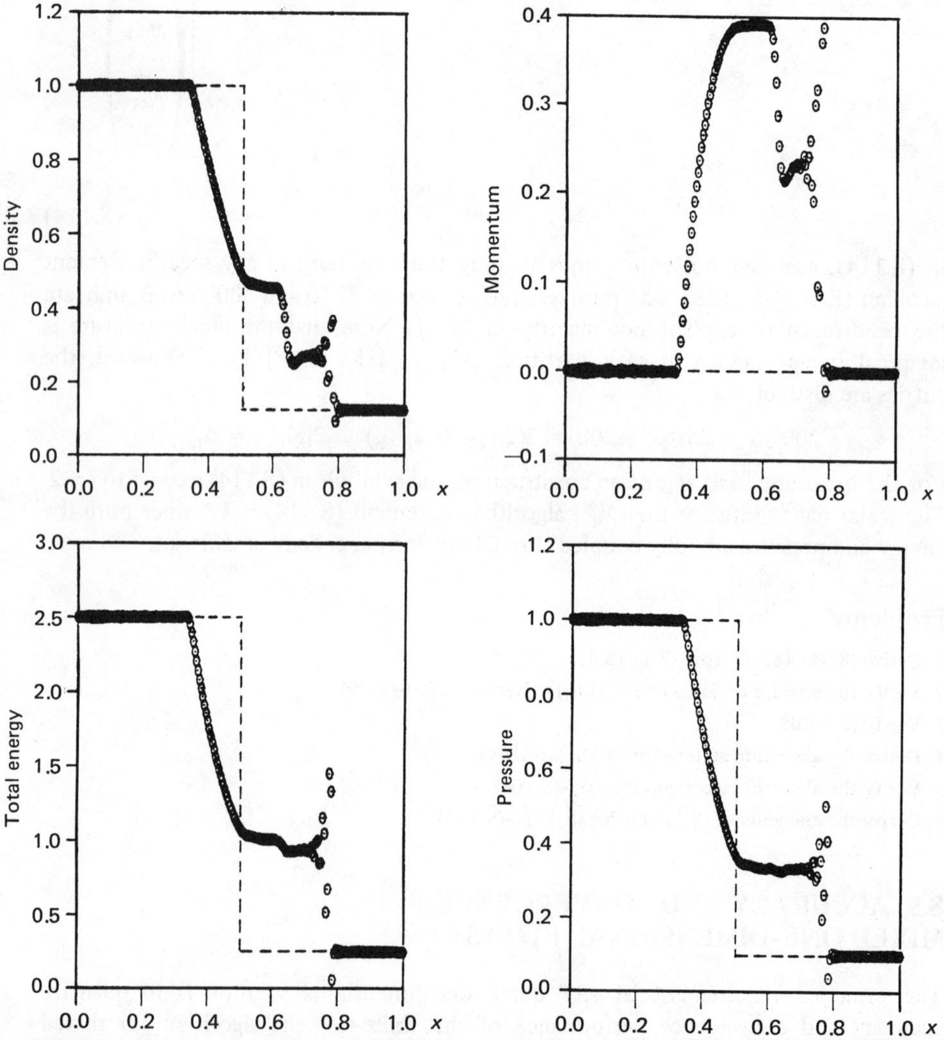

Figure 8.4 $M = 400$, $k = 1$ finite-element algorithm solution, Riemann shock tube, $t = 0.14154$ s, $\nu_\alpha^1 \equiv \nu \equiv \nu_\alpha^2, \nu_m^1 \equiv 0$. (– – –) Denotes initial conditions.

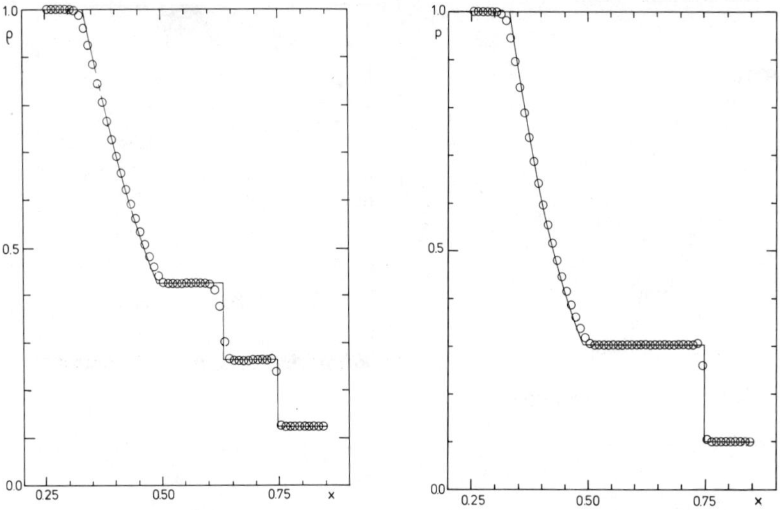

Figure 8.5 Solution for Riemann shock tube generated by the MUSCL code, reported by van Leer (1979); Courant number = 0.9, $\Delta x = 0.01$, $t = 0.14154$ s, reprinted with permission.

For the finite-element algorithm assessment, Baker (1982), the diaphragm is placed midway in a duct of uniform cross section, with the unit length discretized into $12 \leqslant M \leqslant 400$ finite elements R_e^1 of uniform measure Δ. The $k = 1$, $M = 100$ discretization corresponds to the definition of Sod (1978), with initial condition specifications $u(x) = 0$, $p = 1 = \rho$ on $0 \leqslant x \leqslant 0.5$, $p = 0.1$ and $\rho = 0.125$ on $0.5 < x \leqslant 1.0$, and $\gamma = 1.4$. Figure 8.4 graphs the $k = 1$ solution variable set $\{QI(n\,\Delta t)\}$ at $t =$ 0.14154 s, as obtained using the Raymond-Garder order-of-accuracy optimized parameter set $\nu_\alpha^1 \equiv \nu \equiv \nu_\alpha^2$, $\nu_m^1 = 0$, and $\nu \equiv (15)^{-1/2}$. Each symbol corresponds to a nodal coordinate of q_α^h, and the dashed lines denote the initial conditions. The shock is centered at $x = 0.75$, the contact discontinuity is centered at $x = 0.62$, and the rarefaction wave lies upstream of $x = 0.5$, the diaphragm location. For comparison, Fig. 8.5 is a graph of the $M = 99$ solution for ρ^h and p^h, on the region $0.25 \leqslant x \leqslant 0.75$, as generated by the lagrangian-rezone eulerian MUSCL finite-difference algorithm of van Leer (1979). The analytical solution is shown as solid lines. The $k = 1$ finite-element solution is considerably smoother, with less well-defined gradients and plateaus, and with excessive overshoot/undershoot about the shock. Figure 8.6 is an improved $k = 1$, $M = 200$, $\{N_1\}$ algorithm solution, obtained with the "numerically optimized" dissipation parameter set $\nu_\alpha^1 = \nu\{3/8,\ 0,\ 1/4\}$ and $\nu_\alpha^2 = \nu\{3/4,\ 2,\ 1\}$, $\nu \equiv (15)^{-1/2}$ and $1 \leqslant \alpha \leqslant 3$. Each of the characteristic Riemann solution features is accurately predicted including planar plateau regions and a crisply defined shock with negligible overshoot.

The solution fields of principal engineering interest for the Riemann problem are velocity and internal energy (temperature) distributions. Figure 8.7*a* graphs the $M = 99$ MUSCL code solution and the analytical solution (solid line). The ν_α optimized, $k = 1$, $M = 200$ and $M = 100$ finite-element solutions are graphed in Figs. 8.7*b*–8.7*c*, respectively. In addition, Fig. 8.7*d* shows the $M = 100$ solution obtained using the

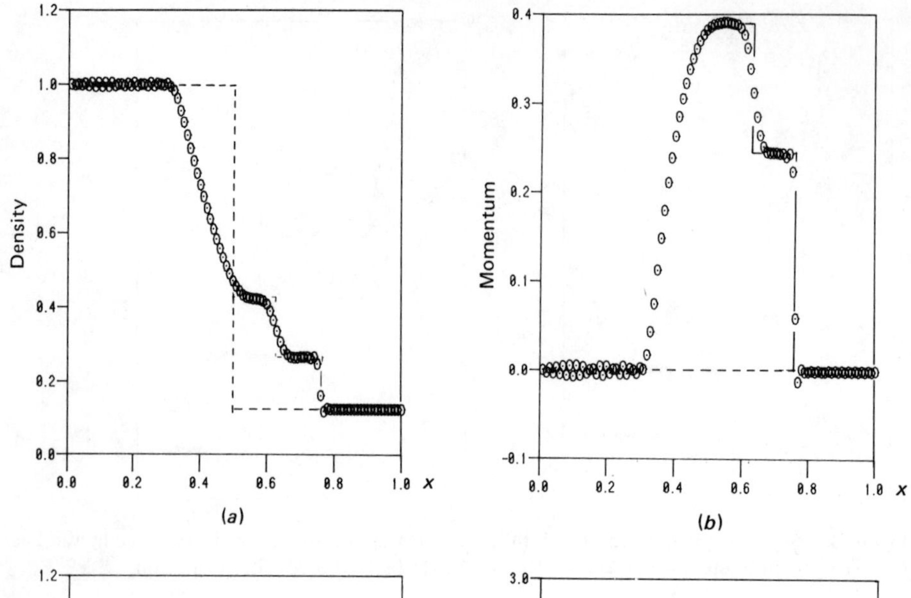

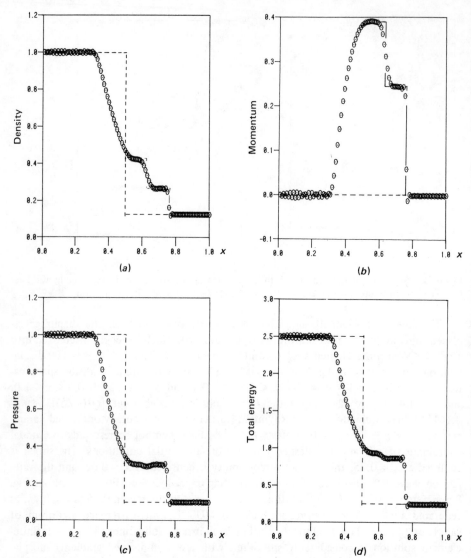

Figure 8.6 $M = 200$, $k = 1$ finite-element solution, Riemann shock tube $\nu_{\alpha}^{1} = \nu\{3/8,\ 0,\ 1/4\}$, $\nu_{\alpha}^{2} = \nu\ \{3/4, 2, 1\}$, $t = 0.14154$ s. (– – –) Denotes initial conditions.

Crank-Nicolson finite-difference algorithm equivalent of the $k = 1$ finite-element algorithm with $\nu_{\alpha}^{1} = 0$ and $\nu_{\alpha}^{2} = \nu\{1,\ 1,\ 1\}$. Increasing the dissipation level ν_{α}^{2} would moderate the illustrated excessive shock overshoot, at the expense of farther diffusing the shock over more than the present five domains. In comparison, the $M = 100$, $k = 1$ finite-element algorithm data interpolate the shock over only two element domains with negligible overshoot, for the identical CPU and main memory requirements. The $M = 100$, $k = 1$ finite-element data (Fig. 8.7*c*), compare favorably with the MUSCL code data. The velocity resolution of the shock and the planarity in the high temperature plateau are nominally identical. The MUSCL code interpolates the contact discontinuity over five domains, while the $k = 1$ data has smeared it over nine finite elements. Considering that the eulerian finite element algorithm is not at all "hard-wired" for this problem, this accuracy is quite acceptable.

The accuracy of the $k = 2$ finite-element algorithm for the Riemann problem is nominally identical. The optimized dissipation parameter set was determined as $\nu_\alpha^1 = 0$, and $\nu_\alpha^2 = \nu\{1/4,\ 3/4,\ 1/2\}$ (Baker, 1982). Figure 8.8 graphs the resulting

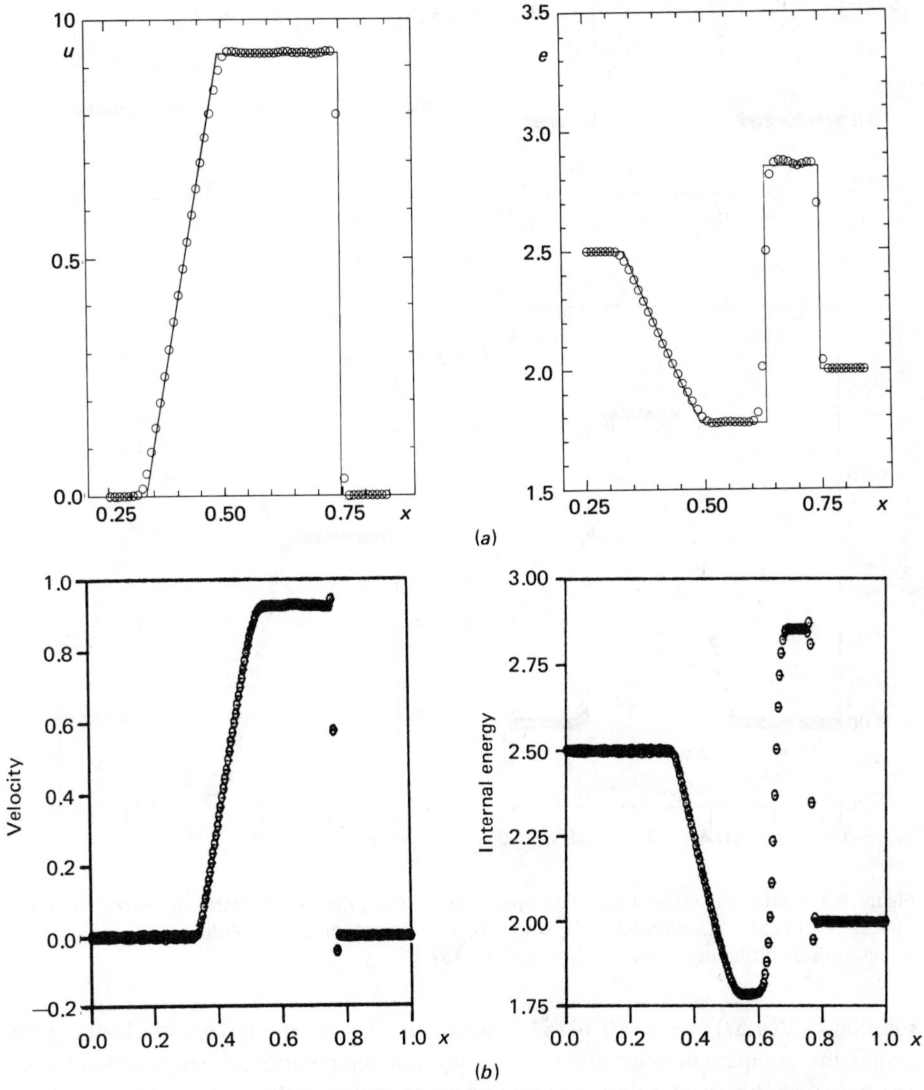

Figure 8.7 Finite-element and finite-difference algorithm solution comparisons, Riemann shock tube; $t = 0.14154$ s. (*a*) MUSCL code solution of van Leer (1978); (——) analytical solution, reprinted with permission; (*b*) $M = 200, k = 1$ finite-element solution, ν_{opt}.

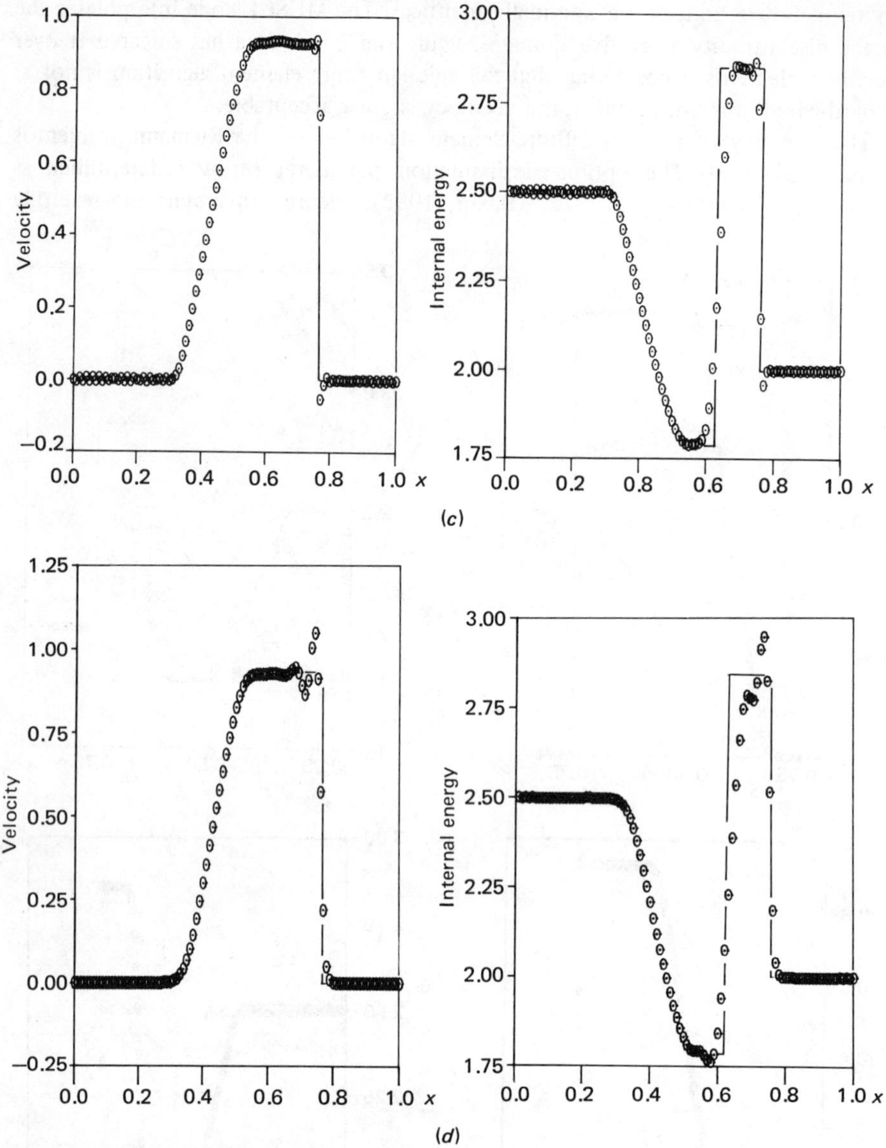

Figure 8.7 Finite-element and finite-difference algorithm solution comparisons; Riemann shock tube, $t = 0.14154$ s (*Continued*). (*c*) $M = 100$, $k = 1$ finite-element solution, ν_{opt}. (*d*) Crank-Nicolson finite-difference solution, $\nu_\alpha^1 = 0$, $\nu_\alpha^2 = (15)^{-1/2}$.

solution $\{QI(n\,\Delta t)\}$ at $t = 0.14154$ s, using an $M = 50$ discretization. Figure 8.9*a* graphs the companion solutions for velocity and temperature, where the solid lines are traces of the exact solution. In comparison to Fig. 8.7*a*–*c*, accuracy is excellent with a noticeable improvement in definition of the contact discontinuity. For the case of the diagonalized finite-difference equivalent of the $k = 2$ algorithm, since

$\nu_\alpha^1 = 0$ is "optimal," the algorithm results are not measurable degraded (see Fig. 8.9*b*). The Newton iteration algorithm jacobian construction (8.114) approximates the theoretical quadratic convergence rate. For example, Table 8.1 summarizes location and magnitude of extremum elements of $\{\delta QI\}$ for a typical integration step.

The sharply defined solutions, as obtained using minimal levels for ν_α^2, typically require 80 steps and 250 iterations to reach $t = 0.14154$ s, at a Courant number ($C = |u + a|\,\Delta t/\Delta x$) of approximately 0.33. Since the algorithm is implicit, the sole constraint on Courant number is accuracy. For these results, a Richardson extrapolation step at $t = 0.14154$ s confirmed that the significant digit in $\|q^h\|$ was unaffected

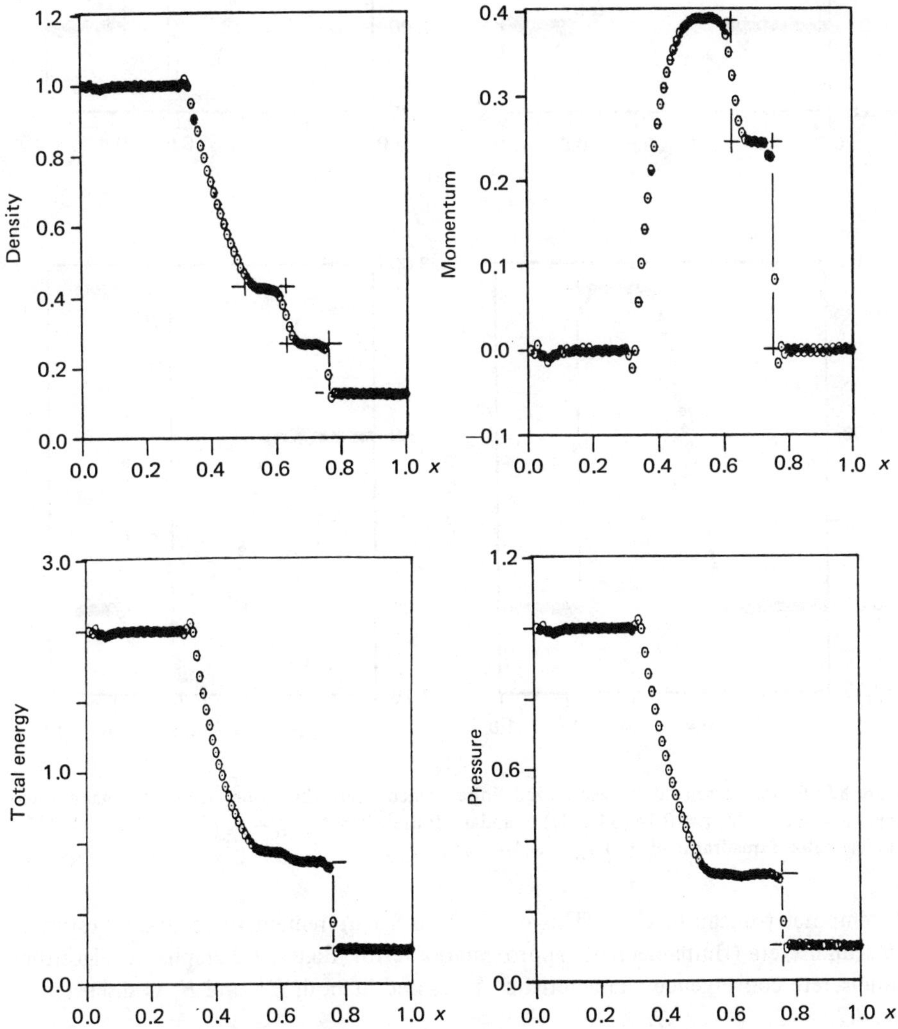

Figure 8.8 $M = 50$, $k = 2$ finite-element algorithm solution, Riemann shock tube, $t = 0.14154$ s, $\nu_\alpha^1 = 0, \nu_\alpha^2 = \nu\{1/4, 3/4, 1/2\}$.

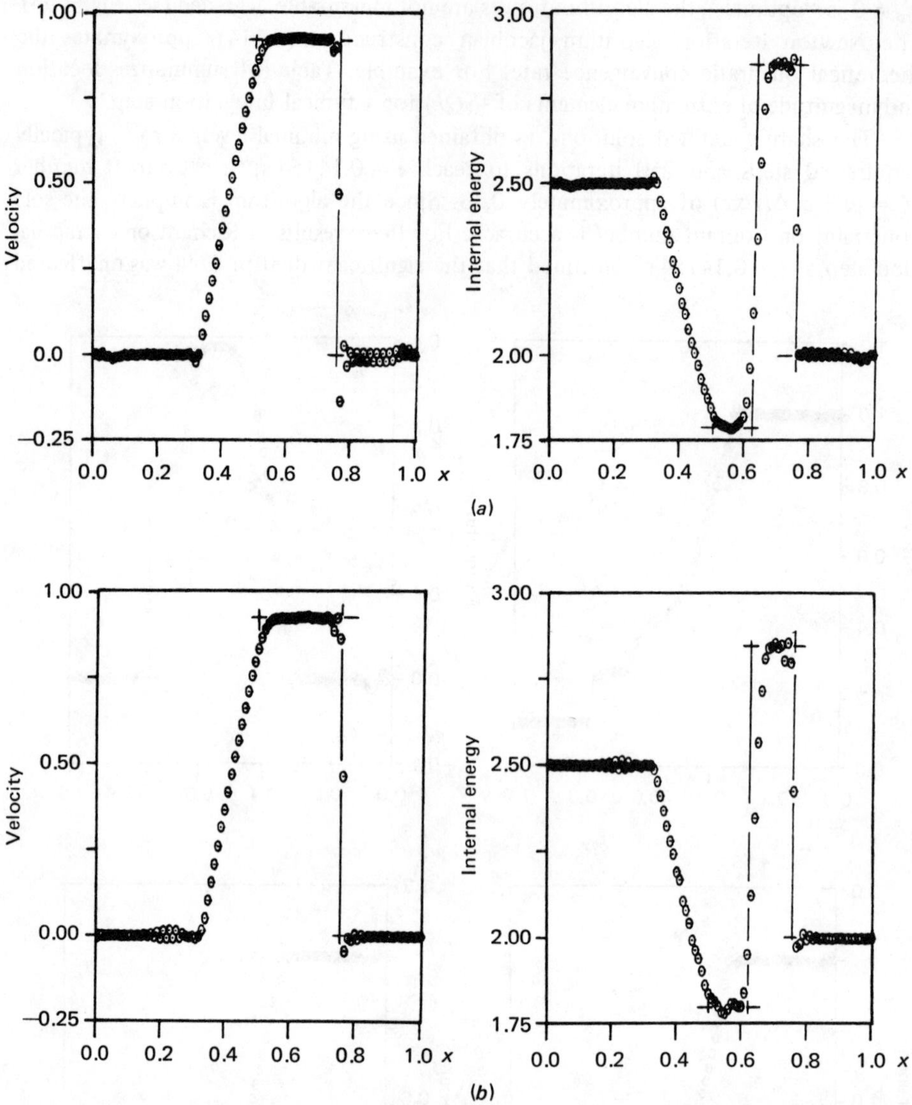

Figure 8.9 Finite-element and diagonalized finite-element algorithm comparisons, Riemann shock tube, $M = 50$, $k = 2$, $t = 0.14154$ s. (*a*) Standard finite element, $\nu^1_\alpha = 0$, $\nu^2_\alpha = \nu\{1/4, 3/4, 1/2\}$; (*b*) diagonalized quadratic, $\nu^1_\alpha = 0$, $\nu^2_\alpha = \nu\{1/4, 3/4, 1/2\}$.

by temporal truncation error. This of course is a requirement to accurately estimate the semidiscrete (finite-element) approximation error. Figure 8.2 graphs the algorithm semidiscrete convergence characteristics, measured in both H^1 and E, as discussed in Sec. 8.7.

Solution efficiency is principally determined by discretization (M) and integration time step (C), in concert with the convergence requirement for the Newton iteration

Table 8.1 Newton iteration convergence in $\{\delta QI\}$ Riemann shock tube ($M = 100$, $k = 1$, $\epsilon = 0.001$)

Iteration	$\{\delta R\}_{max}$	Node	$\{\delta M\}_{max}$	Node
1	0.026	70	0.051	70
2	0.0018	69	−0.0028	69
3	0.000082	69	−0.0038	69
Iteration	$\{\delta G\}_{max}$	**Node**	$\{\delta P\}_{max}$	**Node**
1	0.14	70	0.049	70
2	−0.0072	70	0.0048	71
3	0.00032	70	0.0026	68

algorithm. Table 8.2 summarizes for the $M = 100$, $k = 1$ Reimann solution, the effect of decreasing solution cost by increasing C. Solution cost is nominally halved by doubling the Courant number, to a certain point. Thereafter, diminishing returns are encountered as additional Newton iterations are required for the same convergence level. In all data for $C > 0.33$, the significant digit in the semidiscrete E norm is directly affected by temporal truncation error. Hence, solution accuracy is degraded monotonically with increasing C. It is noteworthy that the $k = 1$ finite-element algorithm accuracy in E, obtained at $C = 1.41$, is uniformly superior to the $C = 0.33$ finite-difference solution (see Fig. 8.2), and was obtained at 40 percent of the computer cost.

Since the finite-element algorithm is fully implicit, the entirety of R^1 is in continuous communication, even those regions where the flow is locally supersonic. An interesting test occurs for a mixed-flow situation, wherein boundary data modifications in a subsonic region require an adjustment to flow in a supersonic region. For example, off-design operation of a de Laval nozzle yields a strong shock in the diverging section, such that the specified mass flow can diffuse to the exit chamber pressure. A modest increase in the exit pressure requires the shock to relocate upstream of its original location, wherein the flow is uniformly supersonic. During this period of adjustment, the supersonic flow upstream of the shock must not respond to

Table 8.2 Accuracy and efficiency summary, Riemann shock tube ($M = 100$, $k = 1$, $\epsilon = 0.001$)

Courant number C	Number of integration time steps	Number of algorithm passes	GO step CPU	Energy norm $\|\|q_\alpha^h\|\|_E^2$ ρ	m	g
0.33	80	229	1.00	1.54	2.43	17.9
0.44	60	180	0.79	1.50	2.39	17.4
0.67	40	121	0.54	1.46	2.29	16.8
0.90	30	92	0.42	1.41	2.15	16.0
1.41	20	82	0.38	1.34	1.90	14.4

the subsonic exit pressure level, the shock must progressively weaken as it moves upstream into regions of smaller cross section, and the flow downstream of the shock must diffuse smoothly to the new exit condition.

Figure 8.10 summarizes an $M = 74$, $k = 1$ algorithm steady-state solution for off-design nozzle flow with $M_1 = 1.35$ before the shock, using ν_{opt} and $\frac{1}{2}\nu_{\text{opt}}$. The solid line is the exact solution, and the $\frac{1}{2}\nu_{\text{opt}}$ solution is in excellent agreement on shock strength and definition. It is interesting how the momentum solution inter-

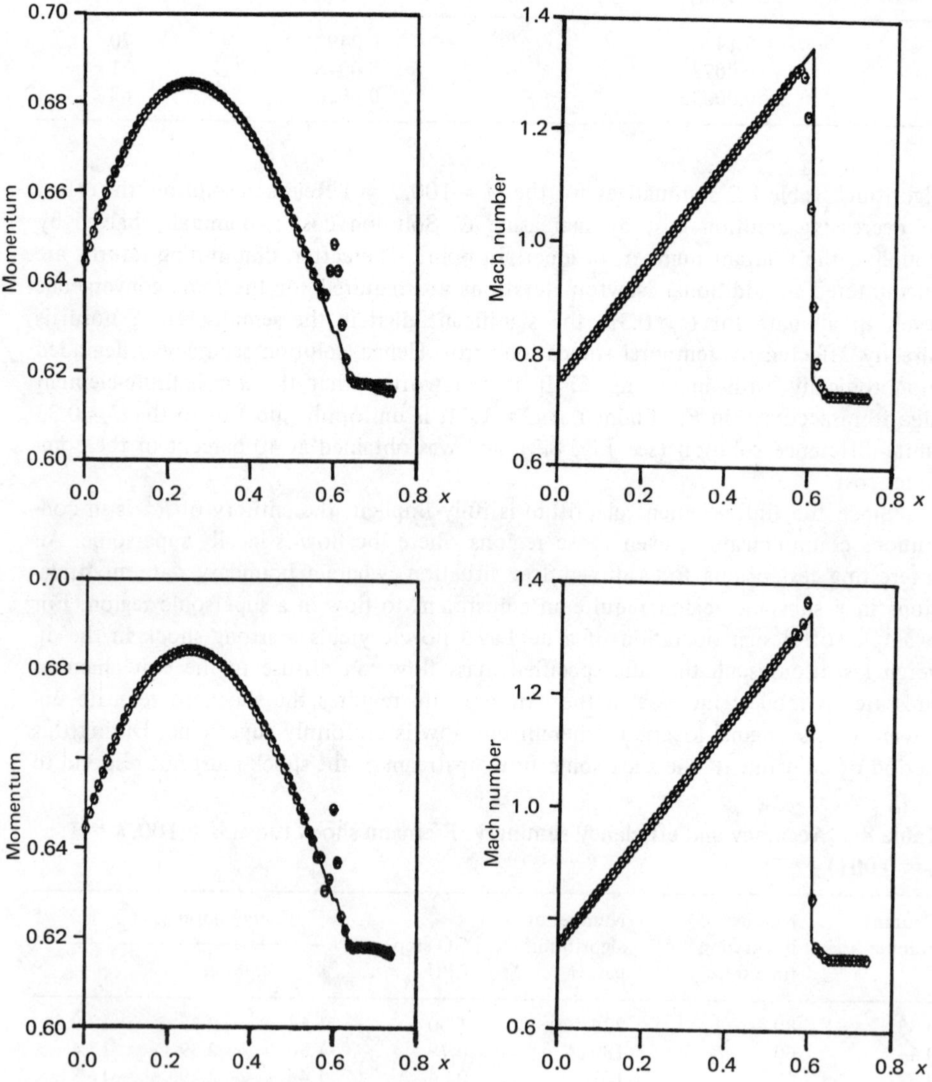

(b)

Figure 8.10 Finite-element algorithm steady-state solution, off-design de Laval nozzle flow; $M = 74, k = 1$; (a) $\nu_\alpha = \nu_{\text{opt}}$; (b) $\nu_\alpha = \frac{1}{2}\nu_{\text{opt}}$.

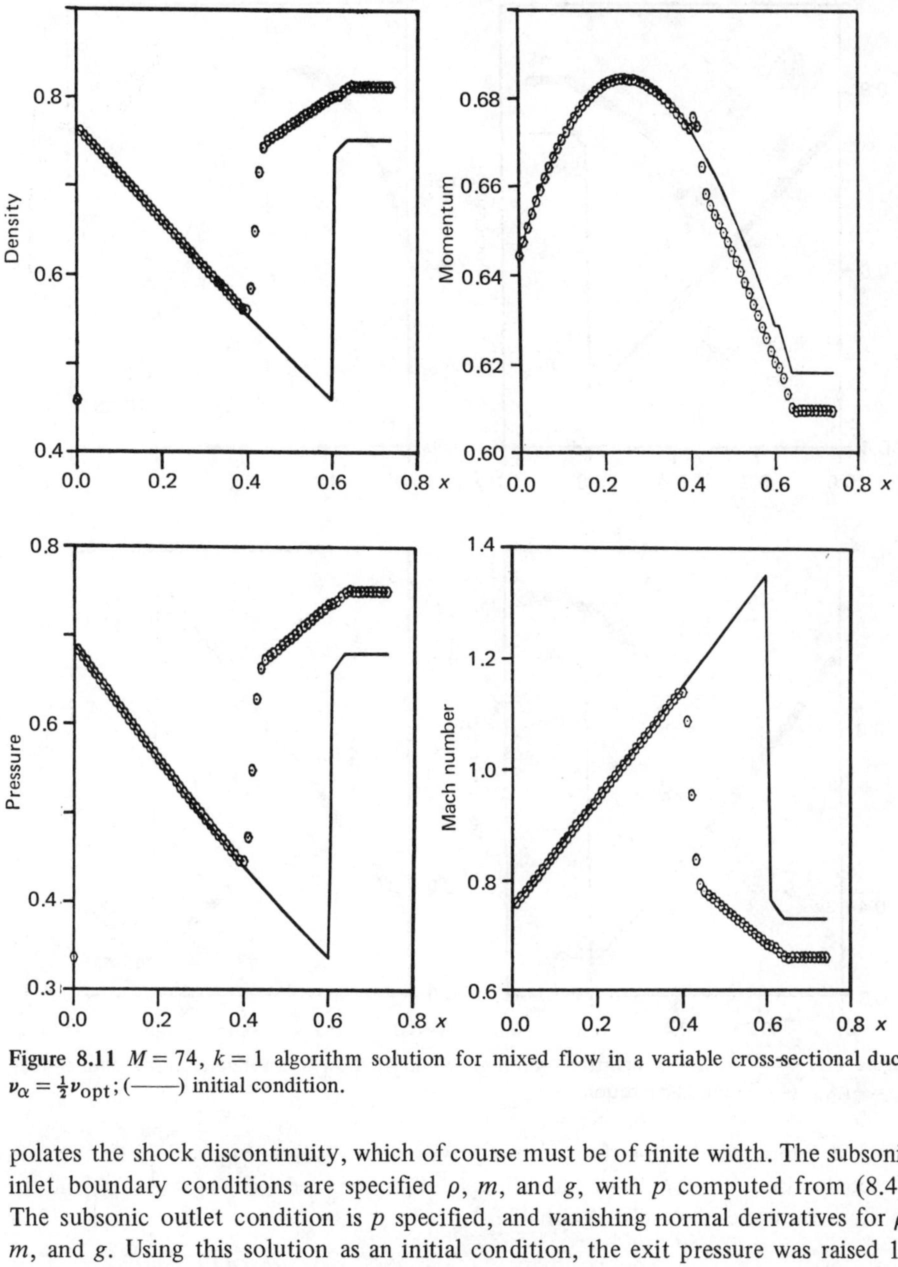

Figure 8.11 $M = 74$, $k = 1$ algorithm solution for mixed flow in a variable cross-sectional duct, $\nu_\alpha = \frac{1}{2}\nu_{\text{opt}}$; (——) initial condition.

polates the shock discontinuity, which of course must be of finite width. The subsonic inlet boundary conditions are specified ρ, m, and g, with p computed from (8.4). The subsonic outlet condition is p specified, and vanishing normal derivatives for ρ, m, and g. Using this solution as an initial condition, the exit pressure was raised 15 percent and held fixed. Figure 8.11 summarizes the $k = 1$ algorithm solution at the new steady-state, where the solid lines show the initial conditions. The flow has adjusted to the modified subsonic exit pressure, with a new shock Mach number of $M_1 = 1.15$. The flow upstream of the shock is unaltered from the initial conditions, and a smooth subsonic expansion to exit conditions is predicted downstream. The

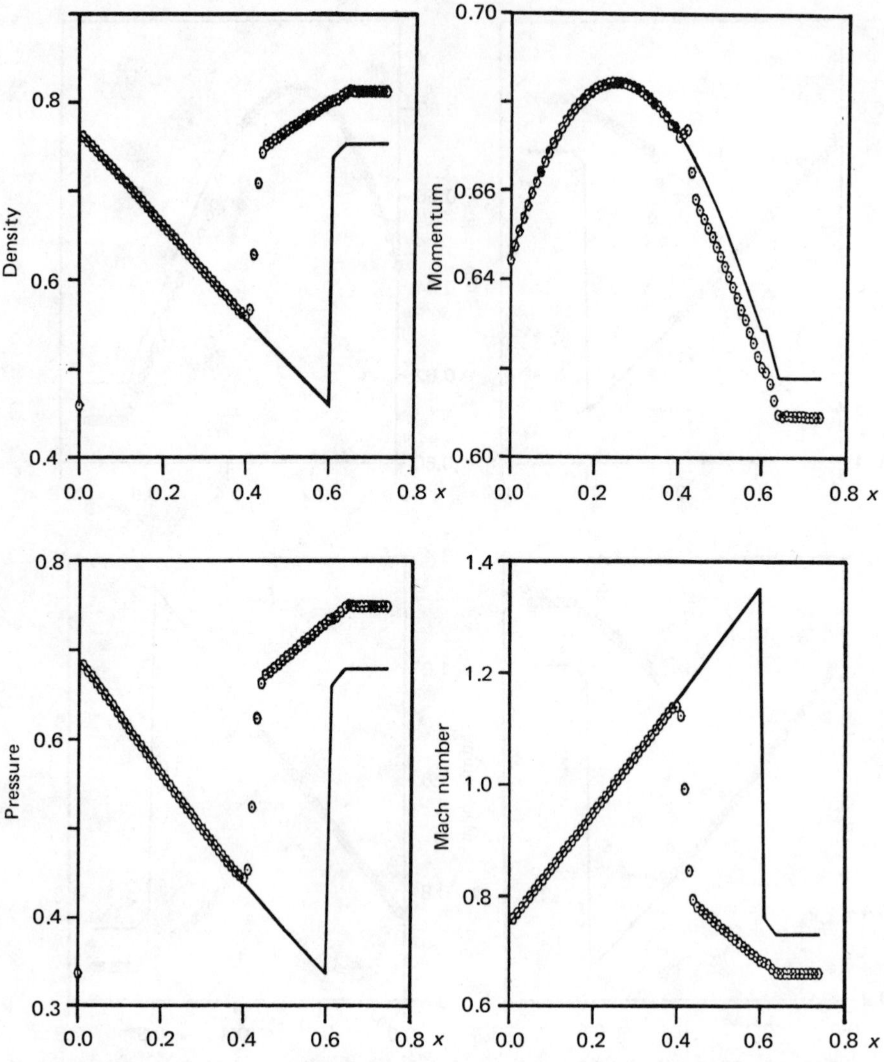

Figure 8.12 $M = 37$, $k = 2$ algorithm solution for mixed flow in a variable cross-sectional duct, $\nu_\alpha = \frac{1}{2}\nu_{\text{opt}}$; (——) initial condition.

shock is interpolated across four elements with no overshoot. Figure 8.12 summarizes the comparison $M = 37$, $k = 2$ algorithm solution obtained using $\nu_\alpha = \frac{1}{2}\nu_{\text{opt}}$, and the solution accuracies are indistinguishable.

8.10 TWO-DIMENSIONAL FORMULATION, LINEAR TENSOR PRODUCT BASIS

As noted in Sec. 8.1, a wide variety of methodologies exist for approximate generation of the inverse coordinate transformation $\eta_i = \eta_i(x_j)$; see (8.37). For example, Fig. 8.13

illustrates such body-fitted coordinate systems, for various two-dimensional aerodynamic configurations, as generated using Poisson equation techniques (Thames et al., 1977). The principal requirement is to render contours coincident with aerodynamic surfaces, symmetry, or periodicity boundaries, to be coordinate curves of the η_i system. The next requirement, from the standpoint of solution accuracy, is to avoid distorted computational cells in critical flow regions, e.g., about stagnation points.

With respect to the developed finite-element algorithm, each of the illustrated

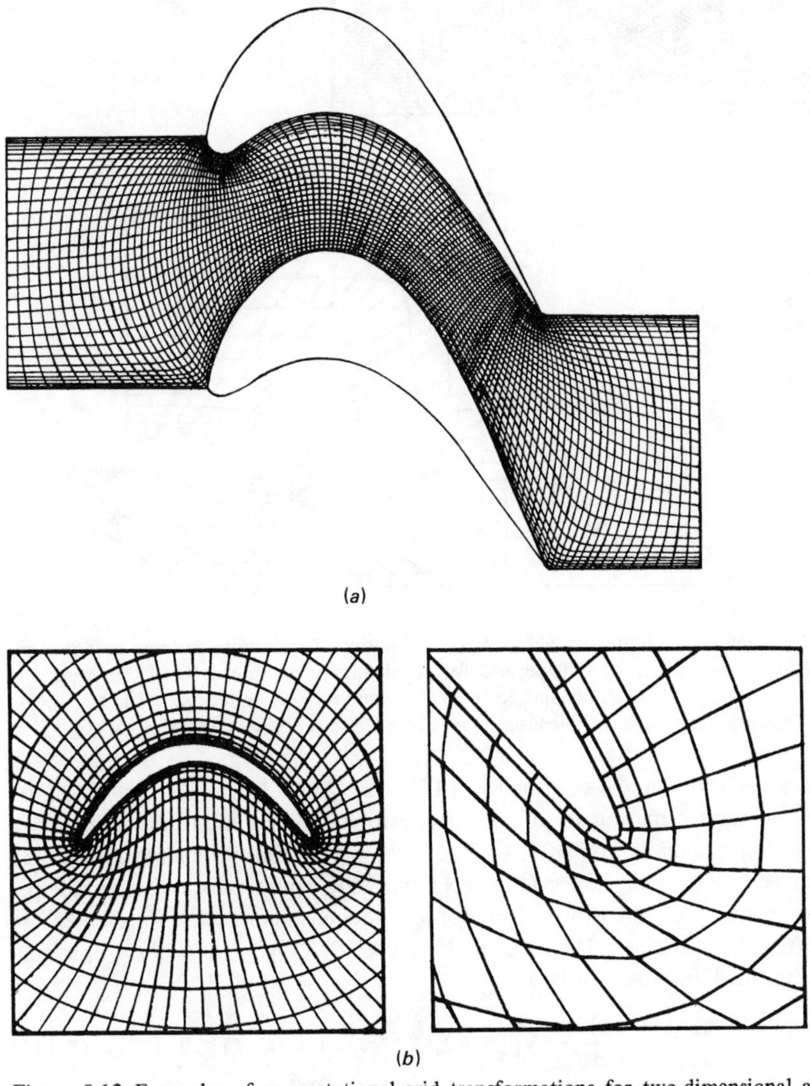

Figure 8.13 Examples of computational grid transformations for two-dimensional aerodynamic flow predictions. (*a*) Turbine cascade. From Ghia and Ghia (NASA, 1980, p. 302). (*b*) Highly cambered airfoil and trailing edge close-up. From Sorenson and Steger (NASA, 1980, p. 456).

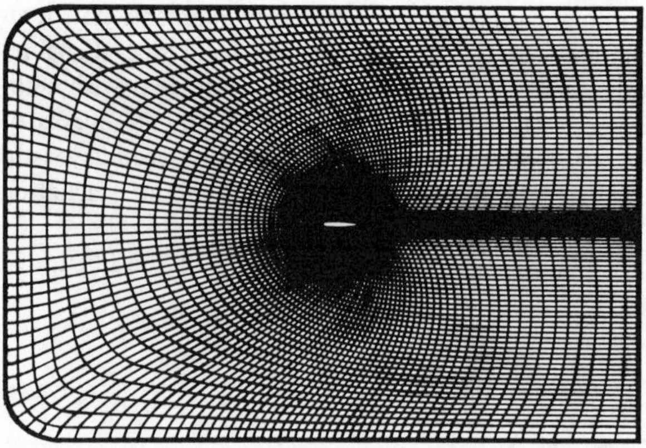

(c)

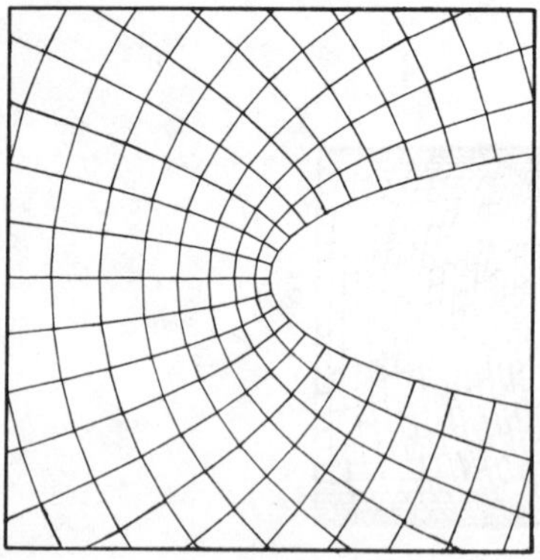

(d)

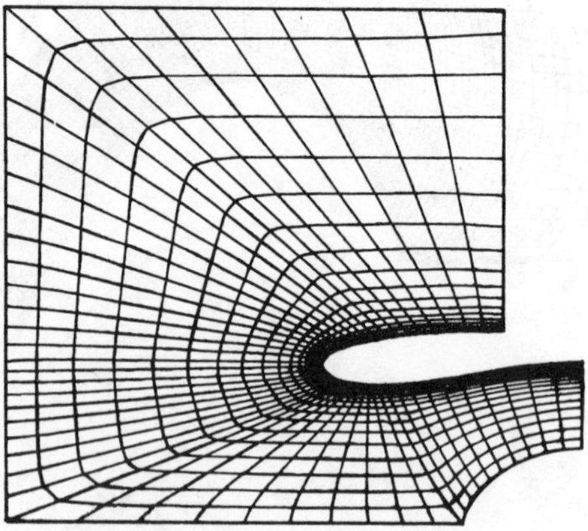

(e)

Figure 8.13 Examples of computational grid transformations for two-dimensional aerodynamic flow prediction (*Continued*). (*c*) C-Type grid for airfoil in a wind tunnel. From Sorenson and Steger (NASA, 1980, p. 458). (*d*) Leading edge detail. From Sorenson and Steger (NASA, 1980, p. 457). (*e*) C-Type grid for macelle with center body. From Kowalski (NASA, 1980, p. 349).

grids defines the set of nodal coordinates $\{XI\} \equiv \Sigma_e \{XI\}_e$, $1 \leqslant e \leqslant M$, $1 \leqslant I \leqslant 2$, required for the transformation (8.38). For exposition, restrict attention to the two-dimensional bilinear basis $\{N_1^+(\eta)\}$, (8.39). The master finite-element domain R_e^2 then contains only vertex nodes (Fig. 8.1). For the counterclockwise numbering convention, starting in the lower left corner, the element node coordinates are $\{XI\}_e \equiv \{XI,\ YI,\ 1 \leqslant I \leqslant 4\}$. The elemental array $\{ETAKJ\}_e$, $1 \leqslant (K, J) \leqslant 2$, is constructed from the definition (8.43), as

$$\left(\frac{\partial \eta_k}{\partial x_j}\right)_e \equiv \frac{1}{\det J_e} \{N_1\}^T \{ETAKJ\}_e \qquad 1 \leqslant (K, J) \leqslant 2 \tag{8.115}$$

Noting that $(\det J)_e^{-1}$ cancels in the algebra, (8.43), the matrix elements of $\{ETAKJ\}_e$ are readily determined as

$$\{ETAKJ\}_e = \frac{1}{2}\left\{\begin{matrix} \{Y4-Y1, Y3-Y2, Y3-Y2, Y4-Y1\}_e^T, (1,1) \\ \{X1-X4, X2-X3, X2-X3, X1-X4\}_e^T, (1,2) \\ \{Y1-Y2, Y1-Y2, Y4-Y3, Y4-Y3\}_e^T, (2,1) \\ \{X2-X1, X2-X1, X3-X4, X3-X4\}_e^T, (2,2) \end{matrix}\right\} \tag{8.116}$$

The numbers in parenthesis indicate the indices (K, J) in $\{ETAKJ\}_e$. The corresponding definition for det $[J]_e$ is

$$\det [J]_e \equiv \{N_1\}^T\{DET\}_e \tag{8.117}$$

yielding

$$\{DET\}_e = \frac{1}{4}\left\{\begin{matrix} (X2-X1)(Y4-Y1)-(X4-X1)(Y2-Y1) \\ (X2-X1)(Y3-Y2)-(X3-X2)(Y2-Y1) \\ (X3-X4)(Y3-Y2)-(X3-X2)(Y3-Y4) \\ (X3-X4)(Y4-Y1)-(X4-X1)(Y3-Y4) \end{matrix}\right\}_e \tag{8.118}$$

The contravariant convection velocity approximation $\bar{u}_k^h$, (8.46), on the domain R_e^2 is defined as

$$\bar{u}_k^h \equiv \{N_1\}^T\{UBARK\}_e \tag{8.119}$$

and the algebra yields

$$\{UBARK\}_e = \{ETAKJ\}_e\{N_1\}^T\{UJ\}_e \tag{8.120}$$

Since (8.120) is defined on a nodal basis, the elements of $\{N_1\}$ reduce to the Kronecker delta, hence,

$$\{UBARK\}_e = UJ_e\{ETAKJ\}_e \tag{8.121}$$

Summation is implied over J, and at the nodes $UJ \equiv MJ/R$, that is, $u_j \equiv m_j/\rho$.

The tensor product jacobian formulation, given for the quasi-one-dimensional flow, is modified only to account for alignment with either the η_1 or η_2 coordinate axis. The cardinal basis remains as given in (8.98), and DET_e is equal to one-half the element measure (8.100). Hence, for (8.74)-(8.79), and using Pythagoras' rule,

$$\{DETK\}_e = \tfrac{1}{2}\left(\sqrt{(XKR-XKL)^2+(YKR-YKL)^2}\right)_e \begin{Bmatrix} 1 \\ 1 \end{Bmatrix} \tag{8.122}$$

where R and L denote right and left, respectively, for the specific η alignment. Correspondingly, the elements of $\{ETAKJ\}_e$ are equal to the direction cosines of the local affine coordinate transformation between x_i and η_j. Denoting θ^k as the angle between the global coordinate x_1, and the local η_k axis on R_e^1 (see Fig. 8.14), then

$$\{ETAKJ\}_e = \left\{\begin{matrix} \{\ \cos\theta^k, \sin\theta^k\}^T, (1,1) \\ \{-\sin\theta^k, \cos\theta^k\}^T, (1,2) \end{matrix}\right\}_e \tag{8.123}$$

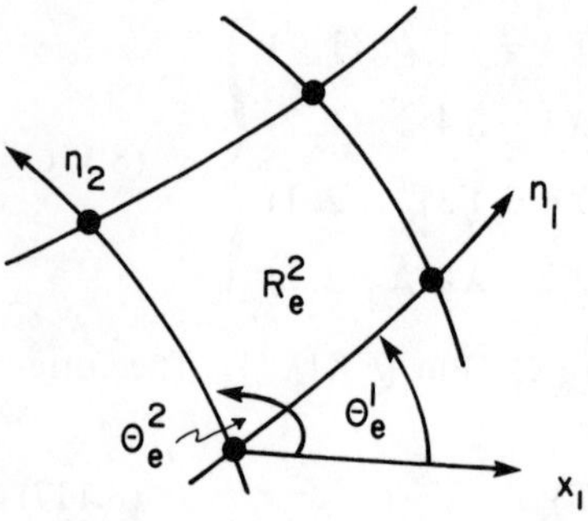

Figure 8.14 Definition of coordinate rotation angle θ_e^k.

The numbers in parentheses again indicate the indices (K, J). Using (8.123), the element node definition for convection velocity in each $[J_\eta]$ is [cf. (8.121)]

$$\{UBARK\}_e = UJ_e\{ETAKJ\}_e \tag{8.124}$$

with $\{ETAKJ\}_e$ provided by (8.123).

No further comments are required concerning evaluation of the algorithm matrices $\{FI\}$, (8.50)-(8.58). The Newton jacobian matrix tensor product solution is [cf. (8.59)-(8.62)]

$$[J_1]\{PI\}_{j+1}^{p+1} = -\{FI\}_{j+1}^{p} \qquad [J_2]\{\delta QI\}_{j+1}^{p+1} = \{PI\}_{j+1}^{p+1} \tag{8.125}$$

The generalization of (8.109) for the two-step solution procedure (8.125) is best illustrated by assuming the x_i and η_k coordinate systems are parallel, hence, $\{ETAKJ\}_e = \{0, 1\}$. For the first solution sweep in (8.125), assumed to be executed parallel to the η_1 coordinate direction, the Newton statement (8.109) takes the form

$$S_e \begin{bmatrix} [JRR]_e & [JRM1]_e & 0 & 0 & 0 & 0 & 0 \\ [JM1R]_e & [JM1M1]_e & 0 & 0 & [JM1P]_e & [JM1SIJ]_e & 0 \\ [JM2R]_e & [JM2M1]_e & [JM2M2]_e & 0 & 0 & 0 & 0 \\ [JGR]_e & [JGM1]_e & 0 & [JGG]_e & [JGP]_e & [JGSIJ]_e & [JGQI]_e \\ [JPR]_e & [JPM1]_e & 0 & [JPG]_e & [JPP]_e & 0 & 0 \\ [JSIJR]_e & [JSIJM1]_e & 0 & 0 & 0 & [JSIJSIJ]_e & 0 \\ [JQIR]_e & [JQIM1]_e & 0 & [JQIG]_e & 0 & 0 & [JQIQI]_e \end{bmatrix} \{PI\}$$

$$= -\{FI\} \tag{8.126}$$

For the second sweep parallel to η_2, (8.109) is the form

$$\begin{bmatrix} [JRR]_e & 0 & [JRM2]_e & 0 & 0 & 0 & 0 \\ [JM1R]_e & [JM1M1]_e & [JM1M2]_e & 0 & 0 & 0 & 0 \\ [JM2R]_e & 0 & [JM2M2]_e & 0 & [JM2P]_e & [JM2SIJ]_e & 0 \\ [JGR]_e & 0 & [JGM2]_e & [JGG]_e & [JGP]_e & [JGSIJ]_e & [JGQI]_e \\ [JPR]_e & 0 & [JPM2]_e & [JPG]_e & [JPP]_e & 0 & 0 \\ [JSIJR]_e & 0 & [JSIJM2]_e & 0 & 0 & [JSIJSIJ]_e & 0 \\ [JQIR]_e & 0 & [JQIM2]_e & [JQIG]_e & 0 & 0 & [JQIQI]_e \end{bmatrix} \{\delta QI\}$$

$$= \{PI\} \tag{8.127}$$

In (8.126)-(8.127), the tensor indices in SIJ and QI range $1 \leqslant (I, J) \leqslant 2$, and the zeros indicate no contribution on that sweep.

The individual contributions to $S_e\,[JQQ]$, and the other terms in (8.126)-(8.127), are assembled as illustrated by (8.114). The maximum band width of the jacobian α-block structure is nominally 30, which is three times the number of nodal dependent variables, i.e., degrees of freedom per node. Rearrangement of the order of variables in $\{\delta QI\}$ can reduce this number for each specific sweep.

Problems

1 Derive (8.116) from (8.115) and (8.39).

2 Establish (8.118) from (8.117) and (8.39).

3 Verify (8.120)-(8.121).

4 Expand (8.122) and verify its appropriateness for the tensor matrix product jacobians (8.74)-(8.79).

5 Verify (8.126) and expand it in the form (8.114).

6 Verify (8.127) and expand it in the form (8.114).

8.11 TWO-DIMENSIONAL INVISCID AND VISCOUS FLOW

Several issues basic to accuracy and convergence aspects of the tensor matrix product formulation of the generalized coordinates finite-element Navier-Stokes algorithm are reported by Baker (1982). Particular aspects studied include application of gradient boundary conditions, Newton algorithm convergence, prediction accuracy for shocks oblique to the mesh and computed in nonprincipal coordinates, and a shock-boundary layer interaction at $\text{Re} = 10^5$.

The test problem definition is the two-dimensional generalization of the Riemann shock tube discussed in Sec. 8.9. By using the linear tensor product basis $\{N_1^+\}$, solutions were generated on discretizations of $M = 32 \times N$, where $4 \leqslant N \leqslant 20$ dependent upon whether the problem was defined as inviscid or viscous. For reference, Fig. 8.15 graphs the coarse-grid ($M = 32$), one-dimensional $k = 1$ algorithm solution prediction of velocity and internal energy for the Riemann problem. The solid lines are traces of the $M = 200$, $k = 1$ solution from Fig. 8.7*b*, and each open symbol is a nodal solution value obtained using $\nu_\alpha^\gamma = \nu_{\text{opt}}$. Interestingly, on this coarse grid, the importance of $\nu_\alpha^1 > 0$ on accuracy becomes diminished. The solid symbols in Fig. 8.15 are the comparison nodal values, as obtained using $\nu_\alpha^1 \equiv 0$, $\nu_\alpha^2 = \nu\{3/4, 2, 1\}$ in the $k = 1$ algorithm solution, at locations where the two solutions differed. These differences are truly negligible; hence, each two-dimensional Riemann solution was executed using $\nu_\alpha^1 = 0$ and $\nu_\alpha^2 = \nu_{\text{opt}}^2$.

Computational assessments are reported (Baker, 1982) evaluating vanishing gradient boundary conditions applied on the transverse walls of the two-dimensional inviscid flow Riemann shock tube. Figure 8.16 graphs the $M = 32 \times 6$, $k = 1$ solution at $t = 0.14154$ s, for the shock tube axis aligned parallel with the principal coordinate x_1. As a consequence, the entire momentum solution is carried by m_1, and m_2 was computed equal to zero to three significant digits for the Newton convergence set at $\epsilon = 0.01$. The $M = 32 \times 6$ solution agrees exactly with the comparison $M = 32$ one-dimensional $k = 1$ algorithm solution (Fig. 8.17), even to prediction of the small amplitude "$2\,\Delta x$" waves in the zero velocity region upstream of the rarefaction wave. The solution required two iterations per step for convergence, and executed in 27 time steps. Figure 8.18 graphs the solution for the more demanding case corresponding to insertion of the diaphragm at an angle to the tube axis. This yields the algorithm requirement to predict a shock oblique to the mesh. The algorithm results

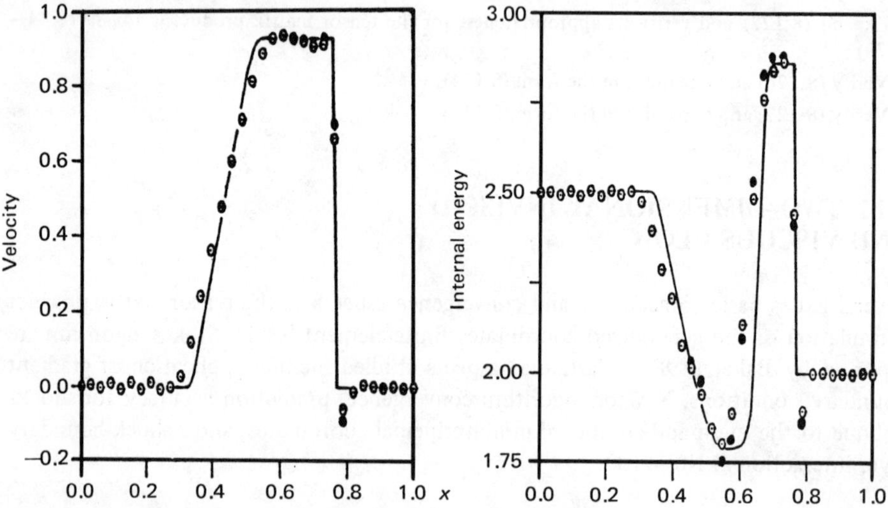

Figure 8.15 $M = 32 \times 1$, $k = 1$ finite-element solution parameters, Riemann shock tube; (——) $M = 200$ solution; (•) $\nu_\alpha^1 = 0$, $\nu_\alpha^2 = \nu_{\text{opt}}$.

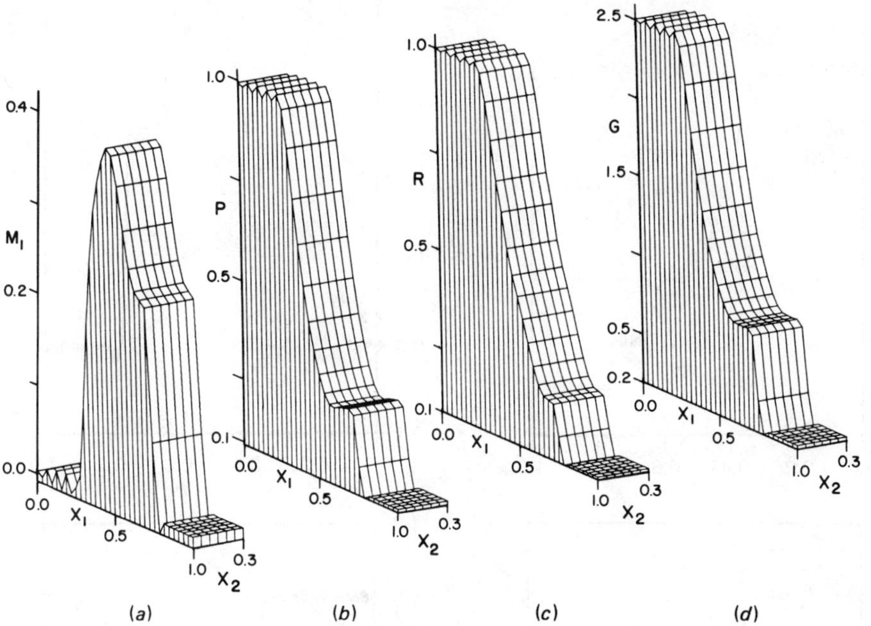

Figure 8.16 $M = 32 \times 6$, $k = 1$ finite-element solution, two-dimensional Riemann shock tube, $t = 0.14154$ s, $\nu^1_\alpha = 0$, $\nu^2_\alpha = \nu\{3/4, 2, 2, 1\}$. (*a*) Momentum m_1; (*b*) pressure p; (*c*) density ρ; (*d*) energy g.

exhibit comparable accuracy, and experience no difficulty in enforcing the gradient boundary for steep solution gradients oblique to the walls. A slightly enhanced "$2\,\Delta x$" trashiness occurs in the solution right rear corner, and a modest no-zero distribution for m_2 was also computed.

Figure 8.19 graphs the $M = 32 \times 6$, $k = 1$ algorithm solution for the shock tube misaligned with the principal coordinates of the momentum vector m_i. As a consequence, both momentum equations generate non-zero solutions. As can be seen by comparing Fig. 8.16, the shock does not appear prominent in these m_i solutions (Fig. 8.19*b–c*). However, computation of the component of $\bar{u}_k$ parallel to η_1 [cf. (8.120)], which is the coordinate parallel to the shock tube axis, confirms existence of the shock (Fig. 8.19*c*). Further, the predicted internal energy distribution (Fig. 8.19*d*) is also in good agreement with the "correct" solution (Fig. 8.15).

The final evaluation reported is for the aligned shock tube definition, reexecuted as a viscous problem at $\text{Re} \equiv 10^5$ on an $M = 32 \times 20$ uniform discretization. The corresponding momentum boundary conditions on the transverse walls are now no-slip, i.e., $m_1 = 0 = m_2$. The cold wall boundary condition was defined for the energy equation $\epsilon \equiv \epsilon_0$ in (8.7), and a vanishing normal derivative applied for the density solution (8.1). No boundary condition specifications are appropriate for p, σ_{ij}, or q_j, since each is defined by an algebraic equation. The integration time step and Newton convergence requirement were maintained identical to those of the inviscid test case (Fig. 8.16). Figure 8.20 graphs the $k = 1$ algorithm solution at $t = 0.14154$ s. In

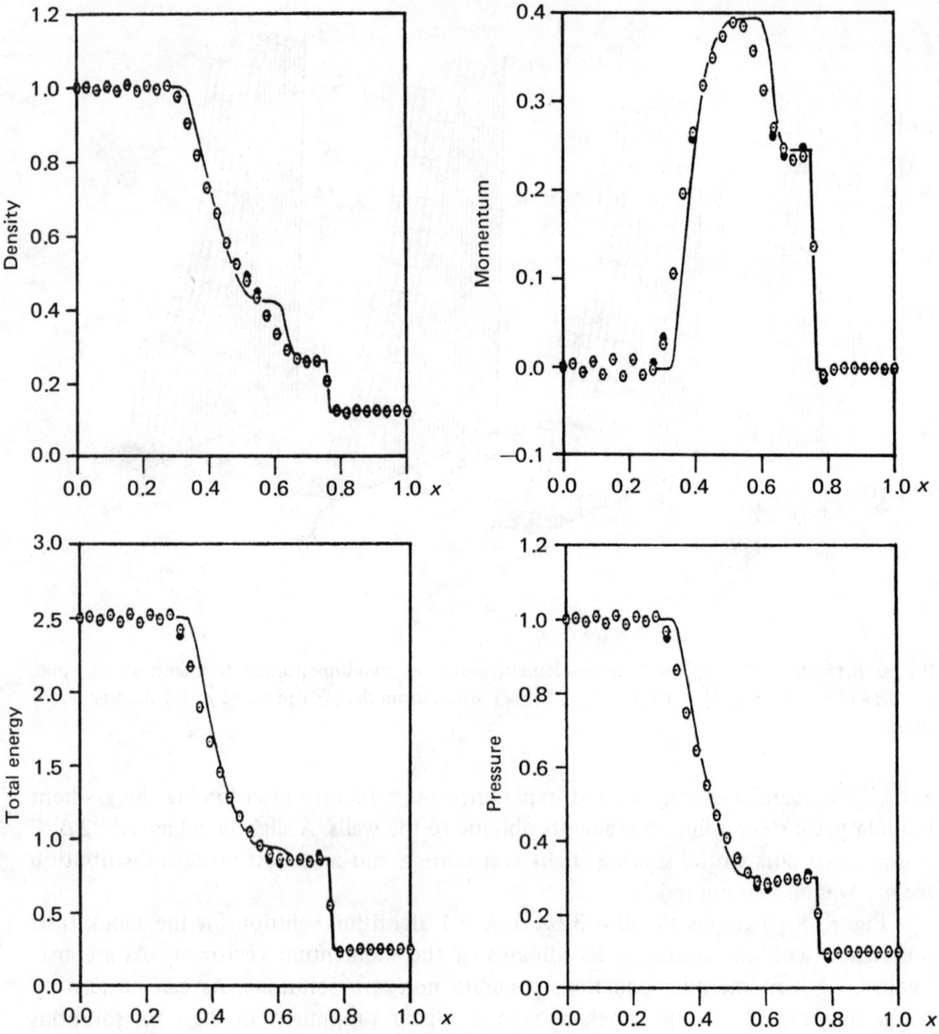

Figure 8.17 $M = 32 \times 1$, $k = 1$ finite-element solution for Riemann shock tube; (——) $M = 200$ solution, (●) $\nu_\alpha^1 = 0$, $\nu_\alpha^2 = \nu_{\text{opt}}$, $t = 0.14154$ s.

the centroidal region, away from the influence of the no-slip wall, the viscous solution agrees essentially exactly with the comparison one-dimensional inviscid solution (Fig. 8.16). The influence of the viscous boundary conditions is clearly evident in all dependent variables. The growth of the laminar boundary layer behind the traveling shock is just visible in the solution for m_1. The solution for m_2 is quite oscillatory, but the peak value is only about 10 percent of the maximum m_1. The σ_{12} shear stress solution is sharply peaked at the wall, with a steep front adjacent to the shock. The solution is non-zero only in the vicinity of the wall, and exhibits the required skew symmetries.

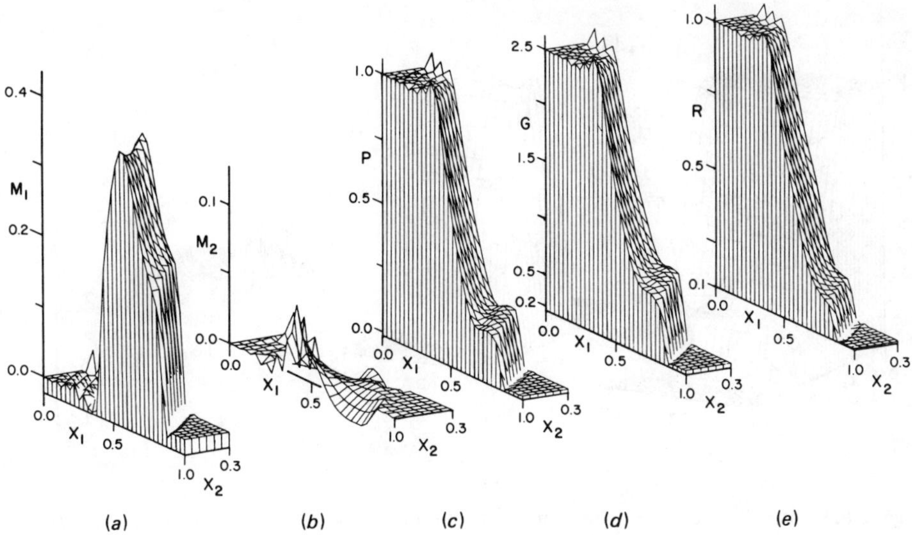

Figure 8.18 $M = 32 \times 6$, $k = 1$ finite-element algorithm solution, two-dimensional Riemann shock tube, oblique diaphragm; $t = 0.14154$ s. (*a*) Momentum m_1; (*b*) momentum m_2; (*c*) pressure p; (*d*) energy g; (*e*) density ρ.

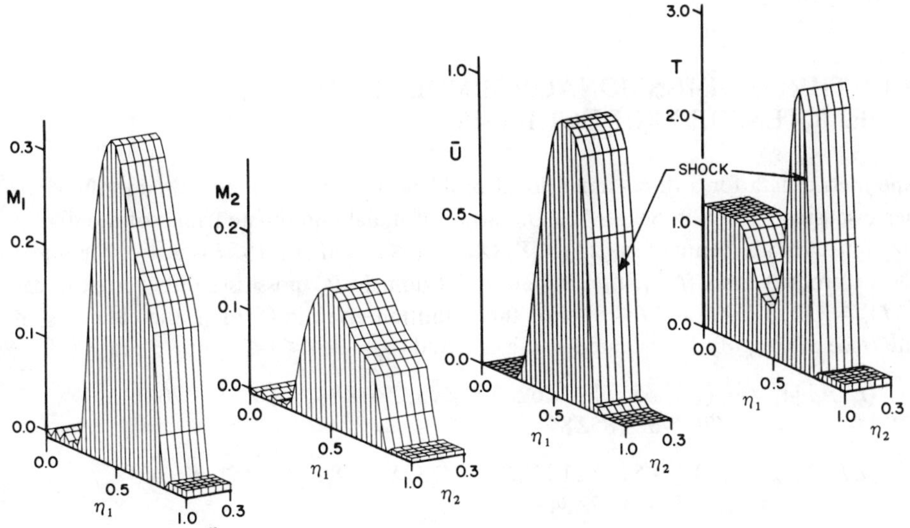

Figure 8.19 $M = 32 \times 6$, $k = 1$ finite-element solution, two-dimensional Riemann shock tube; $\beta = 26°$, $t = 0.14154$ s. (*a*) Momentum m_1; (*b*) momentum m_2; (*c*) convection velocity $\bar{u}_1$; (*d*) internal energy.

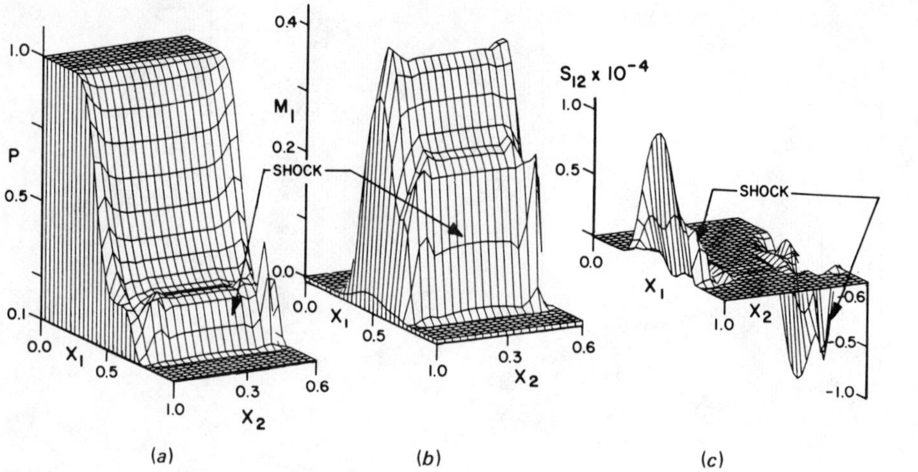

Figure 8.20 $M = 32 \times 20$, $k = 1$ finite-element solution, two-dimensional viscous Riemann shock tube; $\mathrm{Re} = 10^5$, $t = 0.14154$ s. (*a*) Pressure p; (*b*) momentum m_1; (*c*) shear stress σ_{12}.

This test problem specification possessed 10 dependent variables per nodal coordinate, plus five pieces of nodal metric data, yielding approximately 10,000 nodal degrees of freedom to handle. The Newton convergence character was reported similar to the inviscid flow test case, following a few extra iterations at start-up. The solution employed 27 time steps to reach t_f, required 90 iterations, and utilized 70 K words of central memory on an IBM 370-3031 computer.

8.12 THREE-DIMENSIONAL FORMULATION, LINEAR TENSOR PRODUCT BASIS

The metric data for a three-dimensional problem definition are generated in the manner discussed for R^2 in Sec. 8.10. The array of nodal coordinate triples of the discretization $\cup R_e^3$ are denoted as $\{XI\} \equiv \Sigma_e \{XI\}_e$, $1 \leqslant e \leqslant M$ and $1 \leqslant I \leqslant 3$. For the linear tensor product basis $\{N_1^+\}$, the finite-element domain R_e^3 possesses only vertex nodes $\{XI\}_e \equiv \{XI, YI, ZI, 1 \leqslant I \leqslant 8\}$. For the definition given in (8.115), the elements on the trace of $[\partial\eta_k/\partial x_j]$, evaluated at the centroid ($\eta_i = 0$, $1 \leqslant i \leqslant 3$) of R_e^3 are

$$\begin{aligned}
\{ETA11\}_e^T &= \tfrac{1}{4}\{Y41Z51, Y32Z62, Y32Z73, Y41Z84, Y85Z51, Y76Z62,\\
&\qquad Y76Z73, Y85Z84\}_e\\
\{ETA22\}_e^T &= \tfrac{1}{4}\{X21Z51, X21Z62, X34Z73, X34Z84, X65Z51, X65Z62,\\
&\qquad X78Z73, X78Z84\}_e\\
\{ETA33\}_e^T &= \tfrac{1}{4}\{X21Y41, X21Y32, X34Y32, X34Y41, X65Y85, X65Y76,\\
&\qquad X78Y76, X78Y85\}_e
\end{aligned} \tag{8.128}$$

For a rectangular domain, $\{ETAKJ\}_e = \{0\}$ for $K \neq J$, and the notation in (8.128) is defined as, for example,

$$Y41Z51 \equiv (Y4 - Y1)(Z5 - Z1) \tag{8.129}$$

In the same notation, the elements of $\{DET\}_e$ evaluated at the origin of the domain R_e^3 are

$$\{DET\}_e^T = \tfrac{1}{64}\{X21Y41Z51, X21Y32Z62, X34Y32Z73, X34Y41Z84, X65Y85Z51, X65Y76Z62, X78Y76Z73, X78Y85Z84\}_e \tag{8.130}$$

In the instance of R_e^3 being a rectangular parallelepiped, then $\{DET\}_e = \Delta_e\{1\}/64$, where Δ_e is the element volume. For (8.128)-(8.130), nodes 1-4 are defined in the lower plane (see Fig. 8.1*b*), with node 1 in the lower left corner. Nodes 5-8 are also ordered counterclockwise, in the upper plane, with node 5 above node 1.

For the tensor product jacobians (8.74)-(8.79),

$$\{DETK\}_e = \tfrac{1}{2}\sqrt{(XKR - XKL)^2 + (YKR - YKL)^2 + (ZKR - ZKL)^2}\begin{Bmatrix}1\\1\end{Bmatrix} \tag{8.131}$$

where R and L denote right and left, respectively, for the specific η_k alignment. As occurred for R_e^2, the components of $\{ETAKJ\}_e$ are the direction cosines of the local affine transformation between x_i and η_j, $1 \leqslant (i, j) \leqslant 3$ [see (8.123)]. The definition for $\{UBARK\}_e$ is also unchanged from (8.124).

No consequential solutions using the three-dimensional algorithm are reported in the literature. However, Baker (1982) does document the three-dimensional tensor product jacobian construction for the three-dimensional equivalent of the Riemann shock tube.

8.13 CLOSURE

This concludes the derivation and examination of the theoretical and practical aspects of finite-element computational fluid mechanics. The reader has–it is hoped–benefitted from the experience. It should be quite obvious that this science is in its infancy, with regard to application to the complete Navier-Stokes equations. Nevertheless, the theoretical structures are rich in classical mechanics, and the formulational procedures have fully utilized calculus and vector field theory. Hopefully, the robustness of this methodology will prompt continued refinement and examination of its application to real-world problem classes in computational fluid mechanics.

REFERENCES

Baker, A. J. (1982). Research on a Finite Element Numerical Algorithm for the Three-dimensional Navier-Stokes Equations, U.S.A.F. Tech. Rept. AFWAL-TR-81.

Beam, R. M. and Warming, R. F. (1978). An Implicit Factored Scheme for the Compressible Navier-Stokes Equations, *AIAA J.*, vol. 16, pp. 393–402.

Briley, W. R. and McDonald, H. (1977). Solution of the Multi-Dimensional Compressible Navier-Stokes Equations by a Generalized Implicit Method, *J. Comp. Phys.*, vol. 24, p. 372.

Cebeci, T. and Smith, A. M. O. (1974). *Analysis of Turbulent Boundary Layers*, Academic Press, New York.

Halmos, P. R. (1958). *Finite Dimensional Vector Spaces*, Van Nostrand, Princeton, New Jersey.

Hanjalic, K. and Launder, B. E. (1972). A Reynolds Stress Model of Turbulence and its Application to Thin Shear Flows, *J. Fluid Mech.*, vol. 52, pt. 4, pp. 609–638.

Launder, B. E., Reece, G. J., and Rodi, W. (1975). Progress in the Development of a Reynolds-Stress Turbulence Closure, *J. Fluid Mech.*, vol. 68, pt. 3, pp. 537–566.

MacCormack, R. W. (1969). The Effect of Viscosity in Hypervelocity Impact Cratering, Tech. Paper AIAA-69-354.

MacCormack, R. W. (1977). An Efficient Explicit-Implicit-Characteristic Method for Solving the Compressible Navier-Stokes Equations, *Proceedings of the SIAM-AMS Symposium on Computational Fluid Dynamics*, New York.

MacCormack, R. W. (1981). A Numerical Method for Solving the Equations of Compressible Viscous Flow, Tech. Paper AIAA-81-0110.

Morkovin, M. V. (1964). Effects of Compressibility on Turbulent Flow, in Favre and Breach (eds), *The Mechanics of Turbulence*, National Center for Scientific Research, France.

Marvin, J. G. (1982). Turbulence Modeling for Computational Aerodynamics, Tech. Paper AIAA-82-0164.

NASA (1980). NASA Workshop on Numerical Grid Generation Techniques for Partial Differential Equations, Proceedings, NASA Rept. CP-2166.

Raymond, W. H. and Garder, A. (1976). Selective Damping in a Galerkin Method for Solving Wave Problems with Variable Grids, *Mon. Weather Rev.*, vol. 104, pp. 1583–1590.

Shapiro, A. H. (1953). *The Dynamics and Thermodynamics of Compressible Fluid Flow*, vol. II, Ronald Press, New York.

Sod, G. A. (1978). A Survey of Several Finite Difference Methods for Systems of Non-Linear Hyperbolic Conservation Laws, *J. Comp. Phys.*, vol. 27, pp. 1–31.

Steger, J. L. and Pulliam, T. H. (1980). An Implicit Finite Difference Code for Inviscid and Viscous Cascade Flow, Tech. Paper AIAA-80-1427.

Steger, J. L. (1981). Finite Difference Simulation of Compressible Flows, Presented at ASME-AIAA Symposium on Computers in Flow Predictions and Fluid Dynamics Experiments, ASME Winter Annual Meeting, November, Washington, D.C.

Tennekes, H. and Lumley, J. L. (1974). *A First Course in Turbulence*, MIT Press, Cambridge, Mass.

Thames, F. G., Thompson, J. F., Mastin, C. W., and Walker, R. L. (1977). Numerical Solutions for Viscous and Potential Flow about Arbitrary Two-dimensional Bodies using Body-Fitted Coordinate Systems, *J. Comp. Phys.*, vol. 24, no. 1, pp. 245–273.

van Leer, B. (1979). Towards the Ultimate Conservative Difference Scheme. V. A Second-Order Sequel to Godunov's Method, *J. Comp. Phys.*, vol. 32, pp. 101–136.

von Neumann, J. and Richtmyer, R. D. (1950). A Method for the Numerical Calculation of Hydrodynamic Shocks, *J. Appl. Phys.*, vol. 21, pp. 232–237.

Zalesak, S. T. (1980). High Order ZIP Differencing of Convective Terms, U.S. Navy Memo. Rept. NRL-4218.

APPENDIX

A

CARDINAL BASIS AND HYPERMATRIX CONSTRUCTION

Efficient utilization of the uniformity of the finite-element algorithmic procedure is enhanced by cardinal basis functions and a unified notation. These concepts, which are extendible to multidimensional space, are best introduced on one-dimensional space. Figure A.1 shows a one-dimensional element with vertex nodes 1 and 2. Linear interpolation of the distribution of a variable $q(x)$ over R_e^1 is

$$q_e(x) = a + b \frac{x}{\Delta_e} \tag{A.1}$$

The coefficients in (A.1) are easily reexpressed in terms of the nodal values Q_i of q_e as

$$q_e(x) = Q_1\left(1 - \frac{\bar{x}}{\Delta_e}\right) + Q_2\left(\frac{\bar{x}}{\Delta_e}\right) \tag{A.2}$$

where the origin of $\bar{x}$ is at node 1. Rewriting Eq. (A.2) as a matrix inner product produces the linear one-dimensional cardinal basis $\{N_1(\bar{x})\}$:

$$\{N_1(\bar{x})\} \equiv \begin{Bmatrix} 1 - \dfrac{\bar{x}}{\Delta_e} \\[2ex] \dfrac{\bar{x}}{\Delta_e} \end{Bmatrix} \tag{A.3}$$

Equation (A.3) defines the linearly dependent, normalized natural coordinate system ζ_i for a one-dimensional space, that is, $\{\zeta\} \equiv \{N_1(\bar{x})\}$. The ζ_i system is also

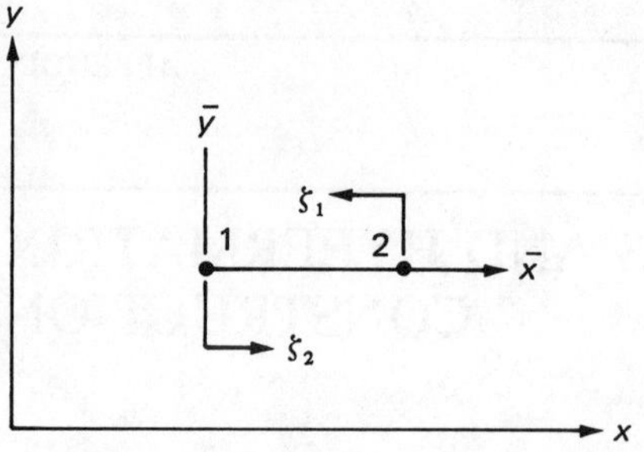

Figure A.1 One-dimensional finite element coordinate systems.

shown in Fig. A.1, and all cardinal basis on R_e^1 can be written as polynomials on ζ_i. Equation (A.1), for a general degree interpolation, is

$$q_e(x) = a + b\,\frac{x}{\Delta_e} + C\left(\frac{x}{\Delta_e}\right)^2 + d\left(\frac{x}{\Delta_e}\right)^3 + \cdots \tag{A.4}$$

Equation (A.4), rewritten in terms of the kth degree cardinal basis $\{N_k\}$, yields the basic definition statement:

$$q_e(x) = \{N_k(\zeta)\}^T\{Q\}_e \tag{A.5}$$

Figure A.2 illustrates coordinates, and the numbering system minimizing matrix bandwidth, of the additional nodes (x) required for Eq. (A.5). The resulting cardinal basis definitions are directly determined to be

$$k = 1: \qquad \{N_1\} = \{\zeta\} = \begin{Bmatrix} \zeta_1 \\ \zeta_2 \end{Bmatrix} \tag{A.6}$$

$$k = 2: \qquad \{N_2\} = \begin{Bmatrix} \zeta_1(2\zeta_1 - 1) \\ 4\zeta_1\zeta_2 \\ \zeta_2(2\zeta_2 - 1) \end{Bmatrix} \tag{A.7}$$

$$k = 3: \qquad \{N_3\} = \frac{9}{2}\begin{Bmatrix} \zeta_1(\zeta_2^2 - \zeta_2 + \frac{2}{9}) \\ \zeta_1\zeta_2(2 - 3\zeta_2) \\ \zeta_1\zeta_2(3\zeta_2 - 1) \\ \zeta_2(\zeta_2^2 - \zeta_2 + \frac{2}{9}) \end{Bmatrix} \tag{A.8}$$

$$k = 3': \qquad \{N_3'\} = \begin{Bmatrix} 1 - (\zeta_2)^2(1 + 2\zeta_1) \\ [\zeta_1\zeta_2 - \zeta_1(\zeta_2)^2]\,\Delta_e \\ (\zeta_2)^2(1 + 2\zeta_1) \\ [-\zeta_1(\zeta_2)^2]\,\Delta_e \end{Bmatrix} \tag{A.9}$$

Note that only for the Hermite cubic, $k \equiv 3'$ (which involves derivative degrees of freedom as well as the dependent variable at vertex nodes), is the basis function explicitly dependent on the element measure Δ_e. Also note that all elements in Eqs. (A.6)–(A.9) could be written in terms of ζ_1 or ζ_2 only, since they are linearly dependent [see Eq. (A.3)]. The selected forms display parent symmetry.

One utility of the cardinal basis construction is that the integrals of a finite-element algorithm statement are readily evaluated, since pth degree polynomials in ζ_i are integrated in closed form as

$$\int_{R_e^1} \zeta_1^{p_1} \zeta_2^{p_2}\, d\bar{x} \equiv \Delta_e \frac{p_1!p_2!}{(1 + p_1 + p_2)!} \tag{A.10}$$

For example, the elemental one-dimensional initial value matrix $[C]_e$, defined in Chap. 4 and evaluated using the quadratic cardinal basis $\{N_2\}$, Eq. (A.7), becomes

$$[C]_e = \int_{R_e^1} \{N_2\}\{N_2\}^T\, dx$$
$$= \int_{R_e^1} \begin{Bmatrix} \zeta_1(2\zeta_1 - 1) \\ 4\zeta_1\zeta_2 \\ \zeta_2(2\zeta_2 - 1) \end{Bmatrix} \{\zeta_1(2\zeta_1 - 1),\ \ 4\zeta_1\zeta_2,\ \ \zeta_2(2\zeta_2 - 1)\}\, dx \tag{A.11}$$

With repeated use of Eq. (A.10), the resultant matrix is

$$[C]_e \equiv \Delta_e[A200] = \frac{\Delta_e}{60}\begin{bmatrix} 8 & 4 & -2 \\ 4 & 32 & 4 \\ -2 & 4 & 8 \end{bmatrix} \tag{A.12}$$

Equation (A.12) illustrates definition of a standard matrix nomenclature. For the matrix $[A200]$, the A signifies a matrix on one-dimensional space, the first 2 indicates two cardinal bases form the matrix, and both O's indicate neither basis is differentiated. The rank of $[A200]$ equals $k + 1$, where k is the degree of the selected cardinal basis. No additional specific nomenclature is usually used to signify the value of k, but one could easily be defined, for example, $[A200_2]$. Irrespective

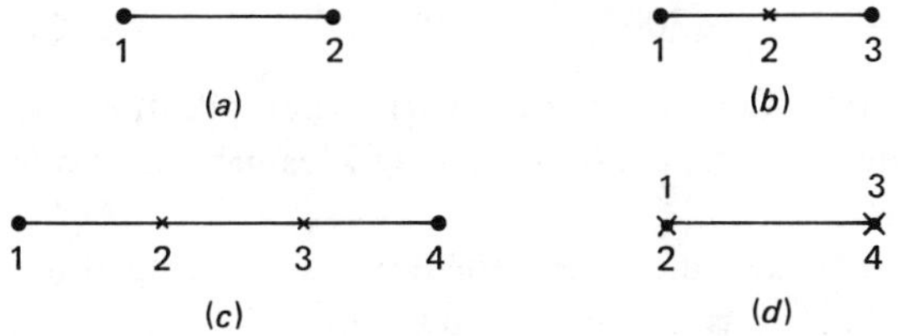

Figure A.2 Node locations for a one-dimensional domain spanned by various degree cardinal basis $\{N_k\}$. (*a*) Linear, $k = 1$; (*b*) quadratic, $k = 2$; (*c*) cubic Lagrange, $k = 3$; (*d*) cubic Hermite, $k = 3'$.

of k, the matrix coefficients are element independent, and the integers and divisor reside in a DATA statement.

To illustrate mixed interpolation, reevaluate $[C]_e$ on a one-dimensional space spanned by a cylindrical coordinate system. Then, interpolating r in terms of its nodal coordinates on R_e^1 yields

$$dx \Rightarrow r\, dr\, d\theta = 2\pi \{R\}_e^T \{N_1\}\, dx \tag{A.13}$$

which is exact. Hence, with scalar rearrangement and dividing by 2π,

$$[C]_e = \int_{R_e^1} \{R\}_e^T \{N_1\} \{N_2\} \{N_2\}^T\, dx$$

$$= \{R\}_e^T \int_{R_e^1} \begin{Bmatrix} \zeta_1 \\ \zeta_2 \end{Bmatrix} \begin{Bmatrix} \zeta_1(2\zeta_1 - 1) \\ 4\zeta_1\zeta_2 \\ \zeta_2(2\zeta_2 - 1) \end{Bmatrix} \{\zeta_1(2\zeta_1 - 1),\quad 4\zeta_1\zeta_2,\quad \zeta_2(2\zeta_2 - 1)\}\, dx \tag{A.14}$$

From Eq. (A.11), the outer product on $\{N_2\}$ forms a square matrix of rank 3. Therefore, recalling the definition of scalar multiplication of a matrix, the premultiplication by $\{N_1\}$ yields a square matrix with elements that are themselves column matrices. With this rearrangement, each element in Eq. (A.14) is directly integrated using Eq. (A.10), yielding

$$[C]_e \equiv \Delta_e \{R\}_e^T [A3000] = \frac{\Delta_e}{60} \{R\}_e^T \begin{bmatrix} \begin{Bmatrix} 7 \\ 1 \end{Bmatrix} & \begin{Bmatrix} 4 \\ 0 \end{Bmatrix} & \begin{Bmatrix} -1 \\ -1 \end{Bmatrix} \\ & \begin{Bmatrix} 16 \\ 16 \end{Bmatrix} & \begin{Bmatrix} 0 \\ 4 \end{Bmatrix} \\ (\text{sym}) & & \begin{Bmatrix} 1 \\ 7 \end{Bmatrix} \end{bmatrix} \tag{A.15}$$

The matrix $[A3000]$ is a hypermatrix of degree one; it is element-independent, and the rank of each hyperelement equals that of the left contraction matrix. Note that if the elements of $\{R\}_e$ are a uniform constant, the premultiplication can be completed, yielding the useful identity.

$$\{ONE\}^T [A3000] = \{1, 1\} [A3000] = [A200] \tag{A.16}$$

Using the hypermatrix nomenclature, the order of matrix multiplication is restrained. In particular, postmultiplication of $[A3000]$ by $\{Q\}_e$ cannot be completed before premultiplication by $\{R\}_e^T$.

The hypermatrix construction generalizes nicely for equation nonlinearity. For example, the element convection matrix $[U]_e$ is also defined in Chap. 4 as

$$[U]_e = \int_{R_e^1} \{U\}_e^T \{N_k\} \{N_k\} \frac{d}{dx} \{N_k\}^T \, d\bar{x} \tag{A.17}$$

The derivative of $\{N_k\}$ with x is directly evaluated using the chain rule; see Eqs. (A.6)-(A.9). Assuming for illustration that $k = 2$, Eq. (A.17) becomes

$$[U]_e \equiv \Delta_e \{U\}_e^T [A3001]$$

$$= \frac{8}{\Delta_e} \{U\}_e^T \int_{R_e^1} \begin{Bmatrix} \zeta_1(2\zeta_1 - 1) \\ 4\zeta_1\zeta_2 \\ \zeta_2(2\zeta_2 - 1) \end{Bmatrix} \begin{Bmatrix} \zeta_1(2\zeta_1 - 1) \\ 4\zeta_1\zeta_2 \\ \zeta_2(2\zeta_2 - 1) \end{Bmatrix}$$

$$\cdot \{1 - 4\zeta_1, \quad 4(\zeta_1 - \zeta_2), \quad 4\zeta_2 - 1\} \, dx \tag{A.18}$$

and differentiation of $\{N_2\}$ has extracted the multiplier Δ_e^{-1}. Resultant integration using Eq. (A.10) will produce Δ_e in the numerator; hence, $[U]_e$ is independent of the element measure. Proceeding through the algebra, the quadratic cardinal basis matrix equivalent for convection becomes

$$[A3001] = \frac{1}{30\,\Delta_e} \begin{bmatrix} \begin{Bmatrix} -10 \\ -6 \\ 1 \end{Bmatrix} & \begin{Bmatrix} 12 \\ 8 \\ 0 \end{Bmatrix} & \begin{Bmatrix} -2 \\ -2 \\ -1 \end{Bmatrix} \\ \begin{Bmatrix} -6 \\ -16 \\ 2 \end{Bmatrix} & \begin{Bmatrix} 8 \\ 0 \\ -8 \end{Bmatrix} & \begin{Bmatrix} -2 \\ 16 \\ 6 \end{Bmatrix} \\ \begin{Bmatrix} 1 \\ 2 \\ 2 \end{Bmatrix} & \begin{Bmatrix} 0 \\ -8 \\ -12 \end{Bmatrix} & \begin{Bmatrix} -1 \\ 6 \\ 10 \end{Bmatrix} \end{bmatrix} \tag{A.19}$$

As with the mixed interpolation hypermatrix, the premultiplication of Eq. (A.19) by $\{U\}_e^T$ is required prior to any conventional matrix operations.

The diffusion term in an equation requires evaluating integrals of products of derivatives. Assuming the diffusion coefficient $k_e(x)$ interpolated linearly, the elemental diffusion matrix equivalent $[K]_e$ is

$$[K]_e \equiv \{k\}_e^T \int \{N_1\} \frac{d}{dx} \{N_k\} \frac{d}{dx} \{N_k\}^T \, d\bar{x} = \Delta_e \{k\}_e^T [A3011] \tag{A.20}$$

For $1 \leqslant k \leqslant 3$, the matrices $[A3011]$ are

$$k = 1: \qquad [A3011] = \frac{1}{\Delta_e^2}\begin{bmatrix} \begin{Bmatrix} 1 \\ 1 \end{Bmatrix} & \begin{Bmatrix} -1 \\ -1 \end{Bmatrix} \\ \begin{Bmatrix} -1 \\ -1 \end{Bmatrix} & \begin{Bmatrix} 1 \\ 1 \end{Bmatrix} \end{bmatrix} \tag{A.21}$$

$$k = 2: \qquad [A3011] = \frac{1}{6\,\Delta_e^2}\begin{bmatrix} \begin{Bmatrix} 11 \\ 3 \end{Bmatrix} & \begin{Bmatrix} -12 \\ -4 \end{Bmatrix} & \begin{Bmatrix} 1 \\ 1 \end{Bmatrix} \\ \begin{Bmatrix} -12 \\ -4 \end{Bmatrix} & \begin{Bmatrix} 16 \\ 16 \end{Bmatrix} & \begin{Bmatrix} -4 \\ -12 \end{Bmatrix} \\ \begin{Bmatrix} 1 \\ 1 \end{Bmatrix} & \begin{Bmatrix} -4 \\ -12 \end{Bmatrix} & \begin{Bmatrix} 3 \\ 11 \end{Bmatrix} \end{bmatrix} \tag{A.22}$$

$$k = 3: \qquad [A3011] = \frac{1}{80\,\Delta_e^2}\begin{bmatrix} \begin{Bmatrix} 262 \\ 34 \end{Bmatrix} & \begin{Bmatrix} -327 \\ -51 \end{Bmatrix} & \begin{Bmatrix} 78 \\ 30 \end{Bmatrix} & \begin{Bmatrix} -13 \\ -13 \end{Bmatrix} \\ \begin{Bmatrix} -327 \\ -51 \end{Bmatrix} & \begin{Bmatrix} 594 \\ 270 \end{Bmatrix} & \begin{Bmatrix} -297 \\ -297 \end{Bmatrix} & \begin{Bmatrix} 30 \\ 78 \end{Bmatrix} \\ \begin{Bmatrix} 78 \\ 30 \end{Bmatrix} & \begin{Bmatrix} -297 \\ -297 \end{Bmatrix} & \begin{Bmatrix} 270 \\ 594 \end{Bmatrix} & \begin{Bmatrix} -51 \\ -327 \end{Bmatrix} \\ \begin{Bmatrix} -13 \\ -13 \end{Bmatrix} & \begin{Bmatrix} 30 \\ 78 \end{Bmatrix} & \begin{Bmatrix} -51 \\ -327 \end{Bmatrix} & \begin{Bmatrix} 34 \\ 262 \end{Bmatrix} \end{bmatrix} \tag{A.23}$$

Extension of the hypermatrix formulation to a multidimensional problem definition is straightforward, although the algebra becomes quite detailed. These concepts are introduced in Chap. 3, with extensions given in Chaps. 5–8.

APPENDIX

B

FINITE-ELEMENT ALGORITHM HYPERMATRICES

B.1 LINEAR AND QUADRATIC BASIS ON ONE-DIMENSIONAL SPACE

B.1.1 Linear Basis $\{N_1\}$

Note: Δ_e = element length

$$\{A10\} = \frac{1}{2}\begin{Bmatrix} 1 \\ 1 \end{Bmatrix}$$

$$[A200] = \frac{1}{6}\begin{bmatrix} 2 & 1 \\ 1 & 2 \end{bmatrix}$$

$$[A201] = \frac{1}{2\,\Delta_e}\begin{bmatrix} -1 & 1 \\ -1 & 1 \end{bmatrix}$$

$$[A210] = \frac{1}{2\,\Delta_e}\begin{bmatrix} -1 & -1 \\ 1 & 1 \end{bmatrix}$$

$$[A3000] = \frac{1}{12}\begin{bmatrix} \begin{Bmatrix} 3 \\ 1 \end{Bmatrix} & \begin{Bmatrix} 1 \\ 1 \end{Bmatrix} \\ \begin{Bmatrix} 1 \\ 1 \end{Bmatrix} & \begin{Bmatrix} 1 \\ 3 \end{Bmatrix} \end{bmatrix}$$

$$[A3001] = \frac{1}{6\,\Delta_e}\begin{bmatrix} \begin{Bmatrix} -2 \\ -1 \end{Bmatrix} & \begin{Bmatrix} 2 \\ 1 \end{Bmatrix} \\ \begin{Bmatrix} -1 \\ -2 \end{Bmatrix} & \begin{Bmatrix} 1 \\ 2 \end{Bmatrix} \end{bmatrix}$$

$$[A3010] = \frac{1}{6\,\Delta_e}\begin{bmatrix} \begin{Bmatrix} -2 \\ -1 \end{Bmatrix} & \begin{Bmatrix} -1 \\ -2 \end{Bmatrix} \\ \begin{Bmatrix} 2 \\ 1 \end{Bmatrix} & \begin{Bmatrix} 1 \\ 2 \end{Bmatrix} \end{bmatrix}$$

$$[A3100] = \frac{1}{6\,\Delta_e}\begin{bmatrix} \begin{Bmatrix} -2 \\ 2 \end{Bmatrix} & \begin{Bmatrix} -1 \\ 1 \end{Bmatrix} \\ \begin{Bmatrix} -1 \\ 1 \end{Bmatrix} & \begin{Bmatrix} -2 \\ 2 \end{Bmatrix} \end{bmatrix}$$

$$[A3011] = \frac{1}{2\,\Delta_e^2}\begin{bmatrix} \begin{Bmatrix} 1 \\ 1 \end{Bmatrix} & \begin{Bmatrix} -1 \\ -1 \end{Bmatrix} \\ \begin{Bmatrix} -1 \\ -1 \end{Bmatrix} & \begin{Bmatrix} 1 \\ 1 \end{Bmatrix} \end{bmatrix}$$

$$[A3110] = \frac{1}{2\,\Delta_e^2}\begin{bmatrix} \begin{Bmatrix} 1 \\ -1 \end{Bmatrix} & \begin{Bmatrix} 1 \\ -1 \end{Bmatrix} \\ \begin{Bmatrix} -1 \\ 1 \end{Bmatrix} & \begin{Bmatrix} -1 \\ 1 \end{Bmatrix} \end{bmatrix}$$

$$[A40000] = \frac{1}{60}\begin{bmatrix} \begin{bmatrix} 12 & 3 \\ 3 & 2 \end{bmatrix} & \begin{bmatrix} 3 & 2 \\ 2 & 3 \end{bmatrix} \\ \begin{bmatrix} 3 & 2 \\ 2 & 3 \end{bmatrix} & \begin{bmatrix} 3 & 3 \\ 3 & 12 \end{bmatrix} \end{bmatrix}$$

$$[A40001] = \frac{1}{12\,\Delta_e}\begin{bmatrix} \begin{bmatrix} -3 & 3 \\ -1 & 1 \end{bmatrix} & \begin{bmatrix} -1 & 1 \\ -1 & 1 \end{bmatrix} \\ \begin{bmatrix} -1 & 1 \\ -1 & 1 \end{bmatrix} & \begin{bmatrix} -1 & 1 \\ -3 & 3 \end{bmatrix} \end{bmatrix}$$

$$[A40010] = \frac{1}{12\,\Delta_e}\begin{bmatrix} \begin{bmatrix} -3 & -1 \\ -1 & -1 \end{bmatrix} & \begin{bmatrix} 3 & 1 \\ 1 & 1 \end{bmatrix} \\ \begin{bmatrix} -1 & -1 \\ -1 & -3 \end{bmatrix} & \begin{bmatrix} 1 & 1 \\ 1 & 3 \end{bmatrix} \end{bmatrix}$$

$$[A41000] = \frac{1}{12\,\Delta_e}\begin{bmatrix} \begin{bmatrix} -3 & -1 \\ 3 & 1 \end{bmatrix} & \begin{bmatrix} -1 & -1 \\ 1 & 1 \end{bmatrix} \\ \begin{bmatrix} -1 & -1 \\ 1 & 1 \end{bmatrix} & \begin{bmatrix} -1 & -3 \\ 1 & 3 \end{bmatrix} \end{bmatrix}$$

$$[A40011] = \frac{1}{6\,\Delta_e}\begin{bmatrix} \begin{bmatrix} 2 & -2 \\ 1 & -1 \end{bmatrix} & \begin{bmatrix} -2 & 2 \\ -1 & 1 \end{bmatrix} \\ \begin{bmatrix} 1 & -1 \\ 2 & -2 \end{bmatrix} & \begin{bmatrix} -1 & 1 \\ -2 & 2 \end{bmatrix} \end{bmatrix}$$

$$[A40110] = \frac{1}{6\,\Delta_e^2}\begin{bmatrix} \begin{bmatrix} 2 & 1 \\ 1 & 2 \end{bmatrix} & \begin{bmatrix} -2 & -1 \\ -1 & -2 \end{bmatrix} \\ \begin{bmatrix} -2 & -1 \\ -1 & -2 \end{bmatrix} & \begin{bmatrix} 2 & 1 \\ 1 & 2 \end{bmatrix} \end{bmatrix}$$

$$[A41100] = \frac{1}{6\,\Delta_e^2}\begin{bmatrix} \begin{bmatrix} 2 & 1 \\ -2 & -1 \end{bmatrix} & \begin{bmatrix} 1 & 2 \\ -1 & -2 \end{bmatrix} \\ \begin{bmatrix} -2 & -1 \\ 2 & 1 \end{bmatrix} & \begin{bmatrix} -1 & -2 \\ 1 & 2 \end{bmatrix} \end{bmatrix}$$

$$[A40101] = \frac{1}{6\,\Delta_e^2}\begin{bmatrix} \begin{bmatrix} 2 & -2 \\ -2 & 2 \end{bmatrix} & \begin{bmatrix} 1 & -1 \\ -1 & 1 \end{bmatrix} \\ \begin{bmatrix} 1 & -1 \\ -1 & 1 \end{bmatrix} & \begin{bmatrix} 2 & -2 \\ -2 & 2 \end{bmatrix} \end{bmatrix}$$

B.1.2 Quadratic Basis $\{N_2\}$

$$\{A10\} = \frac{1}{6}\begin{Bmatrix} 1 \\ 4 \\ 1 \end{Bmatrix}$$

$$[A200] = \frac{1}{30}\begin{bmatrix} 4 & 2 & -1 \\ 2 & 16 & 2 \\ -1 & 2 & 4 \end{bmatrix}$$

$$[A201] = \frac{1}{6\,\Delta_e}\begin{bmatrix} -3 & 4 & -1 \\ -4 & 0 & 4 \\ 1 & -4 & 3 \end{bmatrix}$$

$$[A210] = \frac{1}{6\,\Delta_e}\begin{bmatrix} -3 & -4 & 1 \\ 4 & 0 & 4 \\ -1 & 4 & 3 \end{bmatrix}$$

$$[A3000] = \frac{1}{420}\begin{bmatrix} \begin{Bmatrix} 39 \\ 20 \\ -3 \end{Bmatrix} & \begin{Bmatrix} 20 \\ 16 \\ -8 \end{Bmatrix} & \begin{Bmatrix} -3 \\ -8 \\ -8 \end{Bmatrix} \\ \begin{Bmatrix} 20 \\ 16 \\ -8 \end{Bmatrix} & \begin{Bmatrix} 16 \\ 192 \\ 16 \end{Bmatrix} & \begin{Bmatrix} -8 \\ 16 \\ 20 \end{Bmatrix} \\ \begin{Bmatrix} -3 \\ -8 \\ -3 \end{Bmatrix} & \begin{Bmatrix} -8 \\ 16 \\ 20 \end{Bmatrix} & \begin{Bmatrix} -3 \\ 20 \\ 39 \end{Bmatrix} \end{bmatrix}$$

$$[A3001] = \frac{1}{90\,\Delta_e}\begin{bmatrix} \begin{Bmatrix} -30 \\ -18 \\ 3 \end{Bmatrix} & \begin{Bmatrix} 36 \\ 24 \\ 0 \end{Bmatrix} & \begin{Bmatrix} -6 \\ -6 \\ -3 \end{Bmatrix} \\ \begin{Bmatrix} -18 \\ -48 \\ 6 \end{Bmatrix} & \begin{Bmatrix} 24 \\ 0 \\ -24 \end{Bmatrix} & \begin{Bmatrix} -6 \\ 48 \\ 18 \end{Bmatrix} \\ \begin{Bmatrix} 3 \\ 6 \\ 6 \end{Bmatrix} & \begin{Bmatrix} 0 \\ -24 \\ -36 \end{Bmatrix} & \begin{Bmatrix} -3 \\ 18 \\ 30 \end{Bmatrix} \end{bmatrix}$$

$$[A3010] = \frac{1}{30\,\Delta_e}\begin{bmatrix} \begin{Bmatrix} -10 \\ -6 \\ 1 \end{Bmatrix} & \begin{Bmatrix} -6 \\ -16 \\ 2 \end{Bmatrix} & \begin{Bmatrix} 1 \\ 2 \\ 2 \end{Bmatrix} \\ \begin{Bmatrix} 12 \\ 8 \\ 0 \end{Bmatrix} & \begin{Bmatrix} 8 \\ 0 \\ -8 \end{Bmatrix} & \begin{Bmatrix} 0 \\ -8 \\ -12 \end{Bmatrix} \\ \begin{Bmatrix} -2 \\ -2 \\ -1 \end{Bmatrix} & \begin{Bmatrix} -2 \\ 16 \\ 6 \end{Bmatrix} & \begin{Bmatrix} -1 \\ 6 \\ 10 \end{Bmatrix} \end{bmatrix}$$

$$[A3100] = \frac{1}{30\,\Delta_e}\begin{bmatrix} \begin{Bmatrix} -10 \\ 12 \\ -2 \end{Bmatrix} & \begin{Bmatrix} -6 \\ 8 \\ -2 \end{Bmatrix} & \begin{Bmatrix} 1 \\ 0 \\ -1 \end{Bmatrix} \\ \begin{Bmatrix} -6 \\ 8 \\ -2 \end{Bmatrix} & \begin{Bmatrix} -16 \\ 0 \\ 16 \end{Bmatrix} & \begin{Bmatrix} 2 \\ -8 \\ 6 \end{Bmatrix} \\ \begin{Bmatrix} 1 \\ 0 \\ -1 \end{Bmatrix} & \begin{Bmatrix} 2 \\ -8 \\ 6 \end{Bmatrix} & \begin{Bmatrix} 2 \\ -12 \\ 10 \end{Bmatrix} \end{bmatrix}$$

$$[A3011] = \frac{1}{30\,\Delta_e^2}\begin{bmatrix} \begin{Bmatrix} 37 \\ 36 \\ -3 \end{Bmatrix} & \begin{Bmatrix} -44 \\ -32 \\ -4 \end{Bmatrix} & \begin{Bmatrix} 7 \\ -4 \\ 7 \end{Bmatrix} \\ \begin{Bmatrix} -44 \\ -32 \\ -4 \end{Bmatrix} & \begin{Bmatrix} 48 \\ 64 \\ 48 \end{Bmatrix} & \begin{Bmatrix} -4 \\ -32 \\ -44 \end{Bmatrix} \\ \begin{Bmatrix} 7 \\ -4 \\ 7 \end{Bmatrix} & \begin{Bmatrix} -4 \\ -32 \\ -44 \end{Bmatrix} & \begin{Bmatrix} -3 \\ 36 \\ 37 \end{Bmatrix} \end{bmatrix}$$

$$[A3110] = \frac{1}{30\,\Delta_e^2}\begin{bmatrix} \left\{\begin{matrix} 37 \\ -44 \\ 7 \end{matrix}\right\} & \left\{\begin{matrix} 36 \\ -32 \\ -4 \end{matrix}\right\} & \left\{\begin{matrix} -3 \\ -4 \\ 7 \end{matrix}\right\} \\ \left\{\begin{matrix} -44 \\ 48 \\ -4 \end{matrix}\right\} & \left\{\begin{matrix} -32 \\ 64 \\ -32 \end{matrix}\right\} & \left\{\begin{matrix} -4 \\ 48 \\ 44 \end{matrix}\right\} \\ \left\{\begin{matrix} 7 \\ 4 \\ -3 \end{matrix}\right\} & \left\{\begin{matrix} -4 \\ -32 \\ 36 \end{matrix}\right\} & \left\{\begin{matrix} 7 \\ -44 \\ 37 \end{matrix}\right\} \end{bmatrix}$$

$$[A40000] = \frac{1}{630}\begin{bmatrix} \begin{bmatrix} 46 & 16 & -3 \\ 16 & 16 & -2 \\ -3 & -2 & -1 \end{bmatrix} & \begin{bmatrix} 16 & 16 & -2 \\ 16 & 16 & -8 \\ -2 & -8 & -2 \end{bmatrix} & \begin{bmatrix} -3 & -2 & 1 \\ -2 & -8 & -2 \\ 1 & -2 & -3 \end{bmatrix} \\ \begin{bmatrix} 16 & 16 & -2 \\ 16 & 16 & -8 \\ -2 & -8 & -2 \end{bmatrix} & \begin{bmatrix} 16 & 16 & -8 \\ 16 & 256 & 16 \\ -8 & 16 & 16 \end{bmatrix} & \begin{bmatrix} -2 & -8 & -2 \\ -8 & 16 & 16 \\ -2 & 16 & 16 \end{bmatrix} \\ \begin{bmatrix} -3 & -2 & 1 \\ -2 & -8 & -2 \\ 1 & -2 & -3 \end{bmatrix} & \begin{bmatrix} -2 & -8 & -2 \\ -8 & 16 & 16 \\ -2 & 16 & 16 \end{bmatrix} & \begin{bmatrix} 1 & -2 & -3 \\ -2 & 16 & 16 \\ -3 & 16 & 46 \end{bmatrix} \end{bmatrix}$$

$$[A40001] = \frac{1}{420\,\Delta_e}\begin{bmatrix} \begin{bmatrix} -105 & 132 & -27 \\ -44 & 48 & -4 \\ 9 & -12 & 3 \end{bmatrix} & \begin{bmatrix} -44 & 48 & -4 \\ -48 & 64 & -16 \\ 8 & 0 & -8 \end{bmatrix} & \begin{bmatrix} 9 & -12 & 3 \\ 8 & 0 & -8 \\ -3 & 12 & -9 \end{bmatrix} \\ \begin{bmatrix} -44 & 48 & -4 \\ -48 & 64 & -16 \\ 8 & 0 & -8 \end{bmatrix} & \begin{bmatrix} -48 & 64 & -16 \\ -192 & 0 & 192 \\ 16 & -64 & 48 \end{bmatrix} & \begin{bmatrix} 8 & 0 & -8 \\ 16 & -64 & 48 \\ 4 & -48 & 44 \end{bmatrix} \\ \begin{bmatrix} 9 & -12 & 3 \\ 8 & 0 & -8 \\ -3 & 12 & -9 \end{bmatrix} & \begin{bmatrix} 8 & 0 & -8 \\ 16 & -64 & 48 \\ 4 & -48 & 44 \end{bmatrix} & \begin{bmatrix} -3 & 12 & -9 \\ 4 & -48 & 44 \\ 27 & -132 & 105 \end{bmatrix} \end{bmatrix}$$

$$40010] = \frac{1}{420\,\Delta_e}\begin{bmatrix} \begin{bmatrix} -105 & -44 & 9 \\ -44 & -48 & 8 \\ 9 & 8 & -3 \end{bmatrix} & \begin{bmatrix} 132 & 48 & -12 \\ 48 & 64 & 0 \\ -12 & 0 & 12 \end{bmatrix} & \begin{bmatrix} -27 & -4 & 3 \\ -4 & -16 & -8 \\ 3 & -8 & -9 \end{bmatrix} \\ \begin{bmatrix} -44 & -48 & 8 \\ -48 & -192 & 16 \\ 8 & 16 & 4 \end{bmatrix} & \begin{bmatrix} 48 & 64 & 0 \\ 64 & 0 & -64 \\ 0 & -64 & -48 \end{bmatrix} & \begin{bmatrix} -4 & -16 & -8 \\ -16 & 192 & 48 \\ -8 & 48 & 44 \end{bmatrix} \\ \begin{bmatrix} 9 & 8 & -3 \\ 8 & 16 & 4 \\ -3 & 4 & 27 \end{bmatrix} & \begin{bmatrix} -12 & 0 & 12 \\ 0 & -64 & -48 \\ 12 & -48 & -132 \end{bmatrix} & \begin{bmatrix} 3 & -8 & -9 \\ -8 & 48 & 44 \\ -8 & 44 & 105 \end{bmatrix} \end{bmatrix}$$

$$41000] = \frac{1}{420\,\Delta_e}\begin{bmatrix} \begin{bmatrix} -105 & -44 & 9 \\ -44 & -48 & 8 \\ 9 & 8 & -3 \end{bmatrix} & \begin{bmatrix} -44 & -48 & 8 \\ -48 & -192 & 16 \\ 8 & 16 & 4 \end{bmatrix} & \begin{bmatrix} 9 & 8 & -3 \\ 8 & 16 & 4 \\ -3 & 4 & 27 \end{bmatrix} \\ \begin{bmatrix} 132 & 48 & -12 \\ 48 & 64 & 0 \\ -12 & 0 & 12 \end{bmatrix} & \begin{bmatrix} 48 & 64 & 0 \\ 64 & 0 & -64 \\ 0 & -64 & -48 \end{bmatrix} & \begin{bmatrix} -12 & 0 & 12 \\ 0 & -64 & -48 \\ 12 & -48 & -132 \end{bmatrix} \\ \begin{bmatrix} -27 & -4 & 3 \\ -4 & -16 & -8 \\ 3 & -8 & -9 \end{bmatrix} & \begin{bmatrix} -4 & -16 & -8 \\ -16 & 192 & 48 \\ -8 & 48 & 44 \end{bmatrix} & \begin{bmatrix} 3 & -8 & -9 \\ -8 & 48 & 44 \\ -9 & 44 & 105 \end{bmatrix} \end{bmatrix}$$

$$40011] = \frac{1}{210\,\Delta_e^2}\begin{bmatrix} \begin{bmatrix} 184 & -228 & 44 \\ 94 & -104 & 10 \\ -19 & 24 & -5 \end{bmatrix} & \begin{bmatrix} -228 & 288 & -60 \\ -104 & 96 & 8 \\ 24 & -48 & 24 \end{bmatrix} & \begin{bmatrix} 44 & -60 & 16 \\ 10 & 8 & -18 \\ -5 & 24 & -19 \end{bmatrix} \\ \begin{bmatrix} 94 & -104 & 10 \\ 176 & -128 & -48 \\ -18 & 8 & 10 \end{bmatrix} & \begin{bmatrix} -104 & 96 & 8 \\ -128 & 256 & -128 \\ 8 & 96 & -104 \end{bmatrix} & \begin{bmatrix} 10 & 8 & -18 \\ -48 & -128 & 176 \\ 10 & -104 & 94 \end{bmatrix} \\ \begin{bmatrix} -19 & 24 & -5 \\ -18 & 8 & 10 \\ 16 & -60 & 44 \end{bmatrix} & \begin{bmatrix} 24 & -48 & 24 \\ 8 & 96 & -104 \\ -60 & 288 & -228 \end{bmatrix} & \begin{bmatrix} -5 & 24 & -19 \\ 10 & -104 & 94 \\ 44 & -228 & 184 \end{bmatrix} \end{bmatrix}$$

$$[A40110] = \frac{1}{210\,\Delta_e^2}\left[\begin{array}{ccc}
\begin{bmatrix} 184 & 94 & -19 \\ -228 & -104 & 24 \\ 44 & 10 & -5 \end{bmatrix} & \begin{bmatrix} -228 & -104 & 24 \\ 288 & 96 & -48 \\ -60 & 8 & 24 \end{bmatrix} & \begin{bmatrix} 44 & 10 & -5 \\ -60 & 8 & 24 \\ 16 & -18 & -19 \end{bmatrix} \\
\begin{bmatrix} 94 & 176 & -18 \\ -104 & -128 & 8 \\ 10 & -48 & 10 \end{bmatrix} & \begin{bmatrix} -104 & -128 & 8 \\ 96 & 256 & 96 \\ 8 & -128 & -104 \end{bmatrix} & \begin{bmatrix} 10 & -48 & 10 \\ 8 & -128 & -104 \\ -18 & 176 & 94 \end{bmatrix} \\
\begin{bmatrix} -19 & -18 & 16 \\ 24 & 8 & -60 \\ -5 & 10 & 44 \end{bmatrix} & \begin{bmatrix} 24 & 8 & -60 \\ -48 & 96 & 288 \\ 24 & -104 & -228 \end{bmatrix} & \begin{bmatrix} -5 & 10 & 44 \\ 24 & -104 & -228 \\ -19 & 94 & 184 \end{bmatrix}
\end{array}\right]$$

$$[A41100] = \frac{1}{210\,\Delta_e^2}\left[\begin{array}{ccc}
\begin{bmatrix} 184 & 94 & -19 \\ -228 & -104 & 24 \\ 44 & 10 & -5 \end{bmatrix} & \begin{bmatrix} 94 & 176 & -18 \\ -104 & -128 & 8 \\ 10 & -48 & 10 \end{bmatrix} & \begin{bmatrix} -19 & -18 & 16 \\ 24 & 8 & -60 \\ -5 & 10 & 44 \end{bmatrix} \\
\begin{bmatrix} -228 & -104 & 24 \\ 288 & 96 & -48 \\ -60 & 8 & 24 \end{bmatrix} & \begin{bmatrix} -104 & -128 & 8 \\ 96 & 256 & 96 \\ 8 & -128 & -104 \end{bmatrix} & \begin{bmatrix} 24 & 8 & -60 \\ -48 & 96 & 288 \\ 24 & -104 & -228 \end{bmatrix} \\
\begin{bmatrix} 44 & 10 & -5 \\ -60 & 8 & 24 \\ 16 & -18 & -19 \end{bmatrix} & \begin{bmatrix} 10 & -48 & 10 \\ 8 & -128 & -104 \\ -18 & 176 & 94 \end{bmatrix} & \begin{bmatrix} -5 & 10 & 44 \\ 24 & -104 & -228 \\ -19 & 94 & 184 \end{bmatrix}
\end{array}\right]$$

$$[A40101] = \frac{1}{210\,\Delta_e^2}\left[\begin{array}{ccc}
\begin{bmatrix} 184 & -228 & 44 \\ -228 & 288 & -60 \\ 44 & -60 & 16 \end{bmatrix} & \begin{bmatrix} 94 & -104 & 10 \\ -104 & 96 & 8 \\ 10 & 8 & -18 \end{bmatrix} & \begin{bmatrix} -19 & 24 & -5 \\ 24 & -48 & 24 \\ -5 & 24 & -19 \end{bmatrix} \\
\begin{bmatrix} 94 & -104 & 10 \\ -104 & 96 & 8 \\ 10 & 8 & -18 \end{bmatrix} & \begin{bmatrix} 176 & -128 & -48 \\ -128 & 256 & -128 \\ -48 & -128 & 176 \end{bmatrix} & \begin{bmatrix} -18 & 8 & 10 \\ 8 & 96 & -104 \\ 10 & -104 & 94 \end{bmatrix} \\
\begin{bmatrix} -19 & 24 & -5 \\ 24 & -48 & 24 \\ -5 & 24 & -19 \end{bmatrix} & \begin{bmatrix} -18 & 8 & 10 \\ 8 & 96 & -104 \\ 10 & -104 & 94 \end{bmatrix} & \begin{bmatrix} 16 & -60 & 44 \\ -60 & 288 & -228 \\ 44 & -228 & 184 \end{bmatrix}
\end{array}\right]$$

B.2 BILINEAR TENSOR PRODUCT BASIS ON TWO-DIMENSIONAL SPACE

Note: $\Delta_e \Rightarrow \det J_e$

$$\{B10\} = \begin{Bmatrix} 1 \\ 1 \\ 1 \\ 1 \end{Bmatrix}$$

$$[B200] = \frac{1}{9}\begin{bmatrix} 4 & 2 & 1 & 2 \\ & 4 & 2 & 1 \\ & & 4 & 2 \\ (\text{sym}) & & & 4 \end{bmatrix}$$

$$[B3000] = \frac{1}{36}\begin{bmatrix} 9 & 3 & 1 & 3 \\ 3 & 3 & 1 & 1 \\ 1 & 1 & 1 & 1 \\ 3 & 1 & 1 & 3 \\ 3 & 3 & 1 & 1 \\ 3 & 9 & 3 & 1 \\ 1 & 3 & 3 & 1 \\ 1 & 1 & 1 & 1 \\ 1 & 1 & 1 & 1 \\ 1 & 3 & 3 & 1 \\ 1 & 3 & 9 & 3 \\ 1 & 1 & 3 & 3 \\ 3 & 1 & 1 & 3 \\ 1 & 1 & 1 & 1 \\ 1 & 1 & 3 & 3 \\ 3 & 1 & 3 & 9 \end{bmatrix}$$

$$[B3001] = \frac{1}{36}\begin{bmatrix} -6 & 6 & 2 & -2 \\ -3 & 3 & 1 & -1 \\ -1 & 1 & 1 & -1 \\ -2 & 2 & 2 & -2 \\ -3 & 3 & 1 & -1 \\ -6 & 6 & 2 & -2 \\ -2 & 2 & 2 & -2 \\ -1 & 1 & 1 & -1 \\ -1 & 1 & 1 & -1 \\ -2 & 2 & 2 & -2 \\ -2 & 2 & 6 & -6 \\ -1 & 1 & 3 & -3 \\ -2 & 2 & 2 & -2 \\ -1 & 1 & 1 & -1 \\ -1 & 1 & 3 & -3 \\ -2 & 2 & 6 & -6 \end{bmatrix} \qquad [B3010] = \frac{1}{36}\begin{bmatrix} -6 & -3 & -1 & -2 \\ -3 & -6 & -2 & -1 \\ -1 & -2 & -2 & -1 \\ -2 & -1 & -1 & -2 \\ 6 & 3 & 1 & 2 \\ 3 & 6 & 2 & 1 \\ 1 & 2 & 2 & 1 \\ 2 & 1 & 1 & 2 \\ 2 & 1 & 1 & 2 \\ 1 & 2 & 2 & 1 \\ 1 & 2 & 6 & 3 \\ 2 & 1 & 3 & 6 \\ -2 & -1 & -1 & -2 \\ -1 & -2 & -2 & -1 \\ -1 & -2 & -6 & -3 \\ -2 & -1 & -3 & -6 \end{bmatrix}$$

$$[B3002] = \frac{1}{36}\begin{bmatrix} -6 & -2 & 2 & 6 \\ -2 & -2 & 2 & 2 \\ -1 & -1 & 1 & 1 \\ -3 & -1 & 1 & 3 \\ -2 & -2 & 2 & 2 \\ -2 & -6 & 6 & 2 \\ -1 & -3 & 3 & 1 \\ -1 & -1 & 1 & 1 \\ -1 & -1 & 1 & 1 \\ -1 & -3 & 3 & 1 \\ -2 & -6 & 6 & 2 \\ -2 & -2 & 2 & 2 \\ -3 & -1 & 1 & 3 \\ -1 & -1 & 1 & 1 \\ 2 & -2 & 2 & 2 \\ -6 & -2 & 2 & 6 \end{bmatrix} \qquad [B3020] = \frac{1}{36}\begin{bmatrix} -6 & -2 & -1 & -3 \\ -2 & -2 & -1 & -1 \\ -1 & -1 & -2 & -2 \\ -3 & -1 & -2 & -6 \\ -2 & -2 & -1 & -1 \\ -2 & -6 & -3 & -1 \\ -1 & -3 & -6 & -2 \\ -1 & -1 & -2 & -2 \\ 2 & 2 & 1 & 1 \\ 2 & 6 & 3 & 1 \\ 1 & 3 & 6 & 2 \\ 1 & 1 & 2 & 2 \\ 6 & 2 & 1 & 3 \\ 2 & 2 & 1 & 1 \\ 1 & 1 & 2 & 2 \\ 3 & 1 & 2 & 6 \end{bmatrix}$$

$$[B3011] = \frac{1}{36}\begin{bmatrix} 4 & -4 & -1 & 1 \\ 4 & -4 & -1 & 1 \\ 1 & -1 & -1 & 1 \\ 1 & -1 & -1 & 1 \\ -4 & 4 & 1 & -1 \\ -4 & 4 & 1 & -1 \\ -1 & 1 & 1 & -1 \\ -1 & 1 & 1 & -1 \\ -1 & 1 & 1 & -1 \\ -1 & 1 & 1 & -1 \\ -1 & 1 & 4 & -4 \\ -1 & 1 & 4 & -4 \\ 1 & -1 & -1 & 1 \\ 1 & -1 & -1 & 1 \\ 1 & -1 & -4 & 4 \\ 1 & -1 & -4 & 4 \end{bmatrix} \qquad [B3012] = \frac{1}{36}\begin{bmatrix} 4 & 2 & -2 & -4 \\ 2 & 4 & -4 & -2 \\ 1 & 2 & -2 & -1 \\ 2 & 1 & -1 & -2 \\ -4 & -2 & 2 & 4 \\ -2 & -4 & 4 & 2 \\ -1 & -2 & 2 & 1 \\ -2 & -1 & 1 & 2 \\ -2 & -1 & 1 & 2 \\ -1 & -2 & 2 & 1 \\ -2 & -4 & 4 & 2 \\ -4 & -2 & 2 & 4 \\ 2 & 1 & -1 & -2 \\ 1 & 2 & -2 & -1 \\ 2 & 4 & -4 & -2 \\ 4 & 2 & -2 & -4 \end{bmatrix}$$

$$[B3022] = \frac{1}{36}\begin{bmatrix} 4 & 1 & -1 & -4 \\ 1 & 1 & -1 & -1 \\ 1 & 1 & -1 & -1 \\ 4 & 1 & -1 & -4 \\ 1 & 1 & -1 & -1 \\ 1 & 4 & -4 & -1 \\ 1 & 4 & -4 & -1 \\ 1 & 1 & -1 & -1 \\ -1 & -1 & 1 & 1 \\ -1 & -4 & 4 & 1 \\ -1 & -4 & 4 & 1 \\ -1 & -1 & 1 & 1 \\ -4 & -1 & 1 & 4 \\ -1 & -1 & 1 & 1 \\ -1 & -1 & 1 & 1 \\ -4 & -1 & 1 & 4 \end{bmatrix} \qquad [B3021] = \frac{1}{36}\begin{bmatrix} 4 & -4 & -2 & 2 \\ 2 & -2 & -1 & 1 \\ 1 & -1 & -2 & 2 \\ 2 & -2 & -4 & 4 \\ 2 & -2 & -1 & 1 \\ 4 & -4 & -2 & 2 \\ 2 & -2 & -4 & 4 \\ 1 & -1 & -2 & 2 \\ -2 & 2 & 1 & -1 \\ -4 & 4 & 2 & -2 \\ -2 & 2 & 4 & -4 \\ -1 & 1 & 2 & -2 \\ -4 & 4 & 2 & -2 \\ -2 & 2 & 1 & -1 \\ -1 & 1 & 2 & -2 \\ -2 & 2 & 4 & -4 \end{bmatrix}$$

$$
[B40000] = \frac{1}{900}\begin{bmatrix}
144 & 36 & 9 & 36 & 36 & 24 & 6 \\
36 & 24 & 6 & 9 & 24 & 36 & 9 \\
9 & 6 & 4 & 6 & 6 & 9 & 6 \\
36 & 9 & 6 & 24 & 9 & 6 & 4 \\
36 & 24 & 6 & 9 & 24 & 36 & 9 \\
24 & 36 & 9 & 6 & 36 & 144 & 36 \\
6 & 9 & 6 & 4 & 9 & 36 & 24 \\
9 & 6 & 4 & 6 & 6 & 9 & 6 \\
9 & 6 & 4 & 6 & 6 & 9 & 6 \\
6 & 9 & 6 & 4 & 9 & 36 & 24 \\
4 & 6 & 9 & 6 & 6 & 24 & 36 \\
6 & 4 & 6 & 9 & 4 & 6 & 9 \\
36 & 9 & 6 & 24 & 9 & 6 & 4 \\
9 & 6 & 4 & 6 & 6 & 9 & 6 \\
6 & 4 & 6 & 9 & 4 & 6 & 9 \\
24 & 6 & 9 & 36 & 6 & 4 & 6
\end{bmatrix}
$$

$$
[B40010] = \frac{1}{900}\begin{bmatrix}
-36 & -12 & -3 & -9 & 36 & 12 & 3 \\
-12 & -12 & -3 & -3 & 12 & 12 & 3 \\
-3 & -3 & -2 & -2 & 3 & 3 & 2 \\
-9 & -3 & -2 & -6 & 9 & 3 & 2 \\
-12 & -12 & -3 & -3 & 12 & 12 & 3 \\
-12 & -36 & -9 & -3 & 12 & 36 & 9 \\
-3 & -9 & -6 & -2 & 3 & 9 & 6 \\
-3 & -3 & -2 & -2 & 3 & 3 & 2 \\
-3 & -3 & -2 & -2 & 3 & 3 & 2 \\
-3 & -9 & -6 & -2 & 3 & 9 & 6 \\
-2 & -6 & -9 & -3 & 2 & 6 & 9 \\
-2 & -2 & -3 & -3 & 2 & 2 & 3 \\
-9 & -3 & -2 & -6 & 9 & 3 & 2 \\
-3 & -3 & -2 & -2 & 3 & 3 & 2 \\
-2 & -2 & -3 & -3 & 2 & 2 & 3 \\
-6 & -2 & -3 & -9 & 6 & 2 & 3
\end{bmatrix}
$$

9	9	6	4	6	36	9	6	24
6	6	9	6	4	9	6	4	6
4	4	6	9	6	6	4	6	9
6	6	4	6	9	24	6	9	36
6	6	9	6	4	9	6	4	6
9	9	36	24	6	6	9	6	4
6	6	24	36	9	4	6	9	6
4	4	6	9	6	6	4	6	9
4	4	6	9	6	6	4	6	9
6	6	24	36	9	4	6	9	6
9	9	36	144	36	6	9	36	24
6	6	9	36	24	9	6	24	36
6	6	4	6	9	24	6	9	36
4	4	6	9	6	6	4	6	9
6	6	9	36	24	9	6	24	36
9	9	6	24	36	36	9	36	144

9	9	3	2	6	–9	–3	–2	–6
3	3	3	2	2	–3	–3	–2	–2
2	2	2	3	3	–2	–2	–3	–3
6	6	2	3	9	–6	–2	–3	–9
3	3	3	2	2	–3	–3	–2	–2
3	3	9	6	2	–3	–9	–6	–2
2	2	6	9	3	–2	–6	–9	–3
2	2	2	3	3	–2	–2	–3	–3
2	2	2	3	3	–2	–2	–3	–3
2	2	6	9	3	–2	–6	–9	–3
3	3	9	36	12	–3	–9	–36	–12
3	3	3	12	12	–3	–3	–12	–12
6	6	2	3	9	–6	–2	–3	–9
2	2	2	3	3	–2	–2	–3	–3
3	3	3	12	12	–3	–3	–12	–12
9	9	3	12	36	–9	–3	–12	–36

$$[B40020] = \frac{1}{360} \left[\begin{array}{rrrrrrr}
-36 & -9 & -3 & -12 & -9 & -6 & -2 \\
-9 & -6 & -2 & -3 & -6 & -9 & -3 \\
-3 & -2 & -2 & -3 & -2 & -3 & -3 \\
-12 & -3 & -3 & -12 & -3 & -2 & -2 \\
-9 & -6 & -2 & -3 & -6 & -9 & -3 \\
-6 & -9 & -3 & -2 & -9 & -36 & -12 \\
-2 & -3 & -3 & -2 & -3 & -12 & -12 \\
-3 & -2 & -2 & -3 & -2 & -3 & -3 \\
-3 & -2 & -2 & -3 & -2 & -3 & -3 \\
-2 & -3 & -3 & -2 & -3 & -12 & -12 \\
-2 & -3 & -9 & -6 & -3 & -12 & -36 \\
-3 & -2 & -6 & -9 & -2 & -3 & -9 \\
-12 & -3 & -3 & -12 & -3 & -2 & -2 \\
-3 & -2 & -2 & -3 & -2 & -3 & -3 \\
-3 & -2 & -6 & -9 & -2 & -3 & -9 \\
-12 & -3 & -9 & -36 & -3 & -2 & -6
\end{array} \right.$$

$$[B40100] = \frac{1}{360} \left[\begin{array}{rrrrrrr}
-36 & -12 & -3 & -9 & -12 & -12 & -3 \\
-12 & -12 & -3 & -3 & -12 & -36 & -9 \\
-3 & -3 & -2 & -2 & -3 & -9 & -6 \\
-9 & -3 & -2 & -6 & -3 & -3 & -2 \\
36 & 12 & 3 & 9 & 12 & 12 & 3 \\
12 & 12 & 3 & 3 & 12 & 36 & 9 \\
3 & 3 & 2 & 2 & 3 & 9 & 6 \\
9 & 3 & 2 & 6 & 3 & 3 & 2 \\
9 & 3 & 2 & 6 & 3 & 3 & 2 \\
3 & 3 & 2 & 2 & 3 & 9 & 6 \\
2 & 2 & 3 & 3 & 2 & 6 & 9 \\
6 & 2 & 3 & 9 & 2 & 2 & 3 \\
-9 & -3 & -2 & -6 & -3 & -3 & -2 \\
-3 & -3 & -2 & -2 & -3 & -9 & -6 \\
-2 & -2 & -3 & -3 & -2 & -6 & -9 \\
-6 & -2 & -3 & -9 & -2 & -2 & -3
\end{array} \right.$$

−3	9	6	2	3	36	9	3	12
−2	6	9	3	2	9	6	2	3
−2	2	3	3	2	3	2	2	3
−3	3	2	2	3	12	3	3	12
−2	6	9	3	2	9	6	2	3
−3	9	36	12	3	6	9	3	2
−3	3	12	12	3	2	3	3	2
−2	2	3	3	2	3	2	2	3
−2	2	3	3	2	3	2	2	3
−3	3	12	12	3	2	3	3	2
−9	3	12	36	9	2	3	9	6
−6	2	3	9	6	3	2	6	9
−3	3	2	2	3	12	3	3	12
−2	2	3	3	2	3	2	2	3
−6	2	3	9	6	3	2	6	9
−9	3	2	6	9	12	3	9	36

−3	−3	−3	−2	−2	−9	−3	−2	−6
−3	−3	−9	−6	−2	−3	−3	−2	−2
−2	−2	−6	−9	−3	−2	−2	−3	−3
−2	−2	−2	−3	−3	−6	−2	−3	−9
3	3	3	2	2	9	3	2	6
3	3	9	6	2	3	3	2	2
2	2	6	9	3	2	2	3	3
2	2	2	3	3	6	2	3	9
2	2	2	3	3	6	2	3	9
2	2	6	9	3	2	2	3	3
3	3	9	36	12	3	3	12	12
3	3	3	12	12	9	3	12	36
−2	−2	−2	−3	−3	−6	−2	−3	−9
−2	−2	−6	−9	−3	−2	−2	−3	−3
−3	−3	−9	−36	−12	−3	−3	−12	−12
−3	−3	−3	−12	−12	−9	−3	−12	−36

$$[B40200] = \frac{1}{360}\left[\begin{array}{rrrrrrr}
-36 & -9 & -3 & -12 & -9 & -6 & -2 \\
-9 & -6 & -2 & -3 & -6 & -9 & -3 \\
-3 & -2 & -2 & -3 & -2 & -3 & -3 \\
-12 & -3 & -3 & -12 & -3 & -2 & -2 \\
-9 & -6 & -2 & -3 & -6 & -9 & -3 \\
-6 & -9 & -3 & -2 & -9 & -36 & -12 \\
-2 & -3 & -3 & -2 & -3 & -12 & -12 \\
-3 & -2 & -2 & -3 & -2 & -3 & -3 \\
9 & 6 & 2 & 3 & 6 & 9 & 3 \\
6 & 9 & 3 & 2 & 9 & 36 & 12 \\
2 & 3 & 3 & 2 & 3 & 12 & 12 \\
3 & 2 & 2 & 3 & 2 & 3 & 3 \\
36 & 9 & 3 & 12 & 9 & 6 & 2 \\
9 & 6 & 2 & 3 & 6 & 9 & 3 \\
3 & 2 & 2 & 3 & 2 & 3 & 3 \\
12 & 3 & 3 & 12 & 3 & 2 & 2
\end{array}\right.$$

$$[B40110] = \frac{1}{360}\left[\begin{array}{rrrrrrr}
24 & 12 & 3 & 6 & -24 & -12 & -3 \\
12 & 24 & 6 & 3 & -12 & -24 & -6 \\
3 & 6 & 4 & 2 & -3 & -6 & -4 \\
6 & 3 & 2 & 4 & -6 & -3 & -2 \\
-24 & -12 & -3 & -6 & 24 & 12 & 3 \\
-12 & -24 & -6 & -3 & 12 & 24 & 6 \\
-3 & -6 & -4 & -2 & 3 & 6 & 4 \\
-6 & -3 & -2 & -4 & 6 & 3 & 2 \\
-6 & -3 & -2 & -4 & 6 & 3 & 2 \\
-3 & -6 & -4 & -2 & 3 & 6 & 4 \\
-2 & -4 & -6 & -3 & 2 & 4 & 6 \\
-4 & -2 & -3 & -6 & 4 & 2 & 3 \\
6 & 3 & 2 & 4 & -6 & -3 & -2 \\
3 & 6 & 4 & 2 & -3 & -6 & -4 \\
2 & 4 & 6 & 3 & -2 & -4 & -6 \\
4 & 2 & 3 & 6 & -4 & -2 & -3
\end{array}\right.$$

–3	–3	–2	–2	–3	–12	–3	–3	–12
–2	–2	–3	–3	–2	–3	–2	–2	–3
–2	–2	–3	–9	–6	–3	–2	–6	–9
–3	–3	–2	–6	–9	–12	–3	–9	–36
–2	–2	–3	–3	–2	–3	–2	–2	–3
–3	–3	–12	–12	–3	–2	–3	–3	–2
–3	–3	–12	–36	–9	–2	–3	–9	–6
–2	–2	–3	–9	–6	–3	–2	–6	–9
2	2	3	3	2	3	2	2	3
3	3	12	12	3	2	3	3	2
3	3	12	36	9	2	3	9	6
2	2	3	9	6	3	2	6	9
3	3	2	2	3	12	3	3	12
2	2	3	3	2	3	2	2	3
2	2	3	9	6	3	2	6	9
3	3	2	6	9	12	3	9	36

–6	–6	–3	–2	–4	6	3	2	4
–3	–3	–6	–4	–2	3	6	4	2
–2	–2	–4	–6	–3	2	4	6	3
–4	–4	–2	–3	–6	4	2	3	6
6	6	3	2	4	–6	–3	–2	–4
3	3	6	4	2	–3	–6	–4	–2
2	2	4	6	3	–2	–4	–6	–3
4	4	2	3	6	–4	–2	–3	–6
4	4	2	3	6	–4	–2	–3	–6
2	2	4	6	3	–2	–4	–6	–3
3	3	6	24	12	–3	–6	–24	–12
6	6	3	12	24	–6	–3	–12	–24
–4	–4	–2	–3	–6	4	2	3	6
–2	–2	–4	–6	–3	2	4	6	3
–3	–3	–6	–24	–12	3	6	24	12
–6	–6	–3	–12	–24	6	3	12	24

$$
[B40220] = \frac{1}{360}\begin{bmatrix}
24 & 6 & 3 & 12 & 6 & 4 & 2 \\
6 & 4 & 2 & 3 & 4 & 6 & 3 \\
3 & 2 & 4 & 6 & 2 & 3 & 6 \\
12 & 3 & 6 & 24 & 3 & 2 & 4 \\
6 & 4 & 2 & 3 & 4 & 6 & 3 \\
4 & 6 & 3 & 2 & 6 & 24 & 12 \\
2 & 3 & 6 & 4 & 3 & 12 & 24 \\
3 & 2 & 4 & 6 & 2 & 3 & 6 \\
-6 & -4 & -2 & -3 & -4 & -6 & -3 \\
-4 & -6 & -3 & -2 & -6 & -24 & -12 \\
-2 & -3 & -6 & -4 & -3 & -12 & -24 \\
-3 & -2 & -4 & -6 & -2 & -3 & -6 \\
-24 & -6 & -3 & -12 & -6 & -4 & -2 \\
-6 & -4 & -2 & -3 & -4 & -6 & -3 \\
-3 & -2 & -4 & -6 & -2 & -3 & -6 \\
-12 & -3 & -6 & -24 & -3 & -2 & -4
\end{bmatrix}
$$

$$
[B40120] = \frac{1}{144}\begin{bmatrix}
9 & 3 & 1 & 3 & 3 & 3 & 1 \\
3 & 3 & 1 & 1 & 3 & 9 & 3 \\
1 & 1 & 1 & 1 & 1 & 3 & 3 \\
3 & 1 & 1 & 3 & 1 & 1 & 1 \\
-9 & -3 & -1 & -3 & -3 & -3 & -1 \\
-3 & -3 & -1 & -1 & -3 & -9 & -3 \\
-1 & -1 & -1 & -1 & -1 & -3 & -3 \\
-3 & -1 & -1 & -3 & -1 & -1 & -1 \\
-3 & -1 & -1 & -3 & -1 & -1 & -1 \\
-1 & -1 & -1 & -1 & -1 & -3 & -3 \\
-1 & -1 & -3 & -3 & -1 & -3 & -9 \\
-3 & -1 & -3 & -9 & -1 & -1 & -3 \\
3 & 1 & 1 & 3 & 1 & 1 & 1 \\
1 & 1 & 1 & 1 & 1 & 3 & 3 \\
1 & 1 & 3 & 3 & 1 & 3 & 9 \\
3 & 1 & 3 & 9 & 1 & 1 & 3
\end{bmatrix}
$$

3	−6	−4	−2	−3	−24	−6	−3	−12
2	−4	−6	−3	−2	−6	−4	−2	−3
4	−2	−3	−6	−4	−3	−2	−4	−6
6	−3	−2	−4	−6	−12	−3	−6	−24
2	−4	−6	−3	−2	−6	−4	−2	−3
3	−6	−24	−12	−3	−4	−6	−3	−2
6	−3	−12	−24	−6	−2	−3	−6	−4
4	−2	−3	−6	−4	−3	−2	−4	−6
−2	4	6	3	2	6	4	2	3
−3	6	24	12	3	4	6	3	2
−6	3	12	24	6	2	3	6	4
−4	2	3	6	4	3	2	4	6
−3	6	4	2	3	24	6	3	12
−2	4	6	3	2	6	4	2	3
−4	2	3	6	4	3	2	4	6
−6	3	2	4	6	12	3	6	24

1	−3	−3	−1	−1	−9	−3	−1	−3
1	−3	−9	−3	−1	−3	−3	−1	−1
1	−1	−3	−3	−1	−1	−1	−1	−1
1	−1	−1	−1	−1	−3	−1	−1	−3
−1	3	3	1	1	9	3	1	3
−1	3	9	3	1	3	3	1	1
−1	1	3	3	1	1	1	1	1
−1	1	1	1	1	3	1	1	3
−1	1	1	1	1	3	1	1	3
−1	1	3	3	1	1	1	1	1
−3	1	3	9	3	1	1	3	3
−3	1	1	3	3	3	1	3	9
1	−1	−1	−1	−1	−3	−1	−1	−3
1	−1	−3	−3	−1	−1	−1	−1	−1
3	−1	−3	−9	−3	−1	−1	−3	−3
3	−1	−1	−3	−3	−3	−1	−3	−9

$$[B40210] = \frac{1}{144}\left[\begin{matrix} 9 & 3 & 1 & 3 & -9 & -3 & -1 \\ 3 & 3 & 1 & 1 & -3 & -3 & -1 \\ 1 & 1 & 1 & 1 & -1 & -1 & -1 \\ 3 & 1 & 1 & 3 & -3 & -1 & -1 \\ 3 & 3 & 1 & 1 & -3 & -3 & -1 \\ 3 & 9 & 3 & 1 & -3 & -9 & -3 \\ 1 & 3 & 3 & 1 & -1 & -3 & -3 \\ 1 & 1 & 1 & 1 & -1 & -1 & -1 \\ -3 & -3 & -1 & -1 & 3 & 3 & 1 \\ -3 & -9 & -3 & -1 & 3 & 9 & 3 \\ -1 & -3 & -3 & -1 & 1 & 3 & 3 \\ -1 & -1 & -1 & -1 & 1 & 1 & 1 \\ -9 & -3 & -1 & -3 & 9 & 3 & 1 \\ -3 & -3 & -1 & -1 & 3 & 3 & 1 \\ -1 & -1 & -1 & -1 & 1 & 1 & 1 \\ -3 & -1 & -1 & -3 & 3 & 1 & 1 \end{matrix}\right.$$

B.3 TRILINEAR TENSOR PRODUCT BASIS ON THREE-DIMENSIONAL SPACE

Note: $\Delta_e \Rightarrow \det J_e$

$$[C200] = \frac{1}{8}\begin{bmatrix} 8 & 4 & 2 & 4 & 4 & 2 & 1 & 2 \\ 4 & 8 & 4 & 2 & 2 & 4 & 2 & 1 \\ 2 & 4 & 8 & 4 & 1 & 2 & 4 & 2 \\ 4 & 2 & 4 & 8 & 2 & 1 & 2 & 4 \\ 4 & 2 & 1 & 2 & 8 & 4 & 2 & 4 \\ 2 & 4 & 2 & 1 & 4 & 8 & 4 & 2 \\ 1 & 2 & 4 & 2 & 2 & 4 & 8 & 4 \\ 2 & 1 & 2 & 4 & 4 & 2 & 4 & 8 \end{bmatrix}$$

$$
\left.\begin{matrix}
-3 & -3 & -1 & -1 & -3 & 3 & 1 & 1 & 3 \\
-1 & -1 & -1 & -1 & -1 & 1 & 1 & 1 & 1 \\
-1 & -1 & -1 & -3 & -3 & 1 & 1 & 3 & 3 \\
-3 & -3 & -1 & -3 & -9 & 3 & 1 & 3 & 9 \\
-1 & -1 & -1 & -1 & -1 & 1 & 1 & 1 & 1 \\
-1 & -1 & -3 & -3 & -1 & 1 & 3 & 3 & 1 \\
-1 & -1 & -3 & -9 & -3 & 1 & 3 & 9 & 3 \\
-1 & -1 & -1 & -3 & -3 & 1 & 1 & 3 & 3 \\
1 & 1 & 1 & 1 & 1 & -1 & -1 & -1 & -1 \\
1 & 1 & 3 & 3 & 1 & -1 & -3 & -3 & -1 \\
1 & 1 & 3 & 9 & 3 & -1 & -3 & -9 & -3 \\
1 & 1 & 1 & 3 & 3 & -1 & -1 & -3 & -3 \\
3 & 3 & 1 & 1 & 3 & -3 & -1 & -1 & -3 \\
1 & 1 & 1 & 1 & 1 & -1 & -1 & -1 & -1 \\
1 & 1 & 1 & 3 & 3 & -1 & -1 & -3 & -3 \\
3 & 3 & 1 & 3 & 9 & -3 & -1 & -3 & -9
\end{matrix}\right]
$$

$$
[C201] = \frac{1}{12}\begin{bmatrix}
-4 & 4 & 2 & -2 & -2 & 2 & 1 & -1 \\
-4 & 4 & 2 & -2 & -2 & 2 & 1 & -1 \\
-2 & 2 & 4 & -4 & -1 & 1 & 2 & -2 \\
-2 & 2 & 4 & -4 & -1 & 1 & 2 & -2 \\
-2 & 2 & 1 & -1 & -4 & 4 & 2 & -2 \\
-2 & 2 & 1 & -1 & -4 & 4 & 2 & -2 \\
-1 & 1 & 2 & -2 & -2 & 2 & 4 & -4 \\
-1 & 1 & 2 & -2 & -2 & 2 & 4 & -4
\end{bmatrix}
$$

$$[C202] = \frac{1}{12}\begin{bmatrix} -4 & -2 & 2 & 4 & -2 & -1 & 1 & 2 \\ -2 & -4 & 4 & 2 & -1 & -2 & 2 & 1 \\ -2 & -4 & 4 & 2 & -1 & -2 & 2 & 1 \\ -4 & -2 & 2 & 4 & -2 & -1 & 1 & 2 \\ -2 & -1 & 1 & 2 & -4 & -2 & 2 & 4 \\ -1 & -2 & 2 & 1 & -2 & -4 & 4 & 2 \\ -1 & -2 & 2 & 1 & -2 & -4 & 4 & 2 \\ -1 & -2 & 2 & 1 & -2 & -4 & 4 & 2 \\ -2 & -1 & 1 & 2 & -4 & -2 & 2 & 4 \end{bmatrix}$$

$$[C211] = \frac{1}{8}\begin{bmatrix} 4 & -4 & -2 & 2 & 2 & -2 & -1 & 1 \\ -4 & 4 & 2 & -2 & -2 & 2 & 1 & -1 \\ -2 & 2 & 4 & -4 & -1 & 1 & 2 & -2 \\ 2 & -2 & -4 & 4 & 1 & -1 & -2 & 2 \\ 2 & -2 & -1 & 1 & 4 & -4 & -2 & 2 \\ -2 & 2 & 1 & -1 & -4 & 4 & 2 & -2 \\ -1 & 1 & 2 & -2 & -2 & 2 & 4 & -4 \\ 1 & -1 & -2 & 2 & 2 & -2 & -4 & 4 \end{bmatrix}$$

$$[C222] = \frac{1}{8}\begin{bmatrix} 4 & 2 & -2 & -4 & 2 & 1 & -1 & -2 \\ 2 & 4 & -4 & -2 & 1 & 2 & -2 & -1 \\ -2 & -4 & 4 & 2 & -1 & -2 & 2 & 1 \\ -4 & -2 & 2 & 4 & -2 & -1 & 1 & 2 \\ 2 & 1 & -1 & -2 & 4 & 2 & -2 & -4 \\ 1 & 2 & -2 & -1 & 2 & 4 & -4 & -2 \\ -1 & -2 & 2 & 1 & -2 & -4 & 4 & 2 \\ -2 & -1 & 1 & 2 & -4 & -2 & 2 & 4 \end{bmatrix}$$

$$[C233] = \frac{1}{8}\begin{bmatrix} 4 & 2 & 1 & 2 & -4 & -2 & -1 & -2 \\ 2 & 4 & 2 & 1 & -2 & -4 & -2 & -1 \\ 1 & 2 & 4 & 2 & -1 & -2 & -4 & -2 \\ 2 & 1 & 2 & 4 & -2 & -1 & -2 & -4 \\ -4 & -2 & -1 & -2 & 4 & 2 & 1 & 2 \\ -2 & -4 & -2 & -1 & 2 & 4 & 2 & 1 \\ -1 & -2 & -4 & -2 & 1 & 2 & 4 & 2 \\ -2 & -1 & -2 & -4 & 2 & 1 & 2 & 4 \end{bmatrix}$$

$$[C203] = \frac{1}{12}\begin{bmatrix} -4 & -2 & -1 & -2 & 4 & 2 & 1 & 2 \\ -2 & -4 & -2 & -1 & 2 & 4 & 2 & 1 \\ -1 & -2 & -4 & -2 & 1 & 2 & 4 & 2 \\ -2 & -1 & -2 & -4 & 2 & 1 & 2 & 4 \\ -4 & -2 & -1 & -2 & 4 & 2 & 1 & 2 \\ -2 & -4 & -2 & -1 & 2 & 4 & 2 & 1 \\ -1 & -2 & -4 & -2 & 1 & 2 & 4 & 2 \\ -2 & -1 & -2 & -4 & 2 & 1 & 2 & 4 \end{bmatrix}$$

$$[C210] = \frac{1}{12}\begin{bmatrix} -4 & -4 & -2 & -2 & -2 & -2 & -1 & -1 \\ 4 & 4 & 2 & 2 & 2 & 2 & 1 & 1 \\ 2 & 2 & 4 & 4 & 1 & 1 & 2 & 2 \\ -2 & -2 & -4 & -4 & -1 & -1 & -2 & -2 \\ -2 & -2 & -1 & -1 & -4 & -4 & -2 & -2 \\ 2 & 2 & 1 & 1 & 4 & 4 & 2 & 2 \\ 1 & 1 & 2 & 2 & 2 & 2 & 4 & 4 \\ -1 & -1 & -2 & -2 & -2 & -2 & -4 & -4 \end{bmatrix}$$

$$[C220] = \frac{1}{12}\begin{bmatrix} -4 & -2 & -2 & -4 & -2 & -1 & -1 & -2 \\ -2 & -4 & -4 & -2 & -1 & -2 & -2 & -1 \\ 2 & 4 & 4 & 2 & 1 & 2 & 2 & 1 \\ 4 & 2 & 2 & 4 & 2 & 1 & 1 & 2 \\ -2 & -1 & -1 & -2 & -4 & -2 & -2 & -4 \\ -1 & -2 & -2 & -1 & -2 & -4 & -4 & -2 \\ 1 & 2 & 2 & 1 & 2 & 4 & 4 & 2 \\ 2 & 1 & 1 & 2 & 4 & 2 & 2 & 4 \end{bmatrix}$$

$$[C230] = \frac{1}{12}\begin{bmatrix} -4 & -2 & -1 & -2 & -4 & -2 & -1 & -2 \\ -2 & -4 & -2 & -1 & -2 & -4 & -2 & -1 \\ -1 & -2 & -4 & -2 & -1 & -2 & -4 & -2 \\ -2 & -1 & -2 & -4 & -2 & -1 & -2 & -4 \\ 4 & 2 & 1 & 2 & 4 & 2 & 1 & 2 \\ 2 & 4 & 2 & 1 & 2 & 4 & 2 & 1 \\ 1 & 2 & 4 & 2 & 1 & 2 & 4 & 2 \\ 2 & 1 & 2 & 4 & 2 & 1 & 2 & 4 \end{bmatrix}$$

INDEX